M000007031

Thermodynamics

From concepts to applications

Thermodynamics

From concepts to applications

ARTHUR SHAVIT AND CHAIM GUTFINGER

FACULTY OF MECHANICAL ENGINEERING
TECHNION - ISRAEL INSTITUTE OF TECHNOLOGY
HAIFA, ISRAEL

PRENTICE HALL
London New York Toronto Sydney Tokyo Singapore Madrid Mexico City Munich

First published 1995 by
Prentice Hall International (UK) Limited
Campus 400, Maylands Avenue
Hemel Hempstead
Hertfordshire, HP2 7EZ
A division of
Simon & Schuster International Group

Typeset in 10/12pt Times
by Columns Design and Production Services Ltd, Reading

Printed and bound in Great Britain at the University Press, Cambridge

Library of Congress Cataloging-in-Publication Data

Shavit, Arthur.
Thermodynamics : from concepts to applications / Arthur Shavit and Chaim Gutfinger.
p. cm.
Includes index.
ISBN 0-13-288267-1 (pbk.)
1. Thermodynamics. I. Gutfinger, Chaim. II. Title.
QC311.S513 1995
536'.7–dc20 94-29081
CIP

British Library Cataloguing in Publication Data

A catalogue record for this book is available from the British Library

ISBN 0-13-288267-1 (pbk)

1 2 3 4 5 99 98 97 96 95

Contents

Preface

The writing of this book was triggered by the need to provide the new student with a basic textbook on thermodynamics that is rigorous and accurate. There are many thermodynamic texts that present the subject in a scientifically correct manner. Unfortunately, they present the material at a level too high for the beginner . On the other hand, many of the popular basic texts on thermodynamics seem to lack a rigorous presentation of the theoretical material. The present book aims to bridge the gap between these two approaches.

Thermodynamics is considered by many students to be a difficult subject. Even though the mathematics used is rather simple, students find it difficult to solve thermodynamic problems. This is probably due to the fact that many concepts encountered by beginners have not been made clear to them. The authors, therefore, set out to write this book with the main purpose of presenting the student with a text that is relatively simple to comprehend without compromising rigor and accuracy. It is assumed that the reader has had at least one year of basic engineering education which includes mathematics and physics. Although the theory of thermodynamics is emphasized, each new concept that is introduced is supplemented by examples of practical applications.

The objective of a course based on this book is to direct the student to think in clear, consistent, and correct terms of thermodynamics; to make the student understand the basic principles of the subject; and to provide the student with sufficient knowledge to solve real engineering problems. Some of the terms used in thermodynamics are also used in everyday life. These terms that may be used loosely in everyday life have, however, a very specific meaning in thermodynamics. Thermodynamics has historically been developed around the concepts of work, heat, energy, temperature, and entropy. Still, in many modern textbooks no clear definitions of some of these terms are given. At times, these important concepts are explained intuitively and the student is left to make his or her own interpretations. In this book each concept is clearly defined in scientifically correct terms that, nevertheless, are within the grasp of the new student.

The book presents the theory of thermodynamics structured somewhat similarly to geometry. Definitions of the basic terms are given with the understanding that whenever a term is used it always has the same meaning. Axioms, which represent extensions of experimental facts, are given. These are known as the laws of thermodynamics.

Corollaries of the definitions and the laws are then developed. The theory of thermodynamics is comprised of a combination of definitions, laws, and corollaries. Thermodynamic practice makes use of these laws to solve actual engineering problems. At each stage of the development of the theory the student is exposed directly and by means of examples to applications that illustrate the use of the theory.

The book starts with definitions of the basic concepts of thermodynamics, such as system, property, state, path, interaction, process, etc. The definitions are posed in simple, yet rigorous and exact, terms. It continues with an exposition of the concepts of work in general, and work in quasistatic processes. The first law of thermodynamics is then introduced in terms of adiabatic work, from which the concept of energy follows.

The idea of a simple system then follows. Properties of simple systems are given in Chapter 4 in the form of graphs and tables for real substances, such as steam, and in Chapter 5 in terms of equations, presented for the ideal gas. Access to real material properties allows the student to tackle some actual engineering problems and make meaningful calculations at a fairly early stage of the course. The thermodynamic theory is extended in Chapter 6 to open systems leading to many practical examples and applications.

Having presented the first law of thermodynamics, both for closed and open systems, the book goes on to introduce the second law of thermodynamics. This is done in Chapters 7 and 8 in the traditional way through PMM2. The concepts of reversibility and entropy are introduced and their importance is shown. The student is made aware that the changes in properties are not the same when the processes are reversible or irreversible. Moreover, the directions of the deviations of the changes of properties, in an actual irreversible process, are given in terms of appropriate inequalities. The concepts developed in these two chapters are then used in applications presented in Chapter 9.

Chapter 10 deals with the analysis of exergy. The concept of exergy is most useful in the evaluation of the merits of processes, and as such is utilized in the analysis of various thermodynamic processes involving cycles, mixtures, and chemical reactions, presented in subsequent chapters.

Chapters 11 and 12 provide further applications of the first and second laws of thermodynamics. Chapter 11 deals with applications to power and refrigeration cycles. Examples showing all elements of a power station and multistage refrigeration are presented and supplemented by exergy analysis. Chapter 12 deals with ideal gas mixtures and applications to humid-air processes.

Chapters 13 to 16 consider more advanced topics of thermodynamics such as the relations between thermodynamic properties and their application to the development of equations of state for real substances. Criteria for equilibrium are introduced. These are used in applications to physical and chemical equilibria discussed in Chapters 17–19, such as osmosis, absorption refrigeration, and combustion.

The program of studies that engineering students cover is crowded with subjects competing for time allocation. As a result of this competition, thermodynamics is set as a one-semester required course for the majority of the students. This course has to endow them with a basic understanding of thermodynamics, and also introduce them to the fundamental vocabulary used in the field. On the other hand, for students who specialize in thermal sciences, this one-semester course is just the first in a series of courses, which must, therefore, serve as a solid foundation and minimize the need for later repetitions.

This book may be used for the one-semester required course in thermodynamics. It is also suitable for a two-semester more comprehensive course, depending on the emphasis put on thermodynamics in the curriculum of the particular program involved. Special programs may emphasize certain chapters and skip others. The structure of the book allows such flexibility. At Technion, for example, the basic core course in thermodynamics covers Chapters 1–9 and 11–12 of the book, and a more advanced elective course covers Chapter 10 and Chapters 12–19.

CHAPTER ONE

Introduction

Thermodynamics is a branch of science that deals with the properties of matter as related to changes of temperature. An important aspect of thermodynamics is the relationship between energy, heat and work. As a matter of fact the word thermodynamics, which comes from the Greek, means *the power of heat.*

Thermodynamics is an important basic tool in the development of many branches of science, such as fluid and solid mechanics, heat and mass transfer, material science, chemistry and biology and life sciences. It determines the direction in which processes proceed, and provides conservation relationships for material and energy balances. Classical thermodynamics, which is the subject of this book, takes no account of the atomic structure of matter, but considers matter as a continuum. It is based on a number of laws and postulates that enable the state of matter, which is affected by a vast quantity of properties, to be expressed in terms of a small number of properties. For example, a detailed description of air in a room would require the specification of the location and velocity of each and every molecule of the air, a rather impossible task. Still, the observed behavior of the air can be adequately described, using classical thermodynamics, by a small number of properties, say temperature and pressure.

The need for the science of thermodynamics arose with the development of the steam engine by Thomas Newcomen (1712) and James Watt (1769), which marked the beginning of the industrial revolution. Once the steam engine became a working reality, the question of the equivalence of heat and work became relevant, as well as the question of the maximum power a steam engine could produce for a given heat input.

1.1 Historical background

The term energy is central to thermodynamics. The concepts of work and energy, and the interrelations between them, have been used in mechanics since Newton's time. Huygens (1661) showed that he could calculate the height which a pendulum could reach from energy considerations. The laws of energy conservation, in purely mechanical systems, have also been known for a long time. What troubled scientists till the middle of the nineteenth century was that the laws of energy conservation described well physical phenomena in many cases but in others did not seem to be true. For example, although the height that a pendulum would reach could be fairly accurately calculated from the velocity at the lowest point, the fact that the pendulum would stop eventually seemed to contradict the purely mechanical law of conservation of energy.

The concept of heat, and the distinction between heat and temperature, was also problematic. For a very long period of time people did not understand the difference between the two. The first scientific thermometer was invented by Galileo in the sixteenth century, who used it to measure the 'heat' of various bodies.

Joseph Black (1759) was the first to make a distinction between heat and temperature. He showed that there exists a quantity which is conserved in certain experiments, and this quantity is the heat and not the temperature, whereas the temperature is the measure of the *intensity* of heat.

As a result of Black's experiments, the *caloric theory* was developed. This theory prevailed in science for about 100 years. The caloric theory postulated the existence of the caloric, or the heat substance, a pseudo-fluid that obeyed certain conservation properties. The theory never developed to the point of providing clear and exact statements and definitions of the basic concepts. A partial exposition of the caloric theory was proposed by Cleghorn (1779) and is essentially as follows:

- The caloric is a fluid whose particles repel each other – to account for thermal expansion.
- The caloric is conserved – to account for calorimetry.
- Caloric particles are attracted differently to different particles of matter – to account for different specific heats.
- The caloric may be sensible or latent – to account for phase changes.
- The caloric has weight – to account for the change of weight in oxidation.

The caloric theory came under strong attack by Benjamin Thomson. In a series of experiments he showed that there is no change in the weight of bodies upon heating or cooling. While watching the process of boring cannon barrels in Munich, using horses to turn the drill, he observed that there was no limit to the amount of heat that could be produced, as long as work was being supplied by the horses. He thus concluded that the caloric, as described by the calorists, is an impossible matter since it has no weight, is not conserved and could be produced without limit.

Even though the main ideas of the caloric theory were refuted some of its terms, e.g. the term specific heat, were adopted in modern thermodynamics. Caloric theory is also credited with providing the scientific basis for calorimetry and as such it is used till this day.

The relationship between work and heat was first asserted and calculated by Robert Mayer (1842). He calculated theoretically the conversion factor between heat and work, from the difference between the specific heat at constant pressure and the specific heat at constant volume. Unfortunately for him, his ideas were not accepted at that time, and he could not even publish his results. The credit for finding the mechanical work equivalence of heat went to James P. Joule, who in a series of methodical experiments, performed during 1840–1848, measured the amount of heat produced per unit work input.

The concept of work, even though it has been used since the seventeenth century, was given a new emphasis in the work of Sadi Carnot, who in 1824 wrote a book on the theory of the steam engine, entitled *The Motive Power of Fire*. In this book he defined work as *weight lifted through a height*. This definition, with some modifications, is still used today. Carnot tried to find the maximum efficiency that a steam engine, or indeed any thermal engine, could attain. He found that this maximum depends only on the highest and the lowest temperatures to which the engine is exposed. Carnot himself subscribed to the caloric theory, and believed that heat is neither created nor destroyed. He made an analogy between heat and water. Work can be obtained from water falling from a higher to a lower level, without changing the amount of water. Similarly, he proposed that heat "falling" from a higher to a lower temperature could produce work without changing the amount of heat. Though Carnot's premise is wrong, his conclusions regarding the maximum efficiency of an engine that uses heat to produce work are correct, and form the basis of what is known as the second law of thermodynamics.

Lord Kelvin pointed out in 1849 that the work of Joule was in contradiction to the work of Carnot, and proposed some additional experiments to resolve the differences. About a year later, in 1850, Clausius managed to unify the two views, without performing a single experiment. He stated two principles, which he termed the first and second laws of thermodynamics, which together are the basis of modern thermodynamics.

This was the turning point for the development of thermodynamics as a science on its own that would be applied beyond the realm of steam engines to form one of the pillars of modern science and engineering.

1.2 Applications of thermodynamics

Thermodynamics can provide answers to many general and diverse questions concerning energy sources, power supply, water desalination, chemical processes and many others. The following examples illustrate the wide range of problems to which thermodynamics can be applied.

The maximum amount of work that can be obtained from a given amount of fuel can be determined purely on the basis of thermodynamics, without even specifying the equipment that is needed for this purpose. Thus one may decide whether there is room for improvement in the thermal efficiency of a given automobile engine.

Another example is the ocean, which contains a very large amount of energy. Yet thermodynamics shows that it is almost useless as a source of power generation.

It is well known that fresh water can be produced from sea water by evaporation and subsequent condensation of the vapor. Such an evaporation process requires a large quantity of heat, usually supplied as fuel. Thermodynamics can provide the basic calculations of the least amount of fuel that is required to perform that task. Once again the actual process can be compared to the most efficient process, and an intelligent decision as to the areas of improvement can be made.

An alternative method of desalination is the process of reverse osmosis where pressurized saline water is passed along a special semipermeable membrane that allows water to pass through. Thermodynamics can assess the minimum pumping power needed to perform the desalination by reverse osmosis. It can also show the relationship between the minimum heat in the evaporation process and the minimum pumping power in the reverse osmosis process.

Thermodynamic considerations determine the point where salt starts to precipitate when a saline solution is being slowly cooled.

Biological processes like the oxygenation of blood are also subject to thermodynamic considerations. Thermodynamics can be used to determine the conditions of oxygen transfer into the bloodstream, or transfer of carbon dioxide from the bloodstream into the environment. Carbon dioxide, which by itself is not poisonous, could in high concentration in the environment be fatal by blocking the removal of carbon dioxide from the bloodstream. Thermodynamics can explain this phenomenon and calculate the level of danger.

The scope of thermodynamics is very wide indeed. It may be difficult to cover all the aspects of thermodynamics in one book. In this book we therefore focus our attention mostly on subjects that are of interest to students of engineering.

CHAPTER TWO

Basic concepts

This chapter introduces the terminology and definitions used in the study of thermodynamics. It starts by providing definitions for the basic concepts encountered in the subject. Definitions should be stated in exact terms allowing no room for ambiguity, thus providing a common language for all users of the subject. One can define any concept or entity, regardless of whether these exist in reality or not. For example, a mermaid may be clearly defined as a creature having an upper part of a young woman and a lower part of a fish; yet, the very fact that it can be well defined does not guarantee its actual existence.

Thermodynamics also makes use of experimental facts. By an experimental fact we mean an experiment that may be repeated many times, always yielding the same result. Examples of experimental facts are: the earth rotating around the sun, an apple falling from a tree to the ground, a hot copper block contracting when placed in cold water, etc. We encounter many experimental facts which may or may not be related to each other.

Generalizations and extensions of experimental facts are known as laws or axioms. A law is formulated on the basis of all the experimental facts available without a single fact to contradict it. Laws are not only applicable to the experimental facts on which they are based, but also assumed to apply to new situations. Of course, if we were to find even a single experimental fact that contradicts the law then we would have to modify the law or dispense with it altogether. In the course of the development of science it happened that laws accepted at one time were modified or completely discarded later on. An example of modified laws are Newton's laws of motion that were later modified by Einstein. Examples of discarded laws are the ancient Greek laws stating that any substance is made of four basic elements: fire, earth, water and air; or the laws of the caloric theory stating that heat is conserved.

Although a law represents the best accumulation of scientific knowledge, it cannot be proven. Even if an overwhelmingly large number of experimental facts may support the validity of the law, there is no assurance that no single experimental fact will ever be found to contradict it. The following analogy may clarify this point. A young inhabitant of the Arctic Circle may formulate a law, on the basis of repeated observations, that all the people in the world live in dwellings made of ice. Although this "law" represents his best knowledge, it will have to be modified once the young man leaves the Arctic Circle. Still, laws are used in all branches of science as if they were absolute truths. Theorems and corollaries can be formulated and proven on the basis of laws and definitions. Once formulated they can be used to solve a variety of practical problems.

We now begin by defining and explaining some basic concepts used in thermodynamics.

2.1 The thermodynamic system

For the purpose of thermodynamic analysis we usually focus our attention on a finite amount of matter, which is separated from its surroundings, and is called a system.

A system is defined by whatever is enclosed within a clearly specified boundary.

In order to define a system one must specify its boundaries and describe the contents within these boundaries. If matter is not allowed to cross the boundary, the system is referred to as a *closed system* or simply as a *system*. Obviously, when no matter crosses the boundary, the amount of matter within the closed system is constant, ignoring the effects of relativity.

If matter is allowed to cross the boundary, the system is referred to as an *open system**. The open system is contained within a *control volume* and surrounded by a *control surface*. The terms *open system* and *control volume* are interchangeable.

The boundary of the system may be real, namely physical, or imaginary, i.e. mathematical, and may be stationary or changing with time; it must, however, be well defined at all times.

Anything outside the boundary of the system is called the *surroundings* or the *environment*. It is important that at any given time the system can be isolated from its environment. *Isolation* means that the system and its environment do not affect each other. To simplify the thermodynamic analysis, the environment is limited only to regions which may influence the system. The environment may also be viewed as a system.

As an example of a system consider the air enclosed by the cylinder and piston shown in Fig. 2.1. The boundary of this system consists of the internal surfaces of the cylinder and piston, shown by the dashed line. The boundary may change by moving the piston up or down. The environment can be the piston, weight, cylinder and outside atmosphere.

Now let us consider only the oxygen which is part of the air inside the cylinder. We cannot select the oxygen by itself as a system, since no boundary that encloses the oxygen only and separates it from its environment can be specified, given that the oxygen is very well mixed with the nitrogen of the air.

2.2 Properties and state

In defining a system all we need to describe is its boundary and contents. The definition does not give any information on the condition of the system at any given time. In order to do so we introduce additional attributes which characterize the system, known as prop-

* From now on a closed system will be referred to simply as *a system* while an open system will be designated explicitly as such.

Figure 2.1 **A system with a boundary.**

erties. We distinguish between primitive properties and derived properties.

A primitive property is a characteristic quantity of the system which can be determined by a test, i.e. a measurement. The outcome of the measurement is the value of the property.

The test, or measurement, should not be dependent on prior knowledge of the system whose property is being determined, nor should it require any change in the system. Volume, for example, is a primitive property. A test could be prescribed in which the amount of water displaced by the system is a measure of its volume. This test can, in principle, be performed without requiring any changes in, or prior knowledge of, the system. Examples of primitive properties are length, pressure, mass, density, number of pages in a book, etc. The cost of a book, on the other hand, even though it may be a characteristic of the book, is not a property in the thermodynamic sense. No test can be performed on the book itself, by which its cost can be definitely deduced without any prior knowledge.

A system can be characterized by a large number of properties, each of which may assume different values. Assigning a value to each primitive property and taking all of them together defines the state of the system. Thus:

The state of the system is defined by the set of the values of all its primitive properties.

Identical states

If all the corresponding properties of a system at two given states have equal values then the two states are called *identical states*. Two states are considered to be different if at least one property does not have the same value. A change of state occurs if the value of at least one property changes.

It is possible to consider each property as a coordinate in a multidimensional property space. A point in this space defines uniquely the values of each of the properties and, therefore, also describes the state of the system. In thermodynamics the terms *state* and *point* are used interchangeably. Two identical states will be described by the same point in the property space while different states correspond to different points.

Path

During a change of state the system may pass through a series of intermediate states. The succession of states through which a system passes during a change of state is called a *path*. A path may be described by a line in the multidimensional property space.

Interaction

Some changes of state can be brought about without any changes in its environment, while other changes require some corresponding changes in the environment.

If a change of state in one system requires corresponding changes in another system, it is said that there is an interaction *between the two systems.*

For an interaction to take place, at least two systems with a common boundary must be involved. One of the systems may be the environment. There is no meaning for an interaction if only one system is involved. The interaction takes place through the common boundary.

As an example of an interaction, consider the air in Fig. 2.1 to be the system, and everything else the environment. Compressing the air in the cylinder by lowering the weighted piston results in an interaction between the system, i.e. the air and its environment, namely, the weighted piston. This interaction can be identified at the boundary between the system and its environment as an applied force acting over a distance. On the other hand, if the system is defined to include the air together with the weighted piston, the compression of the air, as well as the lowering of the weighted piston, are both changes that take place within the system. Hence, no interaction of the combined system takes place. If no interaction can take place between the system and its environment, the system is said to be isolated.

Process

A basic concept in thermodynamics, which describes what is happening to a system, is a *process*. When a change of state takes place in a system, with or without interactions, the system is said to undergo a process.

A process is completely specified by the end states, the path and the interactions that take place at the boundary.

When a system goes through the same changes of state but with different interactions at the boundary the processes are different even though the paths are identical. The specification of a process must include all the information on the changes that occur in the system, as well as the interactions at the boundaries.

Cycle

A process whose final state is identical to its initial state is called a *cycle*. Consequently, the properties of a system suffer no net change during a cycle. Alternatively, the cyclic change of any property is zero.

General definition of a property

We have seen that primitive properties have the following characteristics:

- the change of a primitive property between two end states is independent of the path, and
- the change of a primitive property in a cycle is zero.

We can use these characteristics of primitive properties to extend the definition to define a general property as follows:

A property is defined as a quantity whose change in any non-cyclic process depends on the end states only, or whose change in any cycle is zero.

Derived properties

A general property, as defined, certainly includes the class of primitive properties. It may, however, also define other quantities as properties. Properties that are not primitive properties are called *derived properties.* While a primitive property is defined by a test that may be performed without requiring a change of state, a derived property is defined through a specified process or procedure between two end states. Obviously, before a derived property can be defined one must know the end states which are specified by sets of primitive properties. A derived property can, therefore, always be described in terms of the primitive properties.

For example, the depth of the tread of a given automobile tire is a primitive property which can be measured without a change in the state of the tire. On the other hand, the number of miles the tire may travel is not a property, since it depends not only on the initial and final states, but also on the conditions under which the tire was driven. We may define a quantity called "rated tire mileage" as the number of miles traveled under prescribed standard load, speed, road and weather conditions. This quantity depends only on the end states of the tire, as characterized by the tread depth, and is, therefore, a derived property. As a matter of fact, a chart may be devised that would correlate the tread depth with the rated mileage of the tire.

The measurement of a derived property requires a change of state.

Once properties are given, new properties may be defined in terms of the given properties. Thus, for example, if u, p and v are properties, we may define a new property h as $h = u + pv$.

In general, any single-valued algebraic function of a property or several properties is also a property. Obviously, that function has a unique value for any given state. For example, if V is a property so are V^2 and $\ln V$, since for a given state there is one unique value for V and also for V^2 and $\ln V$. Some combinations of properties are important in thermodynamics while others may be completely useless. Nevertheless, all these are properties.

Extensive and intensive properties

Properties may also be classified as *extensive* and *intensive*. A property is called extensive if it is proportional to the extent of the system. Mass, volume and kinetic energy are examples of extensive properties. Their value for a combination of two systems in identical states is the sum of the respective properties of the individual systems.

A property is called intensive if it can be defined at a point in a system and if it is independent of the extent of the system. Pressure, temperature and chemical composition are examples of intensive properties, since they can be measured at any given point irrespective of the size of the system.

There may be other properties that are neither extensive nor intensive, since they cannot be defined at a point, nor are they proportional to the extent of the system. The volume squared, V^2, is a property, since its value is fixed by the state, yet it is neither intensive nor extensive. Fortunately, such properties are of little importance in thermodynamics.

Quantity of matter

The amount of matter of a system is given by the mass enclosed within its boundary. The standard SI unit of mass is 1 kilogram (kg).

An alternative way to measure the amount of matter is by the number n of kilomoles (kmol): 1 kmol is a quantity of matter that contains a number of molecules equal to that of 12 kg of carbon-12. That number of molecules is the Avogadro number which is equal to

$$N_0 = 6.023 \times 10^{26} \text{ molecules/kmol} \tag{2.1}$$

The mass of 1 kmol of a given subtance is called its *molar mass*, or its *molecular weight*. It is denoted by the letter M. Obviously, the molar mass of carbon-12 is 12 kg/kmol or 12 g/mol. In this book the term *molecular weight* is used, following the convention of the SI system of units. The relation between mass, molecular weight and the number of kilomoles is

$$m = nM \tag{2.2}$$

Table 19.1 in Chapter 19 lists the molecular weights of some of the common substances.

Specific property

Any extensive property, when divided by any other extensive property, yields an intensive property. Dividing an extensive property by the mass yields a specific property. For example, specific volume, v, is defined as

$$v = \frac{V}{m} \tag{2.3}$$

In thermodynamics it is customary to denote extensive properties (other than mass) by capital letters and the specific properties by the corresponding lower case letters.

Dividing an extensive property by the number of kilomoles yields a molar specific property. For example, molar specific volume, $\bar{v}$, is defined as

$$\bar{v} = \frac{V}{n} = \frac{VM}{m} \tag{2.4}$$

Density

Dividing an extensive property by the volume yields a property density. For example, the mass per unit volume is the mass density, ρ

$$\rho = \frac{m}{V} \tag{2.5}$$

and the electric charge, Q, per unit volume is the electric charge density, ρ_Q

$$\rho_Q = \frac{Q}{V} \tag{2.6}$$

In thermodynamics equations are usually written in terms of specific properties rather than densities.

2.3 Some characteristics of properties

Let us return to the definition of a property, as stated in the previous section. A property was defined as a quantity whose change in a process depends on the end states only or, alternatively, whose change in a cycle is always zero. We now rephrase this statement mathematically.

Let Π be some property of a system, and denote an infinitesimal change in Π as $d\Pi$. Then a finite change of Π between two given states, 1 and 2, is given by

$$\int_1^2 d\Pi = \Pi_2 - \Pi_1 \tag{2.7}$$

For a cyclic process Eq. (2.7) leads to

$$\oint d\Pi = 0 \tag{2.8}$$

Equations (2.7) and (2.8) indicate that a change of a property is determined by the end states only and is not dependent on the details of the change, i.e. the change can be evaluated without knowledge of the process that brought about that change nor the path between the end states. In that respect an infinitesimal change in a property corresponds mathematically to an exact differential. The integration of an exact differential between two given points is independent of the path of the integration, while the cyclic integral of an exact differential is zero.

Not every infinitesimal change constitutes an exact differential. Mathematics offers a test to identify exact differentials. Thus, if some quantity u is a function of x and y, i.e. $u = u(x, y)$, and a small change in u is given as

$$du = M(x, y)\,dx + N(x, y)\,dy \tag{2.9}$$

then du is an exact differential if and only if the following condition is met:

$$\frac{\partial M(x,y)}{\partial y} = \frac{\partial N(x,y)}{\partial x} \tag{2.10}$$

Equation (2.10) is useful in determining whether a given function represents a property.

EXAMPLE 2.1

Given that H, U, V, and p are properties, determine and explain which of the following quantities describes a property or a change in a property and which does not.

a. $x = U\sqrt{p^2 H}$

b. $y = \ln(U/p)$

c. $dz = d\left(\frac{\ln(U/p)}{T}\right)$

d. $dv = -Hdp$

SOLUTION

a. x is a property since it is an algebraic function of the given properties.
b. y is a property since it is an algebraic function of the given properties.
c. z is a property since the right hand side is an exact differential.
d. In general v is not a property. The property H may be a function of several variables in which case the integration with respect to p is not a unique function of the end states. If, however, H is a function of p only then v is a property.

2.4 Equilibrium

Classical thermodynamics deals with states of equilibrium. The concept of equilibrium is fundamental to thermodynamics.

In mechanics the special case of *mechanical equilibrium* is defined as a state that cannot change by itself. This implies that for a system in mechanical equilibrium the sum of all the forces and the sum of all the moments acting on the system must equal zero. To change the state of a system in mechanical equilibrium an additional external force has to be exerted on the system. Thus, if no additional forces or moments are applied by the environment on the system no change of state can take place. Mechanical equilibrium is but one aspect of equilibrium considered in thermodynamics. A more general definition for the state of equilibrium used in thermodynamics is as follows:

An equilibrium state is a state that cannot be changed without interactions with the environment.

This definition includes that of mechanical equilibrium, but it is a more general one. Any system in thermodynamic equilibrium is, obviously, also in mechanical equilibrium, but the converse is not always true. Systems may be in mechanical equilibrium while not in thermodynamic equilibrium. Consider, for example, a system consisting of a block of hot copper resting on a block of cold copper, Fig. 2.2. Although the system is obviously in mechanical equilibrium (all forces are balanced) and cannot by itself change its position, it is not in thermodynamic equilibrium, since other changes in the system may take place without requiring any interaction with the environment. Indeed, the hot copper will cool down while the cold copper will warm up. Changes of state will continue until the temperature becomes uniform throughout the system, and equilibrium is reached.

As a second example, consider the container of Fig. 2.3 at uniform temperature and pressure, divided by a partition into two parts, one containing nitrogen and the other oxygen. A small hole in the partition allows the flow of the gases from one part to the other. Here again the system is in mechanical equilibrium, but not in thermodynamic equilibrium. Changes within the system will take place without any interaction with the environment, and will continue until a uniform composition in the whole system is reached.

The question of whether a system is in a state of equilibrium may be determined by analyzing the system itself without any reference to its environment. If there is no way to change the state of the system without leaving some effects outside it, the system is in a state of equilibrium. We often encounter situations where the system changes continuously but still goes through states of equilibrium at any instant of time during the change. That, of course, is not contradictory to the concept of equilibrium since those changes in the system take place while corresponding changes take place in the environment. The following example may illustrate that point.

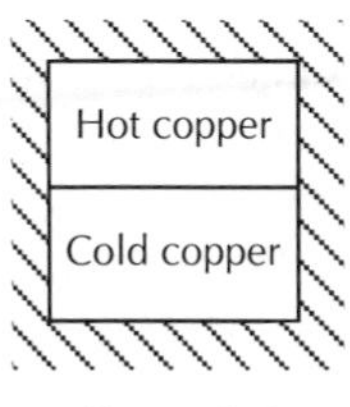

Figure 2.2

Consider a gas, enclosed in a cylinder–piston assembly, for which all the intensive properties, such as the pressure, the temperature, the density, etc., are uniform. That system is in a state of equilibrium regardless of whether the pressure in the environment is higher, lower, or equal to that inside the cylinder. If the pressure outside and inside are equal, no change will take place in the system nor in the environment and the situation is easy to associate with equilibrium. Even if the pressures are not equal, and the piston may start to move and thus change the properties of the gas, the gas may still be in equilibrium. All that is needed to ascertain that the system is in a state of equilibrium is to check whether changes would continue once we stop the interaction with the environment, say by placing a stop on the piston that prevents further motion. If in that case the state of the gas could not be changed any further, then it is an equilibrium state.

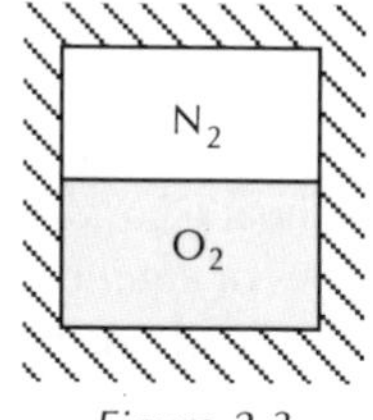

Figure 2.3

2.5 Stable equilibrium

A state of equilibrium is not a state that cannot be changed. Indeed, it is possible to change the state of a system in equilibrium, but in order to do so something must also change in the environment.

A system in a state of stable equilibrium can be changed only if there is a corresponding change in the environment outside the system. The change in the environment is not arbitrary. It must be of the same order of magnitude as the change in the system and it must continue as long as the change in the system takes place. In this book we shall be concerned mainly with states of stable equilibria. Unless otherwise stated we shall refer to a state of stable equilibrium as a *stable state* or simply as an *equilibrium state*. The state of stable equilibrium is defined below:

A system is in a state of stable equilibrium if no change in the system can take place without a corresponding change in the environment; a finite change in the system requires a net finite change in the environment.

An illustration of a system in stable equilibrium, taken from mechanics, is shown in Fig. 2.4. The system consists of a ball which is positioned inside a vessel. Different positions of the ball in the vessel represent different states. The state where the ball is at the bottom of the vessel is the stable equilibrium state. It would not change by itself without some interaction with its environment. The state (the position) of the ball can be changed to another state if a force is applied by another system, say by lowering a weight tied to the ball by a string. If we want to double the height of the ball then we must also double the drop in elevation of the weight. The change in the environment, the weight, is of the same order of magnitude as the change in the state of the system, i.e. the ball. The change in the environment is not temporary, i.e. as long as the ball is in a new state the weight cannot be restored to its original position.

Other examples of stable equilibria are the system in Fig. 2.2 after the temperature in the two blocks equalizes and the one in Fig. 2.3 after the two gases mix completely.

Other types of equilibria

In mechanics, four types of equilibria are encountered, according to the kind of change that is required in the environment relative to the change that takes place in the system. These four types of equilibria are stable, unstable, neutral and metastable. All four types are relevant in thermodynamics, but the most important one is that of stable equilibrium. The other types of equilibria are important in more advanced topics.

Common to all the types of equilibria is the fact that no change of state can take place without a corresponding change in the environment. We distinguish between the different types of equilibria according to the kind of change that is required in the environment relative to the change in the system.

> *Stable equilibrium:* A system is in a state of stable equilibrium if a finite change of state requires a change of the same order of magnitude in the environment.
>
> *Unstable equilibrium* is a state of equilibrium such that a finite change of state as well as a finite rate of change of state can be achieved by a temporary change of a smaller order of magnitude in the environment.
>
> *Neutral equilibrium* is a state of equilibrium such that a finite change of state can be achieved by a temporary change of a smaller order of magnitude in the environment. A finite rate of change in the system, however, requires a finite and continuous change in the environment.
>
> *Metastable equilibrium* is a state of equilibrium such that a small finite change of state requires a change of the same order of magnitude in the environment, provided these do not exceed a certain limit. If the limit is exceeded then a finite

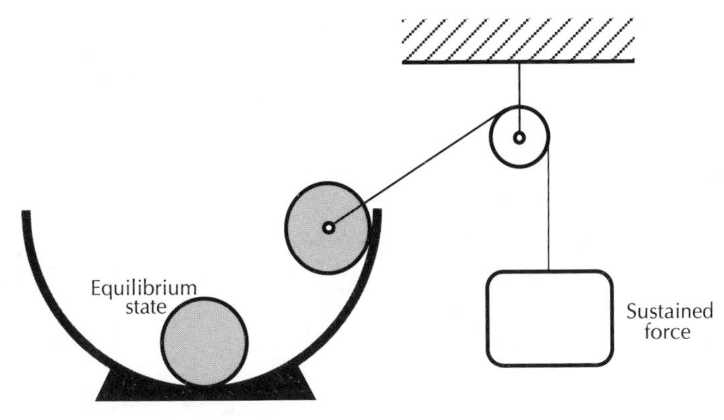

Figure 2.4 **Equilibrium.**

change as well as a finite rate of change may take place by a temporary change in the environment.

2.6 Mutual equilibrium

Consider two systems, each in stable equilibrium. These two systems, when brought into contact, may or may not interact depending on their states. If no interaction takes place, the systems are said to be in mutual equilibrium. Another way of looking at it is that mutual equilibrium exists if a combined system comprised of the original two systems is in a state of stable equilibrium. It should be noted that two systems may each be in equilibrium, yet not in mutual equilibrium. In that case, when the systems are brought into contact, an interaction will take place. The interaction will continue until mutual equilibrium is reached.

Consider, for example, a block of copper taken out from a hot oven and left to cool in an ambient atmosphere. If the properties are uniform throughout the copper block (even though they may change with time) the block may be considered at any instant of time in stable equilibrium, since changes in the block cannot take place without corresponding changes in the environment, complying with the definition of stable equilibrium. Similar comments can be made about the atmosphere; namely, if its properties are uniform, it may also be considered in stable equilibrium. However, the copper block and the atmosphere are not in mutual equilibrium, and therefore an interaction between them can take place.

2.7 The zeroth law of thermodynamics

The concept of equilibrium may now be used to formulate what is known as the zeroth law of thermodynamics:

Two systems, each in mutual equilibrium with a third system, are also in mutual equilibrium with each other in the same manner.

The meaning of the zeroth law of thermodynamics is illustrated in Fig. 2.5. Let system A and system B be each in mutual equilibrium with system C. Namely, if communication between systems A and C were allowed, no interactions would result. The same holds for systems B and C. The zeroth law of thermodynamics asserts that system A and system B are also in mutual equilibrium.

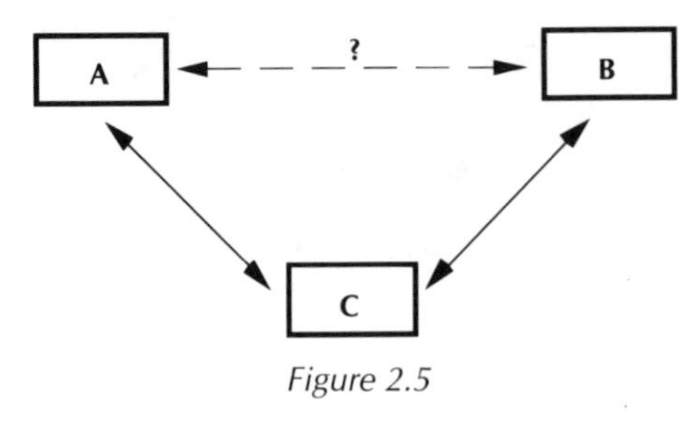

Figure 2.5

This law cannot be proven on the basis of previous laws. It is accepted since it is in agreement with all known experimental facts with no exception.

The zeroth law may seem so obvious that a question may be asked: why bother at all to state such a law? True, for thermodynamic systems there are no exceptions. However, if one tries to apply a similar law to social behavior it might result in failure. If one replaced the notion "mutual equilibrium" with the notion "mutual love", then it would not be so obvious that, if Mary is in mutual love with John, and Mary is in mutual love with her daddy, then John and daddy are also in mutual love.

The zeroth law of thermodynamics is used in the definition and measurement of temperature. This will be discussed in Chapter 3, after the concept of heat is introduced.

PROBLEMS

2.1 State which of the following items must be specified when a system is defined: boundary, matter content, distribution of matter inside the boundaries, cost, location, walls internal to boundaries, walls external to boundaries, date of observation, ownership, limitation to changes, volume, pressure at a given point.

2.2 Declare which of the following items must be specified when a state of a well-defined system is described: boundary, matter content, distribution of matter inside the boundaries, cost, location, walls internal to boundaries, walls external to boundaries, date of observation, ownership, limitation to changes, volume, pressure at a given point.

2.3 Must the boundaries of a system be physical entities? Could the boundaries be given mathematically? Could matter cross the boundary at one specific point?

2.4 A system is selected to allow the analysis of a real situation. Is it possible, in your opinion, to describe exactly all the aspects of a real situation? Explain in a few words and support your answer with an example.

2.5 Would it be possible to define only derived properties for a given system without ever defining its primitive properties?

2.6

a. Could a primitive property be an independent property?
b. Is it possible to construct an exact set of independent properties that consists of only primitive properties?

2.7

a. Could a derived property be an independent property?
b. Is it possible to construct a complete set of independent properties that consists only of derived properties?

2.8 Try to fit a thermodynamic system to each of the following entities. If you can, describe the boundary and give two – three properties. If you think that no system can be defined, explain why not.

a. 5 kg of carbon dioxide contained in a steel cylinder–piston assembly.
b. 5 kg of air contained in a steel cylinder–piston assembly.
c. 1 kg of oxygen in 5 kg of air contained in a steel cylinder–piston assembly.
d. Half a rod of copper whose diameter is 0.2 m and length 1.3 m.
e. A magnetic rod whose diameter is 0.2 m and length 1.3 m.
f. Half the magnetic rod, whose diameter is 0.2 m and length 1.3 m, that includes the north magnetic pole.
g. One of two neighboring stars.
h. A drop of gasoline with air enclosed in a steel cylinder–piston assembly.
i. The air that was originally in a leaky container.
j. The air that was originally enclosed in half a rigid container after the partition was broken. The other part of the container was originally void.
k. The oxygen that was originally enclosed in half a rigid container after the partition was broken. The other part of the container originally contained air.

2.9 If p, V and T are properties and R is a constant, determine which of the following equations describes a change in property and which one does not. Explain in brief.

a. $dx = RdT + pdV$ b. $dy = pdV + Vdp$ c. $dz = pdV - Vdp$

d. $dx = d\left(\frac{pV}{T}\right)$ e. $dy = -Vdp$ f. $dz = \frac{p}{T}dV$

2.10

a. Could an equilibrium state be changed?
b. If a state of a system does not change in a period of 15 seconds, does that mean that the system is in a state of stable equilibrium?
c. If a state of a system does not change in a period of 15 hours, does that mean that the system is in a state of stable equilibrium?
d. If a state of a system does not change in a period of 15 days does that mean that the system is in a state of stable equilibrium?
e. Can one be sure that a state of equilibrium exists once the concept is well defined?

2.11 Car batteries are rated in terms of two quantities: voltage and ampere-hours.

a. Define these quantities and describe a method for measuring them.
b. Does the quantity voltage represent a thermodynamic property? If yes, is it a primitive or derived property?
c. Does the quantity ampere-hours represent a thermodynamic property? If yes, is it a primitive or derived property?

2.12 A closed pressure vessel contains 80 kg of liquid water and 2 kg of water vapor. The volume of the liquid is 95.2 liters and the remainder of the vessel is occupied by vapor. The specific volume of the vapor is 0.08619 m^3/kg.

a. Define the system and its boundaries.
b. Find the volume of the vessel.
c. Find the specific volume of the liquid.
d. What is the density of the vapor?
e. Find the average specific volume of the vapor–liquid mixture.

2.13 A closed vessel contains 50 kg of liquid ammonia and 1 kg of ammonia vapor. The specific volume of the liquid is 0.00158 m^3/kg and the specific volume of the vapor is 0.2517 m^3/kg.

a. Define the system and its boundaries.
b. Find the volume of the liquid phase.
c. Find the volume of the vessel.
d. What are the densities of the liquid and the vapor?
e. Find the average specific volume of the vapor–liquid mixture.

2.14 Given a property $P = P(x, y)$, the exact differential of P is given as

$$dP = \left(\frac{\partial P}{\partial x}\right)dx + \left(\frac{\partial P}{\partial y}\right)dy$$

Compare this expression to Eq. (2.9) and show that Eq. (2.10) is indeed a sufficient condition for P to be an exact differential.

2.15 An intensive property can be defined at each point of a system.
Must an intensive property of a system have a unique value, or would it be possible to have different values of an intensive property at different points of a system? Support your answer with an example.

2.16 Must an extensive property of a system have a unique value, or would it be possible to have different values of an extensive property at different points of a system? Support your answer with an example.

2.17 The state of a certain non-isolated system is continuously changing. It is claimed that at any time during the process the system is in states of equilibrium.
Is such a claim possible? If not explain why. If yes, give an example.

CHAPTER THREE

Work, energy, and heat – first law of thermodynamics

The terms work, heat, and energy are used in everyday language, sometimes interchangeably. Intuitive understanding of these terms is not sufficient for thermodynamic analysis, and may lead occasionally to erroneous results.

In this chapter the terms work, energy, and heat are carefully defined. It is shown that they represent three discrete non-interchangeable concepts with a distinct relationship among them. The first law of thermodynamics is stated for a closed system and is shown to lead to the law of conservation of energy.

3.1 Work in mechanical systems

Work in mechanics is defined as the scalar product of a force and the displacement of its point of application. For a differential displacement the work is

$$dW = \mathbf{F} \cdot d\,\mathbf{r} \tag{3.1}$$

In thermodynamics, where interactions are regarded from the point of view of a system, this definition may be interpreted as follows: when a system applies a force on its surroundings, causing a displacement at the boundary, the scalar product of the force and the boundary displacement is the work of the system. This work obviously causes changes in the environment, for example the change in level of a weight in a gravitational field, or the stretching of a spring. As far as the system is concerned all these changes are equivalent insofar as they are caused by identical changes in the system and at its boundaries.

So far, only modes of work, where the force and the displacement can be easily identified, have been described. In other types of work related to electric, magnetic and other nomena, it may be difficult to identify the force and the displacement. The definition of work in thermodynamics is such that it covers all the possible modes, and of course also includes the definition of work in mechanics.

3.2 Work in thermodynamic systems

In thermodynamics work is defined as follows:

Work is an interaction between two systems such that whatever happens in each system and its boundary could have happened, exactly, with the only effect external to that system being a change in the level of a weight in a gravitational field.

Work, by definition, is an interaction; hence, it requires at least two systems. Indeed, there is no meaning to work if only one system is involved. Not every interaction is work. To be considered work an interaction must pass the test expressed in the definition above. The following examples clarify this point.

EXAMPLE 3.1

Consider a weight attached by a string, passing over a frictionless pulley, to a block sliding on a horizontal plane, Fig. 3.1. Lowering the weight causes the block to slide on the plane overcoming friction.

By defining the block and the plane as system A, and the weight as system B, an interaction between systems A and B can be identified. This interaction may be recognized at the boundary, by observing the motion of the stretched string.

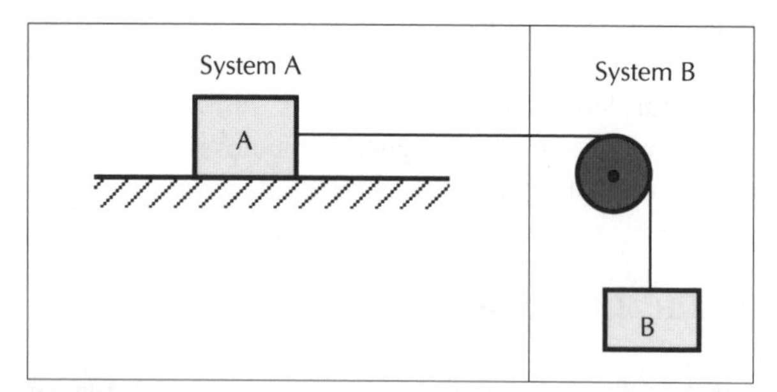

Figure 3.1

To show that this is indeed a work interaction, two tests must be devised, one for each system, as follows: the test for system A may be provided by system B itself, since the only effect outside of system A is a change in the level of the weight in system B.

In order to test system B, system A is replaced by a test system, "Test B" in Fig. 3.2, consisting of a weight on a

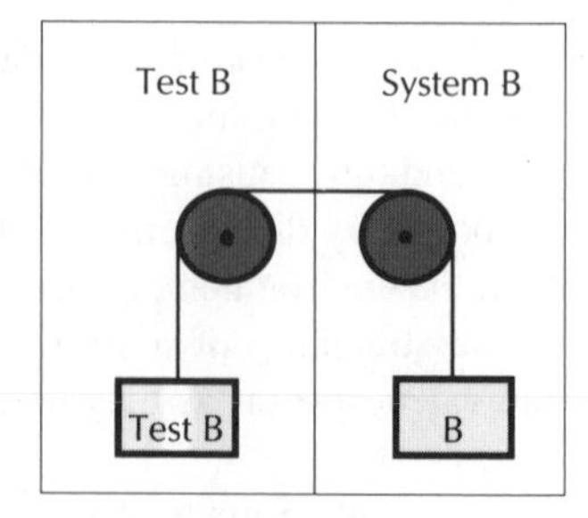

Figure 3.2

string passing over a frictionless pulley. Now in "Test B" the only change is the raising of the level of the weight, while system B repeats, exactly, the original process. The motion of the string under tension at the boundary is also repeated exactly as in the original process. Since we have demonstrated that both systems A and B comply with the definition of work the interaction is work.

If one selects the combination of the block, plane and weight as a single system, no work can be identified in the thermodynamic sense, even though changes do occur within the system.

EXAMPLE 3.2

Consider a light bulb connected to a storage battery as shown in Fig. 3.3. By closing the switch, a process takes place in the system. Current crosses the boundary through the circuit causing the bulb to light up.

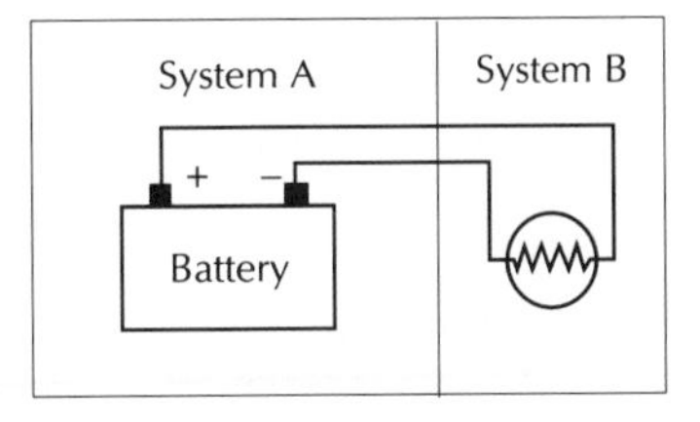

Figure 3.3

Defining the battery as system A and the light bulb as system B, an interaction can be identified, since what happens in system B depends on the changes in system A and vice versa. Even though no weight has changed its level in either system it can be shown that this interaction is work, by again devising two tests, one for each system. A test system for system A could consist of a frictionless electric motor which is used to lift weights. Whatever occurred in system A and at its boundary during the actual process can now be repeated exactly so that the only change in "test A" is the raising of a weight.

Similarly, the battery of system A could be replaced by a frictionless electric generator driven by a falling weight, resulting in effects in system B identical to those of the original process. Hence, it is a work interaction.

Obviously, if instead of a light bulb an electric heater were connected to the battery, once again the interaction between the battery and the heater would be work.

3.2.1 An example where work cannot be identified

Consider system A, a block of copper taken out from a refrigerator. This system is brought into contact with system B, a block of copper taken out of a hot oven (Fig. 3.4a). No other systems are involved. Obviously, an interaction between the systems takes place.

A test for system A can be devised as follows: a frictionless electric generator driven by a falling weight supplies the current to a resistance heater in system B. Whatever happened in system A in the original interaction could thus be repeated where the only external effect (in test A, Fig. 3.4b) is the falling of a weight. However, no test for system B can be found in which the only external effect would be a change in the level of a weight. Since only one test for work was found, the interaction could not be shown to be work. This interaction will be identified later on as a heat interaction.

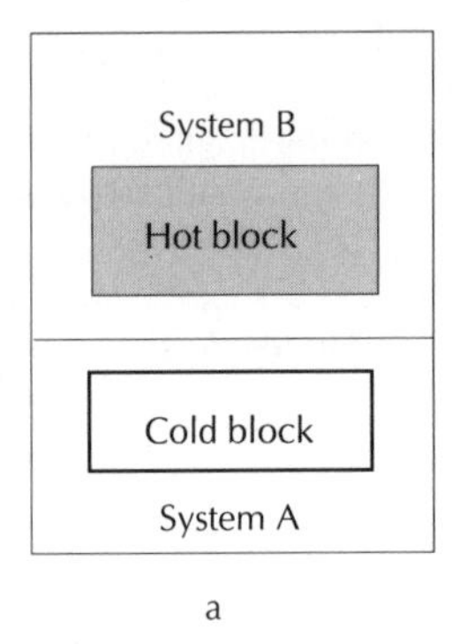

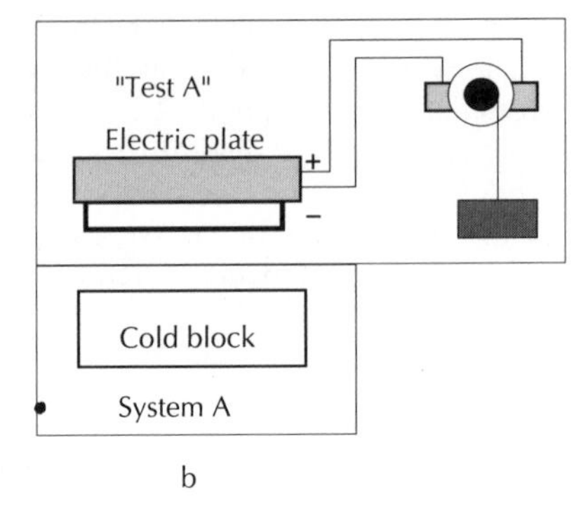

Figure 3.4

3.3 Measure of work

In the test for each system undergoing a work interaction, the only effect was a change in the level of a weight. This change may be used to measure the amount of work of that system.

The measure of the work of a system is defined by the product of the weight and the change of its level in the test. The work of the system is taken as positive when the weight in the external test is raised and negative when it is lowered. When the work is positive the system is said to be doing work on its environment, while when it is negative the environment is doing work on the system.

3.4 Work in adiabatic processes

A process that involves no interactions other than work is called an adiabatic process.

An adiabatic process may therefore involve no interactions at all or work interactions only. An adiabatic boundary is one through which no interactions, other than work, can take place. A system whose boundaries are adiabatic can undergo only adiabatic processes.

3.5 Work in non-adiabatic processes

As seen in the previous sections, work interactions were always associated with phenomena that occurred on the boundary. In Example 3.1, the boundary phenomenon was the motion of a string under tension. In Example 3.2, electric current passed through the boundary. Both phenomena could be directly translated into a change in the level of a weight. In non-adiabatic processes such boundary phenomena could take place in combination with other boundary phenomena. Work under those conditions would be the same as that caused by the same boundary phenomena in adiabatic processes.

EXAMPLE 3.3

A 5 kg block is attached to a linear spring and is resting on a support, Fig. 3.5. The spring is under zero tension. When the support is removed, the block drops and after several oscillations assumes a new position. If the spring constant is k = 500 N/m, calculate the work interaction of the spring, neglecting air resistance.

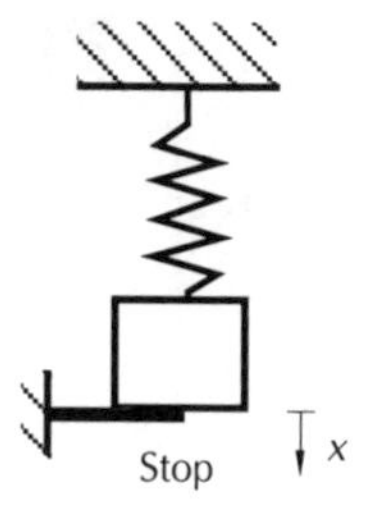

Figure 3.5

SOLUTION

The spring displacement is calculated from the condition of mechanical equilibrium between the block and the spring:

$$kx = mg$$

$$x = \frac{mg}{k} = \frac{5 \times 9.80665}{500} = 0.0981 \text{ m}$$

Defining the spring as system A and the block as system B, the only effect outside system A is a change in the level of a weight. Thus the work is

$$W = -mgx = -5 \times 9.81 \times 0.0981 = -4.81 \text{ J}$$

The minus sign indicates that work is done on the spring, i.e. the work of the spring is negative.

3.6 Work at a moving boundary

When a force is acting at a system boundary, resulting in motion, work is performed. The work of the system can be calculated from

$$W = -\int_1^2 \mathbf{F} \cdot d\mathbf{x} \tag{3.2}$$

where $\mathbf{F}$ is the force, applied by the surroundings, on the boundary of the system. The minus sign accounts for the fact that the work of the system is negative, i.e. work is done *on* the system.

3.7 Work of a compressible system

Consider a closed system comprised of a gas contained in a cylinder, under pressure by a weighted piston, Fig. 3.6. Initially the piston is prevented from rising by a pin. The pin is removed and the piston rises due to the gas pressure until it finally stops. It is easy in this case to calculate the work of the piston, W_p, since it is equal to the change of the level of a weight in a test (for the piston), which in turn is equal to

$$W_p = m_p g(z_1 - z_2) = \frac{m_p g}{A}[A(z_1 - z_2)] = p_2(V_1 - V_2)$$

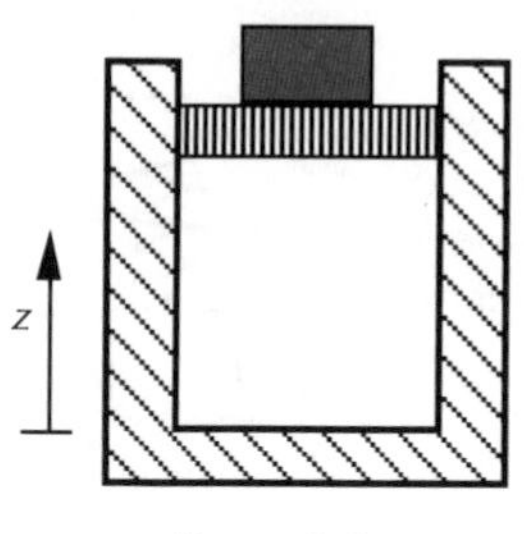

Figure 3.6

The work of the gas, W, in this process, is obviously equal in magnitude, but opposite in sign to the work of the piston:

$$W = -W_p = p_2(V_2 - V_1) \tag{3.3}$$

Note that the pressure at the final state, p_2, is equal to the piston weight divided by its area, and the volume change of the gas is equal to the piston area multiplied by the change of its level.

One can further note that, even though the initial state (before removing the pin) and the final state are both equilibrium states, all the intermediate states are of non-equilibrium character. The final pressure, p_2, can be easily determined since it is equal to the weight of the piston divided by its area. During the process, the pressure of the gas may be not uniform within the cylinder and the piston may have varying accelerations. The exact value of the pressure, p, measured at some point in the gas is not known. It is, however, larger than the final pressure, p_2 throughout the process. Thus,

$$W = p_2(V_2 - V_1) < \int_1^2 p dV \tag{3.4}$$

since $p_2 < p$ throughout the process.

To summarize, the work of the system on the environment can be viewed as follows: the resistance that the system has to overcome during a volume change can be expressed by an external equivalent pressure, p_e, exerted by the environment on the system. Hence, the work done by the system on the environment is, in general,

$$W = \int_1^2 p_e dV \tag{3.5}$$

Obviously, for compression work, the volume change is negative, and $p_e > p$. It follows that in general

$$\int_1^2 p_e dV < \int_1^2 p\, dV$$

where the inequality sign was inverted, due to the fact that in compression $dV < 0$.

3.8 Quasistatic process and quasistatic work

When a system undergoes changes it passes through a sequence of states some of which may be essentially equilibrium states and some far away from equilibrium. For example, consider a system consisting of a gas inside a cylinder covered by a piston. If the pressure of the gas is substantially higher then the external force per unit area of the piston (the external equivalent pressure), the piston will be accelerated. During this acceleration the conditions of the gas at a given instant may be far from equilibrium, that is such a state could be changed without any interaction with the environment. On the other hand, it is possible to think of processes where the system will be in equilibrium, at any instant during the process. In the example of the gas in the cylinder, if we make sure that the external equivalent pressure is equal (or essentially equal) to the pressure of the gas throughout the expansion process, then at any instant during the process the gas could be essentially in equilibrium.

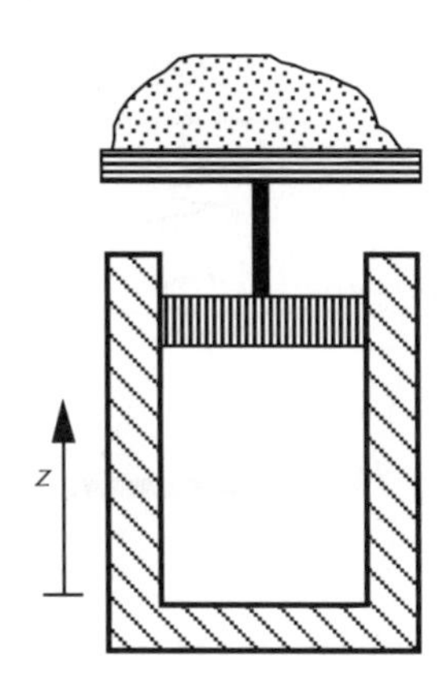

Figure 3.7

A process where the system passes through equilibrium states during the change of state is called a *quasistatic process*. The work of a quasistatic process is called *quasistatic work*.

To visualize a quasistatic process, consider Fig. 3.7 showing a cylinder containing gas under a piston loaded by sand so that the gas pressure exactly supports the weight of the piston plus the sand. Now one grain of sand is removed and the gas expands by a small amount until its pressure supports the sand-loaded piston. One grain of sand does not change substantially the weight of the piston and sand; thus the state inside the gas is very close to equilibrium. The finer the sand the smaller the deviation from equilibrium. This is true for all the states throughout the process. Eventually, the final state is reached. For very fine sand this process is an example of a quasistatic process.

Since the internal pressure is equal to the external equivalent pressure, the work in this case can be calculated by

$$W = \int_1^2 p_e dV \tag{3.6}$$

Note that in general the work may be equal to or less than the integral, namely

$$\int_1^2 p_e dV \leq \int_1^2 p_e x dV \tag{3.7}$$

where the equality holds for quasistatic processes and the inequality otherwise.

Quasistatic processes are, obviously, not limited to compressible systems. Consider, for example, the spring–weight arrangement in vacuum discussed in Example 3.3. The process of stretching a spring can be performed quasistatically by starting with zero load and increasing the tension on the spring by continuously adding fine grains of sand to the load, as shown in Fig. 3.8. The process can be terminated when the total load on the spring is 5 kg, as in Example 3.3. The spring displacement will also be the same, i.e. 0.0981m. At any instant the spring is in mutual equilibrium with the load and therefore the process is quasistatic. The work can therefore be calculated from

$$W_s = \int_1^2 F dx = \int_1^2 -kx dx = -\frac{k}{2}(x_2^2 - x_1^2) \tag{3.8}$$

Substituting $k = 500$ N/m into Eq. (3.8) yields

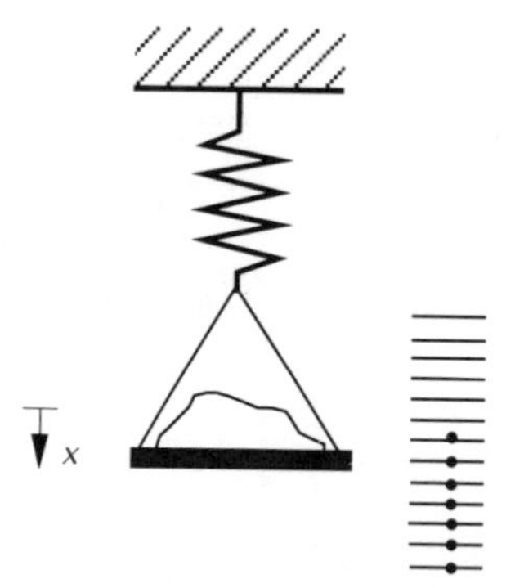

Figure 3.8 **Quasistatic work.**

$$W_q = -(500/2) \times 0.0981^2 = -2.41 \text{ J}$$

which is half of the work obtained for the non-quasistatic process of Example 3.3.

Table 3.1 lists various modes of work for quasistatic processes. In each mode, we distinguish a generalized driving force, e.g. pressure, magnetic field, and a generalized displacement, e.g. change of volume, change of magnetization. The expression for the quasistatic work is also given in the table.

Table 3.1 **Modes of quasistatic work.**

Mode of work	Generalized force		Generalized displacement		Expression for δW
Mechanical	Force	F	Displacement	dx	$\delta W = -Fdx$
Compression	Pressure	p	Volume change	dV	$= pdV$
Surface tension	Surface tension	σ	Area change	dA	$= -\sigma dA$
Torsion	Moment	M_T	Angle change	$d\omega$	$= -M_T d\omega$
Electric	Electric field	$\mathbf{E}$	Electric displacement	$d\mathbf{D}$	$= -\mathbf{E}\cdot d\mathbf{D}$
Magnetic	Magnetic field	$\mathbf{H}$	Magnetization	$d\mathbf{M}$	$= -\mathbf{H}\cdot d\mathbf{M}$

The driving force is an *intensive* property which may or may not change during the work interaction. On the other hand, the displacement is an *extensive* property that must change in order to have a quasistatic work interaction. Therefore, the displacement is used to characterize the quasistatic work mode and is called the *quasistatic work parameter*.

For example, in compression work, $\delta W = pdV$, the driving force, p, is an *intensive* property. The pressure may change or remain constant during the interaction. On the other hand the volume must change during the process in order to have a non-zero work interaction. Therefore, the volume is the quasistatic parameter for this work mode.

3.9 The first law of thermodynamics

A change of state in a system can be achieved by means of different processes. It has been shown by experiment that, when a system goes from state A to state B by different adiabatic processes, the work of the system, as measured by the change in the level of a weight, is the same for each one of the adiabatic processes.

Consider, for example, the system in Fig. 3.9 consisting of water in which a stirrer and

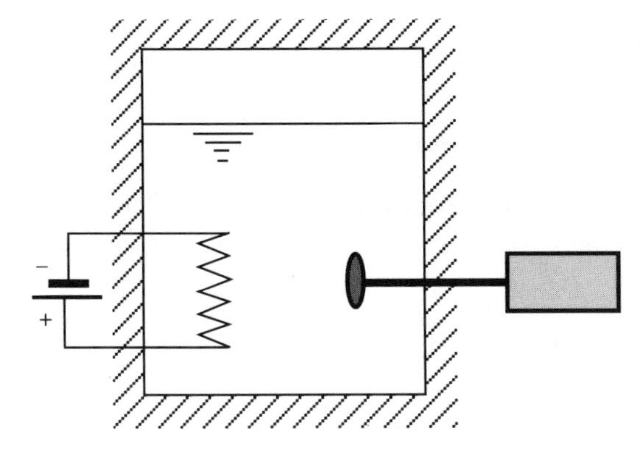

Figure 3.9

an electric resistor are immersed. This system is contained in an adiabatic vessel through which the shaft of the stirrer and the wires of the resistor pass. Now, consider two different processes resulting in the same change of state of the system. In the first process, the shaft is being rotated by means of a falling weight, till the desired end state is reached. In the second process, starting from the same initial state, the desired final state is reached by passing an electric current through the resistor. The current is generated by means of a generator driven by a falling weight.

Careful measurements have shown that the amounts of work between the given end states of the system were the same in both processes. This illustrates an experimental fact that for various adiabatic processes between two given states the work is identical, and does not depend on the details of the process, as long as it is adiabatic. The first law of thermodynamics is a generalization of this and similar experimental facts. It may be stated as follows:

The work of a system for any adiabatic process connecting given end states depends on the end states only.

Since work in an adiabatic process depends only on the end states, and not on the details of the process, it can be used to define a change of a property, as shown in Chapter 2. Indeed, the adiabatic work is used to define a property called energy. More formally:

Energy, E, is a property the change of which is measured by the adiabatic work between two given end states.

The change of energy in a cycle is equal to zero, as is the case for any property. It is conventional to define energy so that it increases when the work of the system is negative, that is when work is done on the system:

$$E_2 - E_1 = \Delta E = -W_{adiab} \tag{3.9}$$

In non-adiabatic processes the change in energy, ΔE, is not necessarily equal to the work input ($-W$), and a correction should be made to account for other, non-work, interactions. These are called heat interactions, denoted as Q. Thus, the energy change of a system in any process is equal to the work and the heat inputs into the system:

$$E_2 - E_1 = Q + (-W) \text{ or } \Delta E = Q - W \tag{3.10}$$

Equation (3.10) constitutes the general statement of the first law of thermodynamics. It expresses the concept of conservation of energy in systems undergoing interactions.

3.10 Work, heat, and energy

Work, heat, and energy have the same dimensions and are denoted by the same units. The basic unit of energy is the joule, which equals the work required to lift a weight of 1 newton by 1 meter. Other units are the kJ, the calorie, the Btu, the kWh, etc. The relationships between these units are given in the Appendix.

Energy describes a property that has a distinct value for each state. Work and heat on the other hand are interactions and not properties; hence, it is impossible to assign a value for work or heat to any state. Work and heat depend on the details of the process connecting two states. They can, therefore, be measured during a change of state only. The notation used to describe these quantities reflects these notions.

The differential change of energy between two adjacent states is denoted by dE, which is an exact differential in the mathematical sense. Therefore, a finite change between two states is

$$\Delta E = \int_1^2 dE = E_2 - E_1 \tag{3.11}$$

and

$$\oint dE = 0 \tag{3.12}$$

The integration in Eq. (3.11) can be performed even if the exact process between states 1 and 2 is not known.

The differential quantities of work and heat *during* a process connecting two adjacent states are denoted by δW and δQ, respectively. The results of the integration between two states are

$$\int_1^2 \delta Q = Q_{12} \tag{3.13}$$

and

$$\int_1^2 \delta W = W_{12} \tag{3.14}$$

The symbol δ indicates a small quantity which is not an exact differential. Integration requires knowledge of the process, and it does not describe the change of a property between states 1 and 2. The difference in notation between Eqs (3.13)–(3.14) and that of Eq. (3.11) accounts for this fact.

Although both are interactions, expressible at the boundary of a system, work and heat differ from one another. Work is an interaction which passes the test for equivalence of the change in the level of a weight, as shown above. Heat, on the other hand, does not.

Heat is an interaction that may take place between two systems, each being in equilibrium but not in mutual equilibrium. In the next section, the property of temperature will be introduced through the concept of mutual equilibrium. It will also be shown that heat interactions are associated with a temperature difference between the interacting systems. For work, at least one system, the one that does the work, cannot be in equilibrium. The ability to have an interaction between systems in equilibrium is the main feature that distinguishes heat from work. This notion will be taken up in detail after the second law of thermodynamics is introduced.

EXAMPLE 3.4

A system is undergoing a cycle which consists of three processes. During the first process the work is 5 kJ and the heat is 23 kJ. In the second one no work takes place and the heat interaction is –50 kJ. The third process is adiabatic.

a. Find the energy change in each process.
b. Find the work in the third process.

SOLUTION

a. We may write the first law of thermodynamics, Eq. (3.10), for each process of the cycle:

$$\Delta E_1 = Q_1 - W_1$$

$$\Delta E_2 = Q_2 - W_2$$

$$\Delta E_3 = Q_3 - W_3$$

For the complete cycle, the change of energy is zero, and hence

$$\Delta E_1 + \Delta E_2 + \Delta E_3 = 0$$

Therefore,

$$\Delta E_1 = 23 - 5 = 18 \text{ kJ}$$

$$\Delta E_2 = -50 - 0 = -50 \text{ kJ}$$

$$\Delta E_3 = -(\Delta E_1 + \Delta E_2) = -(18 - 50) = 32 \text{ kJ}$$

$$\Delta E_3 = Q_3 - W_3 = 0 - W_3$$

b. The third process is adiabatic; hence

$$W_3 = -\Delta E_3 = -32 \text{ kJ}$$

3.11 Temperature

Temperature is a property which is closely related to thermal equilibrium. Systems are in thermal equilibrium if no heat interaction results after bringing the systems into good contact with each other. If a heat interaction does take place the systems are not in thermal equilibrium. Conversely, if systems not in thermal equilibrium are brought in good contact, a heat interaction will result. The zeroth law of thermodynamics, which was introduced in Chapter 2, also applies to thermal equilibrium.

Thus, if system A and system B are each in thermal equilibrium with system C, they must, by the zeroth law, be in thermal equilibrium with each other.

In fact, if any number of systems are each in thermal equilibrium with a given test system, they must also be in thermal equilibrium with each other. All these systems form a group that has a common property, namely that of being in thermal equilibrium with the test system. This property is called *temperature*.

Needless to say, a system which does not belong to the group (i.e. it is not in thermal equilibrium with the given test system) is not in thermal equilibrium with any of the systems of the group, and hence does not have the same temperature.

Temperature is a property that is equal in all systems which are in thermal equilibrium with each other.

The above definition of temperature does not tell us by itself how to assign a value to temperature. This can be done by selecting a standard system, called a thermometer, that has only one independent property, e.g. the level of mercury in a glass tube. Certain reference states, that can be easily reproduced in any good laboratory, are assigned preselected values of temperature. The combination of these reference states and a standard thermometer constitute a temperature scale.

Celsius and Fahrenheit scales are the most common in everyday use. Each can be assigned to a thermometer of mercury inside a glass tube. The reference states are the ice point, 0 °C and 32 °F for the Celsius and the Fahrenheit scales, respectively, and the steam (boiling) point, where the respective values are 100 °C and 212 °F for the two scales. The two temperature scales are related to each other by

$$T(°\mathrm{F}) = 1.8 \times T(°\mathrm{C}) + 32 \qquad (3.15)$$

These scales depend on a physical standard thermometer by which all other thermometers must be calibrated. A thermodynamic temperature scale, based on the second law of thermodynamics, will be introduced in Chapter 8. This thermodynamic scale is not dependent on the specific selection of a thermometer.

PROBLEMS

3.1 For each of the following cases choose a suitable system, if possible, and describe its boundaries and surroundings. Indicate if the work done is positive, negative or zero.

a. A balloon is inflated by means of a hand pump. Assume that the balloon, pump and connectors are adiabatic.
b. A liquid moving inside a rigid vessel comes slowly to rest.

c. Hydrogen (H_2) and oxygen (O_2) in a rigid vessel undergo a chemical reaction and water is formed.
d. A pressure cooker containing water is put on a stove and the pressure inside rises.
e. An electric capacitor is connected to a battery. The voltage across the capacitor is rising.
f. An electric resistor is put inside a thermos bottle. The resistor is connected to a battery and current flows through it for an hour.
g. A package of butter falls from a table onto a very hard floor.

3.2 A gas is compressed from a state of 0.30 m^3 and 1.0 bar, to a state of 0.10 m^3 and 4.0 bars, in a process that can be represented by a straight line on a *p–V* diagram. Determine the work of the gas.

3.3 The force that a balloon exerts on its contents is proportional to its volume. The balloon is inflated from zero volume to a final volume of $V_2 = 0.34$ m^3 and a final pressure of $p_2 = 130$ kPa. Calculate the work done on the balloon.

3.4 Determine which of the following sets of data satisfy the first law of thermodynamics:

a.	$W = 50$ kJ	$Q = 170$ kJ	$\Delta E = 120$ kJ
b.	$W = 100$ Btu	$Q = -110$ Btu	$\Delta E = -210$ Btu
c.	$W = 100$ Btu	$Q = -110$ Btu	$\Delta E = -210$ Wh
d.	$W = 250$ kJ	$Q = -110$ kJ	$\Delta E = -100$ Wh
e.	$W = -50$ Wh	$Q = 130$ Wh	$\Delta E = 50$ kJ
f.	$W = 44$ kPa m^3	$Q = 188$ kJ	$\Delta E = 40$ Wh
g.	$W = 44$ kPa m^3	$Q = 188$ kJ	$\Delta E = 40$ kN m

3.5 A refrigerator is working with its door open inside a completely insulated room. Determine if the energy change of the room is positive, negative or zero.

3.6 A cylinder contains 5.0 kg of CO_2 and is closed by a piston of negligible mass. In a certain experiment the pressure and volume were measured at different states and the following results were obtained:

p	bar	3.45	2.75	2.07	1.38	0.69
v	m^3/kg	0.125	0.150	0.187	0.287	0.474

Determine the work of the system which includes the cylinder, the piston and the gas if:

a. The process is quasistatic.
b. A pressure of 0.35 bars is required to overcome the internal friction.

3.7 A closed system consisting of an unknown gas undergoes a cycle consisting of three quasistatic processes, as shown in Fig. 3.10.
Process 1–2 is adiabatic and its energy change is –50 kJ.
Process 2–3 is at constant pressure.
Process 3–1 is at constant volume.

a. Find the work done by the gas in each stage.
b. Find the work of the system for the complete cycle.
c. Find the heat interaction for the complete cycle.

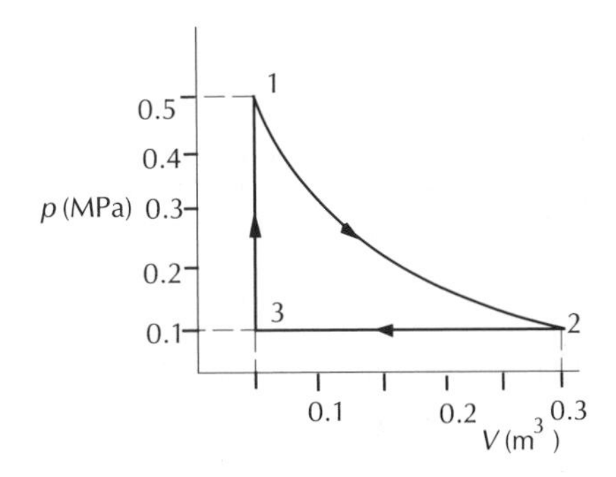

Figure 3.10

3.8 Indicate whether the following statements are true, sometimes true, or false.

a. Work is a derived property.
b. The pressure change from a state 1 to state 2 depends on the work of the system.
c. Pressure is a primitive property.
d. Energy is a primitive property.

e. Heat interaction is a derived property.
f. Pressure is an intensive property.
g. In gas expansion the energy change is positive.
h. Equilibrium is a state that cannot be changed.
i. The product of pressure and volume is an intensive property.
j. The product of pressure and volume is an extensive property.
k. The enthalpies of two systems in mutual equilibrium are equal.
l. The heat interaction in an isobaric process is positive.
m. The heat interaction in an isothermal process is positive.
n. Work in an adiabatic process is equal to zero.
o. When a gas is being compressed in a cylinder its energy decreases.
p. In a cycle where the work is positive, the energy of the system decreases.
q. Energy is an intensive property.

3.9 Determine the energy change in kilojoules for each of the following situations:

a. $Q = -5$ kcal, $W = 30$ kJ
b. $Q = 20$ Btu, $W = 0$
c. $Q = 0.05$ kWh, $W = 400$ kgf.m
d. $Q = 0$, $W = 1000$ ftlb

3.10 A 12 inch diameter spherical balloon is filled with gas at 25 psi. Owing to a heat interaction of 40 kJ the diameter of the balloon increases to 16 inches. During the process the pressure in the balloon:

I. stays constant;
II. increases proportionally to the diameter;
III. changes inversely proportional to the diameter.

a. Find the work done by the gas for each of the above situations.
b. Find the energy change of the gas.

3.11 A system of unknown contents interacts with the environment such that only the effects described below take place. Analyze the nature of the interaction and its sign in each of the following situations. Could it be work, heat or both?

a. A string passing through the boundary of the system results in a weight rising in the environment.
b. A string passing through the boundary of the system results in a weight being lowered in the environment.
c. Water in an insulated electric kettle is brought close to boiling.
d. Water in an uninsulated electric kettle is brought close to boiling.
e. An electric capacitor is discharged.
f. An electric capacitor is charged.
g. A cold body is heated.
h. A hot body is cooled.
i. A spring is stretched.
j. A stretched spring is released.

3.12 An automobile battery which is originally fully charged gradually discharges while sitting on a shelf at a constant temperature of 40 °C, producing no electric work but resulting in a heat transfer of 1000 kJ to its environment. The battery is then recharged to its initial state by means of a process involving work *input* of 440 Wh. Find the heat interaction of the *battery* during this charging process. Justify your answer thermodynamically.

3.13 A PMM1 is defined as an adiabatic system for which the work in a cycle is not zero. Is the first law equivalent to the statement that a PMM1 is impossible?

3.14 Consider a capacitor which undergoes the following processes:

Process a. The capacitor, initially uncharged, is fully charged by connecting it to the terminals of a battery. During this process the temperature of the battery, the wires, and the capacitor is kept constant by a constant-temperature bath. The energy of the battery decreases by

CHAPTER FOUR

Simple systems

The laws of thermodynamics are applicable to any system, regardless of its complexity. It is sometimes helpful to model certain aspects of the system, and thus substantially simplify the analysis. In this chapter we introduce the concept of a simple system, which has only one mode of quasistatic work. In many applications this simplified concept is fairly accurate in describing real substances.

We present the terms enthalpy and specific heats, and explain the structure of tables of properties, e.g. the steam tables. These are then combined with the first law of thermodynamics to formulate solutions to some simple problems.

4.1 Independent and dependent properties

In Chapter 2 a state is defined by the collection of all its properties. The question may be asked whether all the properties of the system are actually needed in order to define its state, or whether there is a minimum number of properties by which a state may be completely defined.

It turns out that there is no need to list all the properties in order to define a state, since some properties are dependent on others. In other words, there exists a set called *independent properties*, whose values, once specified, fix all the other properties of the system. A property whose value is determined by the set of independent properties is called a dependent property. For example, a triangle as a system has many properties. However, three properties, say one side and two angles, are sufficient to define a triangle completely and all its other properties, such as its area, circumference, bisectors, etc. This set of three independent properties is not unique. Three sides could also have been selected. However, three angles could not, since they are not mutually independent; their sum is 180°, and setting two angles fixes the third.

The number of independent properties that a thermodynamic system may have is determined by a thermodynamic law known as the *state postulate*. This number depends on the complexity of the system.

15 Wh and there is a heat interaction of 20 kJ *to the bath.*

Process b. The charged capacitor is then disconnected from the battery and discharged completely by connecting it across a 100 Ω resistor. Again the temperature of the capacitor, the wires, and the resistor is kept constant by the bath.

Determine the heat interaction in process b. Is it positive or negative?

3.15 A vertical cylinder is covered by a 5.0 kg piston whose area is 20 cm². Initially the gas in the cylinder is at atmospheric pressure of 1.03 bars and the piston is held by a stop at a height of 10 cm.

The stop is removed and the piston descends to a new equilibrium state.

a. Determine the final pressure of the gas.
b. Find the work interaction of the gas, given that $p_1V_1 = p_2V_2$.

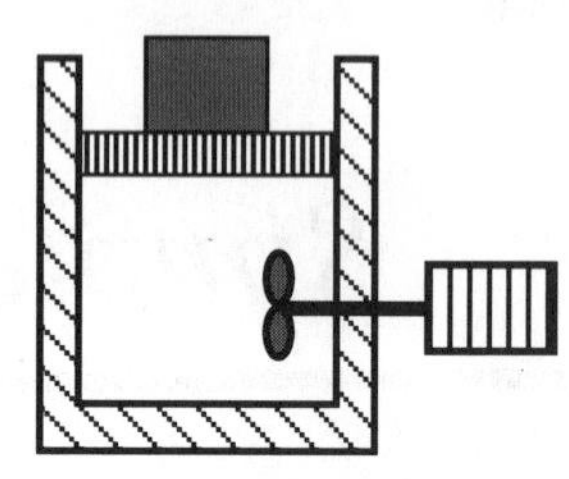

Figure 3.11

3.16 A gas is contained in an insulated cylinder covered by a weighted piston that maintains a constant pressure of 0.50 MPa, Fig. 3.11. A 1.0 hp mixer is turned on for 1hour causing the gas in the cylinder to expand from 30 L to 90 L.

Find the energy change of the gas.

3.17 The average amount of heat that a person emits to the environment is 100 kcal/h. The air-conditioning system in an auditorium containing 1000 people stops working for 15 minutes. Assuming that the walls are perfectly insulated:

a. Find the energy change of everything included within the auditorium walls.
b. Find the change of energy of the auditorium air.
c. Would the temperature in the auditorium change in these 15 minutes? Explain.

3.18 The density of liquid water at 0 °C and 1.0 bar is 1000 kg/m³ while that of ice is 917 kg/m³. Find the work of a system of 1.0 kg of ice that melts at 0 °C and 1.0 bar.

3.19 A system of 1 kg expands quasistatically from 1 m³ and 1.0 MPa to 3 m³.

Find the work of the system if during the process:

a. $p = \text{const.}$
b. $pv = \text{const.}$
c. $pv^2 = \text{const.}$
d. The relationship between p and v is given as:

v	m³/kg	1.00	1.50	2.00	2.50	3.00
p	MPa	1.00	0.906	0.75	0.531	0.25

3.20 A cylinder contains 2.0 kg of gas and is covered by a piston. The gas expands from an initial state of 0.020 m³, 7.0 bars, to a final pressure of 1 bar.

Find the work done by the gas if during the expansion:

a. $pV = \text{const.}$
b. $pV^2 = \text{const.}$
c. $pV^n = \text{const.}$

4.2 The state postulate

The stable equilibrium state of a system is uniquely determined by all its quasistatic work parameters and its energy.

The state postulate fixes the number of independent properties of a system in a stable state*. For example, consider a system consisting of helium inside a spherical flying balloon. We can arbitrarily change the volume and the elevation of the helium. These two properties are its quasistatic work parameters, corresponding to work of volume expansion and work of elevation change in a gravitational field, respectively. In addition, we can also change the energy of the system, say by heating the helium. Once these three properties have been fixed all other properties, e.g. pressure, temperature, density, specific volume, are uniquely defined.

For the system described above only three properties are independent while all the other properties are dependent. The selection of the three independent properties is not unique. One could just as well specify the pressure, temperature and energy as the independent properties and determine from these the elevation and volume. Not every set of three properties can be selected as independent. Energy, volume, and density would not do, since the volume and the density are not independent for this system, as the product of volume and density is fixed and equal to the mass of the helium. The state postulate assures, however, that a set consisting of the quasistatic work parameters and the energy is always a set of mutually independent properties.

4.3 Simple systems

A system that has only one relevant mode of quasistatic work is called a simple system.

Hence, a simple compressible system has a quasistatic work mode associated with a change of its volume only. A simple elastic system has a quasistatic work mode due to elastic deformation only.

Simple systems can also have other work interactions, but these would not be quasistatic and would always be negative. For example, consider the system in Fig. 4.1, consisting of a gas which is enclosed in a horizontal cylinder and a piston. The only possible quasistatic work is that of piston displacement while the pressure inside the gas is uniform and equal to the force per unit area applied by the piston. Other work interactions are also possible, such as an electric current passing through the boundary, or a propeller doing work while mixing the gas. These works are non-quasistatic and negative. For simple systems the state postulate reduces to:

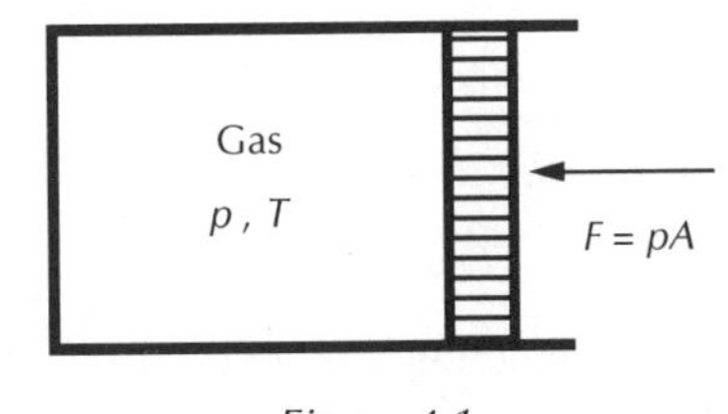

Figure 4.1

* It is surprising to note that a principle as basic as the state postulate was formulated as late as 1956 in a paper by S.J. Kline and F.O. Koenig, "The State Principle – Some General Aspects of the Relationship among the Properties of Systems" *J. Appl. Mech.*, **23**, pp. 1–6 (1956).

The stable equilibrium state of a simple system is determined by its quasistatic work parameter and its energy.

Therefore, two independent properties fix the stable state of a simple system. It should be noted that non-equilibrium states of simple systems cannot be characterized by two properties only. Indeed, in order to characterize a state that is not in equilibrium additional information is required. Non-equilibrium states are treated in detail in more advanced books*.

In this book we deal mainly with simple compressible systems, systems whose only possible quasistatic work is due to a change of volume. Hence, other effects such as those of gravitational, electric, and magnetic fields, as well as the effects of surface tension, strains in solid phases, etc., are absent or cannot produce quasistatic work. In many engineering applications that require thermodynamic analysis, the systems can be considered as simple compressible systems to a high degree of accuracy. These systems will be referred to from now on as simple systems, unless stated specifically otherwise.

As stated above, two independent properties define the state of a simple system. Specifically, the volume (that is, the work parameter) and the energy are a set of independent properties defining the state of the system. Any other property could be written as a function of E and V, for example

$$\Pi_1 = f_1(E,V) \tag{4.1}$$

$$\Pi_2 = f_2(E,V) \tag{4.2}$$

etc. If the two properties, Π_1 and Π_2, are mutually independent Eqs (4.1) and (4.2) can be solved simultaneously to yield E and V, as functions of Π_1 and Π_2:

$$V = F_v(\Pi_1,\Pi_2) \tag{4.3}$$

$$E = F_E(\Pi_1,\Pi_2) \tag{4.4}$$

4.4 Equations of state

If Π_1 and Π_2 are the pressure, p, and the temperature, T, respectively, then Eq. (4.3) takes the form

$$F(p,T,V) = 0 \tag{4.5}$$

or, per unit mass, as

$$f(p,T,v) = 0 \tag{4.6}$$

The functional relationship described by Eq. (4.6) can be given either numerically or by means of an algebraic equation. The latter is called an equation of state. Examples of equations of state are

* See for example S. R. de Groot and P. Mazur, *Thermodynamics of Irreversible Processes*, North-Holland Publishing Co., Amsterdam, 1962.

$$pv = RT \tag{4.7}$$

$$\left(p + \frac{a}{v^2}\right)(v - b) = RT \tag{4.8}$$

$$p(v - b)\exp\left(\frac{a}{RTv}\right) = RT \tag{4.9}$$

where R, a, and b are constants. Whether the relationship between p, v, and T is given by means of a table or by an equation, any one of the properties can be evaluated given the other two.

4.5 Internal energy

Equation (4.4) describes a functional relationship between the energy of a simple system in a stable state and two arbitrarily selected independent properties. This functional relationship is called the internal energy of the simple system, and is designated by U. Hence: *The energy of a simple system in equilibrium is equal to its internal energy.*

$$E_{simple\ \ system} = U(\Pi_1, \Pi_2) \tag{4.10}$$

In a non-simple system (or in non-equilibrium states) the internal energy may still be meaningful; however, it may not necessarily be equal to the energy of the system. While the internal energy is always a function of two properties, the energy of a non-simple system may depend on more than two properties. For example, if a compressible system is also affected by gravity, its energy is a function of its elevation z, in addition to the two properties Π_1 and Π_2 of Eq. (4.10).

$$E = E(\Pi_1, \Pi_2, z) \tag{4.11}$$

For the reference state of $z = 0$ the energy of the system may be taken as equal to its internal energy

$$E_0 = U \tag{4.12}$$

while at elevation z,

$$E = E_0 + mgz \tag{4.13}$$

Combining Eqs (4.12) and (4.13) yields

$$E = U + mgz \tag{4.14}$$

The term mgz is called the potential energy of the system. If a velocity $\mathbf{v}$ is also imparted to the system its energy will be

$$E = U + mgz + \frac{m\mathbf{v}^2}{2} \tag{4.15}$$

where the term $m\mathbf{v}^2/2$ is called the kinetic energy of the system.

Other effects, if present, such as magnetic, electric, and capillary effects, will also affect the energy of the system, and will therefore be included in the expression for the energy of such a non-simple system.

The internal energy, U, is an extensive property. The corresponding *intensive* property, the specific internal energy, u, is the internal energy per unit mass. We now consider a functional relationship which holds for a simple system:

$$u = u(T, v) \tag{4.16}$$

Differentiation of Eq. (4.16) results in

$$du = \left(\frac{\partial u}{\partial T}\right)_v dT + \left(\frac{\partial u}{\partial v}\right)_T dv \tag{4.17}$$

The change in internal energy between two states can be evaluated by integrating Eq. (4.17) provided the parameters $(\partial u / \partial T)_v$ and $(\partial u / \partial v)_T$ are known functions of T and v.

4.6 Basic processes in simple systems

In this section we apply the first law of thermodynamics to some basic processes in simple systems.

The energy of a simple system is the internal energy and therefore the first law of thermodynamics, Eq. (3.10), may be written for a simple system as

$$Q - W = \Delta U \tag{4.18}$$

or in differential form

$$\delta Q - \delta W = dU \tag{4.19}$$

4.6.1 The constant-volume process

A process which involves changes in some of the properties of the system without changing its volume is called a constant-volume (or isochoric) process.

Consider a simple compressible system inside a rigid container. The properties of the system may be changed by several different processes. One way of changing the properties is by having the system undergo a heat interaction, Fig. 4.2a. This interaction may change the temperature, pressure, energy, and other properties of the system. The volume, however, remains fixed owing to the constraints imposed by the rigid container. The process is shown on a p–V diagram, Fig. 4.2c, by a straight vertical line.

The same change of state, where the system passes through the same path, may be obtained by work instead of the heat interaction described above. This work interaction cannot result from a change of volume, since the volume is fixed, and therefore is not

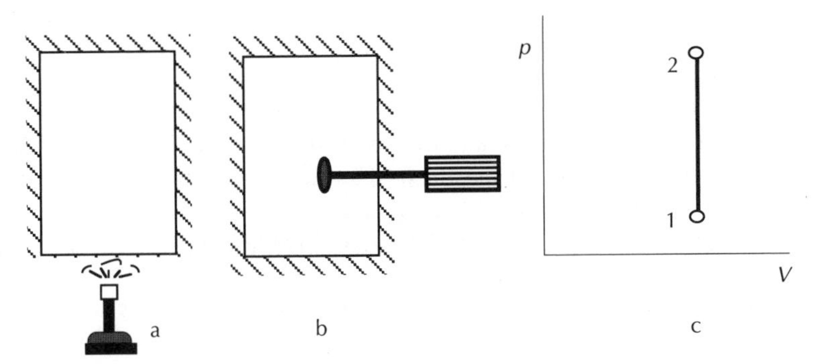

Figure 4.2 **Constant-volume process.**

quasistatic. Nevertheless, work can cross the system boundary through the shaft of a stirrer, Fig. 4.2b.

Applying the first law of thermodynamics, Eq. (4.19), to the first process and noting that $W^I = 0$, one obtains

$$Q^I = \Delta U \tag{4.20}$$

Applying now the first law of thermodynamics to the second process and noting that here there is no heat interaction, $Q^{II} = 0$, yields

$$-W_s^{II} = \Delta U \tag{4.21}$$

where W_s is the work interaction of the system with the stirrer.

We can also effect the same change in the system by a third process that involves both work and heat interactions in suitable amounts W_s^{III} and Q^{III} such that

$$Q^{III} - W_s^{III} = \Delta U \tag{4.22}$$

Even though the processes described above differ from each other by the interactions at the system boundary, they all result in the same changes in the internal energy and the temperature as well as other properties, and have the same representation on the *p–V* diagram, Fig. 4.2c.

The rate of variation of the internal energy with temperature is an important factor in thermodynamics; hence, a new extensive property, denoted by C_v, is defined as

$$C_v = \left(\frac{\partial U}{\partial T}\right)_V \tag{4.23}$$

This property is called *heat capacity at constant volume*. The name is rather misleading, since it has nothing to do with the capacity of the system to store heat. Heat is not a property and cannot be stored. What is actually stored is the internal energy, and the change in the energy of the system can be achieved by either heat or work interactions or by a combination of the two. The term heat capacity is a remnant from the era of the caloric theory when heat was considered to be a property. The heat capacity per unit mass

$$c_v = \frac{C_v}{m} = \left(\frac{\partial u}{\partial T}\right)_v \tag{4.24}$$

is the specific heat capacity at constant volume or in short *specific heat at constant volume*. The units of heat capacity and specific heat are kJ/K and kJ/kg K, respectively.

The specific energy of a simple system is, in general, a function of two independent properties, say $u(T, p)$. It is obvious from Eq. (4.24) that the specific heat at constant volume is also a function of the same independent properties, $c_v(T, p)$.

We now substitute Eq. (4.24) into Eq. (4.17) and obtain an alternative expression for the change in internal energy

$$du = c_v dT + \left(\frac{\partial u}{\partial v}\right)_T dv \tag{4.25}$$

which upon integration between states 1 and 2 yields

$$u_2 - u_1 = \int_1^2 c_v\, dT + \int_1^2 \left(\frac{\partial u}{\partial v}\right)_T dv \tag{4.26}$$

In the case of an isochoric process $dv = 0$, and Eq. (4.26) simplifies to

$$u_2 - u_1 = \int_1^2 c_v dT \tag{4.27}$$

or in terms of extensive properties

$$U_2 - U_1 = m\int_1^2 c_v\, dT \tag{4.28}$$

4.6.2 The constant-pressure process

A process which involves a change in some of the properties of the system without changing the pressure is called a constant-pressure (or isobaric) process.

Consider a simple compressible system inside a piston–cylinder assembly. Properties of the system such as energy, temperature, volume, and others may be changed by several different processes. The pressure of the system, however, is kept constant and equal to the equivalent external pressure imposed by the piston. Figure 4.3c shows the constant-pressure process on a p–V diagram.

One way to change the properties is by having the system undergo a heat interaction, Q^I,as shown in Fig. 4.3a. This constant-pressure interaction results in the movement of the piston and a change of volume. The heat interaction is, therefore, accompanied by a work interaction on the piston. Since the external equivalent pressure is equal to the pressure of the system, p, throughout this process, the work interaction is given by the product of the pressure and the change of volume. Thus

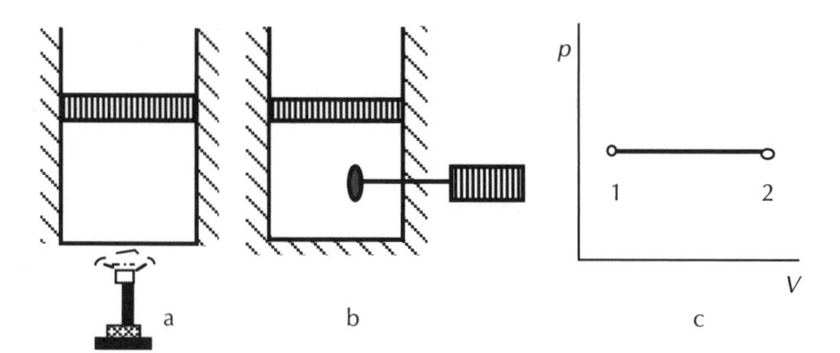

Figure 4.3 **Constant-pressure process.**

$$W = p\Delta V \, . \tag{4.29}$$

The first law of thermodynamics requires that

$$Q^I - p\Delta V = \Delta U \tag{4.30}$$

or

$$Q^I = \Delta U + p\Delta V \, . \tag{4.31}$$

Since the pressure is constant, Eq. (4.31) may be rewritten as

$$Q^I = \Delta(U + pV) \tag{4.32}$$

As with the isochoric process, the same change of state, with the system passing through the same path, may be obtained by the non-quasistatic work of the stirrer, W_s^{II}, instead of the heat interaction described above, Fig. 4.2b. The first law of thermodynamics requires now that

$$-W_s^{II} - p\Delta V = \Delta U \tag{4.33}$$

or

$$-W_s^{II} = \Delta(U + pV) \, . \tag{4.34}$$

Note that two kinds of work are involved in this process: the work associated with the change of volume which is quasistatic, and the work of the stirrer which is not.

We can also effect the same change of state in the system by a third process that involves both work and heat interactions in suitable amounts W_s^{III} and Q^{III} such that

$$Q^{III} - W_s^{III} = \Delta(U + pV) \, . \tag{4.35}$$

The combination of properties $(U + pV)$ describes an extensive property, with units of energy, which often appears in thermodynamics. This property is called *enthalpy* and is denoted by H:

$$H = U + pV \tag{4.36}$$

The corresponding intensive property is the *specific enthalpy*, which is the enthalpy per unit mass:

$$h = \frac{H}{m} = u + pv \tag{4.37}$$

Equation (4.35) may now be written for this constant-pressure process as

$$Q - W_s = \Delta H \tag{4.38}$$

The variation of enthalpy with temperature at constant pressure is also an extensive property called heat capacity at constant pressure and denoted by C_p:

$$C_p = \left(\frac{\partial H}{\partial T}\right)_p \tag{4.39}$$

The corresponding intensive property is the specific heat capacity at constant pressure called for short *specific heat at constant pressure*:

$$c_p = \frac{C_p}{m} = \left(\frac{\partial h}{\partial T}\right)_p \tag{4.40}$$

The specific enthalpy defined above is a function of two independent properties, say T and p:

$$h = h(T, p) \tag{4.41}$$

Differentiating Eq. (4.41) and using Eq. (4.40) yields

$$dh = c_p dT + \left(\frac{\partial h}{\partial p}\right)_T dp \tag{4.42}$$

which for an isobaric process, $dp = 0$, simplifies to

$$dh = c_p dT \tag{4.43}$$

Hence, the change of enthalpy between two states at the same pressure is given by

$$\Delta H = H_2 - H_1 = m\int_1^2 c_p dT \tag{4.44}$$

The ratio of the specific heat at constant pressure to specific heat at constant volume is an intensive property denoted by k and generally it is a function of two independent properties:

$$k = \frac{c_p}{c_v} = k(T, p) \tag{4.45}$$

EXAMPLE 4.1

A coal–oil mixture (COM) is a fuel that can replace heating oil for certain applications. In order to prevent settling of the coal particles, mixing is required before use.

An open tank contains 5000 kg of COM at 22 °C. The COM was stirred for 40 min by a 20 kW paddle mixer. During this operation the temperature of the mixture rose to 27.6 °C. The specific heat of the COM may be assumed to be constant at c_p= 1.4 kJ/kg K.

a. Find the heat interaction of the COM with its surroundings.
b. What would be the temperature rise of the COM if the tank were perfectly insulated?

SOLUTION

a. We use Eq. (4.38) to calculate the heat interaction for this constant-pressure process:

$$Q = \Delta H + W_s$$

ΔH is calculated from Eq. (4.45):

$$\Delta H = m\int_1^2 c_p dT = mc_p(T_2 - T_1) = 5000 \times 1.4 \times (27.6 - 22.0) = 39200 \text{ kJ}$$

The work is

$$W_s = -20 \times 40 \times 60 = -48000 \text{ kJ}$$

The work is negative because it is done on the system. The heat interaction is

$$Q = \Delta H + W_s = 39200 - 48000 = -8800 \text{ kJ}$$

The minus sign indicates that heat is removed from the system.

b. For a perfectly insulated, or adiabatic, process $Q = 0$; hence, from Eq. (4.38),

$$-W_s = \Delta H = +48000 \text{ kJ}$$

The process is isobaric ($dp = 0$) and the specific heat is constant. Equation (4.45) becomes for this case

$$\Delta H = mc_p\Delta T$$

Therefore

$$\Delta T = \frac{\Delta H}{mc_p} = \frac{48000}{5000 \times 1.4} = 6.86 \text{ °C}$$

4.7 Pure substances

A pure substance is one that has a uniform chemical composition throughout the system. A pure substance can be comprised of either a single chemical compound, say water, or a mixture of several chemical compounds, say air, provided its composition is uniform.

A system of a pure substance may consist of several coexisting phases, say gas and liquid. Each of these phases may have different properties. However, as long as the chemical composition is the same throughout, it is considered a pure substance.

4.8 Intensive state

In Chapter 2 we defined a state of a system by means of all its properties, intensive and extensive. It is sometimes useful to describe the condition at a given point of a system, for example when the system is not homogeneous. Only intensive properties can be defined at a point.

The intensive state of a system at a given point is defined by the collection of all the intensive properties at that point. Obviously, not all the intensive properties are required to define an intensive state of a point; the set of independent intensive properties will suffice.

4.9 Phases

A phase is a collection of all parts of a system having the same intensive state. A system may have one or more phases, continuous or discontinuous, in equilibrium. For example, liquid water would be a system of a single phase, provided the pressure, temperature, specific volume, specific energy, etc., have the same value everywhere in the system. On the other hand liquid water with several pieces of ice in it would be a two-phase system, namely that of water and of ice. These phases differ in at least one of the intensive properties, such as density. Note also that the phases need not be spatially continuous. Thus, all the individual pieces of ice belong to the same phase so long as all their intensive properties are identical. Phases are separated from each other by boundaries which are generally surfaces of discontinuity in the intensive state.

Single-phase systems are called homogeneous, while those consisting of more than one phase are heterogeneous systems.

4.10 Properties of a pure substance

It follows from the state principle that any property, B, of a simple compressible system can be determined given its specific energy, u, and its specific volume, v. Thus, on a u versus v diagram any point uniquely defines a state, and no two different states can be represented by the same point. We say, therefore, that there is a one-to-one correspondence between a state of the system and a point on its u– v diagram.

In practice the properties of systems are not given as functions of u and v, but rather as functions of pressure, p, and temperature, T. Usually, the properties p and T are independent of each other and define a single state, but not always; at given values of p and T, when two phases or more can coexist, a state is not uniquely defined. Indeed, for these cases a single set of p and T will correspond to either phase or to any combination thereof. For example, water at 100 °C and 1 atmosphere may exist either as liquid or vapor, or as a mixture of liquid and vapor of arbitrary proportions.

We now proceed to present several diagrams which are used in simple systems. Some of these diagrams, such as p versus v (or p–v), p–h, etc., are useful in solving some ther-

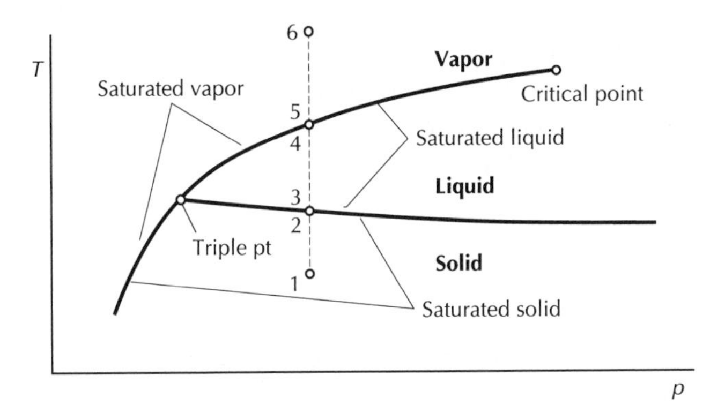

Figure 4.4 **The *T–p* diagram.**

modynamic problems graphically. Other diagrams such as *T–v* or *T–p* are helpful in illustrating the relationships between properties of simple systems.

4.10.1 The *T–p* diagram

Figure 4.4 shows a typical temperature–pressure diagram for a pure substance. The regions marked as solid, liquid and vapor correspond to single-phase regions. In these regions a point on the diagram corresponds to a single state at a given p and T. The different phases are separated on the diagram by saturation lines. Points on these lines represent two-phase regions. The lines intersect at a point known as the triple point, at which the three phases, solid, liquid, and vapor, coexist. The line separating the solid and the liquid phases is the melting line, and the line separating the liquid and the vapor is the vaporization line, while the line on which transition from solid to vapor occurs is the sublimation line.

Consider a constant-pressure process depicted on the *T–p* diagram, Fig. 4.4, by the vertical line 1–2–3–4–5–6. At point 1 the substance is in the solid state. Now the temperature of the solid is raised while keeping the pressure constant, say by a heat interaction. The substance remains solid until state 2 is reached. Further heating will not raise the temperature but rather cause melting of the solid, producing a liquid phase. This process continues until all the solid is melted and state 3 of liquid is reached. As seen on the diagram, points 2 and 3 coincide. Going from state 2 to 3 requires heat even though the pressure and temperature do not change. This heat is called the latent heat of melting (or fusion).

Further heating will raise the temperature of the liquid until point 4 is reached, where a vapor phase starts to form. The temperature again stays constant until all the liquid is evaporated. The heat required for that process is the latent heat of evaporation. Continued heating will raise the temperature without any further change of phase.

If the process described above is repeated at a sufficiently high pressure no transition between liquid and vapor is observed. The pressure above which no liquid–vapor transition can take place is called the critical pressure, the corresponding temperature is the critical temperature and the state defined by these two coordinates is called the critical point.

The *T–p* diagram is useful as a directory to tables describing the properties of pure substances discussed later on in this chapter.

4.10.2 The *p–v* diagram

The *p–v* diagram is useful in assessing the amount of work that the system can do, because the area under the curve of this diagram, $\int pdv$, is equal to the quasistatic work of a simple compressible substance.

A typical *p–v* diagram is shown in Fig. 4.5. This diagram is shown only for the vapor–liquid region above the triple point. The vaporization line of the *T–p* diagram is represented here by the region under the bell-shaped curve. The highest point on this curve is the critical point. The curve to the left of the critical point is the saturated liquid line while that to the right is the saturated vapor line. The region to the left of the saturated liquid line is the region of compressed liquid. The region to the right of the saturated vapor line is that of the superheated vapor. Inside the bell-shaped curve is the two-phase liquid–vapor region.

The isotherms on the *p–v* diagram have different shapes depending on the regions they pass. The one that passes through the critical point is called the critical isotherm. At the critical point the isotherm has an inflection point and its slope is zero. Isotherms above the critical temperature, T_c, decrease monotonically with v. Isotherms below the critical point cross the bell-shaped curve at two points of the same pressure, points A and B in Fig. 4.5. These points represent the two phases, liquid and vapor, in mutual equilibrium at the same temperature and pressure. A substance may be entirely at point A, in which case

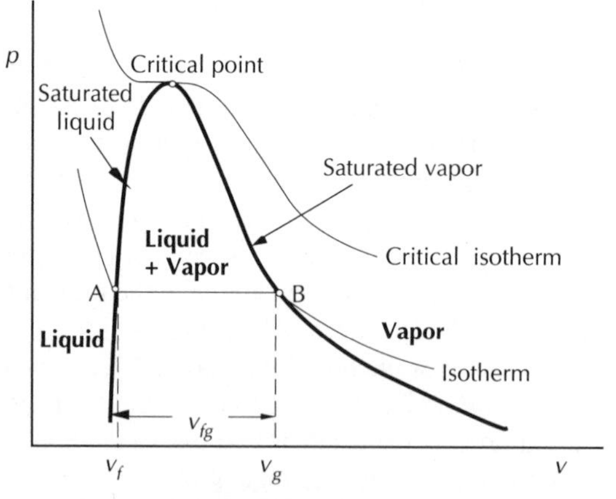

Figure 4.5 **The *p–v* diagram.**

it is only liquid, entirely at B, in which case it is pure vapor, or a combination of the two phases of A and B, at any proportion. We define the quality of the vapor, x, as the ratio of its mass, m_g, to the total mass of the system, m:

$$x = \frac{m_g}{m} = \frac{m_g}{m_f + m_g} \tag{4.46}$$

where m_f is the mass of the liquid. Obviously, the mass fraction of the liquid is $(1-x)$,

$$1 - x = \frac{m_f}{m} \tag{4.47}$$

The total volume of a system consisting of a liquid phase and a vapor phase is

$$V = m_f v_f + m_g v_g \tag{4.48}$$

and the volume per unit mass, v, of the two-phase system is

$$v = V/m \tag{4.49}$$

or

$$v = (1 - x)v_f + xv_g \tag{4.50}$$

Equation (4.50) may be rewritten to read

$$v = v_f + xv_{fg} \tag{4.51}$$

where $v_{fg} = (v_g - v_f)$ is the difference between the specific volume of the saturated vapor and that of the saturated liquid. Equation (4.51) states that the average specific volume of the two-phase mixture, v, is a linear function of x, and equals the specific volume of the liquid plus the volume increase upon vaporization, v_{fg}, times the mass fraction of the system vaporized.

The vapor quality, x, can be expressed explicitly by rearranging Eq. (4.51):

$$x = \frac{v - v_f}{v_{fg}} = \frac{v - v_f}{v_g - v_f} \tag{4.52}$$

Any extensive property of a two-phase system, when divided by the mass, yields an average specific property, which is a linear function of x, and can be represented in a similar form as the volume above, e.g.

$$h = (1 - x)h_f + xh_g = h_f + xh_{fg} \tag{4.53}$$

$$u = (1 - x)u_f + xu_g = u_f + xu_{fg} \tag{4.54}$$

$$s = (1 - x)s_f + xs_g = s_f + xs_{fg} \tag{4.55}$$

4.11 Tables of thermodynamic properties

Properties of pure substances are usually given in tables. Sometimes the properties can be represented by mathematical equations which may be easier to use. These, however, are usually limited in range.

The substance that has been most extensively studied and tabulated is water. Tables of its properties are known as steam tables. Tables for many other substances are also available.

4.11.1 Structure of the steam tables

The steam tables are given in Tables A.1.1–A.1.5. They are arranged according to the regions depicted on the *T–p* diagram, Fig. 4.4. The single-phase regions, vapor and liquid, are given in Tables A.1.3 and A.1.4, respectively. In these regions the pressure and the temperature are independent properties and therefore fix the state uniquely. The vapor–liquid two-phase region depicted on the *T–p* diagram by the line between the triple and the critical points is given by Tables A.1.1 and A.1.2. The sublimation region in which the solid and vapor phases coexist is given in Table A.1.5.

Table A.1.1 gives the properties of each phase in the vapor–liquid saturation region as a function of the temperature. Table A.1.2 is identical to Table A.1.1 except that the independent property there is the pressure. Data for this region can be taken from either table, whichever is more convenient. Besides the temperature and pressure the tables list specific volume, v, specific internal energy, u, specific enthalpy, h, and specific entropy, s. The last property is discussed extensively in Chapter 8. The specific volume is given for the liquid and the vapor, respectively, while the values of internal enthalpy and entropy are arranged in three columns: the first gives the property of the liquid, the last that of the vapor, while the middle one gives the change in property on transition from liquid to vapor.

Table A.1.5 for saturated solid–vapor systems has the same arrangement as Table A.1.1 for saturated liquid–vapor.

In Table A.1.3 for superheated vapor the values of specific volume, internal energy, enthalpy, and entropy are listed in terms of pressure and temperature.

Table A.1.4 for compressed liquid is arranged similarly to Table A.1.3.

4.11.2 Using the steam tables

Two independent properties are needed to fix a state uniquely. It depends on the type and values of the properties as to which table should be used.

Given p and T one begins by finding the saturation pressure p_{sat} corresponding to T.

For $p > p_{sat}$ the point corresponds to compressed liquid and Table A.1.4 is used.

For $p < p_{sat}$ Table A.1.3 for superheated vapor is used.

For $p = p_{sat}$ the point is in the saturation region of Tables A.1.1 and A.1.2. However, the pressure and temperature are not independent and hence an additional property is needed to fix the state.

Given p and v or T and v one finds first v_f and v_g.

If $v_g < v$ then the state is in superheated vapor (Table A.1.3).

If $v_f \leq v \leq v_g$ then the state is in saturation (Table A.1.1 or A.1.2).

If $v_f > v$ then the state is in compressed liquid (Table A.1.4).

Similar procedures are used for the pairs p and u, T and u, p and h T and h, p and s, T and s .

If the two given properties do not include either p or T, a trial and error procedure is required to find the state.

EXAMPLE 4.2

Find the volume, the internal energy, and the enthalpy of 1 kg of H_2O at the following conditions:

a. $T = 300$ °C, $p = 2$ MPa
b. $T = 300$ °C, $p = 20$ MPa
c. $T = 300$ °C, $p = 8.581$ MPa

SOLUTION

From Table A.1.1. we find for 300 °C that: $p_{sat} = 8.581$ MPa.

a. Here $p < p_{sat}$; therefore we turn to Table A.1.3 for superheated vapor and find:

T °C	p MPa	v m³/kg	u kJ/kg	h kJ/kg
300	2.0	0.12547	2772.6	3023.5

The given properties are underlined for clarity.

b. $p > p_{sat}$; therefore we turn to Table A.1.4 for compressed liquid and find the following properties, in SI units:

T °C	p MPa	v m³/kg	u kJ/kg	h kJ/kg
300	2.0	0.0013596	1306.1	1333.3

c. $p = p_{sat}$; therefore additional information is required to fix the state. Under the present conditions only the properties of the saturated liquid and the saturated vapor can be found in Table A.1.1.

EXAMPLE 4.3

Find the properties of 1 kg of H_2O at 300 °C and $x = 0.8$.

SOLUTION

This point is a mixture of 0.8 kg of saturated vapor and 0.2 kg of saturated liquid at 300 °C and 8.581 MPa. Using Table A.1.1 we calculate

$$v = v_f + x(v_g - v_f) = 0.001404 + 0.8 \times (0.02167 - 0.001404) = 0.01762 \text{ m}^3/\text{kg}$$

$$u = u_f + xu_{fg} = 1332.0 + 0.8 \times 1231.0 = 2316.8 \text{ kJ/kg}$$

$$h = h_f + xh_{fg} = 1344.0 + 0.8 \times 1404.9 = 2467.9 \text{ kJ/kg}$$

Summarizing:

T	p	x	v	u	h
300	8.581	0.8	0.01762	2316.8	2467.9

4.11.3 Interpolation

When one of the values is not given in the tables of properties, interpolation is required. In this section we review the rules of linear interpolation.

For example, if we wish to calculate v at a given pressure p, which does not appear explicitly in the table, we look in the table at p_1 which is below p and at p_2 which is just above it and find the corresponding values of v_1 and v_2. The value of v_2 is interpolated from

$$v = v_1 + \frac{p - p_1}{p_2 - p_1}(v_2 - v_1) \tag{4.56}$$

or by rearranging into a different form

$$v = \frac{p_2 - p}{p_2 - p_1} v_1 + \frac{p - p_1}{p_2 - p_1} v_2 \tag{4.57}$$

Substituting $a_1 = (p_2 - p)/(p_2 - p_1)$ and $a_2 = (p - p_1)/(p_2 - p_1)$, Eq. (4.57) is rewritten as

$$v = a_1 v_1 + a_2 v_2 = a_1 v_1 + (1 - a_1) v_2 \tag{4.58}$$

If, for example, the specific volume, v, is required as a function of the known pressure, p, and temperature, T, whose values do not appear explicitly in the table, a double interpolation is used, yielding

$$v = a_1 b_1 v_{11} + a_1 b_2 v_{12} + a_2 b_1 v_{21} + a_2 b_2 v_{22} \tag{4.59}$$

where v_{ij} are depicted in Fig. 4.6 and

	p_1	p_2
T_1	v_{11}	v_{12}
T_2	v_{21}	v_{22}

Figure 4.6 **Double-interpolation scheme.**

$$a_1 = \frac{p_2 - p}{p_2 - p_1} \qquad a_2 = \frac{p - p_1}{p_2 - p_1}$$
$$b_1 = \frac{T_2 - T}{T_2 - T_1} \qquad b_2 = \frac{T - T_1}{T_2 - T_1} \tag{4.60}$$

If another property, say h, is to be found, Eq. (4.59) can be rewritten for h, instead of v, with the same values for the coefficients a_{ij} and b_{ij}.

EXAMPLE 4.4

Find the thermodynamic properties of steam at 2 MPa and 296 °C.

SOLUTION

For p = 2.0 MPa, T_{sat} = 212.42 °C; thus, in our case $T > T_{sat}$; therefore Table A.1.3, for superheated steam, should be used. We interpolate the volume from the table at 2.0 MPa between T_T = 250 °C and T_2 = 300 °C. Using Eq. (4.58) with a_1 and a_2 expressed in terms of temperatures we obtain

$$a_1 = \frac{T - T_1}{T_2 - T_1} = \frac{296-250}{300-250} = 0.92 \qquad a_2 = 1 - a_1 = 0.08$$

$$v = 0.92 \times v(300) + 0.08 \times v(250)$$
$$= 0.92 \times 0.12547 + 0.08 \times 0.11144 = 0.12435 \text{ m}^3/\text{kg}$$

Similarly

$$u = 0.92 \times 2772.6 + 0.08 \times 2679.6 = 2765.2 \text{ kJ/kg}$$
$$h = 0.92 \times 3023.5 + 0.08 \times 2902.5 = 3013.8 \text{ kJ/kg}$$
$$s = 0.92 \times 6.7664 + 0.08 \times 6.5453 = 6.7487 \text{ kJ/kgK}$$

The property s, the entropy, will be discussed later. Summarizing:

State	p	T	v	u	h	s
1	2.0	250	0.11144	2679.6	2902.5	6.5453
given	2.0	296	0.12435	2765.2	3013.8	6.7487
2	2.0	250	0.12547	2772.6	3023.5	6.7664

EXAMPLE 4.5

Given H_2O at $p = 2$ MPa, find the other properties for:

a. $v = 0.15$ m³/kg, and
b. $v = 0.05$ m³/kg.

SOLUTION

We first look at Table A.1.2 and find

$$v_f = 0.001177 \text{ m}^3/\text{kg} \qquad v_g = 0.09963 \text{ m}^3/\text{kg}$$

a. In this case $v > v_g$; therefore Table A.1.3 for the superheated region should be used. We summarize from Table A.1.3:

State	p	T	v	u	h	s
1	2.0	350	0.13857	2059.8	3137.0	6.9563
given	2.0		0.15			
2	2.0	400	0.15120	2945.2	3247.6	7.1271

Calculating a_1 and a_2:

$$a_1 = \frac{v - v_1}{v_2 - v_1} = \frac{0.1500 - 0.13857}{0.1512 - 0.13857} = 0.905 \qquad a_2 = 1 - a_1 = 0.095$$

We use the a_1 and a_2 in Eq. (4.58) to interpolate T, u, h, and s as summarized in the table below:

State	p	T	v	u	h	s
Given	2.0	395.3	0.15	2937.0	3237.1	7.1108

b. In this case $v_f < v < v_g$; hence this point is in the two-phase region, and Table A.1.2 is used to calculate x and the other properties at the saturation temperature $T = 212.42$ °C.

$$x = \frac{v - v_f}{v_g - v_f} = \frac{0.050 - 0.001177}{0.09963 - 0.001177} = 0.4959$$

We calculate u from

$$u = u_f + x u_{fg} = 906.44 + 0.4959 \times 1693.8 = 1746.4 \text{ kJ/kg}$$

The properties h and s are calculated in a similar way, and are summarized in the following table. No interpolation is needed in this problem.

p	T	x	v	u	h	s
2.0	212.42	0.4959	0.15	1746.4	1846.4	4.3782

EXAMPLE 4.6

Find the pressure, p, and temperature, T, for a state for which $u = 3000$ kJ/kg and $v = 0.6$ m³/kg.

SOLUTION

The solution is by trial and error. To find in which table this point is we first look in the saturation table, say A.1.2, for the pressure at which $v = v_g$. This is slightly above $p = 0.3$ MPa. At that point $u_g = 2544 < 3000$; therefore we should look in a table of higher internal energies, in this case, in Table A.1.3.

We now select a pressure and find, by interpolation, the temperature at which $v = 0.6$ m³/kg. Then we calculate the energy for that point and compare it with the given energy, $u = 3000$ kJ/kg. The process is repeated until $\Delta u \rightarrow 0$.

The results of this trial and error search are summarized in the following table:

trial p	$T\|_{v=0.6}$	u_{calc}	$\Delta U = U_{calc} - 3000$
0.4	254.1	2732.6	−267.4
0.5	510.3	3145.3	145.3
0.6	381.7	2933.7	−66.3

From the table we see that our point is between 0.5 and 0.6 MPa, closer to 0.6 MPa. There are no points in the table between these two pressures, and hence the actual point is found by linear interpolation over the energy:

$$p = 0.5 + 0.1 \times \frac{3000 - 3145.3}{2933.7 - 3145.3} = 0.5 + 0.1 \times 0.69 = 0.569 \text{ MPa}$$

and

$$T = 510.3 + (381.7 - 510.3) \times 0.31 = 422.0 \text{ °C}$$

The other properties are found similarly.

If the state in the problem were defined by $v = 0.6$ m³/kg and $u = 2000$ kJ/kg, the point would then lie in the two-phase region. A trial and error procedure would still be required to evaluate p and T. This problem is left as an exercise for the student.

4.12 The first law of thermodynamics for simple systems

We now have sufficient information to solve some problems using the first law of thermodynamics. To solve a problem some or all of the following must be used:

a. Tables of properties or an equation of state.
b. The law of conservation of mass.
c. The law of conservation of energy, i.e. the first law of thermodynamics.
d. A process equation.

We now illustrate the use of these principles by solving several examples for simple systems.

EXAMPLE 4.7

Steam at 8 MPa and 350 °C is contained in a cylinder covered by a weighted piston, which is held in place by a stop. The cylinder is immersed in a thermostatic bath, maintained at 350 °C, see Fig. 4.7. The initial volume of the steam is 0.2 m³.

The stop is removed and the steam expands lifting the piston. When equilibrium is reached the pressure of the steam is 4 MPa.

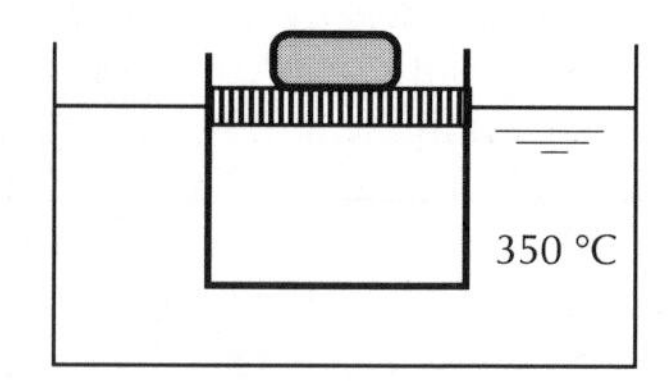

Figure 4.7

a. Find the change in energy and in enthalpy of the steam.
b. Find the work and heat interactions.

SOLUTION

We define the steam in the cylinder as the system. Given the temperature and pressure of the initial and final states of the system we find from the steam tables the specific volume, internal energy, and enthalpy and arrange them in the following table:

State	p (MPa)	T	v	u	h
1	8.0	350	0.02995	2747.7	2987.3
2	4.0	350	0.06645	2826.7	3092.5

We first calculate the mass of the steam from state 1:

$$m = \frac{V}{v_1} = \frac{0.2}{0.02995} = 6.678 \text{ kg}$$

The internal energy change is

$$\Delta U = m(u_2 - u_1) = 6.678 \times (2826.7 - 2747.7) = 527.6 \text{ kJ}$$

and the enthalpy change

$$\Delta H = m(h_2 - h_1) = 6.678(3092.5 - 2987.3) = 702.5 \text{ kJ}$$

The equivalent external pressure, which consists of the atmospheric pressure and the pressure exerted by the piston, is equal to the final equilibrium pressure of the steam, p_2. Thus the work done by the system is

$$W = p_2(V_2 - V_1) = mp_2(v_2 - v_1) = 6.678 \times 4 \times 10^3 \times (0.06645 - 0.02995) = 975.0 \text{ kJ}$$

The heat interaction is calculated from the first law

$$Q = \Delta U + W = 527.6 + 975.0 = 1502.6 \text{ kJ}$$

In the solution of this problem we have used the following:

a. The steam tables to find the initial and final state.
b. Conservation of mass to calculate the constant mass from the specific volume.
c. The first law to calculate the heat.
d. The process equation to calculate the work.

EXAMPLE 4.8

Repeat Example 4.7 for a quasistatic isothermal process between the same end states.

SOLUTION

The change of internal energy and of enthalpy between two end states is independent of the process, and therefore will be the same as in Example 4.7.

The work for this quasistatic process is calculated from

$$W = \int_1^2 p dV = m \int_1^2 p dv \tag{3.6}$$

and a relationship between p and v at 350 °C is obtained from the steam table A.1.3, as follows:

p (MPa)	8.0	7.0	6.0	5.0	4.0
v (L/kg)	29.95	35.24	42.23	51.94	66.45

To find the work, integration of Eq. (3.6) may be carried out either graphically or numerically. We integrate numerically using a simple trapezoidal rule:

$$W = \int_1^2 p dV = m \sum_{i=1}^{k} \frac{p_{i+1} + p_i}{2} \Delta v_i$$

$$= 6.678 \times 0.5 \times [(7+8) \times (35.24 - 29.95) + (6+7) \times (42.23 - 35.24)$$

$$+ (5+6) \times (51.94 - 42.23) + (4+5) \times (66.45 - 51.94)] = 6.678 \times 203.8 = 1361 \text{ kJ}$$

The heat interaction is found again from the first law:

$$Q = \Delta U + W = 527.6 + 1361 = 1889 \text{ kJ}$$

EXAMPLE 4.9

A tank of volume $V = 0.2$ m^3, Fig. 4.8, containing steam at 2 MPa and 500 °C is connected through a valve to a vertical cylinder covered by a heavy piston of area $A = 0.1$ m^2 and weighing 20 kN. The atmospheric pressure is p_0 = 100kPa. The whole tank–cylinder assembly is well insulated.

At the beginning the cylinder contained no steam. The valve is opened and steam flows until the pressures in the cylinder and the tank equalize.

a. Find the final temperature in the cylinder if the final tank temperature is 250 °C.
b. Find the mass of steam that entered the cylinder.
c. What is the piston rise in this process?

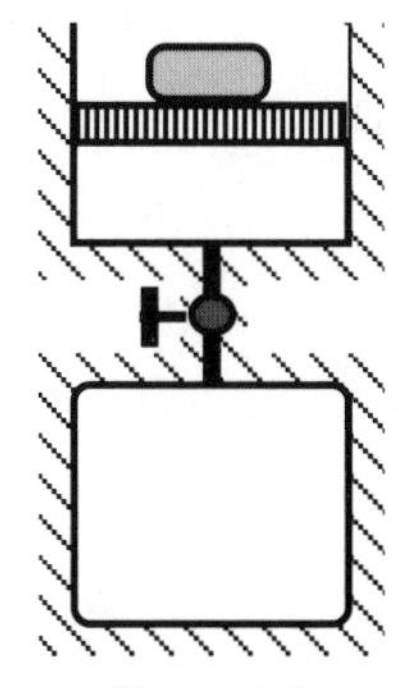

Figure 4.8

SOLUTION

The three relevant states in this problem are labeled as:

1. Initial state in the tank.
2. Final state in the tank.
3. Final state in the cylinder.

The pressure in the final states equals the external equivalent pressure p_e exerted on the system by the weighted piston and the external atmosphere:

$$p_e = p_0 + 20/0.1 = 100 + 200 = 300 \text{ kPa} = 0.3 \text{ MPa}$$

Now states 1 and 2 in the tank are completely defined by both pressure and temperature. In state 3 only the pressure is given.

We arrange the data for the three states in a table underlining the given properties for each state.

State	p MPa	T °C	v m³/kg	h kJ/kg	u kJ/kg	m kg
1	2.0	500	0.17568	3467.6	3116.2	1.1384
2	0.3	250	0.79640	2967.6	2728.7	0.2511
3	0.3					0.8873

The final mass in the cylinder, m_3, was found by the difference, $m_3 = m_1 - m_2$.

To find state 3 an additional property is needed. This is found by the first law of thermodynamics together with the law of conservation of mass:

$$m_1 = m_2 + m_3 \qquad \Delta U = Q - W$$

Since the process is adiabatic $Q = 0$, and

$$W = \int_2^3 p_e dV = p_3 \Delta V = p_3 V_3$$

since the external equivalent pressure equals p_3 and the change of the volume of the system (the steam) equals V_3. Thus

$$\Delta U = -p_3 V_3$$

i.e.

$$(m_3 u_3 + m_2 u_2) - m_1 u_1 = -m_3 p_3 v_3$$

Noting that

$$h_3 = u_3 + p_3 v_3$$

we get

$$m_3 h_3 = m_1 u_1 - m_2 u_2$$

or

$$h_3 = (m_1 u_1 - m_2 u_2)/m_3$$

Substituting the relevant data from the table we obtain

$$h_3 = (1.1384 \times 3116.2 - 0.2511 \times 2728.7)/0.8873 = 3225.9 \text{ kJ/kg}$$

a. For $p_3 = 0.3$ MPa and $h_3 = 3225.9$ kJ/kg we find from Table A.1.3 by interpolation: $T_3 = 376$ °C and $v_3 = 0.9942$ m³/kg
b. The piston rise z_3 is found from

$$V_3 = m_3 v_3 = A_3 z_3$$

Hence,

$$z_3 = \frac{m_3 v_3}{A_3} = \frac{0.8873 \times 0.9942}{0.1} = 8.82 \text{ m}$$

which is rather substantial.

4.13 Summary of equations for simple systems

General definitions

Energy of simple system: $E = U$

Definition of enthalpy: $H = U + pV$

Definition of specific enthalpy: $h = u + pv$

specific heat capacity at constant volume: $c_v = \left(\frac{\partial u}{\partial T}\right)_v$

specific heat capacity at constant pressure: $c_p = \left(\frac{\partial h}{\partial T}\right)_p$

Constant-volume (or isochoric) process

Change of energy: $\Delta U = Q - W_s$

$$\Delta U = U_2 - U_1 = m\int_1^2 c_v dT$$

Constant-pressure (or isobaric) process

Change of enthalpy: $\Delta H = Q - W_s$

$$\Delta H = H_2 - H_1 = m\int_1^2 c_p dT$$

Properties of pure substances

Quality of vapor: $x = \frac{m_g}{m} = \frac{m_g}{m_f + m_g}$

Properties in the vapor–liquid two-phase region:

$$v = v_f + xv_{fg} \qquad u = u_f + xu_{fg} \qquad h = h_f + xh_{fg}$$

PROBLEMS

4.1 For a system containing H_2O in thermodynamic equilibrium, indicate whether the following statements are true, sometimes true, or false:

a. The state of a system is determined by pressure alone.
b. The state is determined by pressure and temperature.
c. The state is determined by volume and energy.
d. The state of superheated vapor is determined by pressure and temperature.
e. The state of superheated vapor is determined by volume and energy.
f. There are two phases in the system.
g. There are three phases in the system.
h. There are four phases in the system.
i. Compressed liquid exists in two phases.
j. When two phases exist the state is determined by pressure alone.
k. When two phases exist the state is determined by pressure and temperature.
l. When two phases exist the state is determined by volume and energy.
m. Two properties determine a state.

4.2 For a simple compressible system, indicate whether the following statements are true, sometimes true, or false:

a. The heat interaction in a cycle is equal to 0.
b. The volume change from state 1 to state 2 depends on the work of the system.
c. Enthalpy is a primitive property of a simple system.
d. When a gas expands, its energy increases.
e. The work of an adiabatic cycle is equal to 0.
f. The work in a cycle is equal to 0.
g. The energy change from state 1 to state 2 depends on the work of the system.
h. The internal energy of a simple system is a derived property.
i. When a gas is compressed in a cylinder, its energy does not change.
j. The work in an adiabatic cycle is positive.

4.3 A closed system of 1 kg of steam undergoes a cycle consisting of three quasistatic processes represented by three straight lines, as shown in Fig. 4.9.

a. Calculate the work of the steam in each stage.

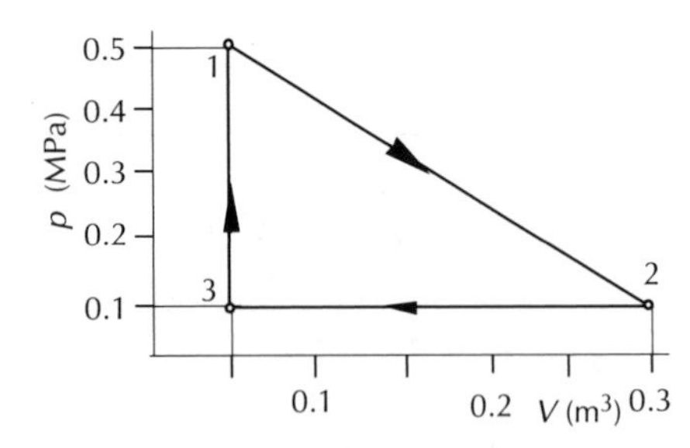

Figure 4.9

b. Find the energy and enthalpy changes in each stage.
c. Determine the heat interaction of the complete process.

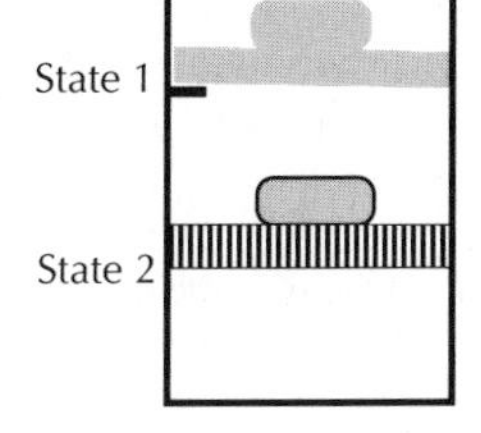

Figure 4.10

4.4 An insulated cylinder is covered by a heavy piston that is held in place by a stop, see Fig. 4.10. The cylinder contains 0.52 kg of H_2O at 3.0 bars, 150 °C (state 1). The stop is removed and the piston drops until the pressure reaches 5.0 bars where it stops (state 2). At this point the insulation is removed and the system is brought in contact with a bath at 150 °C, and the temperatures are allowed to equalize (state 3).

a. Find the temperature and the pressure at state 2.
b. Find the temperature and the pressure at state 3.
c. Determine the heat interaction of the complete process.

4.5 A system of 20 g of Freon-12 at 600 kPa, 130 °C, is contained in a cylinder covered by a heavy piston of 15 cm in diameter and a mass of 720 kg. A stop prevents the piston from moving upward, as shown in Fig. 4.11. The Freon undergoes a quasistatic heat interaction with the environment at 100 kPa, 15 °C, till its volume is reduced to 80% of the initial value.

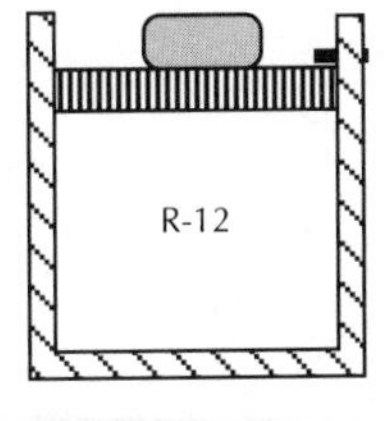

Figure 4.11

a. Find the initial force that the stop exerts on the piston.
b. Find the final state of the system.
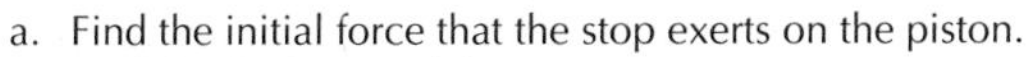
c. Find the heat and work interaction of the system.
d. Now the cylinder is insulated and a stirrer is operated till the initial volume of the system is reached. Find the work of the stirrer.

4.6 An adiabatic vertical cylinder covered by a piston contains gas at $p_1 = 900$ kPa and $V_1 = 0.3$ m^3. The piston has a mass of 1500 kg and an area of 0.1 m^2, and is held in place by a stop. The surrounding pressure is $p_0 = 100$ kPa. The piston is released and the gas expands until a state of equilibrium is reached. The volume of the gas is then $V_2 = 0.8$ m^3.

a. Find the final pressure of the gas.
b. Is the process quasistatic?
c. Does the work in this process depend on the path? Explain!
d. Find the work done by the gas.
e. Find the change in internal energy of the gas.

4.7 A vertical cylinder containing 2 kg of water at 20 °C and 5 bars is covered by a piston, Fig. 4.12. Heat is slowly transferred to the water and the piston rises until it reaches the stops. At this state the volume of the cylinder is 0.6 m^3. Heating continues until the state of saturated steam is reached. Calculate:

a. The final pressure in the cylinder.
b. The heat and work interactions of the water.

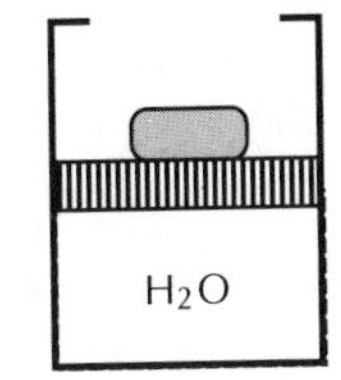

Figure 4.12

4.8 Mercury vapor undergoes a cyclic process shown on the p–V diagram in Fig. 4.13.
Step AB: Adiabatic expansion with $W_{AB} = 4$ kJ.
Step BC: Isochoric heating, $Q_{BC} = 5$ kJ.
Step CA: Isobaric compression.
If $U_A = 110$ kJ and the area enclosed by ABC is 3 kN m:

a. Find U_B and U_C.
b. What is the net work of the cycle?
c. What is the net heat transferred to the gas during the cycle?
d. What is the change in enthalpy of the gas for the complete cycle?

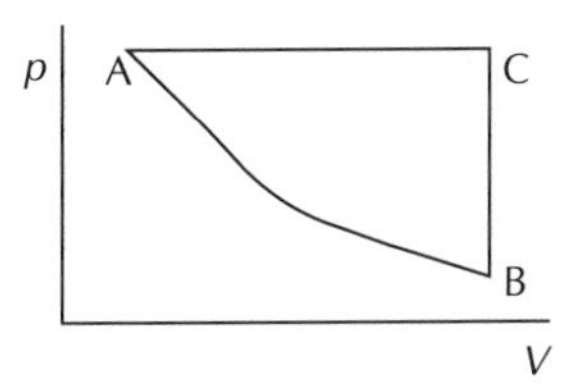

Figure 4.13

4.9 A piston–cylinder assembly contains 4 g of H_2O at 280 °C and a volume of 100 cm^3. The H_2O is compressed isothermally until its internal energy reaches 1227.5 kJ/kg.

a. Sketch the process on a $p-v$ diagram relative to the saturation region.
b. Determine the final pressure of the system.
c. Determine the final volume occupied by the system.
d. Determine the magnitude and direction of the boundary work for this process.
e. Determine the change in specific internal energy of the system.

4.10 A vertical frictionless piston–cylinder assemly contains initially 0.025 kg of steam at 10 °C and 150 kPa. The cylinder is fitted with stationary stops which limit the travel of the piston to a total of 0.10m. The piston has an area of 0.05 m^2 and is weighted so that it maintains a constant pressure of 150 kPa on the steam until the piston reaches the stops. Heat is transferred to the steam until the temperature reaches 150 °C.

a. Show this process on a $p-v$ diagram.
b. Determine the magnitude of the heat transfer required.
c. Find the temperature of the steam when the piston reaches the stops.

4.11 H_2O initially at 2.0 MPa and 260 °C is contained in a closed rigid tank with a volume of 0.225 m^3. The system is cooled until the final pressure is 1.0 MPa

a. Sketch the process on a $p-v$ diagram relative to the saturation region.
b. Determine the change in internal energy for this process.
c. Determine the work interaction for this process.

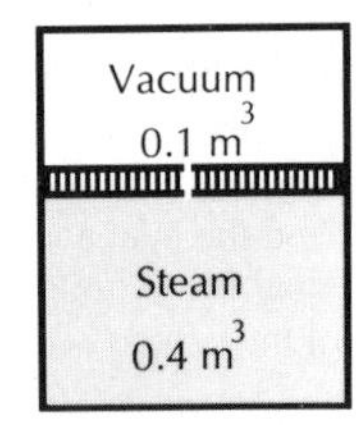

Figure 4.14

4.12 Steam at 0.2 MPa, 150 °C, and 0.4 m^3 is contained in the lower part of a cylinder, under a heavy and frictionless piston, shown in Fig. 4.14. The volume above the piston is 0.1 m^3 and it is evacuated. The cylinder is kept at 150 °C by a thermostatic bath. At a certain moment a hole is punctured in the piston and the steam leaks slowly to the upper part until equilibrium is reached. Find:

a. The pressure at the end of the process.
b. The heat interaction of the container.

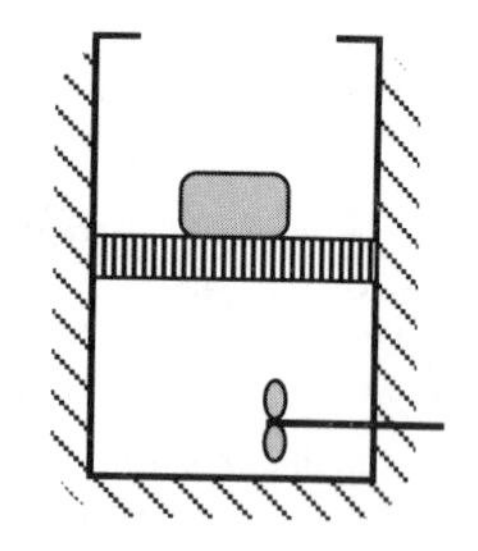

Figure 4.15

4.13 A 2 kg simple system inside an insulated piston–cylinder assembly, equipped with a working mixer, is shown in Fig. 4.15. The system expands isobarically from 0.1 m^3, 1.0 MPa, to 0.2 m^3, where the piston is stopped by a stop. The enthalpy change of the system during this process is 500 kJ. The mixer continues to work until the pressure reaches 5.0 MPa. The total work supplied by the mixer is $W = 1000$ kJ.

a. Draw the processes on a $p-v$ diagram.
b. Find the total heat interaction of the system.
c. Find the work of the system in each process.
d. Find the total enthalpy change of the system.
e. Find the energy change of the system in each process.

4.14 Figure 4.16 shows an insulated tank of 0.25 m^3 with a fixed thin membrane. One side of the tank is empty (vacuum). The other side is filled with 2 kg of steam at 1 MPa and has a volume of 0.16 m^3. The propeller is operated until the steam reaches a state of saturated vapor. At this point the membrane ruptures and the propeller is stopped.

Find the final state of the system and the work interaction.

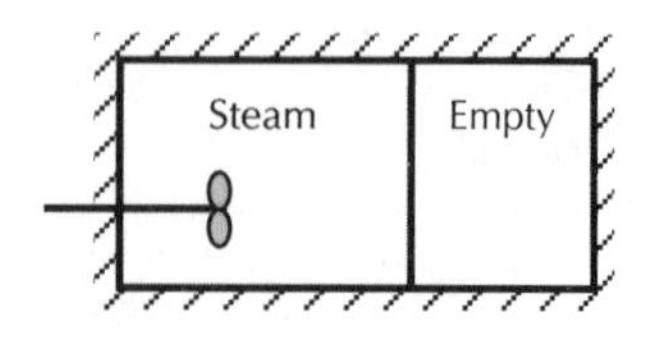

Figure 4.16

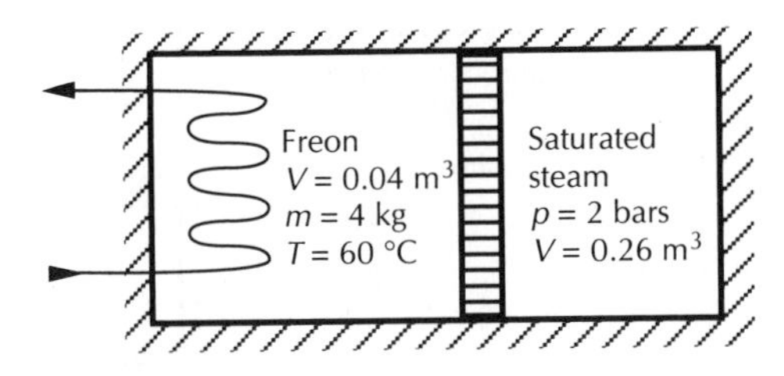

Figure 4.17

4.15 Freon and steam are contained in a cylinder, separated by an insulated frictionless piston, as shown in Fig. 4.17. The piston is held in place by a stop. A heating coil passes through the Freon side of the cylinder. The stop is released and the system reaches equilibrium when the Freon is at 5 bars and 50 °C.

a. Find the initial temperature of the steam and the heat interaction with the coil.
b. Fill out a table with the properties of the gases in the initial and final state.

4.16 The gas inside the piston–cylinder assembly in Fig. 4.18 has a volume of 0.1 m^3 and a pressure of 100 kPa. This pressure balances the weight of the piston exactly such that there is no stress exerted on the spring. Heat in the amount of 130 kJ is transferred to the gas changing its state to 300 kPa, 0.2m^3. During the process the force acting on the spring is proportional to the displacement of the piston.

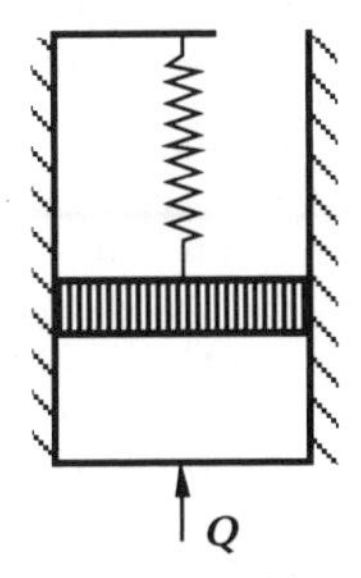

Figure 4.18

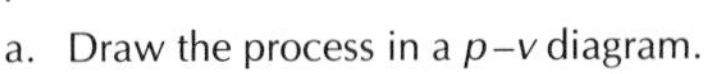

a. Draw the process in a p–v diagram.
b. Find the work of the system. What percentage of it is done on the spring?
c. Find the changes of internal energy and enthalpy during the process.

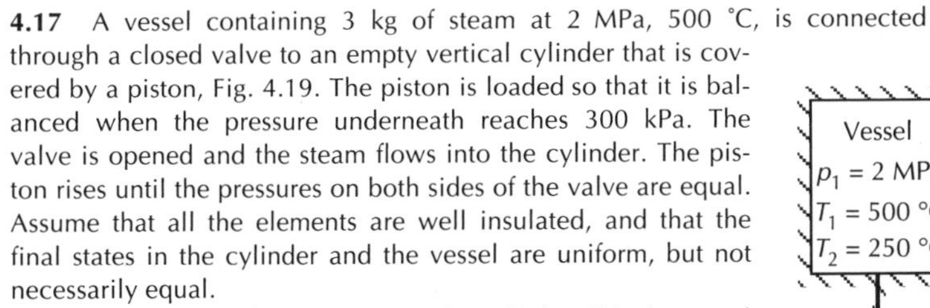

4.17 A vessel containing 3 kg of steam at 2 MPa, 500 °C, is connected through a closed valve to an empty vertical cylinder that is covered by a piston, Fig. 4.19. The piston is loaded so that it is balanced when the pressure underneath reaches 300 kPa. The valve is opened and the steam flows into the cylinder. The piston rises until the pressures on both sides of the valve are equal. Assume that all the elements are well insulated, and that the final states in the cylinder and the vessel are uniform, but not necessarily equal.

Calculate the final temperature in the cylinder, if in the vessel a temperature of 250 °C was measured at the end of the process.

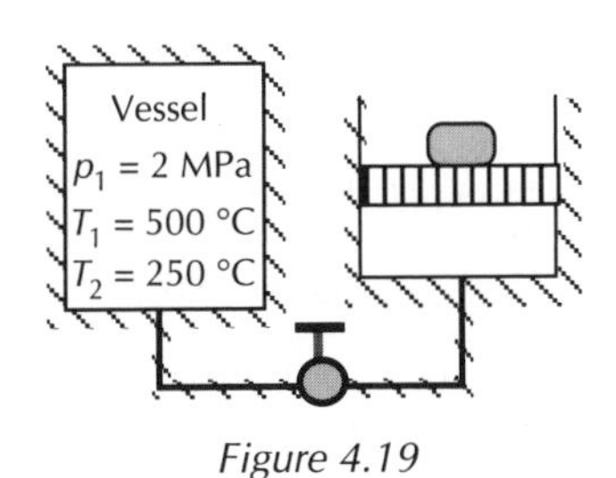

Figure 4.19

4.18 A system undergoes a cycle consisting of three quasistatic processes, as follows:

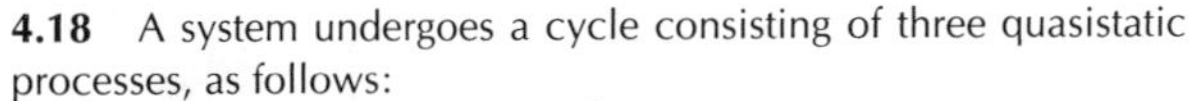

Process 1–2 is adiabatic, with $U_2 - U_1 = -30$ kJ.
Process 2–3 is isochoric.
Process 3–1 is isobaric at 500 kPa from 0.3 m^3 to 0.1 m^3.

a. Find the work of the gas during each process.
b. Find the work and heat interactions for the entire cycle.

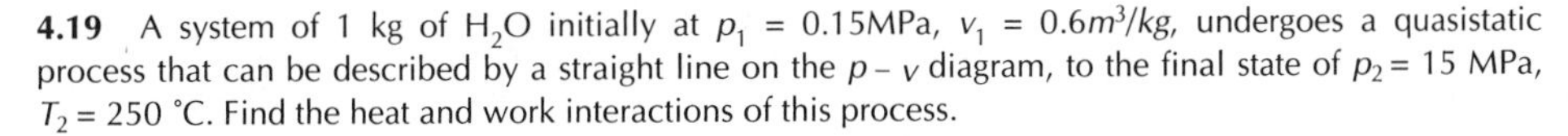

4.19 A system of 1 kg of H_2O initially at p_1 = 0.15MPa, v_1 = 0.6m^3/kg, undergoes a quasistatic process that can be described by a straight line on the $p - v$ diagram, to the final state of p_2 = 15 MPa, T_2 = 250 °C. Find the heat and work interactions of this process.

4.20 An insulated piston–cylinder assembly contains a system of 1 kg of steam at V = 20 L, Fig. 4.20.

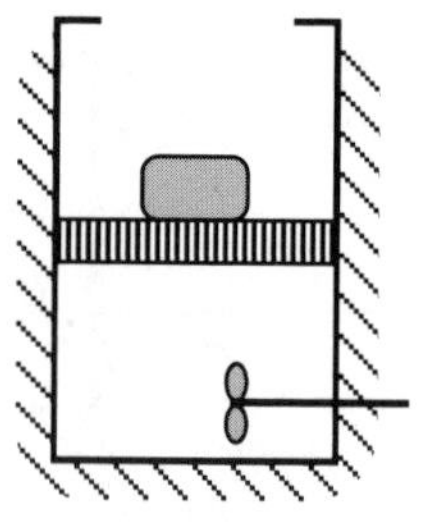
Figure 4.20

Work is supplied to the system by means of a mixer until the steam reaches saturation. The pressure is held constant, at $p = 0.4$ MPa, during the process.

a. Draw the process on a $p - v$ diagram.
b. Find the changes of the energy and the enthalpy of the steam.
c. Find the work of the system.

4.21 The container shown in Fig. 4.21 is divided by a partition into two parts. Part A has a volume of 2 m^3 and contains steam at 2.5 MPa, 400 °C. Part B has a volume of 0.3 m^3 and is evacuated. The partition is removed and the steam reaches a state of equilibrium. Find:

a. The final state of the steam, assuming the container is in good contact with a constant-temperature bath at 400 °C.
b. The interactions that take place with the bath and their magnitude.
c. The final state if the container were adiabatic.

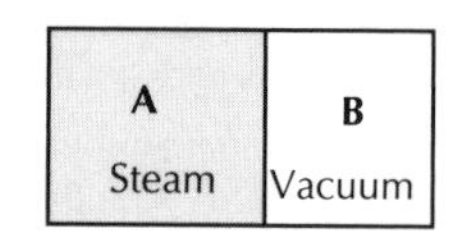

$T = 380$ °C

Figure 4.21

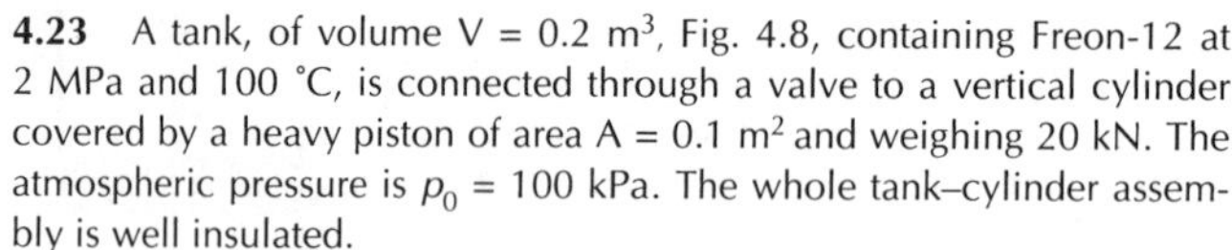

4.22 The specific energy of a certain substance is given by $u = A + Bpv$ where $A = 60$ kJ/kg, $B = 8$, p is in kPa, and v is in m^3/kg.

Find the work done by a system of the above substance when its volume increases adiabatically from 1.5 MPa and 60 L to 150 L.

4.23 A tank, of volume V = 0.2 m^3, Fig. 4.8, containing Freon-12 at 2 MPa and 100 °C, is connected through a valve to a vertical cylinder covered by a heavy piston of area A = 0.1 m^2 and weighing 20 kN. The atmospheric pressure is $p_0 = 100$ kPa. The whole tank–cylinder assembly is well insulated.

At the beginning the cylinder was empty. The valve is opened and Freon flows until the pressures in the cylinder and the tank equalize.

a. Find the final temperature in the cylinder if the final tank temperature is 20 °C.
b. Find the mass of Freon that entered the cylinder.
c. What is the piston rise in this process?

4.24 A marine engineer is investigating the possible causes of a recent submarine disaster, and he comes upon the idea that it may have been due to the explosion of a faulty steam boiler. He hypothesizes that the 3 m^3 boiler accidentally reached a temperature of 700 °C and a pressure of 35 MPa and exploded; the steam then expanded into the boiler room having a volume of 225 m^3.

The engineer feels that the final pressure of the steam may have been high enough to cause the walls of the boiler room to burst and, therefore, he asks you to calculate this pressure for him. Assume that the boiler-room is sealed and that the initial contents of the room may be neglected.

Set up the solution method in detail, discussing all assumptions which you may make, and find the pressure in the room after the explosion.

4.25 In Fig. 4.22, 1kg of water at 20 °C is enclosed in an adiabatic cylinder and piston assembly. The piston maintains a constant pressure of 150 kPa in the cylinder. The water is heated by passing a constant current of 10 A through an 11 Ω resistor.

Find the time required for all the water to evaporate.

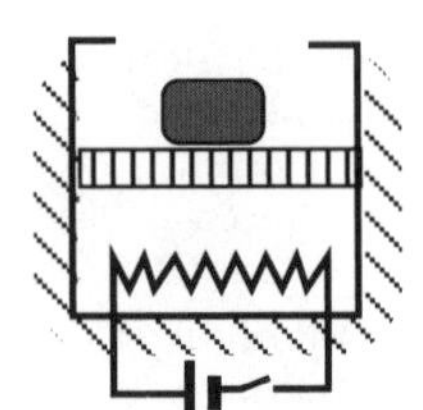
Figure 4.22

4.26 Two vertical, well-insulated, piston–cylinder assemblies, A and B, are connected through an adiabatic turbine, as shown in Fig. 4.23. The pistons are loaded by weights equivalent to pressures of 1.5 and 0.15 MPa, respectively. Initially cylinder A contains 2 kg of steam at a temperature of 400 °C while cylinder B is empty.

Steam is now allowed to flow from cylinder A to cylinder B through the turbine until piston A comes to the bottom of cylinder A. The final temperature of the steam in cylinder

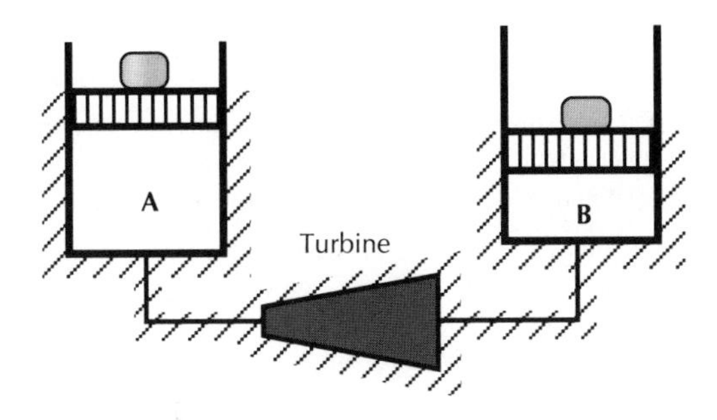

Figure 4.23

B is 140 °C. Assume the volume of the turbine and connecting piping to be negligible. Find the work delivered by the turbine.

4.27 A well-insulated cylinder contains 0.2 kg of steam at 3.5 MPa and 400 °C. The cylinder is covered with a 50 kg insulated piston whose area is 180 cm^2 and is loaded by a weight of 150 kg. The piston is held in place by means of a stop. The stop is removed and the piston moves upward, oscillates for a while, and stops. Assume that the atmospheric pressure is 100 kPa.

Find how much the piston rose.

4.28 A cylinder containing 0.2 kg of steam at 3.5 MPa is maintained at 400 °C by a bath. The cylinder is covered with a 50 kg piston whose area is 180 cm^2 and is loaded by a weight of 150 kg. The piston is held in place by means of a stop. The stop is removed and the piston moves upward, oscillates for a while and stops. Assume that the atmospheric pressure is 100 kPa. Find how much the piston rose.

4.29 A pressure vessel of 2.4 m^3 contains 1.8 m^3 of liquid water and 0.6 m^3 of water vapor at 100 kPa. The vessel is heated until the pressure reaches 5.5 MPa. Find the heat interaction during the process.

4.30 A closed glass tube, whose volume is 0.1 m^3, contains a mixture of liquid water and vapor at 20 °C. The tube is heated slowly and when the temperature reaches 150 °C it contains saturated vapor only.

a. Describe the process on $p-v$ and T–p diagrams.
b. What are the initial and final pressures?
c. Find the change of the specific enthalpy during the process.
d. Determine the heat interaction in the process.

4.31 A system consists of 9.0 kg of water, of which 3.0 kg have a specific internal energy of 20 kJ/kg and the remainder, 30 kJ/kg. A heat interaction takes place, during which 150 kJ are transferred to the system. At the end of the interaction the system attains a stable equilibrium state. Find the final specific internal energy of the system.

4.32 A vessel in good contact with a bath at 400 °C is divided by a stopped piston into two equal parts, Fig. 4.24. One side contains 2.0 kg of steam at 5.0 MPa and the other side is empty. The stop is removed and the piston moves until a new equilibrium state is attained.

a. Determine the pressure at the final state.
b. Find the heat interaction of the steam.

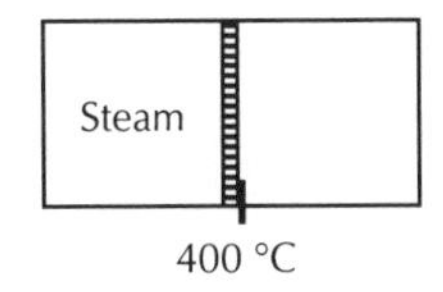

Figure 4.24

4.33 A sealed glass tube of 10 cm³ contains a mixture of water and water vapor at 80 kPa. The quality of the mixture is such that when it is heated it passes through the critical point. Find:

a. The initial quality of the mixture.
b. The heat interaction of the system.

4.34 An adiabatic vessel of 2 m³ is divided by a membrane into two equal parts. One part contains 1kg of steam at 400 °C while the other is evacuated. The membrane ruptures, the steam expands and reaches equilibrium. What is the temperature and pressure of the steam at equilibrium?

4.35 A steam vessel of 2.5 m³ capacity contains 1000 kg of liquid water in equilibrium with its vapor which fills the remainder of the vessel. The temperature is at 200 °C. Now 500 kg of saturated liquid water at 90 °C are pumped into the vessel without removing any steam. How much heat must be added during this process if the pressure and temperature in the steam vessel are to remain at their initial values?

4.36 A balloon made of thin elastic material contains 30 g of steam at 200 °C and 0.2 MPa. The balloon exerts on its contents a pressure difference which is proportional to its volume. The pressure of the surroundings outside the balloon is 1 bar and the temperature 20 °C. The steam undergoes a heat interaction with a reservoir at 400 °C until mutual equilibrium is attained. Find:

a. The final pressure of the steam.
b. The work and heat interactions during the process.

4.37 A cylinder contains steam at 250 °C, 10 bars, behind a piston connected to a linear spring, as shown in Fig. 4.25. The cylinder is immersed in a bath held at 250 °C. In the beginning the piston was held by a stop and the spring was unstressed. Then the stop was removed and the steam expanded to a new equilibrium state at which the pressure was 6 bars.

a. Determine the ratio between the initial and the final volume of the steam.
b. Calculate the heat and the work interactions of the steam.

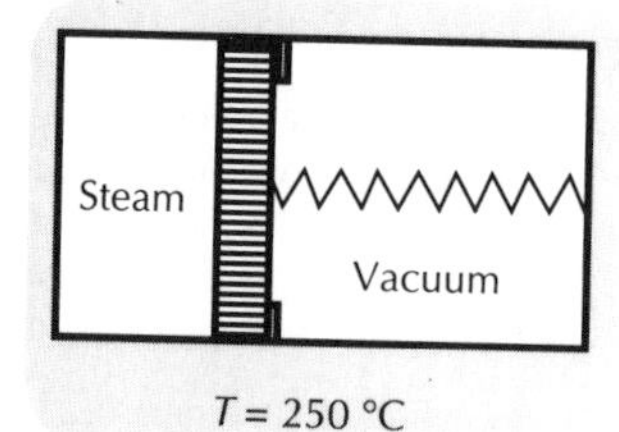

Figure 4.25

4.38 A well-insulated cylinder contains steam at 250 °C, 10 bars, behind a piston connected to a linear spring, as shown in Fig. 4.26. In the beginning the piston was held by a stop and the spring was unstressed. Then the stop was removed and the steam expanded to a new equilibrium state at which the pressure was 6 bars.

Find the final state and the work interaction of the steam.

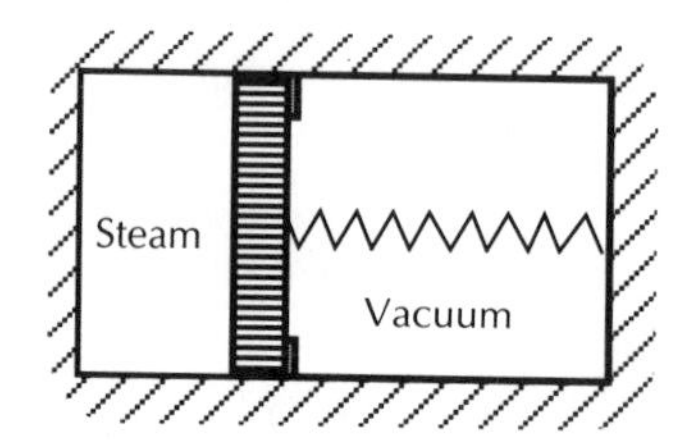

Figure 4.26

CHAPTER FIVE

The ideal gas

In this chapter we introduce the idea of an ideal gas, which is defined in terms of a simple equation of state. An ideal gas so defined has the advantage that all its properties may be calculated mathematically in a closed form without the need to resort to tables. Moreover, quasistatic processes may also be calculated mathematically.

Although the concept of the ideal gas is just a mathematical idea, which does not necessarily have to describe real gas behavior, still for many situations the ideal gas assumption yields very satisfactory results.

5.1 Definition of an ideal gas

It is an experimental fact that for simple substances the property $p\,v/T$ approaches a fixed limit,

$$\lim_{p \to 0} \frac{pv}{T} = \lim_{v \to \infty} \frac{pv}{T} = R \tag{5.1}$$

where R is a constant characteristic of the substance, but independent of temperature. Equation (5.1) is rewritten in terms of molar specific volumes, $\bar{v}$, as

$$\lim_{v \to \infty} \frac{p\bar{v}}{T} = \bar{R} \tag{5.2}$$

where $\bar{R}$ is the universal gas constant, which is independent of the substance.

$$\bar{R} = 8.31434 \frac{\text{J}}{\text{mol K}} = 8.31434 \frac{\text{kJ}}{\text{kmol K}} \tag{5.3}$$

Since $v = \bar{v}/M$ it follows that

$$R = \frac{\bar{R}}{M} \tag{5.4}$$

An ideal gas is defined as one for which the following equation of state holds:

$$pv = RT \tag{5.5}$$

It follows from Eq. (5.1) that all substances approach ideal gas behavior at low densities. Equation (5.5) may be rewritten in several alternative useful forms:

$$p\bar{v} = \bar{R}T \tag{5.6}$$

$$pV = mRT \tag{5.7}$$

$$pV = n\bar{R}T \tag{5.8}$$

where $n = m/M$ is the number of moles of the substance.

There is no real substance that satisfies the ideal gas definition for the entire range of states. Therefore, the ideal gas is a concept rather than a reality. A measure of the deviation of a real substance from the ideal gas behavior is given by a property called the compressibility factor, denoted by Z

$$Z = \frac{pv}{RT} \tag{5.9}$$

At low densities, when ideal gas conditions are approached,

$$\lim_{v \to \infty} Z = 1 \tag{5.10}$$

In general Z is a function of pressure and temperature and may differ from unity. Figure 5.1 shows schematically a typical compressibility chart in terms of reduced properties, $p_r = p/p_c$ and $T_r = T/T_c$.

EXAMPLE 5.1

Using the ideal gas equation of state find the specific volume of steam at 400 °C and at pressures:

a. $p = 0.01$ MPa b. $p = 0.1$ MPa c. $p = 20.0$ MPa

Compare your data with those given in the steam tables and calculate the compressibility factor for each case.

SOLUTION

For steam $R = \bar{R}/M = 8.31434/18.016 = 0.46150$ kJ/kg ; hence

a. $v = RT/p = 0.46150 \times (400 + 273.15)/10 = 31.066\ \text{m}^3/\text{kg}$

b. $v = RT/p = 0.46150 \times 673.15/100 = 3.1066\ \text{m}^3/\text{kg}$

c. $v = RT/p = 0.46150 \times 673.15/20000 = 0.015533\ \text{m}^3/\text{kg}$

For easy reference we arrange the results in a table together with the actual values of v from the steam tables:

Case	p	$v = RT/p$	v_{actual}	$Z = pv_{act}/RT$
a	0.01	31.066	31.063	0.9999
b	0.10	3.1066	3.103	0.9988
c	20.0	0.015533	0.009942	0.6401

As seen, the ideal gas assumption is very good for the high specific volume and low pressure cases a and b, while for the high pressure case c the deviation from ideal gas behavior is quite considerable.

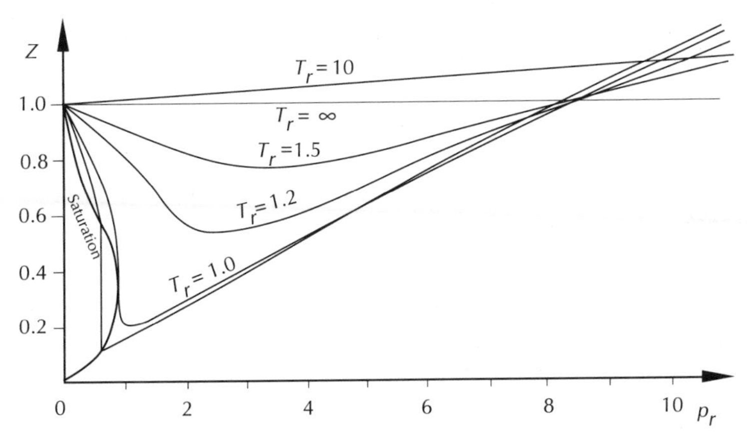

Figure 5.1 **Generalized compressibility chart.**

EXAMPLE 5.2

Repeat Example 5.1 for 50 °C.

SOLUTION

Calculating as in Example 5.1 we arrange the data in a table:

Case	p	$v = RT/p$	v_{actual}	$Z = pv_{act}/RT$
a	0.01	14.9134	14.869	0.9970
b	0.10	1.49134	0.001012	0.000679
c	20.0	0.007457	0.0010038	0.1346

For the low pressure superheated steam of case a $Z \approx 1$, while the compressed liquid of cases b and c has a very low compressibility factor, reflecting the fact that liquids are almost incompressible.

5.2 Internal energy and enthalpy of an ideal gas

For any substance whose equation of state is that of an ideal gas, Eq. (5.5), it can be shown that its internal energy, u, is a function of temperature only, and does not depend on the pressure of the system:

$$u = u(T) \tag{5.11}$$

In order to prove Eq. (5.11), one has to use the so-called Maxwell relationships. This will be done in Chapter 14. At present we accept Eq. (5.11) without proof. The enthalpy of an ideal gas is also a function of temperature only, since

$$h = u + pv = u(T) + RT = h(T) \tag{5.12}$$

We have shown in Eq. (4.26) that generally

$$\Delta u = \int_1^2 c_v dT + \int_1^2 \left(\frac{\partial u}{\partial v} \right)_T dv \tag{4.26}$$

But for an ideal gas it follows from Eq. (5.11) that $(\partial u / \partial v)_T = 0$. Therefore, in this case

$$\Delta u = \int_1^2 c_v dT \tag{5.13}$$

This equation is similar to Eq. (4.27), which was derived for a simple system undergoing a constant-volume process. For an ideal gas, however, Eq. (5.13) applies to any change of state. Similarly, from Eq. (4.43) it follows that for an ideal gas

$$\Delta h = \int_1^2 c_p dT \tag{5.14}$$

which, again, applies for any change of state, and is independent of the process. We now return to Eq. (5.12) and rewrite it as

$$dh = du + d(RT) \quad \Rightarrow \quad c_p dT = c_v dT + RdT$$

which requires that

$$c_p = c_v + R \tag{5.15}$$

Since the internal energy and the enthalpy of an ideal gas are functions of temperature only, so are the specific heats. The specific heat ratio, k, defined by Eq. (4.45), is also a function of temperature only

$$k = c_p / c_v \tag{5.16}$$

Equations (5.15) and (5.16) may be used to express c_v and c_p in terms of R and k:

$$c_v = \frac{1}{k-1} R \qquad c_p = \frac{k}{k-1} R \tag{5.17}$$

5.3 The ideal gas with constant specific heat

Figure 5.2 shows schematically the specific heats at constant volume of typical monatomic and diatomic gases at low pressures. The constant-volume specific heat, c_v, of a monatomic gas does not vary over a wide range of temperatures, and is very nearly equal to $\frac{3}{2}R$. In the case of a diatomic gas, c_v is nearly constant over a moderate range around room temperature, and equals about $\frac{5}{2}R$.

We now introduce the concept of an ideal gas with constant specific heat, which at low pressures is a good approximation of real gases over a considerable range of temperatures. This simplifies considerably the mathematical treatment of thermodynamic processes. If c_v is a constant, c_p and k must also be constant. For a monatomic gas $k = 5/3$, while for a diatomic gas $k = 7/5$. For polyatomic gases values of k between 1.1 and 1.35 are found.

The internal energy and the enthalpy, for an ideal gas with constant specific heat, are

$$\Delta U = mc_v \Delta T \tag{5.18}$$

and

$$\Delta H = mc_p \Delta T \tag{5.19}$$

Making use of the equation of state of an ideal gas together with Eq. (5.17), other useful relationships for ΔU and for ΔH can be obtained. These are summarized below:

$$\Delta U = \frac{1}{k-1}(p_2V_2 - p_1V_1) \qquad \Delta H = \frac{k}{k-1}(p_2V_2 - p_1V_1) \tag{5.20}$$

$$\Delta U = \frac{p_1V_1}{k-1}\left(\frac{T_2}{T_1} - 1\right) \qquad \Delta \mathrm{H} = \frac{kp_1V_1}{k-1}\left(\frac{T_2}{T_1} - 1\right) \tag{5.21}$$

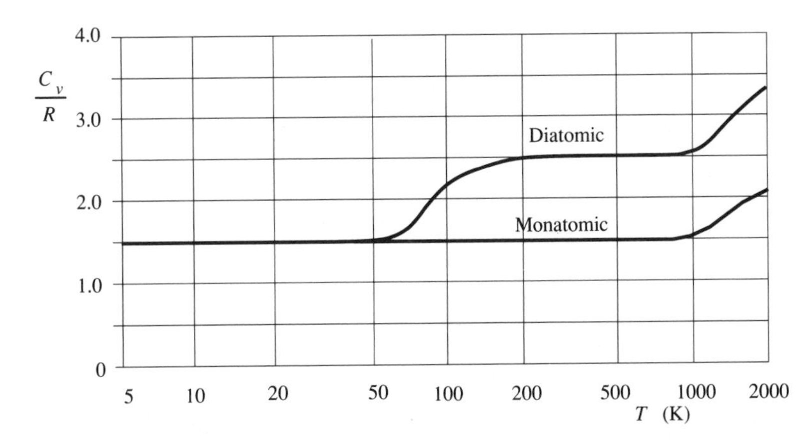

Figure 5.2 **Specific heat at constant volume for monatomic and diatomic gases.**

$$\Delta U = \frac{mRT_1}{k-1}\left(\frac{T_2}{T_1} - 1\right) \qquad \Delta H = \frac{kmRT_1}{k-1}\left(\frac{T_2}{T_1} - 1\right) \tag{5.22}$$

5.4 Quasistatic processes in an ideal gas

We now consider several basic quasistatic processes for ideal gas systems. Since we have an equation of state and formulas for energy and enthalpy, closed form expressions for heat and work interactions can be derived for the quasistatic processes. We recall that for a simple system the work in a quasistatic process can be calculated from

$$W = \int_1^2 p dV \ . \tag{3.6}$$

Thus for a constant-volume process, $dV = 0$, the quasistatic work is zero and the heat interaction is found from the first law of thermodynamics:

$$Q = \Delta U = m\int_1^2 c_v dT \tag{5.23}$$

and for constant c_v

$$Q = \Delta U = mc_v(T_2 - T_1) \tag{5.24}$$

For a constant-pressure process

$$W = p(V_2 - V_1) = mR(T_2 - T_1) \tag{5.25}$$

while the heat interaction is calculated from the first law

$$Q - p\Delta V = \Delta U \qquad \text{or} \qquad Q = \Delta H = \int_1^2 mc_p dT \tag{5.26}$$

which for constant c_p is

$$Q = \Delta H = mc_p(T_2 - T_1) \tag{5.27}$$

For an isothermal process in an ideal gas $\Delta u = \Delta h = 0$ and the first law yields

$$Q = W = \int_1^2 p dV \tag{5.28}$$

Substitution of $p = mRT/V$ and integration results in

$$Q = W = mRT \ln\frac{V_2}{V_1} \tag{5.29}$$

$$Q = W = p_1V_1 \ln\frac{p_1}{p_2} \tag{5.30}$$

For an adiabatic process, $\delta Q = 0$, and the first law of thermodynamics in differential form is

$$dU = -\delta W \tag{5.31}$$

and for a quasistatic process

$$mc_v dT = -pdV \tag{5.32}$$

Dividing both sides of Eq. (5.32) by $mRT = pV$ yields

$$\frac{c_v}{R}\frac{dT}{T} = -\frac{dV}{V} \tag{5.33}$$

which upon integration for constant c_v yields

$$\frac{T_2}{T_1} = \left[\frac{V_1}{V_2}\right]^{k-1} \tag{5.34}$$

or

$$TV^{k-1} = \text{const.} \tag{5.35}$$

Using the equation of state for an ideal gas, other relationships can be obtained. These are summarized in the following table in terms of specific volumes.

Variables	Differential form	Integral form for k = const.	
$T,\ v$	$\frac{dT}{T} + (k-1)\frac{dv}{v} = 0$	$Tv^{k-1} = \text{const.}$	$\frac{T_2}{T_1} = \left(\frac{v_2}{v_1}\right)^{1-k}$
$p,\ v$	$\frac{dp}{p} + k\frac{dv}{v} = 0$	$pv^k = \text{const.}$	$\frac{p_2}{p_1} = \left(\frac{v_2}{v_1}\right)^{-k}$
$T,\ p$	$\frac{dT}{T} - \frac{k-1}{k}\frac{dp}{p} = 0$	$\frac{p^{\frac{k-1}{k}}}{T} = \text{const.}$	$\frac{T_2}{T_1} = \left(\frac{p_2}{p_1}\right)^{\frac{k-1}{k}}$

Since the heat is equal to zero, the work for an adiabatic process is

$$W = -\Delta U \tag{5.36}$$

Hence, using Eqs (5.18)–(5.22) together with Eq. (5.36), the following relationships can be written down for the case of constant specific heat:

$$W = mc_v(T_1 - T_2) \tag{5.37}$$

$$W = \frac{1}{k-1}\left(p_1V_1 - p_2V_2\right) \tag{5.38}$$

$$W = \frac{mRT_1}{k-1}\left[1-\left(\frac{p_2}{p_1}\right)^{\frac{k-1}{k}}\right] \tag{5.39}$$

5.5 The polytropic process

A quasistatic process for which pv^n = const. is called a polytropic process. Special cases of polytropic processes are those discussed in the previous section. These can be summarized as follows:

constant-volume process:	v = const.	pv^{∞} = const.	$n = \infty$
constant-pressure process:	p = const.	pv^0 = const.	$n = 0$
isothermal process:	T = const.	pv^1 = const.	$n = 1$
quasistatic adiabatic process:	$Q = 0$	pv^k = const.	$n = k$

Actual processes of ideal gas compression or expansion are neither adiabatic nor isothermal. Usually these processes can be fairly well approximated by polytropic processes with $1 < n < k$.

The quasistatic work in a polytropic process can be calculated along the path for which $pV^n = p_2V_1^n = p_2V_2^n$ = const. , resulting in

$$W = \int_1^2 pdV = p_1V_1^n\int_1^2\frac{dV}{V^n} = \frac{p_1V_1^n}{1-n}\left(V_2^{1-n}-V_1^{1-n}\right)$$

leading to the following alternative expressions:

$$W = \frac{mR}{n-1}(T_1-T_2) \tag{5.40}$$

$$W = \frac{1}{n-1}(p_1V_1-p_2V_2) \tag{5.41}$$

$$W = \frac{mRT_1}{n-1}\left[1-\left(\frac{p_2}{p_1}\right)^{\frac{n-1}{n}}\right] \tag{5.42}$$

The heat interaction is calculated from the first law

$$Q = \Delta U + W = mc_v(T_2-T_1) + \frac{mR}{n-1}(T_1-T_2) = mR(T_2-T_1)\left[\frac{1}{k-1}-\frac{1}{n-1}\right]$$

and finally

$$Q = \left[\frac{(n-k)mR}{(n-1)(k-1)}\right](T_2 - T_1) = mc_v\left[\frac{n-k}{n-1}\right](T_2 - T_1) = mc_n(T_2 - T_1) \quad (5.43)$$

where

$$c_n = c_v\left[\frac{n-k}{n-1}\right]$$

5.6 The first law of thermodynamics in ideal gas systems

We now solve several examples that illustrate the application of the first law of thermodynamics to ideal gas systems.

EXAMPLE 5.3

A 0.08 m[3] container, shown in Fig. 5.3, is divided by a partition into two parts. The first part, whose volume is 0.03 m[3], contains oxygen at 300 kPa, 27 °C. The second, whose volume is 0.05 m[3], is evacuated. The partition is ruptured and the gas expands to occupy the whole container.

Treat oxygen as an ideal gas for which $M = 32$, $k = 1.4$.

Find the final state of the system, and the work and heat interactions in the process, if

a. The container is in good contact with a reservoir at 27 °C.
b. The container is well insulated.

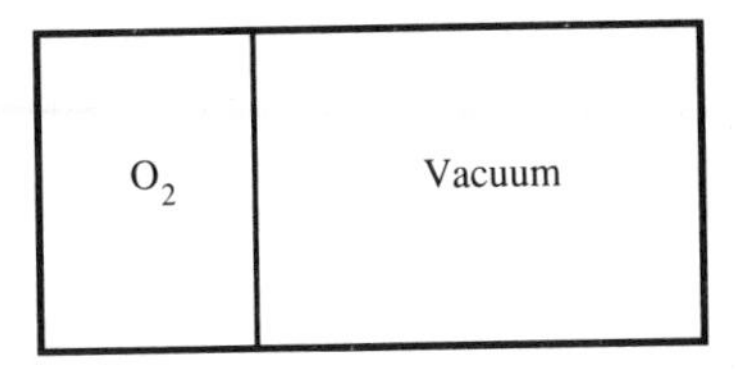

Figure 5.3

SOLUTION

a. In this case, $T_2 = T_1 = 300.15$ K and

$$p_2 = p_1 \frac{V_1}{V_2}\frac{T_2}{T_1} = 300\frac{0.03}{0.08} = 112.5 \text{ kPa}$$

The work of the system is

$$W = \int p_e dV = 0$$

Since resistance to the expansion of the gas is zero, $p_e = 0$. Thus, from the first law

$$\Delta U = Q$$

However, $\Delta U = 0$, since $\Delta T = 0$, and therefore $Q = 0$.

b. In this adiabatic case $Q = 0$, and also $W = 0$ as in case a. Thus

$$\Delta U = Q - W = 0$$

Therefore, the final state in this case is identical to that of case a.

EXAMPLE 5.4

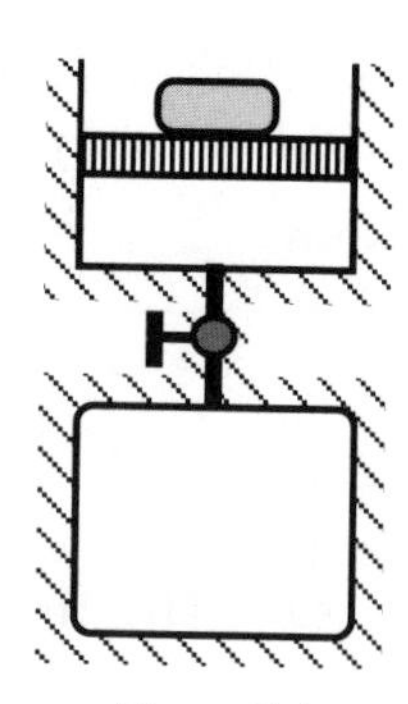
Figure 5.4

A tank of 0.20 m³, Fig. 5.4, contains nitrogen (ideal gas, $M = 28$, $k = 1.4$) at 2 MPa, 500 °C. The tank is connected through a valve to a vertical cylinder covered by a heavy piston weighing 20 kN. The piston area is $A = 0.1$ m². The whole tank–cylinder assembly is well insulated. The atmospheric pressure is 100 kPa.

At the beginning the cylinder contains no nitrogen. The valve is opened and nitrogen flows until the pressures in the cylinder and the tank equalize.

a. Find the final temperature in the cylinder if the final tank temperature is 250 °C.
b. Find the mass of nitrogen that entered the cylinder.
c. What is the piston rise in this process?

SOLUTION

This problem is essentially Example 4.9 with the gas being nitrogen instead of steam. We again denote the initial and final states in the tank by 1 and 2, respectively, and the final state in the cylinder by 3, and calculate the initial and final mass in the tank.

$$m_1 = \frac{p_1 V_1}{RT_1} = \frac{2000 \times 0.2}{(8.3143/28) \times 773.15} = 1.7423 \text{ kg}$$

$$m_2 = \frac{p_2 V_2}{RT_2} = \frac{300 \times 0.2}{(8.3143/28) \times 523.15} = 0.3862 \text{ kg}$$

The mass in the cylinder is found again by the difference

$$m_3 = m_1 - m_2 = 1.3561 \text{ kg}$$

a. To find the temperature, we use the first law for this system, $\Delta U = -W$:

$$(m_2 c_v T_2 + m_3 c_v T_3) - m_1 c_v T_1 = -p_3 V_3$$

or

$$\frac{R}{k-1}(m_2 T_2 + m_3 T_3 - m_1 T_1) = -Rm_3 T_3$$

and finally

$$T_3 = \frac{m_1 T_1 - m_2 T_2}{km_3} = \frac{1.7423 \times 773.15 - 0.3862 \times 523.55}{1.4 \times 1.3561} = 603.1\text{K}$$

b. The piston rise is

$$z_3 = \frac{V_3}{A} = \frac{m_3 RT_3}{p_3 A} = \frac{1.33561 \times 8.3143 \times 603.1}{28 \times 300 \times 0.1} = 8.10 \text{ m}$$

PROBLEMS

5.1 The following units are used in the International Edition of the Steam Tables: bars for pressure, cm^3/g for specific volume, and °C for temperature.

a. What is the numerical value of the universal gas constant in this system of units?
b. Find the specific volume of water vapor at the triple point assuming the vapor is an ideal gas.

5.2 For a system containing an ideal gas in thermodynamic equilibrium, indicate whether the following statements are true, sometimes true, or false:

a. Two properties determine a state.
b. The internal energy increases in an isothermal expansion.
c. The pressure is proportional to the temperature.
d. The temperature decreases in an adiabatic expansion.

5.3 At what temperature is the enthalpy of a certain ideal gas h = 23714 kJ/kmol, while its internal energy is u = 19556 kJ/kmol?

5.4 Find the enthalpy change of air when its state changes from 2.0 bars, 27 °C, to:

a. 4.0 bars, 327 °C.
b. 2.0 bars, 1227 °C.

Calculate the above using the following three methods and compare the results:

1. Using air tables.
2. Assuming air is an ideal gas with constant specific heat (M = 29, k =1.4).
3. Assuming air is an ideal gas whose specific heat is a function of temperature:

$$\frac{c_p}{R} = 3.2991+0.7433\left(\frac{T}{T_0}\right)-0.1081\left(\frac{T}{T_0}\right)^2$$

where T_0 = 1000K.

5.5 Using the ideal gas equation of state find the specific volume of steam at 300 °C and

a. p = 0.01 MPa.
b. p = 0.l MPa.
c. p = 8.581 MPa, x = 0.3.
Compare your results with the steam table values.

5.6 A cylinder containing 0.1 kg of air at 27 °C and 100 kPa is covered by a piston. The air is compressed polytropically at an exponent of n = 1.25, until it reaches 1/8 of its initial volume. Calculate:

a. The pressure and the temperature at the final state.
b. The change in energy and enthalpy of the air.
c. The heat and the work interactions of the air.

5.7 Carbon monoxide gas is contained within a piston–cylinder device at 1 bar, 27 °C. In process A the gas is heated at constant volume until the pressure is doubled. It is then expanded at a constant pressure until the volume is three times its initial value. In process B the gas, from the same initial state, is first expanded at a constant pressure until the volume has tripled, and then the gas is heated at constant volume until it reaches the same final pressure as in A. Find for each of these processes (in kJ/kg):

a. The net heat interaction.
b. The net work.
c. The change of internal energy.

5.8 Calculate the work done by 1 kg of gas during a quasistatic isothermal expansion from an initial volume V_1 to a final volume V_2 if the equation of state of the gas is $p(v-b) = RT$, where b is a positive constant.

If the gas were ideal, would the same process produce more or less work?

5.9 A 0.08 m^3 container is divided by a partition into two parts, Fig. 5.5: the first one is of volume 0.03 m^3 and contains oxygen (ideal gas, M = 32, k = 1.4) at 300 kPa, 25 °C while the other is of volume 0.05 m^3 and contains oxygen at 600 kPa, 225 °C. The partition is ruptured, the gas mixes, and equilibrium is attained. Find the final state and the work and heat interactions of the system, if:

a. The container is well insulated.
b. The container is brought into good contact with a reservoir at 25 °C.

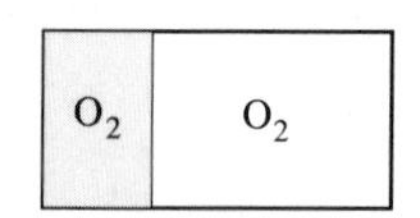

Figure 5.5

5.10 A vertical frictionless piston–cylinder assembly contains initially 0.05 lbm of air at 60 °F and 20 psia. The cylinder is fitted with stationary stops which limit the travel of the piston to a total of 3 inches. The piston has an area of 0.6 ft^2 and is weighted so that it maintains a constant pressure of 20 psia on the air until the piston reaches the stops. Heat is transferred to the air until the temperature reaches 300 °F.

a. Show this process on a $p - v$ diagram.
b. Determine the magnitude of the heat transfer required.
c. Find the temperature of the air when the piston reaches the stops.

5.11 An insulated cylinder is covered by a heavy piston that is held in place by a stop, as shown in Fig. 5.6. The cylinder contains 0.52 kg of air at 3.0 bars and 150 °C (state 1). The stop is removed and the piston drops until it stops at a pressure of 5.0 bars (state 2). At this point the insulation is removed and the system is brought in contact with a bath at 150 °C and the temperatures are allowed to equalize (state 3).

a. Find the temperature and the pressure at state 2.
b. Find the temperature and the pressure at state 3.
c. Calculate the heat interaction of the complete process.

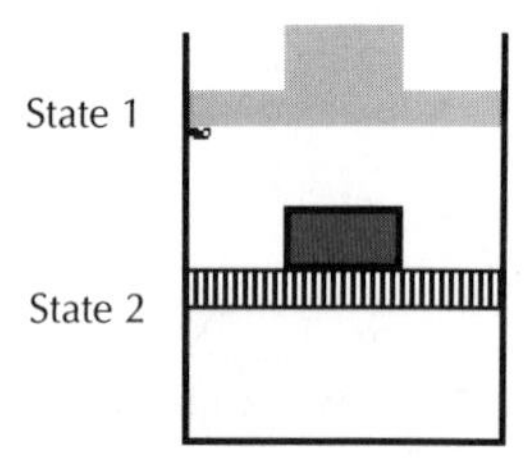

Figure 5.6

5.12 A closed system of 1 kg of air undergoes a cycle consisting of three quasistatic processes represented by three straight lines, as shown in Fig. 5.7.

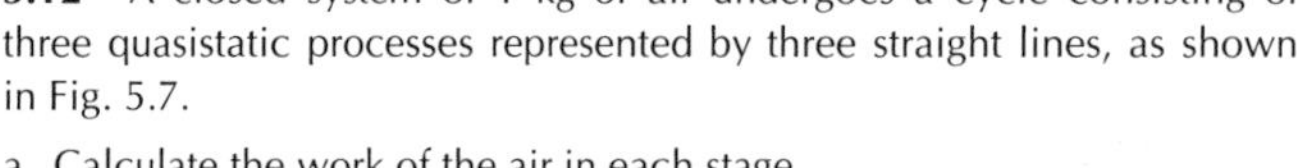

a. Calculate the work of the air in each stage.
b. Find the internal energy and enthalpy changes in each stage.
c. Calculate the heat interaction of the complete process.

5.13 A rigid storage container is divided into two parts by an uninsulated partition which is held in a fixed position. One section of the container contains 0.1 kg of nitrogen initially at 30 bars and 500 °C. The other section of the container contains 0.01 kg of H_2O at 500 °C and 60 bars. The container is cooled by removing energy in the form of heat. When equilibrium is reached the temperature of the contents of the container is found to be 230 °C. Determine:

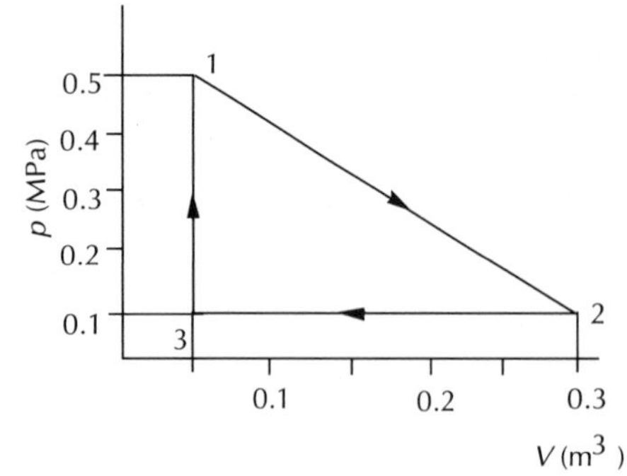

Figure 5.7

a. The final pressure of the H_2O.
b. The final pressure of the nitrogen.
c. The magnitude of the heat transfer (in kJ) for this process.

5.14 A vertical cylinder containing 2 kg of air at 20 °C and 0.5 MPa is covered by a piston, Fig. 5.8. Heat is slowly transferred to the air and the piston rises until it reaches the stops. At this state the volume of the cylinder is 0.8 m³. Heating continues until the pressure reaches 2 MPa. Find:

a. The final temperature in the cylinder.
b. The heat and work interactions of the air.

5.15 A system of 1 kg of oxygen (O_2) at the initial condition of p_1 = 0.15 MPa and v_1 = 0.6 m³/kg undergoes a quasistatic process that can be described by a straight line on the $p - v$ diagram, to the final state of p_2 = 15 MPa, T_2 = 250 °C. Find the heat and work interactions of this process.

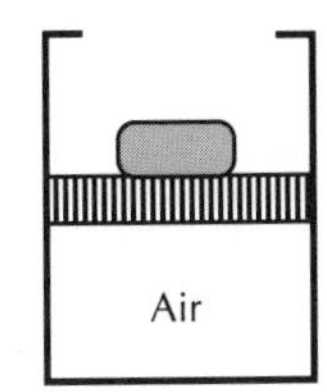

Figure 5.8

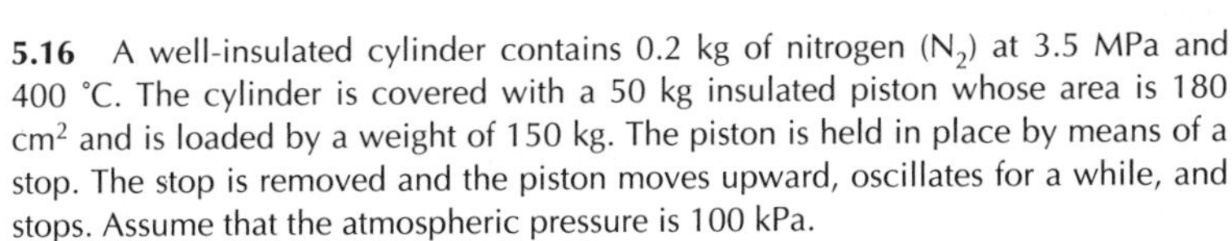

5.16 A well-insulated cylinder contains 0.2 kg of nitrogen (N_2) at 3.5 MPa and 400 °C. The cylinder is covered with a 50 kg insulated piston whose area is 180 cm² and is loaded by a weight of 150 kg. The piston is held in place by means of a stop. The stop is removed and the piston moves upward, oscillates for a while, and stops. Assume that the atmospheric pressure is 100 kPa.

Find how much the piston rose.

5.17 Air (ideal gas, k = 1.4, M = 29) is enclosed in a cylinder, covered by a piston that can travel between two stops, as shown in Fig. 5.9. The cross-sectional area of the cylinder is 0.1 m². The weight of the piston is 2000 N, and the atmospheric pressure is 100 kPa. When the piston is in the lower position the pressure inside the cylinder is 80 kPa and the temperature 100 °C.

The air is heated, and after a while the piston starts moving upward till it is stopped by the upper stop. The heating continues until the temperature of the air reaches 727 °C.

a. Show the process on a $p - v$ diagram.
b. What is the temperature of the air inside the cylinder at the moment the piston starts moving upward?
c. What is the temperature of the air when the piston reaches the upper stop?
d. What is the final pressure of the air inside the cylinder?
e. Find the changes in energy and enthalpy of the air for the complete process.
f. Find the heat and work interactions between the system and the surroundings for the complete process.

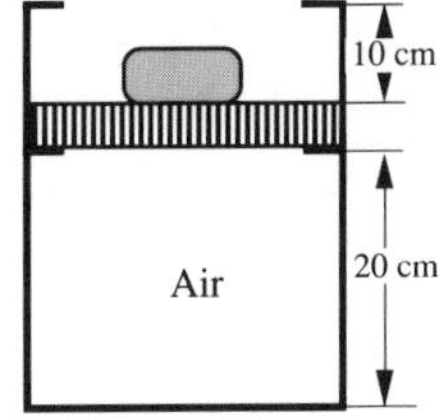

Figure 5.9

5.18 Air (an ideal gas, k = 1.4, M = 29) is enclosed in a stepped cylinder, as shown in Fig. 5.10. The cross-sectional area of the wide part of the cylinder is 0.1 m², while the narrow part has an area of 0.075 m². When the cylinder is in the upper position the pressure inside is 5 MPa and the temperature 327 °C. The air is now cooled, and the piston comes down until it reaches the step. The air continues to cool until its temperature reaches 27 °C.

a. Show the process on a $p - v$ diagram.
b. What is the temperature of the air when it reaches the step?
c. What is the pressure of the air when its temperature reaches 27 °C?
d. Find the heat and work interactions during the complete process.
e. Find the change in energy and the change in enthalpy of the air during the complete process.

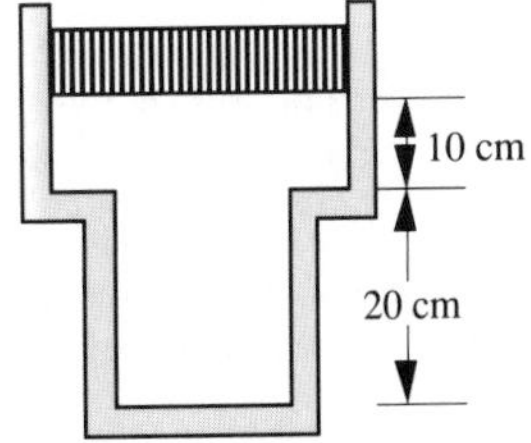

Figure 5.10

5.19 Helium (an ideal gas, M = 4, k = 1.667) is compressed adiabatically from 1 MPa, 27 °C, and 2 m^3 to 2 MPa, 227 °C. Find:

a. The work interaction.
b. The enthalpy change of the helium.

5.20 A piston–cylinder assembly contains 10 kg of air (ideal gas, $M = 29$, $k = 1.4$) at 100 kPa and 40 °C. The air is heated at constant volume till its temperature reaches 260 °C. Find:

a. The change of energy of the air.
b. The change of enthalpy of the air.
c. The work and heat interactions of the air.

5.21 A cylinder covered by a piston contains 10 kg of air (ideal gas, $M = 29$, $k = 1.4$) at 100 kPa and 40 °C. The air is heated at constant pressure till its temperature reaches 260 °C. Find:

a. The change of energy of the air.
b. The change of enthalpy of the air.
c. The work and heat interactions of the air.

5.22 A piston-cylinder assembly contains 2 kg of Argon (ideal gas, $M = 40$, $k = 1.667$) at 20°C and 100 kPa. The Argon undergoes a quasistatic process at the end of which its temperature reaches 300 °C.

Determine the changes in internal energy and enthalpy as well as the work and heat interactions if the process is described by:

a. $p = \text{const.}$
b. $v = \text{const.}$
c. $pv^{1.2} = \text{const.}$
d. $pv^{k} = \text{const.}$

5.23 A 40 L closed, insulated cylinder contains air and water, separated by a piston into two equal parts, as shown in Fig. 5.11. The air is at 0.1 MPa and 250 °C while the water is at 250 °C and $x = 0.6$. The piston has a mass of 100 kg, a cross-sectional area of 80 cm^2, and is held in place by a stop. The stop is released and the piston moves to a new equilibrium state. Find the temperatures, pressures, and volumes of the air and the water, given that the piston is diathermal.

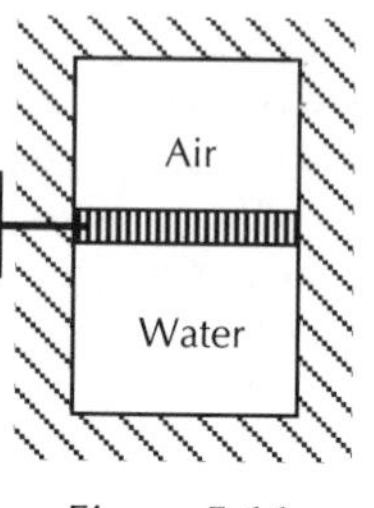

Figure 5.11

5.24 Assuming ideal gas behavior find the mass of each of the following gases required to fill a 200 L tank at 180 °C and 0.8 MPa:

H_2, N_2, O_2, CO_2, CO, H_2O

In the case of H_2O compare your results with those obtained from steam tables.

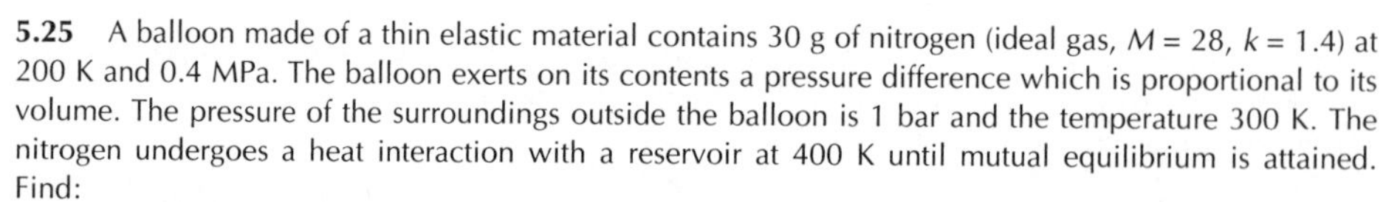

5.25 A balloon made of a thin elastic material contains 30 g of nitrogen (ideal gas, $M = 28$, $k = 1.4$) at 200 K and 0.4 MPa. The balloon exerts on its contents a pressure difference which is proportional to its volume. The pressure of the surroundings outside the balloon is 1 bar and the temperature 300 K. The nitrogen undergoes a heat interaction with a reservoir at 400 K until mutual equilibrium is attained. Find:

a. The final pressure of the nitrogen.
b. The work and heat interactions during the process.

5.26 It is claimed that below 2 atmospheres steam may be assumed to behave as an ideal gas. Consider p and T data for saturated vapor from the steam table at 10, 50, and 100 kPa and calculate the specific volume in m^3/kg, using the ideal gas equation of state.

5.27 Air at 8 MPa and 350 °C is contained in a cylinder covered by a weighted piston, which is held in place by a stop. The initial volume of the air is 0.2 m^3.

The cylinder is immersed in a thermostatic bath, maintained at 350 °C, Fig. 5.12. The stop is removed and the air expands lifting the piston. When equilibrium is reached the pressure of the air is 4 MPa.

Find:

a. The change in energy and in enthalpy of the air.
b. The work and heat interactions.

5.28 An adiabatic vessel of 2 m^3 is divided by a membrane into two equal parts. One part contains 1kg of air at 400 °C while the other is evacuated. The membrane ruptures, the air expands and reaches equilibrium. What is the temperature and pressure of the air at equilibrium?

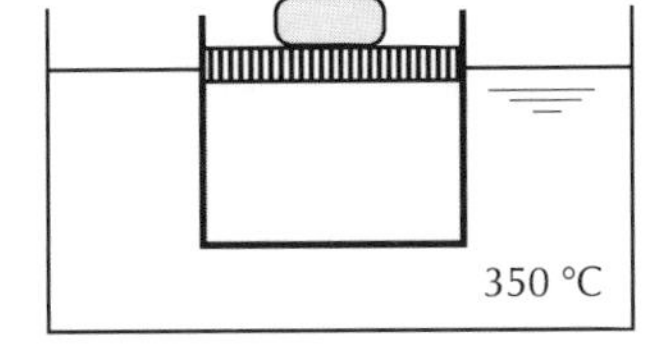

Figure 5.12

5.29 Air at 8 MPa and 350 °C is contained in a well-insulated cylinder covered by a weighted piston, which is held in place by a stop. The initial volume of the air is 0.2 m^3. The stop is removed and the air expands lifting the piston. When equilibrium is reached the pressure of the air is 4 MPa. Find:

a. The change in energy and in enthalpy of the air.
b. The work interaction.

5.30 A system consists of 9.0 kg of oxygen, of which 3.0 kg have a specific internal energy of 20 kJ/kg and the remainder, 30 kJ/kg. A heat interaction takes place with the surroundings, during which 150 kJ are transferred to the system. At the end of the interaction the system attains a stable equilibrium state. Find the final specific internal energy of the system.

5.31 Helium at 0.2 MPa, 150 °C, is contained in the lower part of an adiabatic cylinder, under a heavy and frictionless piston, shown in Fig. 5.13. In the upper part of the cylinder, above the piston, there is a vacuum. At a certain moment a hole is punctured in the piston and the helium leaks slowly to the upper part, until equilibrium is reached. Find the pressure and the temperature at the end of the process.

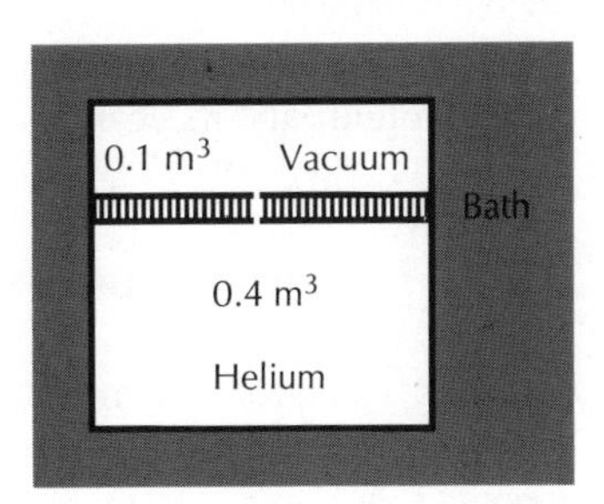

Figure 5.13

5.32 An insulated cylinder, shown in Fig. 5.14, is divided by an adiabatic frictionless piston into two equal compartments, each containing 1.5 kg air at 300 K and 1 bar. Compartment A is slowly heated by an electric heater until a temperature of 500 K is reached. Find:

a. The final pressure.
b. The heat interacion with the heater.

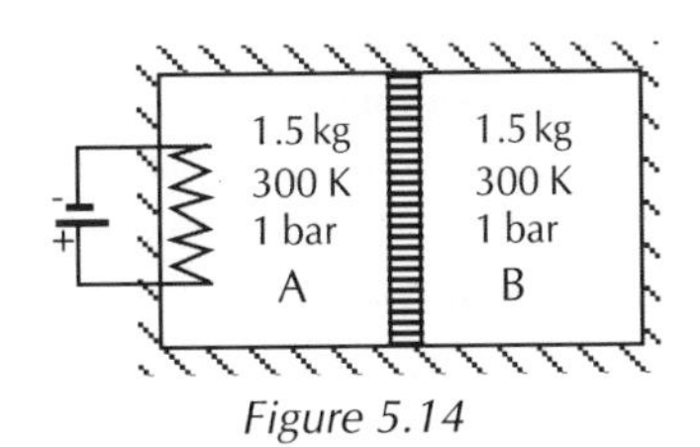

Figure 5.14

CHAPTER SIX

The control volume

Until now we have limited our thermodynamic analysis to closed systems, i.e. to systems in which matter does not cross the surface by which the system is bounded. We now extend our analysis to control volumes, i.e. to open systems in which matter is allowed to cross the system boundary through openings, or ports. The flow through each port is considered homogeneous.

We begin by deriving relationships between the change of an extensive property in a control volume and its change in a suitably selected closed system.

6.1 Transition from system to control volume

Consider a control volume whose boundary is denoted by the solid line in Fig. 6.1. During the process from a state at time t to that at $t + \Delta t$, its boundary may change position and shape. We select a closed system, shown as the hatched area, that coincides with the control volume at the initial state. After some time the previously selected closed system will not coincide with the control volume in regions where matter has crossed the boundary of the control volume.

Consider now the change in some extensive property Π for a process between the times t and $t + \Delta t$. We may look at the change in Π from the point of view of the closed system and write

$$\Delta\Pi = \Pi(t + \Delta t) - \Pi(t) \tag{6.1}$$

For the control volume the change in Π is

$$\Delta\Pi_{cv} = \Pi_{cv}(t + \Delta t) - \Pi_{cv}(t) \tag{6.2}$$

where the subscript cv denotes *control volume*. Since at time t the control volume coincides with the closed system

$$\Pi_{cv}(t) = \Pi(t) \tag{6.3}$$

At time $t + \Delta t$, a property Π, which belongs to the closed system (shown as the hatched

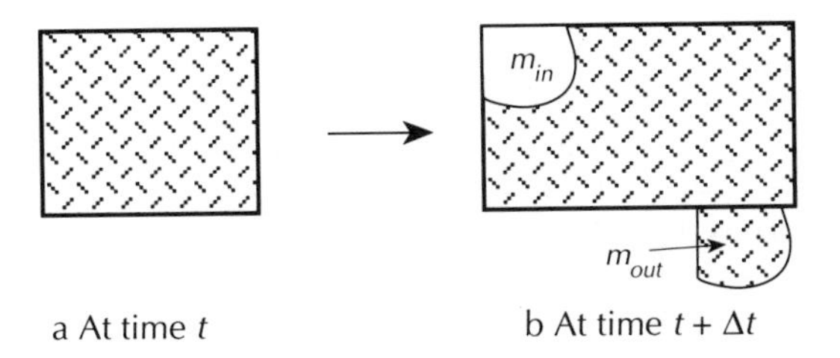

Figure 6.1 **Control volume and the related closed system.**

area in Fig. 6.1), can be related to that belonging to the control volume (within the solid line) by

$$\Pi_{cv}(t+\Delta t) = \Pi(t+\Delta t) + \pi_{in}\dot{m}_{in}\Delta t - \pi_{out}\dot{m}_{out}\Delta t \tag{6.4}$$

where $\pi = \Pi/m$ is the specific property of Π per unit mass, and $\dot{m}$ is the mass flowrate through the boundary. The last two terms of Eq. (6.4) account for the differences between the open and closed systems. The term $\pi_{in}\dot{m}_{in}\Delta t$ is the amount of Π entering the control volume, while the term $\pi_{out}\dot{m}_{out}\Delta t$ is the amount of Π leaving the control volume during the time interval Δt. Combining Eqs (6.2), (6.3), and (6.4) one obtains

$$\Pi_{cv}(t+\Delta t) - \Pi_{cv}(t) = \Pi(t+\Delta t) - \Pi(t) + \pi_{in}\dot{m}_{in}\Delta t - \pi_{out}\dot{m}_{out}\Delta t \tag{6.5}$$

Dividing by Δt and taking the limit as $\Delta t \to 0$, Eq. (6.5) may be rewritten for the more general case of k ports as

$$\left[\frac{d\Pi}{dt}\right]_{cv} = \frac{d\Pi}{dt} + \sum_{i=1}^{k} \pi_i \dot{m}_i \tag{6.6}$$

where $\dot{m}_i$ is positive for matter entering the control volume, and is negative for matter leaving the control volume.

Equation (6.6) can be integrated between times t_1 and t_2 to yield the change of Π between state 1 and state 2:

$$\Delta\Pi_{cv} = \Delta\Pi + \sum_{i=1}^{k} \int_{t_1}^{t_2} \pi_i \dot{m}_i \, dt \tag{6.7}$$

For the special case where π_i are uniform over their respective ports and are not changing with time, the integration is quite simple and Eq. (6.7) simplifies to

$$\Delta\Pi_{cv} = \Delta\Pi + \sum_{i=1}^{k} \pi_i m_i \tag{6.8}$$

where m_i is the total mass that crosses into the control volume through port i. Obviously, if the mass is leaving through port i, the corresponding m_i has a negative value.

Equations (6.6) and (6.8) constitute transformations from closed systems to control volumes, and are useful in extending thermodynamic analysis to control volumes.

6.2 Conservation of mass for a control volume

We now derive the equations of conservation of mass for a control volume, by making use of the relationships (6.6) and (6.8). In this case the extensive property Π is equal to the mass, i.e. $\Pi = m$, and $\pi = 1$. Thus, from Eq. (6.8),

$$\Delta m_{cv} = \Delta m + \sum_{i=1}^{k} m_i \tag{6.9}$$

However, for a closed system, by definition, $\Delta m = 0$, and therefore

$$\Delta m_{cv} = \sum_{i=1}^{k} m_i \tag{6.10}$$

As seen from Eq. (6.10) the mass of a control volume may change, in contrast to that of a closed system. Equation (6.10) indicates that the change of mass inside the control volume equals the net mass inflow through all the ports.

The rate of the mass change inside a control volume can be found from Eq. (6.6):

$$\left(\frac{dm}{dt}\right)_{cv} = \sum_{i=1}^{k} \dot{m}_i \tag{6.11}$$

Equation (6.11) indicates that the rate of mass change inside the control volume is equal to the net mass flowrate through the boundary of the control volume.

For uniform flow through a port the mass flowrate is given as

$$\dot{m} = \rho A \mathbf{v} = \frac{A\mathbf{v}}{v} \tag{6.12}$$

where A is the area of the port and $\mathbf{v}$ the velocity normal to the port. If the flow is not uniform, integration over the port should be performed, resulting in

$$\dot{m} = -\iint \rho \mathbf{v}\, d\mathbf{A} \tag{6.13}$$

The integral on the right hand side of Eq. (6.13) denotes the flow *out* of the control volume and since $\dot{m}$ is defined as the mass inflow, a negative sign is required.

Several special cases of Eqs (6.10) and (6.11) are now considered. For the special case of a control volume with a single port the change of mass between the initial and final states of the control volume is found by simplifying Eq. (6.10):

$$(m_2 - m_1)_{cv} = m_{in} \tag{6.14}$$

Obviously, m_{in} is negative for mass outflow. A corresponding expression for the *rate* of mass change within the control volume is found from Eq. (6.11):

$$\left[\frac{dm}{dt}\right]_{cv} = \dot{m}_{in} \tag{6.15}$$

where $\dot{m}$ is positive for inflow and negative for outflow.

An important special case of Eq. (6.11) is that of steady state.

A steady state is defined as one for which the properties at any point within the control volume do not change with time.

For steady state, Eq. (6.11) simplifies to

$$\sum_{i=1}^{k} \dot{m}_i = 0 \tag{6.16}$$

EXAMPLE 6.1

A coal combustion system requires 8000 kg/h of air. Find the diameter of the air supply pipe if the air pressure is 104 kPa, the temperature is 80 °C, and the velocity in the pipe is 30 m/s. Assume the air to be an ideal gas with $M = 29$ kg/kmol.

SOLUTION

The cross-sectional area of the pipe is found from Eq. (6.12):

$$\dot{m} = \frac{A\mathbf{v}}{v}$$

The specific volume is found from the ideal gas equation of state:

$$v = \frac{RT}{p} = \frac{(8.3143/29) \times (273.15 + 80)}{104} = 0.9735 \text{ m}^3/\text{kg}$$

The area is then

$$A = \frac{8000 \times 0.9735}{3600 \times 30} = 0.07211 \text{ m}^2$$

and the diameter is

$$D = 0.303 \text{ m}$$

6.3 First law of thermodynamics for a control volume

The first law for a closed system is

$$\Delta E = Q - W \tag{6.17}$$

Consider the closed system represented by the dotted area in Fig. 6.2, and the control volume as the one enclosed by the vessel and the bottom surface of the piston. Equation (6.17) which applies to the closed system will now be rewritten for the control volume of Fig. 6.2.

First we rewrite the energy term, ΔE in Eq. (6.17), to make it applicable to the control

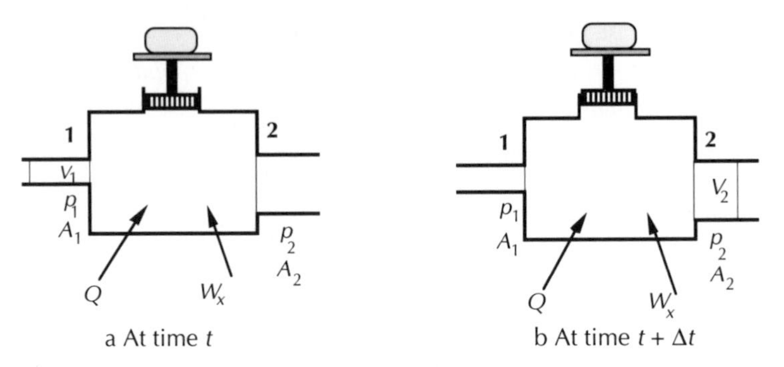

Figure 6.2 **Work of a control volume.**

volume. Using Eq. (6.8) with $\Pi = E$ and $\pi = e$, we obtain

$$\Delta E = \Delta E_{cv} - \sum_{i=1}^{k} e_i m_i \tag{6.18}$$

The work in Eq. (6.17), given for the closed system of Fig. 6.2, is now rewritten in more detail. We consider two categories of work done by the closed system: work done at the boundary corresponding to the ports, and work done everywhere else:

$$W = W_{ports} + W_x \tag{6.19}$$

Referring again to Fig. 6.2, we first consider the work done by the surroundings on the closed system at port 1. The pressure at port 1 is p_1, and the volume of the closed system is reduced here by $\Delta V = -V_1$. Thus at port 1 the work of the system is

$$W_1 = -p_1 V_1 \tag{6.20}$$

Similarly, the work that the system does on its surroundings at port 2 is

$$W_2 = p_2 V_2 \tag{6.21}$$

The volume V_i, crossing port i, is expressible in terms of the specific volume and the crossing mass as $V_i = v_i m_i$. Thus, the work for k ports becomes

$$W_{ports} = -\sum_{i=1}^{k} p_i v_i m_i \tag{6.22}$$

where m_i is positive for the incoming and negative for the outgoing flows. The total work of the corresponding closed system is thus

$$W = W_x - \sum_{i=1}^{k} p_i v_i m_i \tag{6.23}$$

Equations (6.23) and (6.18) are now substituted into Eq. (6.17) resulting in a relationship which is applicable to a control volume:

$$\Delta E_{cv} = Q - W_x + \sum_{i=1}^{k} (e + pv)_i m_i \tag{6.24}$$

The left hand side of Eq. (6.24) represents the total change of energy occurring inside the control volume, while the right hand side of the equation describes what takes place on the boundary causing this change.

We now substitute the specific energy, e, from Eq. (4.15) to yield

$$\Delta E_{cv} = Q - W_x + \sum_{i=1}^{k} \left(u + pv + \frac{\mathbf{v}^2}{2} + gz \right)_i m_i \tag{6.25}$$

and noting that $u + pv = h$

$$\Delta E_{cv} = Q - W_x + \sum_{i=1}^{k} \left(h + \frac{\mathbf{v}^2}{2} + gz \right)_i m_i \tag{6.26}$$

The term $h + \mathbf{v}^2/2 + gz$ appears frequently in flow problems. It is called the stagnation enthalpy and is denoted by h^0,

$$h^0 = h + \mathbf{v}^2/2 + gz \tag{6.27}$$

Substituting Eq. (6.27) into (6.26) yields

$$\Delta E_{cv} = Q - W_x + \sum_{i=1}^{k} h_i^0 m_i \tag{6.28}$$

A rate equation equivalent to Eq. (6.28) is

$$\left(\frac{dE}{dt} \right)_{cv} = \dot{Q} - \dot{W}_x + \sum_{i=1}^{k} h_i^0 \dot{m}_i \tag{6.29}$$

Equations (6.26) and (6.29) are alternative forms of the first law of thermodynamics for a control volume. We now consider several special cases of Eqs (6.26) and (6.29).

6.4 Steady state processes

A steady state process was defined earlier as one for which the properties do not change with time at any point within the system. It follows that within the control surface there is no change with time in both the intensive and extensive properties. Obviously, the intensive properties need not be uniform throughout the system. As a matter of fact, in most engineering systems, they do vary from point to point. However, at each point they are time invariant under steady state conditions.

For a steady state process the left hand sides of Eqs (6.15) and (6.29) vanish by definition, since they describe changes with time of the extensive properties, mass and energy, respectively, within the control surface. Hence, for steady state, conservation of mass is expressed by

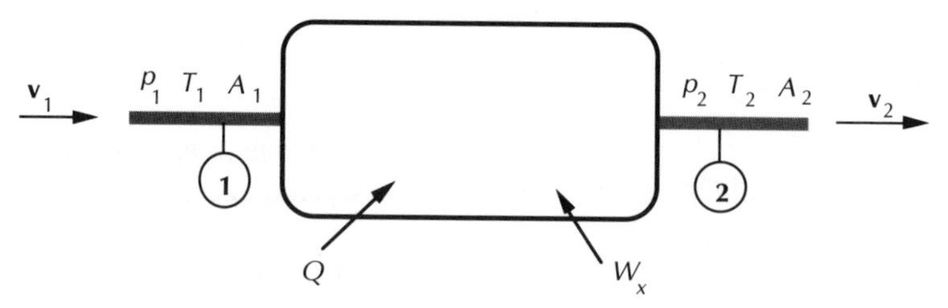

Figure 6.3 **Steady state process in a two-part control volume.**

$$\sum_{i=1}^{k} \dot{m}_i = 0 \tag{6.16}$$

and the first law, Eq. (6.29), becomes

$$\dot{Q} - \dot{W}_x + \sum_{i=1}^{k} h_i^0 \dot{m}_i = 0 \tag{6.30}$$

Many engineering systems operating under steady state conditions have two ports, one inlet and one outlet, as shown in Fig. 6.3. For such cases, conservation of mass simplifies to

$$\dot{m}_1 + \dot{m}_2 = 0 \tag{6.31}$$

$$\dot{m}_1 = -\dot{m}_2 = \dot{m} \tag{6.32}$$

where $\dot{m}$ is the absolute value of the mass flowrate through the control volume. The first law, Eq. (6.30), simplifies for this case to

$$\dot{Q} - \dot{W}_x + \dot{m}_1 h_1^0 + \dot{m}_2 h_2^0 = 0 \tag{6.33}$$

which together with Eq. (6.32) yields

$$\dot{Q} - \dot{W}_x = \dot{m}\left(h_2^0 - h_1^0\right) \tag{6.34}$$

From Eq. (6.34) we see that the heat and work interactions at steady state result in a change of the stagnation enthalpy of the mass flowing through the control volume. Equation (6.34) is sometimes referred to as the *steady flow energy equation*. Written out explicitly it reads

$$\dot{Q} - \dot{W}_x = \dot{m}\left[\left(h_2 - h_1\right) + \frac{\mathbf{v}_2^2 - \mathbf{v}_1^2}{2} + g\left(z_2 - z_1\right)\right] \tag{6.35}$$

or per unit mass flowing through the control volume

$$q - w_x = (h_2 - h_1) + \frac{\mathbf{v}_2^2 - \mathbf{v}_1^2}{2} + g(z_2 - z_1) \tag{6.36}$$

where q, w_x, and h should be in J/kg to be consistent with the units of $\mathbf{v}^2$ and gz.

Equations (6.34)–(6.36) are alternative forms of the steady flow energy equation. They apply to a wide range of engineering devices such as pumps, turbines, compressors, fans, nozzles, pipes and ducts, boilers, condensers, combustion chambers, radiators, etc. These devices are discussed below.

6.4.1 Nozzles and diffusers

Nozzles and diffusers, Fig. 6.4, are devices used to change the velocity of a flowing stream. Nozzles are used to increase the velocity while decreasing the pressure. Diffusers are used to increase the pressure at the expense of the velocity. Nozzles and diffusers are usually short enough to be considered adiabatic. For the same reason the difference in elevation between inlet and outlet can be neglected.

We now apply the first law of thermodynamics for two-port steady state processes, Eq. (6.34), to nozzles and diffusers. These devices are taken as rigid and adiabatic, and therefore $\dot{Q} = 0$ and $\dot{W}_x = 0$. Thus the first law is simplified to

$$h_2^0 = h_1^0 \tag{6.37}$$

Equation (6.37) indicates the fact that the stagnation enthalpy stays constant at any cross-section of the nozzle. Neglecting the difference in elevation simplifies Eq. (6.37) to

$$h_2 + \frac{\mathbf{v}_2^2}{2} = h_1 + \frac{\mathbf{v}_1^2}{2} \tag{6.38}$$

The velocity at any cross-section of the nozzle can be found by rearranging Eq. (6.38):

$$\mathbf{v}_2 = \sqrt{\mathbf{v}_1^2 + 2(h_1 - h_2)} \tag{6.39}$$

The equation derived above applies to nozzles and to diffusers. However, while for nozzles $(h_1 - h_2) > 0$, for diffusers $(h_1 - h_2) < 0$.

When the fluid flowing through the nozzle is an ideal gas Eq. (6.39) becomes

$$\mathbf{v}_2 = \sqrt{\mathbf{v}_1^2 + 2c_p(T_1 - T_2)} \tag{6.40}$$

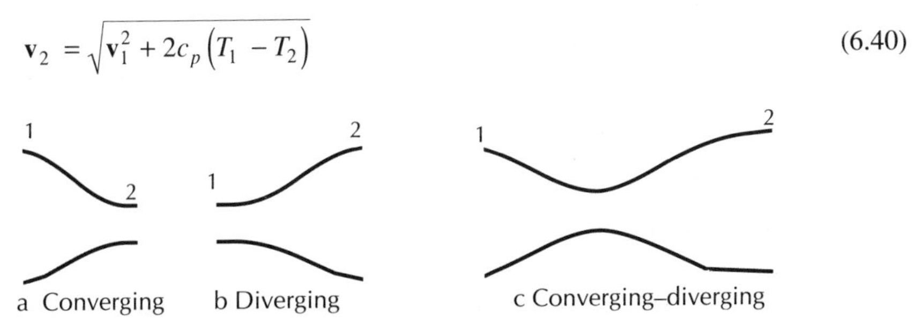

Figure 6.4 **Schematics of nozzles and diffusers.**

EXAMPLE 6.2

Air enters an adiabatic horizontal nozzle at p_1 = 30 bars, T_1= 230 °C, $\mathbf{v}_1$ = 10 m/s, and at a rate of 0.84 kg/s. Assume air to be an ideal gas with constant c_v and M = 29 kg/kmol, k = 1.4. Find:

a. The inlet area.
b. The velocity and area at a point where p_2 = 20 bars, T_2= 180 °C.
c. The velocity and area at a point where p_3 = 5 bars, T_3 = 50 °C.

SOLUTION

a. We first calculate the inlet area from Eq. (6.12):

$$A_1 = \left(\frac{\dot{m}v}{\mathbf{v}}\right)_1$$

with the specific volume given as

$$v_1 = \frac{RT_1}{p_1} = \frac{8.3143 \times 503.15}{29 \times 3000} = 0.04808 \text{ m}^3/\text{kg}$$

Hence

$$A_1 = 0.84 \times 0.04808/10 = 0.00404 \text{ m}^2 = 40.4 \text{ cm}^2$$

b. To find $\mathbf{v}_2$ we use Eq. (6.40) which applies for an ideal gas with constant c_p:

$$\mathbf{v}_2 = \sqrt{\mathbf{v}_1^2 + 2c_p(T_1 - T_2)}$$

Here

$$c_p = \frac{kR}{(k-1)} = \frac{1.4 \times 8.3143}{0.4 \times 29} = 1.0034 \text{ kJ/kg K}$$

Thus

$$\mathbf{v}_2 = \sqrt{10^2 + 2 \times 1.0034 \times 10^3 \times (230 - 180)} = 316.9 \text{ m/s}$$

$$v_2 = \frac{RT_2}{p_2} = \frac{8.3143 \times 453.15}{29 \times 2000} = 0.06496 \text{ m}^3/\text{kg}$$

and

$$A_2 = \frac{\dot{m}v_2}{\mathbf{v}_2} = \frac{0.84 \times 0.06496}{316.9} = 1.72 \times 10^{-4} \text{ m}^2$$

c. Following the same procedure as in b we find

$\mathbf{v}_3$ = 601.1 m/s $\quad$ v_3 = 0.18522 m³/kg $\quad$ A_3 = 2.59 cm²

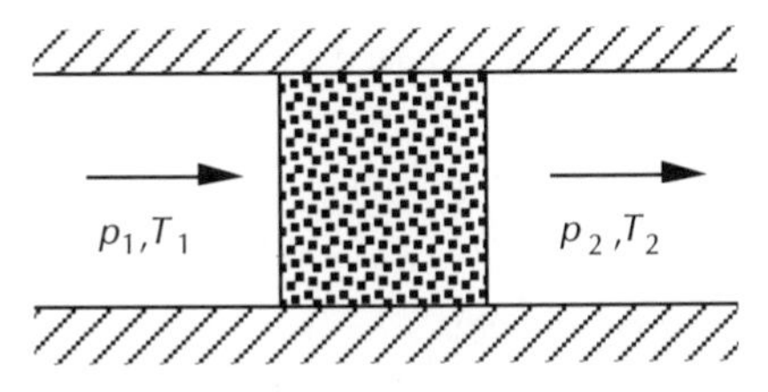

Figure 6.5 **Throttling flow in a pipe.**

6.4.2 Throttling devices

Throttling is a steady state flow process whereby the pressure of a fluid is reduced adiabatically, without involving large velocities. Throttling is used extensively in engineering. A throttling device is shown, schematically, in Fig. 6.5.

A typical application of throttling would be the reduction of the pressure of the fuel–air mixture that enters the cylinder of an internal combustion engine, thus controlling its power. Another application is in refrigeration, where a throttling valve is used to reduce the pressure of a liquid refrigerant to allow its evaporation at a lower temperature.

Throttling devices usually operate at velocities low enough to be negligible in a first-law analysis. Thus Eq. (6.38) which holds for nozzles simplifies for throttling devices to

$$h_2 = h_1 \tag{6.41}$$

Equation (6.41) indicates that flow through a throttling device is a constant-enthalpy, or isenthalpic, process. The throttling phenomenon was the basis of the famous Joule–Thomson experiment, whereby the change in temperature was measured as the pressure was throttled down. The coefficient, c_{JT}, that relates the change of temperature to the change of pressure at constant enthalpy is given by

$$c_{JT} = \left(\frac{\partial T}{\partial p}\right)_h \tag{6.42}$$

and is called the Joule–Thomson coefficient. It is an intensive property, which is easy to measure experimentally. For an ideal gas, $c_{JT} = 0$, since the temperature cannot change while the enthalpy is kept constant. For a non-ideal gas, c_{JT} can be either positive or negative and its value is a measure of the deviation from ideal gas behavior. The Joule–Thomson coefficient data are used extensively in the preparation of tables of properties, such as the steam tables.

EXAMPLE 6.3

The state of wet steam can be characterized by using a throttling calorimeter. A simplified version of a throttling calorimeter, shown schematically in Fig. 6.6, is a valve that reduces adiabatically the pressure of the steam until it gets into the superheated region. The temperature is measured at the exhaust point.

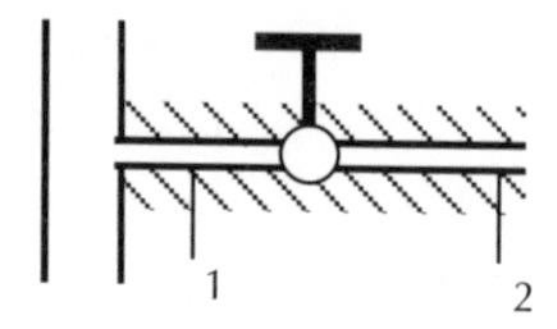

Figure 6.6 **Schematic of a throttling calorimeter.**

The throttling calorimeter of Fig. 6.6 is used on a steam line, in which the pressure is $p_1 = 0.8$ MPa. The exit pressure and temperature are $p_2 = 0.1$ MPa and $T_2 = 100$ °C, respectively.

Find the quality and the specific volume of the steam inside the steam line.

SOLUTION

We first arrange the known data in a table, as follows:

State	p	T	v_f	v_g	h_f	h_g	x	h
1	0.8	170.43	0.001115	0.2404	721.11	2769.1	0.9548	2676.2
2	0.1	100						2676.2

At the exit, the state is completely defined by p_2 and T_2, and thus the enthalpy h_2 can be found.

The throttling process does not change the enthalpy,

$$h_1 = h_2 = 2676.2 \text{ kJ/kg}$$

Hence,

$$x_1 = \frac{h - h_f}{h_g - h_f} = \frac{2676.2 - 721.11}{2769.1 - 721.11} = 0.9548$$

and the specific volume is

$$v_1 = v_f + xv_{fg} = 0.001115 + 0.9548 \times (0.2404 - 0.001115) = 0.2295 \text{ m}^3\text{/kg}$$

6.4.3 Turbines, pumps, and compressors

Turbines, compressors, and pumps, as depicted in Fig. 6.7, are usually two-port systems that operate at steady state. Sometimes transients may also be of interest. Turbines are work-producing devices while compressors and pumps are work-consuming devices.

Turbines are used to produce power at their shaft, so in their analysis we are interested in calculating the power output. Pumps and compressors are used to raise the pressure of a fluid while consuming work. Compressors are used to compress gases and pumps to pump liquids. We are interested in the power output or consumption of these devices.

The power can be calculated from the steady state equation for a control volume, Eq.(6.34):

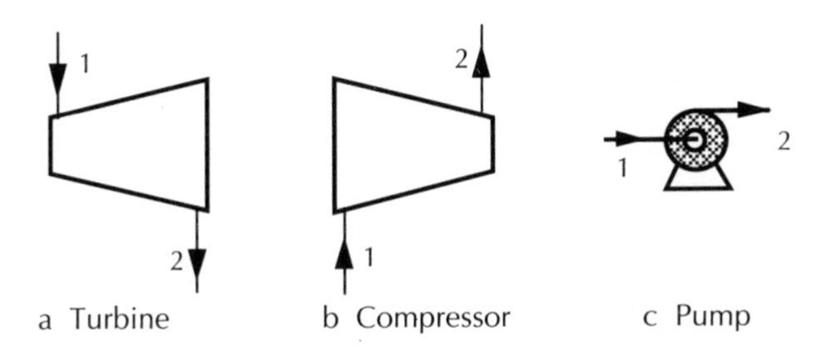

Figure 6.7 **Schematics of turbines, compressors, and pumps.**

$$\dot{W}_x = \dot{m}\left(h_1^0 - h_2^0\right) + \dot{Q} \tag{6.43}$$

where the subscripts 1 and 2 refer to the inlet and outlet, respectively.

As seen in Eq. (6.43), any heat loss from a turbine reduces its power, and therefore proper thermal insulation can improve the power output. On the other hand, heat losses from compressors, which reduce power consumption, are desirable. That is why manufacturers install cooling fins on some compressors.

In many cases heat losses as well as kinetic and potential energy effects can be neglected in the analysis of turbines, compressors, and fans. This simplifies Eq. (6.43) to

$$\dot{W}_x = \dot{m}\left(h_1 - h_2\right) \tag{6.44}$$

Unless otherwise stated, we shall assume that turbines, pumps, and compressors are adiabatic devices operating at steady state with negligible velocities at the ports.

6.4.4 Heat exchangers

One of the most commonly used devices in the process industries is the heat exchanger. Heat exchangers are used to transfer heat from one stream to another, or to heat or cool a given stream. Special purpose heat exchangers include boilers, radiators, condensers, evaporators, and regenerators. A two-stream counter-flow heat exchanger is shown schematically in Fig. 6.8.

In the analysis of heat exchangers it is common to neglect kinetic and potential effects relative to the changes in enthalpy. We may define our control volume to consist either of a single stream, Fig. 6.8a, or of a multiple stream, Fig. 6.8b. In the single-stream case, the analysis is that of the two-port system given in Eq. (6.34), which for $W_x = 0$ and $h^0 = h$ simplifies to

$$\dot{Q} = \dot{m}_c\left(h_2 - h_1\right) \tag{6.45}$$

An analogous equation can be written down for the other stream.

Considering the multistream control volume, we note that the first law for steady state, Eq. (6.30), simplifies to

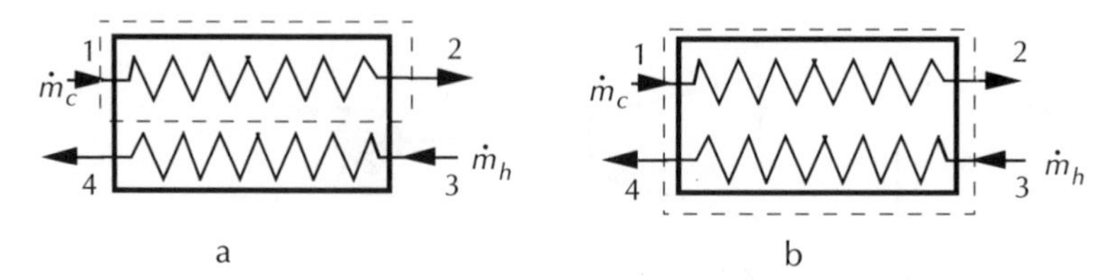

Figure 6.8 **Schematic of a heat exchanger.**

$$\sum_{i=1}^{k} h_i \dot{m}_i = 0 \tag{6.46}$$

Equation (6.46) may be simplified for the special case shown in Fig. 6.8b:

$$\dot{m}_c(h_1 - h_2) + \dot{m}_h(h_3 - h_4) = 0 \tag{6.47}$$

The following example illustrates the use of the first law of thermodynamics in the analysis of various control volumes at steady state.

EXAMPLE 6.4

An industrial system that supplies electric power and process steam, Fig. 6.9, is made up of four basic elements: a pump, a boiler, a turbine, and a heat exchanger. The rate of steam flow through each element is 2.5 kg/s. The conditions at the exit of each element are underlined in the table. Find:

a. The rate of work of the pump.
b. The rate of heat interaction in the boiler.
c. The rate of work of the turbine.
d. The rate of heat interaction in the heat exchanger.
e. The cross-section of the pipe at the exit of each element.

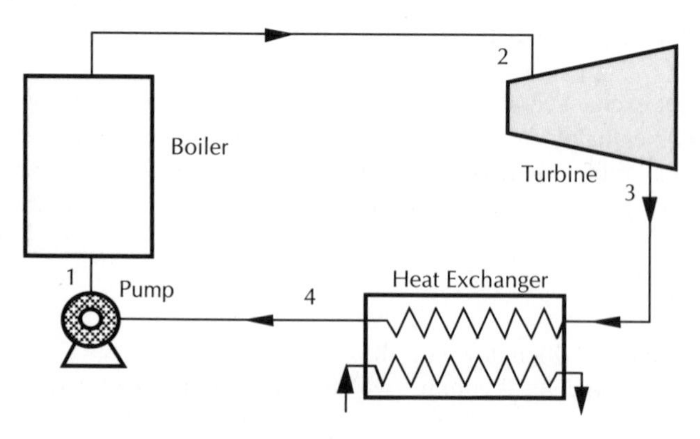

Figure 6.9 **Basic power cycle.**

Exit of element	State	p MPa	T °C	x	$\mathbf{v}$ m/s	z m
Pump	1	10.00	102	–	5	0
Boiler	2	8.00	450	–	20	20
Turbine	3	0.20		0.95	100	10
Heat Exch.	4	0.18	100	–	5	0

SOLUTION

We analyze each element as a steady state two-port open system. The specific volume and the specific enthalpy, for each point, are found in the steam tables, and are listed below. The calculated specific stagnation enthalpies are also shown.

State	p MPa	T °C	x	v m³/kg	h kJ/kg	$\mathbf{v}$ m/s	z m	h^0 kJ/kg
1	10.00	102	–	0.001041	434.91	5	0	434.92
2	8.00	450	–	0.038170	3272.0	20	20	3272.4
3	0.20	120.2	0.95	0.8415	2596.6	100	10	2601.7
4	0.18	100	–	0.001044	419.04	5	0	419.05

The pump and the turbine are assumed to be adiabatic; their work is calculated from Eq. (6.44).

The boiler and the heat exchanger have no work interactions. Their heat interactions are calculated from Eq. (6.45).

a. The rate of work of the pump is

$$\dot{W}_x = \dot{m}(h_4^0 - h_1^0) = 2.5 \times (419.05 - 434.92) = -39.7 \text{ kW}$$

b. The rate of heat interaction in the boiler is

$$\dot{Q} = \dot{m}(h_2^0 - h_1^0) = 2.5 \times (3272.4 - 434.9) = 7094 \text{ kW}$$

c. The rate of work of the turbine is

$$\dot{W}_x = \dot{m}(h_2^0 - h_3^0) = 2.5 \times (3272.4 - 2601.7) = 1676.8 \text{ kW}$$

d. The rate of heat interaction in the heat exchanger is

$$\dot{Q} = \dot{m}(h_4^0 - h_3^0) = 2.5 \times (419.1 - 2601.7) = -5456.5 \text{ kW}$$

Note that the effects of the velocity and elevation are relatively small in this problem and may be neglected.

e. The cross-sectional areas are determined in each point by using Eq. (6.12):

$$A_1 = \frac{\dot{m}v_1}{\mathbf{V}_1} = 2.5 \times \frac{0.001041}{5} = 0.000520 \text{ m}^2 = 5.20 \text{ cm}^2$$

$$A_2 = \frac{\dot{m}v_2}{\mathbf{V}_2} = 2.5 \times \frac{0.03817}{20} = 0.004771 \text{ m}^2 = 47.71 \text{ cm}^2$$

$$A_3 = \frac{\dot{m}v_3}{\mathbf{V}_3} = 2.5 \times \frac{0.8415}{100} = 0.02104 \text{ m}^2 = 210.4 \text{ cm}^2$$

$$A_4 = \frac{\dot{m}v_4}{\mathbf{V}_4} = 2.5 \times \frac{0.001044}{5} = 0.000522 \text{ m}^2 = 5.22 \text{ cm}^2$$

6.5 Unsteady state processes in control volumes

We now turn to control volumes undergoing processes that are not at steady state. In these processes the properties within the control volume change with time and it is generally necessary to use Eq. (6.28) or Eq. (6.29).

We consider some special cases where simplifications can be made. These include discharging a container and filling one from a supply line.

6.6 One-port control volumes

A large class of engineering problems involve open systems that have only one port, where matter crosses the boundary. At the port, the properties of the crossing fluid may be uniform, but not necessarily constant in time. Such situations occur when vessels are being charged or discharged. Obviously, the state within the vessel does not remain constant with time and the flow is unsteady. We now develop the equations that govern the processes in one-port open systems.

Consider a vessel that has only one port, through which matter crosses the boundary. The vessel may have any arbitrary shape. It may be rigid or changing with time. The mass conservation equation, Eq. (6.11), and that of the first law, Eq. (6.29), take a simpler form for this one-port system, since only one term remains in the sum on the right hand side of the equations. We denote that term with the index b, for boundary, thus:

$$\left(\frac{dm}{dt}\right)_{cv} = \dot{m} \tag{6.48}$$

$$\left(\frac{dE}{dt}\right)_{cv} = \dot{Q} - \dot{W}_x + h_b^0 \dot{m} \tag{6.49}$$

Substituting Eq. (6.48) into Eq. (6.49) and assuming the contents of the open system to be a simple system, we obtain

$$\left(\frac{dU}{dt}\right)_{cv} = \dot{Q} - \dot{W}_x + h_b^0 \left(\frac{dm}{dt}\right)_{cv} \tag{6.50}$$

Multiplying throughout by *dt* yields

$$dU = \delta Q - \delta W_x + h_b^0 dm \tag{6.51}$$

where *dU* and *dm* are the respective differential changes in the energy and mass of the open system. An equivalent form of Eq. (6.51) is

$$dH = \delta Q - \delta W_x + h_b^0 dm + d(pV) \tag{6.52}$$

Integration of Eq. (6.51), from the initial state (state 1) to the final state (state 2), results in

$$U_2 - U_1 = Q - W_x + \int_1^2 h_b^0 dm \tag{6.53}$$

Equation (6.53) is now applied to the cases of charging and discharging a vessel.

6.6.1 Charging a vessel

Consider a container that is charged with a fluid, Fig. 6.10, from a supply line, where the conditions stay constant. We select the inside of the container walls as the boundary of the control volume.

The state in the supply line is denoted by index 0; the initial and final states inside the open system are denoted by 1 and 2, respectively. The stagnation enthalpy of the matter that crosses the boundary, h_b^0, is constant and equal to the enthalpy in the supply line, h_0^0 , and Eq. (6.53) yields

$$U_2 - U_1 = Q - W_x + h_0^0 (m_2 - m_1) \tag{6.54}$$

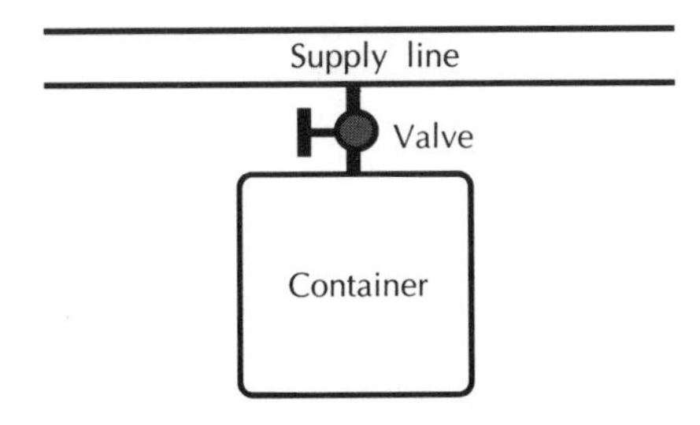

Figure 6.10 **A container charged from a supply line.**

In most cases, the velocity in the main is small enough to be neglected; hence

$$U_2 - U_1 = Q - W_x + h_0(m_2 - m_1) \tag{6.55}$$

An equivalent form of Eq. (6.55) is

$$H_2 - H_1 = Q - W_x + h_0(m_2 - m_1) + p_2V_2 - p_1V_1 \tag{6.56}$$

Some special cases of charging vessels are demonstrated in the following examples.

EXAMPLE 6.5

A rigid insulated container, containing 0.03 kg of helium at 300 °C and 120 kPa, is charged with helium from a main, where the conditions are 0.6 MPa and 300 °C. The charging continues until the flow stops. Assuming that helium is an ideal gas ($M = 4$, $k = 5/3$), find the final mass and temperature of the helium in the container.

SOLUTION

There are three relevant states in this problem. We denote the state in the main by index 0 and the initial and final states inside the control volume by the indices 1 and 2, respectively.

The volume of the container can be calculated from the ideal gas equation of state

$$V = \frac{m_1RT_1}{p_1} = 0.03 \times \left(\frac{8.3143}{4.0}\right) \times \frac{573.15}{120} = 0.2978 \text{ m}^3$$

The container is insulated and rigid. Therefore $Q = 0$ and $W_x = 0$ and Eq. (6.56) becomes

$$H_2 - H_1 = h_0(m_2 - m_1) + V(p_2 - p_1)$$

or

$$m_2(h_2 - h_0) = m_1(h_1 - h_0) + V(p_2 - p_1)$$

Noting that for an ideal gas

$$h = c_pT = \frac{k}{k-1}RT$$

we obtain

$$m_2RT_2 - m_2RT_0 = m_1R(T_1 - T_0) + V(p_2 - p_1)\frac{k-1}{k}$$

but

$$m_2RT_2 = p_2V \text{ and } T_1 = T_0$$

Thus

$$m_2 = \frac{V}{RT_0}\left[p_2 - (p_2 - p_1)\frac{k-1}{k}\right] = \frac{m_1}{k}\left[\frac{p_2}{p_1} + k - 1\right] = \frac{0.03}{5/3}\left(\frac{600}{120} + \frac{2}{3}\right) = 0.102 \text{ kg}$$

The final temperature is

$$T_2 = \frac{p_2 V}{m_2 R} = \frac{600 \times 0.2978}{0.102 \times 8.3143/4} = 842.8 \text{ K}$$

EXAMPLE 6.6

A rigid insulated container, containing 0.03 kg of steam at 300 °C and 120 kPa, is charged with steam from a main, where the conditions are 0.6 MPa and 300 °C. The charging continues until the flow stops. Find the final mass and temperature in the container.

SOLUTION

This example is similar to Example 6.5 with the same notation. The only exception is that the fluid is not an ideal gas, and its properties must be taken from the steam tables. A summary of the properties is shown in the following table (state 1 is found by interpolation). The given properties are underlined.

State	p MPa	T °C	v m³/kg	u kJ/kg	h kJ/kg	m kg	V m³
0	<u>0.60</u>	<u>300</u>	0.4344	2801.0	3061.6	–	–
1	<u>0.12</u>	<u>300</u>	2.1977	2801.0	3073.8	0.030	0.06593
2	<u>0.60</u>						0.06593

The volume of the container is

$$V = m_1 v_1 = 0.03 \times 2.1977 = 0.06593 \text{ m}^3$$

The container is insulated and rigid. Therefore $Q = 0$ and $W_x = 0$, and Eq. (6.56) becomes

$$H_2 - H_1 = h_0 (m_2 - m_1) + V (p_2 - p_1)$$

or

$$m_2 (h_2 - h_0) = m_1 (h_1 - h_0) + V (p_2 - p_1)$$

We note that $V = m_1 v_1 = m_2 v_2$ and therefore

$$\frac{h_2 - h_0}{v_2} = \frac{h_1 - h_0}{v_1} + p_2 - p_1 \tag{6.57}$$

Equation (6.57) gives a relationship between h_2 and v_2:

$$\frac{h_2 - h_0}{v_2} = \frac{3073.8 - 3061.6}{2.1977} + 600 - 120 = 485.55 \text{ kPa}$$

Two additional relationships are implicitly expressed through the steam tables:

$$v_2 = v_2(p_2, T_2) \tag{6.58}$$

and

$$h_2 = h_2(p_2, T_2) \tag{6.59}$$

Now there are three unknowns, T_2, h_2 and v_2, and the three equations, Eqs (6.57)–(6.59), are sufficient to find them. Since the last two equations are given numerically, in tables, the solution is carried out by a trial and error procedure. We guess T_2 and find v_2 and h_2 by using the tables for the data of Eqs (6.58) and (6.59). If v_2 and h_2 balance Eq. (6.57), then the selection is right. If there is no agreement, an additional guess is taken. In general, three–four guesses suffice to converge to the right answer.

The solution for the temperature is found to be T_2 = 424 °C and state 2 is:

State	p MPa	T °C	v m³/kg	u kJ/kg	h kJ/kg	m kg	V m³
2	0.60	424	0.5327	3002.2	3321.8	0.1238	0.06593

6.6.2 Discharging a vessel

Equation (6.51) can also be applied to the process of discharging a vessel, Fig. 6.11. In this case the conditions outside the vessel have no effect on the process, as long as the pressure outside is less than that inside. To solve the problem, it is necessary to know the enthalpy at the boundary. Here the enthalpy is generally not constant, since the state inside the control volume changes continuously.

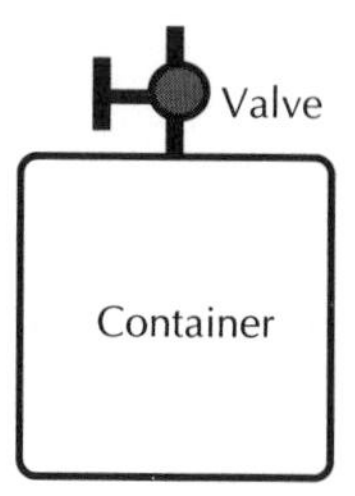

Figure 6.11

The state of the fluid in the vicinity of the port must be known during the entire process. A common case is when the state of the open system is uniform, though it may change with time. In such a case the specific enthalpy at the boundary is equal to that in the vessel, $h_b = h$. Thus, Eqs (6.51) and (6.53) become, respectively,

$$dU = \delta Q - \delta W_x + h dm \tag{6.60}$$

and

$$\Delta U = Q - W_x + \int_1^2 h dm \tag{6.61}$$

Equation (6.61) is the general relationship for discharging a vessel. An alternative relationship can be obtained by rewriting Eq. (6.60) as

$$dH - d(pV) - h dm = \delta Q - \delta W_x$$

or

$$\delta Q - \delta W_x = mdh - d(pV)$$

which for an open system of constant volume simplifies to

$$\delta Q - \delta W_x = mdh - Vdp$$

or,

$$\delta Q - \delta W_x = V\left(\frac{dh}{v} - dp\right) \tag{6.62}$$

Hence, for discharging a rigid vessel we obtain the following relationship:

$$Q - W_x = V\left(\int_1^2 \frac{dh}{v} - \Delta p\right) \tag{6.63}$$

For the special case of discharging an ideal gas under isothermal conditions the integral in Eq. (6.63) vanishes.

EXAMPLE 6.7

A space heater uses $(-W_x)$ of electricity in order to increase the temperature of the air in a room, from T_1 to T_2. The volume of the room is V, the pressure is p, and the heat losses to the environment (the walls, the air outside, etc.) are $-Q$. Derive an expression for the amount of electrical work input, $-W_x$, required for this task.

SOLUTION

The volume, V, of the room is constant and so is the pressure, p, which is usually atmospheric. Hence, if the pressure and the volume are to remain constant, a temperature rise must cause some of the air to leak out of the room. The analysis of this problem is therefore equivalent to that of discharging a vessel of constant volume.

Using Eq. (6.63) the expression for $(-W_x)$ is

$$-W_x = V\left(\int_1^2 \frac{dh}{v} - \Delta p\right) - Q$$

In our case $\Delta p = 0$, $v = RT/p$, and $dh = c_p dT = \left[kR/(k-1)\right]dT$. Hence

$$-W_x = V\int_1^2 \frac{p}{RT}\frac{kR}{k-1}dT - Q$$

which, upon integration, yields the final expression for $-W_x$

$$-W_x = \frac{k}{k-1}pV \ln\frac{T_2}{T_1} - Q$$

At steady state, when the temperature does not change, $T_2 = T_1$ and

$$-W_x = -Q$$

i.e. the electricity input equals the heat loss to the environment.

6.7 Summary of equations for a control volume

Rate of change of a property Π : $\left[\frac{d\Pi}{dt}\right]_{cv} = \left[\frac{d\Pi}{dt}\right]_{sys} + \sum_{i=1}^{k} \pi_i \dot{m}_i$

Discrete change in Π for the special case of $\pi_i = \text{const.}$ during the change of state:

$$\Delta\Pi_{cv} = \Delta\Pi_{sys} + \sum_{i=1}^{k} \pi_i m_i$$

Mass conservation in a control volume:

$$\Delta m_{cv} = \sum_{i=1}^{k} m_i$$

Rate form of conservation of mass: $\left(\frac{dm}{dt}\right)_{cv} = \sum_{i=1}^{k} \dot{m}_i$

Conservation of mass at steady state: $\sum_{i=1}^{k} \dot{m}_i = 0$

First law of thermodynamics for a control volume:

$$\left(\frac{dE}{dt}\right)_{cv} = \dot{Q} - \dot{W}_x + \sum_{i=1}^{k} h_i^0 \dot{m}_i$$

The first law for a steady state: $\dot{Q} - \dot{W}_x + \sum_{i=1}^{k} h_i^0 \dot{m}_i = 0$

First law for one-input–one-output device:

$$\dot{Q} - \dot{W}_x = \dot{m}\left[\left(h_2 - h_1\right) + \frac{\mathbf{v}_2^2 - \mathbf{v}_1^2}{2} + g\left(z_2 - z_1\right)\right]$$

Nozzles and diffusers $h_2 + \frac{\mathbf{v}_2^2}{2} = h_1 + \frac{\mathbf{v}_1^2}{2}$

Throttling devices $h_2 = h_1$

Turbines $\dot{W}_x = \dot{m}\left(h_1^0 - h_2^0\right)$

Pumps and compressors $-\dot{W}_x = \dot{m}\left(h_2^0 - h_1^0\right) - \dot{Q}$

Heat exchangers $\dot{Q} = \dot{m}_c\left(h_{out} - h_{in}\right)_c = \dot{m}_h\left(h_{in} - h_{out}\right)_h$

Unsteady state process in a single-port control volume:

$$m_2u_2 - m_1u_1 = Q - W_x + \int_1^2 h_b^0 dm$$

Charging a vessel from a line: $m_2u_2 - m_1u_1 = Q - W_x + h_0(m_2 - m_1)$

Discharging a vessel: $m_2u_2 - m_1u_1 = Q - W_x + \int_1^2 hdm$

PROBLEMS

6.1 Indicate if the following statements are true, sometimes true, or false.

a. In a control volume at steady state, the mass changes.
b. In a control volume at steady state, the pressure is uniform.
c. The Joule–Thomson coefficient in an ideal gas is equal to zero.
d. The Joule–Thomson coefficient in steam is equal to zero.
e. In a throttling process the temperature change is equal to zero.
f. In a throttling process the enthalpy change is equal to zero.

6.2 Air (ideal gas, $M = 29$, $k = 1.4$) at 10 bars enters an adiabatic turbine at a rate of 1.2 kg/s and a velocity of 9 m/s. The cross-sectional area of the turbine inlet is 300 cm^2. Air leaves the turbine at 1 bar, 30 °C, and a velocity of 35 m/s. Calculate:

a. The power of the turbine.
b. The exit cross-sectional area.

6.3 Steam at 3 MPa and 400 °C enters a turbine nozzle at a speed of 100 m/s. The cross-section at the entrance to the nozzle is 1.6 cm^2. At the nozzle exit the pressure is 140 kPa and the temperature 150 °C.

a. Find the velocity at the exit assuming that the process was adiabatic.
b. What would be the final velocity if the process were not adiabatic and the rate of heat removal were 50 kW?

6.4 In the adiabatic control volume shown in Fig. 6.12 three streams of fluid are coming in and two streams going out. The enthalpy rates of these streams have the values given in the table below. The conditions of the streams and inside the control volume do not change with time, and steady state may be assumed. Find the power produced by the machinery inside the control volume.

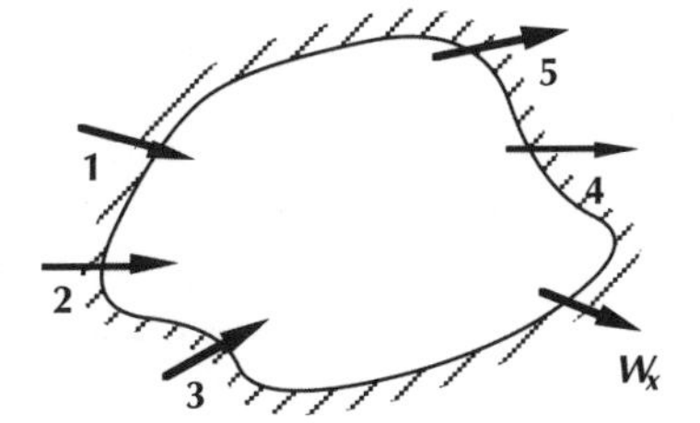

Figure 6.12

Stream #	1	2	3	4	5
Enthalpy (Btu/h)	10000	20000	5000	5000	8000

6.5 Steam at 300 °C and 10 bars is supplied to an adiabatic turbine at the rate of 1.2 kg/s. The velocity at the inlet to the turbine, which is located 15 m above its exit, is 9 m/s. At the turbine exit the pressure is 0.015 bars, the steam quality 0.96, and the velocity 35 m/s. Calculate:

a. The power of the turbine.
b. The error due to neglecting the influence of the velocity and the elevation.

6.6 A high pressure turbine is supplied with 5000 kg/h of steam at 4 MPa and 450 °C. The steam comes out of the turbine saturated at 0.2 MPa.

a. Find the power supplied by the turbine if it is adiabatic. (Neglect kinetic and gravitational terms.)
b. In a real case there is some heat transfer from the surface of the turbine in the amount of 10^5 kJ/h. Find the percentage decrease of power from part a.

6.7 Helium (an ideal gas, M = 4, k = 1.667) enters an adiabatic compressor at 1 MPa, 27 °C, and 120 m/s. At the compressor outlet the cross-sectional area is 260 cm^2, and the helium leaves at 2 MPa, 227 °C, and 20 m/s. Find:

a. The power of the compressor.
b. The internal energy change of the helium passing through the compressor.

6.8 Steam at 200 kPa, enters a vertical supply line at the ground level of a 200m high office building. As it flows up, the steam loses heat in the amount of 15 kJ/kg. It is desired to deliver to the top floor steam at 100 kPa and 90% quality. Find the required temperature and specific volume of the steam at ground level.

6.9 Hydrogen (ideal gas, k = 1.4, M = 2) enters an adiabatic compressor at 27 °C, 1 MPa, and 120 m/s, Fig. 6.13. The exit cross-section of the compressor is 260 cm^2, and the gas leaves at 227 °C, 2 MPa, and 20 m/s. Determine:

a. The power consumption of the compressor.
b. The change in the specific internal energy of the gas that passes through the compressor.

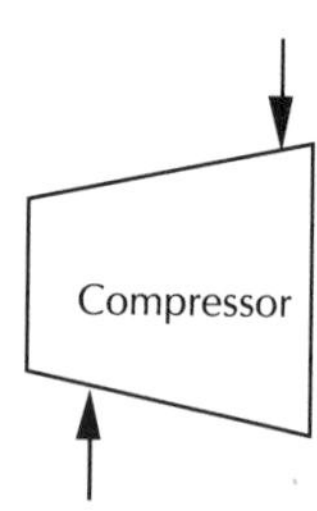

Figure 6.13

6.10 In a certain plant 900 kg/h of saturated steam at 2.5 MPa are needed, while the existing boiler supplies superheated steam at 350 °C and 3.0 MPa. In order to attain the required conditions, the steam is fed into a mixing chamber into which water at 35 °C and 3.2 MPa is sprayed. The exit steam is then throttled down to 2.5 MPa.

a. Describe schematically the mixing chamber.
b. Calculate the mass flowrate of water to be sprayed.

6.11 In a food-processing plant steam at 550 °C, 15 MPa, and a rate of 8 kg/s enters a turbine (point 1 in Fig. 6.14). It leaves the turbine at 1 bar (point 2) and enters a food dryer where it supplies 60 × 10^6 kJ/h before it exhausts (point 3) as a saturated liquid at 100 kPa. Find the power supplied by the turbine.

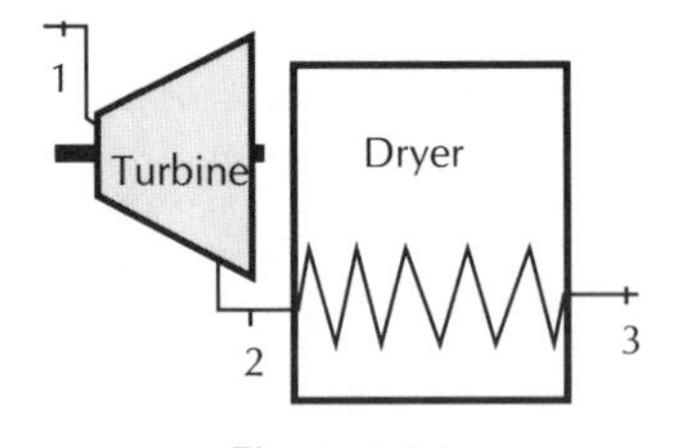

Figure 6.14

6.12 Freon-12 at 44 °C and 12 bars enters a steady flow device at a velocity of 2 m/s through an inlet area of 7 cm^2. At the exit of the device, the pressure is 1.2 bars. The enthalpy of Freon-12 at the exit is the same as the enthalpy at the inlet. Determine:

a. The mass flowrate of Freon-12.
b. The temperature of Freon-12 at the exit.
c. The change in specific volume of the refrigerant in this process.
d. The magnitude of the boundary work for this process.

6.13 Gas methane is transported in a long, well-insulated 4-inch pipe. The gas conditions at the entrance of the pipe are: $p_1 = 1\text{MPa}$, T_1 = 60 °C, **v** = 10m/s. At the exit the pressure is $p_2 = 0.2\text{MPa}$. Assume that methane is an ideal gas (M =16, k = 1.25).

Find the temperature and the velocity of the gas at the exit.

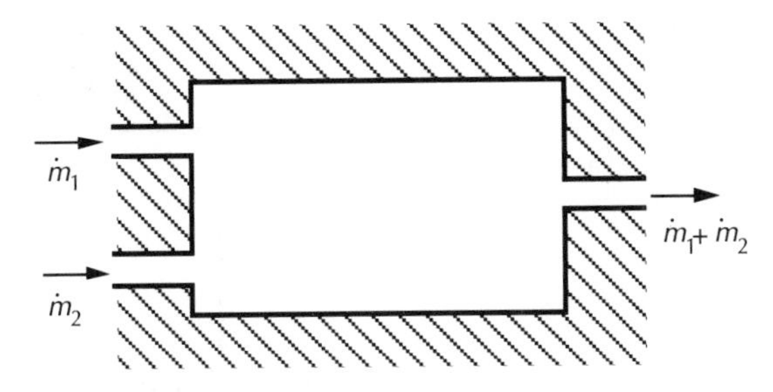

Figure 6.15

6.14 Saturated liquid carbon dioxide at a temperature of 20 °C and a pressure of 6 MPa undergoes throttling to a pressure of 100 kPa. The final temperature is –80 °C.

a. From the pressure–enthalpy diagram for carbon dioxide, find the fraction that is converted to dry ice at 100 kPa.
b. What is the specific volume of the saturated vapor of carbon dioxide at 100 kPa?

6.15 An ejector uses steam at 3 MPa and 400 °C at a rate of $\dot{m}_1$ = 3 kg/s topump water from 70 kPa and 40 °C at a rate of m_2 = l kg/s. The total mixture comes out at 110 kPa, as shown in Fig. 6.15. Assume no heat transfer, steady flow, and negligible velocities at the ports. Find the temperature of the exiting stream.

6.16 A reciprocating engine may be considered a steadyflow device if there is enough "receiver" capacity on either side of it to smooth out variations in pipeline conditions caused by the intermittent action of the engine. The "indicated work" of an engine is the net work done on the piston.

A small reciprocating engine is supplied with steam at 6.5 MPa and 420 °C. The steam exhausts at 2 MPa and 280 °C. If the heat loss from the engine cylinder to the atmosphere is 1.2 kW and the steam flow is 900 kg/h, find the indicated power of the engine.

6.17 A pressure vessel containing water (liquid and vapor) is in good contact with a bath at 370 °C, as shown in Fig. 6.16. A valve at the bottom of the vessel is opened and 2.0 kg of liquid water are withdrawn. At the end of the process there is still both liquid and vapor in the vessel. Assuming that the volume of the vessel is constant during the process, calculate:

a. The change in volume of the vapor in the vessel.
b. The heat interaction of the vessel with the bath.

Note: At 370 °C the volume of the liquid cannot be neglected.

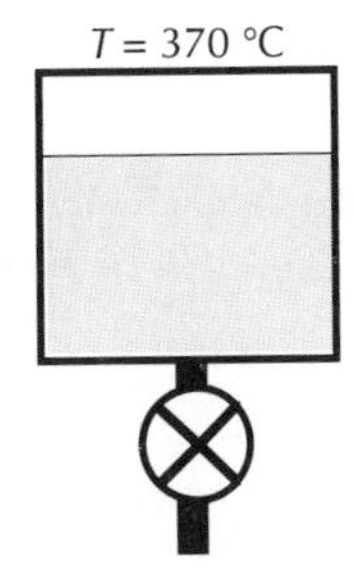

Figure 6.16

6.18 A 40 liter vessel containing oxygen (O_2) at 2.0 MPa and –50 °C is released from a shuttle on the surface of the planet Venus, which has an atmosphere of CO_2 at 220 °C and 0.5 MPa. After some time the vessel reaches the temperature of the surroundings. Now a hole is punctured in the vessel and the oxygen leaks out slowly, such that its temperature is always the same as that of the surroundings.

a. Calculate the heat interaction until the hole is punctured.
b. Calculate the heat interaction until the leak stops.
c. How would your answers be affected if the gas was not ideal? (Write out the appropriate equations.)

6.19 A 0.2 m^3 vessel, shown in Fig. 6.17, contains nitrogen (N_2) at 0.1 MPa and 0 °C. The vessel has a safety valve that prevents the pressure rising above 0.2 MPa. The vessel is heated by a reservoir at 450 °C. When the pressure reaches 0.2 MPa the valve opens and excess nitrogen is released so that the pressure remains 0.2 MPa. When the temperature reaches 400 °C the process is stopped. Find:

a. The mass of N_2 that left through the valve.
b. The heat interaction during the process.

6.20 An insulated vessel of 0.2 m^3, shown in Fig. 6.17, contains nitrogen (N_2, an ideal gas, $M = 28$, $k = 1.4$) at 1 MPa and 200 °C. The valve is opened, and when the pressure reaches 0.2 MPa the valve is closed. Find:

a. The final temperature in the vessel.
b. The mass of N_2 that left through the valve.

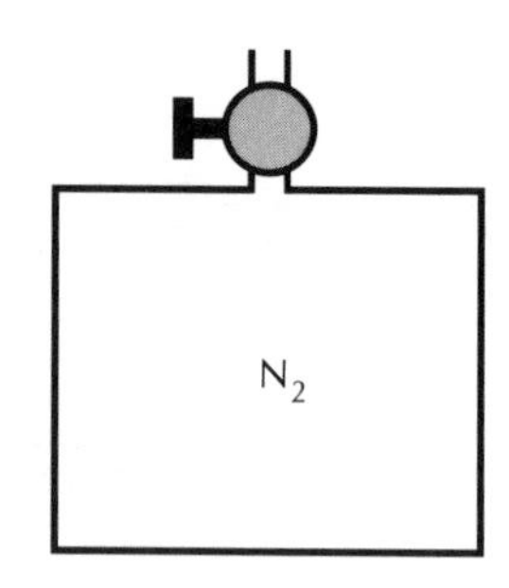

Figure 6.17

6.21 A rigid insulated tank of 5 ft^3, equipped with a paddle wheel, contains air, initially at 20 psia and 80 °F. The paddle wheel rotates, doing work on the air at the rate of 3 Btu/min. The tank is equipped with a relief valve which maintains a constant pressure, by allowing excess air to escape from the tank as the paddle wheel rotates. The paddle wheel is stopped after 20% of the initial mass has escaped.

a. Find the final temperature of the air in the tank.
b. How long must the paddle wheel operate until the final condition is reached?

6.22 Calibration measurements for a defective throttling calorimeter show that for every kilogram of steam flowing through the instrument 30 kJ are lost to the surroundings. When the calorimeter was connected to a pipeline containing wet steam at 3.0 MPa, the conditions at the exit were found to be 115 °C and 100 kPa.

Determine the quality of the steam in the pipeline.

6.23 Steam in a main at 700 kPa and 200 °C is compressed into a constant-volume chamber by a compressor. Initially, the chamber contained 1 kg of steam also at 700 kPa and 200 °C. Assume that the compressor and chamber are adiabatic. Find the temperature in the chamber when its pressure reaches 1400 kPa if the work to the compressor shaft is 32 kJ.

6.24 A 30 L can of air at 1.5 MPa and 40 °C is suspended in a large atmosphere whose pressure is 0.5 MPa and whose temperature is 40 °C. A small hole is made in the can allowing air to escape slowly to the atmosphere. The process is carried out slowly enough so that the temperature of the air in the can does not change until equilibrium is reached. How much heat must be added to or removed from (state which) the can during the process?

6.25 A 30 L can of Freon-12 (R-12) at 1.5 MPa and 40 °C is suspended in a large atmosphere whose pressure is 0.5 MPa and whose temperature is 40 °C. A small hole is made in the can allowing the Freon to escape to the atmosphere. The process is carried out slowly enough so that the temperature of the Freon in the can does not change until equilibrium is reached. How much heat must be added to or removed from (state which) the can during the process?

6.26 Steam flows at 60 m/s through a steam main of 1.6 MPa, 280 °C. Four tanks are connected to this main by pipes which are closed by valves, as shown in Fig. 6.18. Tank A, which has heat-conducting walls, is surrounded by a constant-temperature bath at 280 °C, and is initially evacuated. Tank B is like tank A except that it initially contains steam at 0.8 MPa and 280 °C. Tank C has adiabatic walls and is initially evacuated. Tank D has adiabatic walls and initially contained steam at 0.8 MPa, 280 °C. The valves to the tanks are opened, and closed again when the tanks are filled with steam. Find:

a. The heat transfer to the steam in tank A.
b. The heat transfer to the steam in tank B.
c. The final state in tank C.
d. The final state in tank D.

6.27 A space capsule comes to equilibrium on the surface of Mars. At that time the capsule is completely evacuated and its internal free volume is 2 m^3. However, owing to small leaks, the atmosphere of Mars slowly penetrates into the capsule and after a few hours both temperature and pressure equilib-

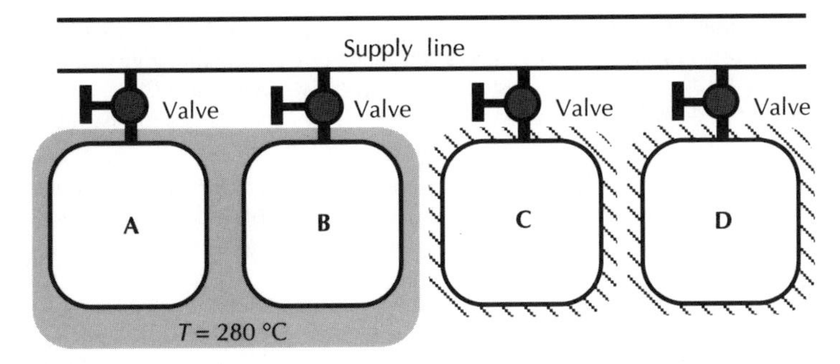

Figure 6.18

rium are established between the inside of the capsule and the atmosphere. Without having any information about the chemical composition of the atmosphere on Mars, we want to calculate the amount and the direction of any heat that might have crossed the boundaries of the capsule during the process described above. We can assume the following:

a. The temperature and pressure of the atmosphere of Mars were constant during the process.
b. The atmosphere of Mars with regard to our process is a simple system.
c. The pressure on the surface of Mars is 70 kPa.

6.28 An empty insulated cylinder, shown in Fig.6.19 contains a piston of negligible weight backed by a linear spring, initially with no tension. Air (ideal gas, $k = 1.4$, $M = 29$) from a main at $p_0 = 1.6$ MPa, $T_0 = 27$ °C, enters under the piston and compresses the spring. When the pressure inside reaches $p_2 = 900$ kPa and the volume 0.04 m^3, the valve is closed. Find:

a. The final temperature in the cylinder.
b. The amount of air that entered.

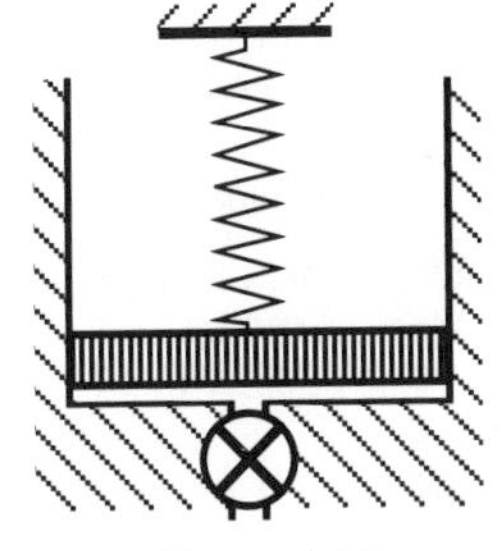

Figure 6.19

6.29 Consider a piston–cylinder device, Fig. 6.20, which is supplied air at a constant mass flowrate $\dot{m}_{in}$ and at constant inlet temperature T_{in} and constant inlet pressure p_{in}. A valve in the outlet line is controlled automatically to keep the outlet mass flowrate always equal to the inlet flowrate, i.e. $\dot{m}_{out} = \dot{m}_{in}$.

The piston is being pushed upward at a constant speed so that the volume of the cylinder is changing at a constant rate $\dot{V}$.

Assume that quasistatic conditions exist at all times and that air is an ideal gas. Suppose that at time $t = t_1$ the mass, the pressure, the temperature, and the volume of the air *inside* the cylinder are m_1, p_1, T_1, and V_1, respectively. Consider a later time t_2 when the volume has decreased to one-half that at t_1 (i.e. $V_2 = \frac{1}{2}V_1$).

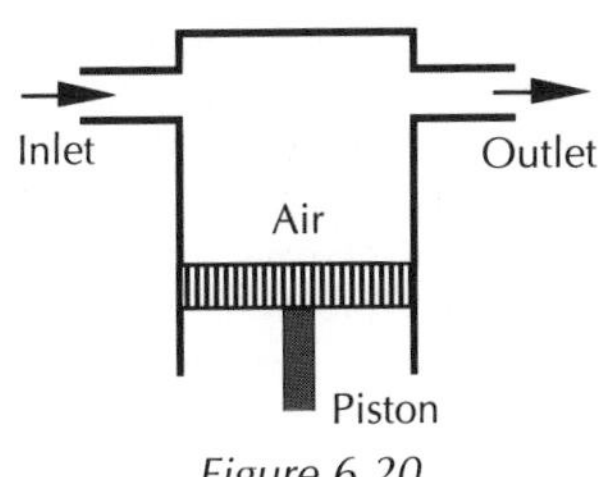

Figure 6.20

a. If a constant-temperature bath is used to maintain a constant temperature of the gas inside the cylinder equal to the inlet temperature T_{in}, derive an expression for the heat interaction Q occurring between time t_1 and t_2 in terms of the given quantities, i.e. $\dot{m}_{in}$, p_{in}, T_{in}, $\dot{V}$, T_1, p_1, m_1, V_1, V_2, T_2, c_v, and c_p.

b. Now assume that we replace the constant-temperature bath by one which automatically and instantaneously adjusts the heat interaction so as to make the process between t_1 and t_2 one of *constant pressure* instead of constant temperature. Again derive an expression in terms of the given quantities for the heat interaction Q occurring between t_1 and t_2.

6.30 A tank initially contains m_1 kilograms of a certain gas having a molecular weight of M. The initial pressure and temperature are p_1 and T_1. The tank is surrounded by a constant-temperature bath so that the gas temperature is *always* maintained constant at $T = T_1$. Now suppose that we open a small valve and allow the gas to flow slowly from the tank. We close the valve after a mass Δm has escaped to the environment.

a. Find an expression for the new pressure p_2 and for the heat interaction Q associated with this process. Assume that the gas in the tank is a semi-ideal gas (i.e. $pV = RT$) and it is maintained at $T = T_1$.
b. If $m_1 = 10$ kg, $\Delta m = 2$ kg, $p_1 = 30$ MPa, and $T_1 = 440$ °C, calculate p_2 and Q for steam using the expressions derived in part a.
c. If steam were to behave as a semi-ideal gas under the above-mentioned conditions, then we would expect that $p_1v_1 = p_2v_2$ since T is held constant. Using the steam tables check if steam actually satisfies the above relation for the conditions described in part b. Discuss your conclusion briefly.
d. Describe how you would solve the problem stated in part b using the steam tables.

6.31 A constant-volume tank of 0.6 m^3 contains initially equal volumes of liquid water and water vapor in equilibrium at 100 kPa. The container is heated at constant volume until the pressure reaches 8 MPa. As heating continues the pressure is maintained at 8 MPa and steam is fed from the container to an adiabatic steam turbine, as shown in Fig. 6.21. The process ends at the point where all of the liquid water in the tank has evaporated. Find:

a. The temperature of the water when the pressure in the tank reaches 8 MPa.
b. The mass of steam that flows out of the tank during the process.
c. The total work of the turbine if the steam exits at 100 kPa and a quality of 80%.
d. The heat interaction of the tank during the above process.

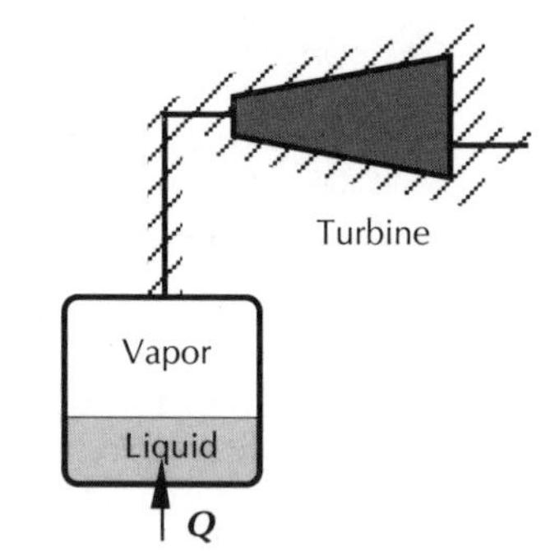

Figure 6.21

6.32 A tank of volume V contains an ideal gas at a high pressure p_1 and temperature T_1. The building containing the tank is set afire by an arsonist. However, the tank is equipped with a thermostatically controlled relief valve which allows gas to escape from the tank so as to keep its internal temperature constant at T_1. How much heat is transferred to the gas inside the tank during the interval in which the pressure is reduced from p_1 to p_2?

6.33 A main supply line in which water flows at 320 °C, 150 MPa, is connected through a valve to an elastic and adiabatic balloon, Fig. 6.22, which exerts on its contents a pressure that is proportional to its volume. At the beginning of the process the volume of the enclosure is zero. The valve is opened and 5 kg of water enter the balloon. The valve closes when the pressure in the balloon reaches 0.8 MPa. Determine the state in the balloon at the end of the process.

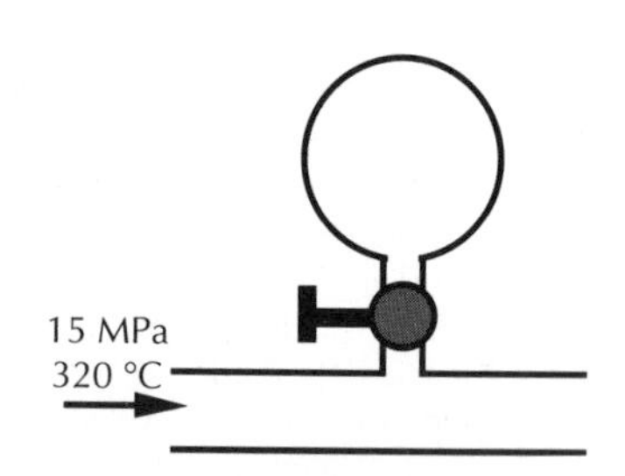

Figure 6.22

6.34 A steam vessel of 2.5m^3 capacity contains 1000 kg of liquid water in equilibrium with its vapor, which fills the remainder of the vessel. The temperature is 200 °C and the corresponding pressure is 1.554 MPa. Now 500 kg of saturated liquid water at 90 °C are pumped into the vessel without removing any steam. How much heat must be added during this process if the pressure and temperature in the steam vessel are to remain at their initial values?

6.35 An insulated, rigid, 18 L vessel contains an ideal gas ($M = 44$, $k = 1.28$) at 140 °C and 0.7 MPa. A valve is opened and the gas leaks slowly into the atmosphere. The conditions of the atmosphere are 0.1 MPa and 30 °C.

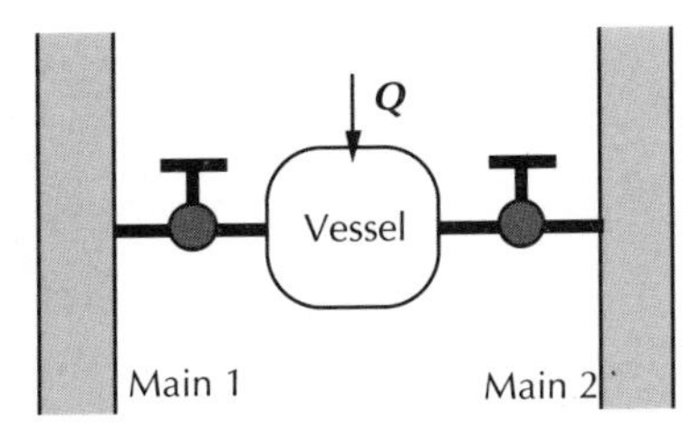

Figure 6.23 **Charging a vessel from two mains.**

a. Determine the state and the mass of the gas remaining in the vessel when the pressure in it reaches 0.3 MPa.
b. Determine the state and the mass of the gas remaining in the vessel when the pressure in it reaches that of the atmosphere.

6.36 In Fig. 6.23, 1 kg of water is admitted from a water main at 20 MPa and 300 °C into an evacuated 60 L vessel. Subsequently superheated steam at 7 MPa and 850 °C is admitted into the vessel from a second main until finally the vessel contains dry saturated steam at 7.0 MPa.

a. Find the mass of steam that enters the vessel from the second main.
b. Calculate the total heat transfer to the H_2O in the vessel.

6.37 A quantity of water is admitted from a water main into an evacuated 60 L adiabatic vessel. The water in the main is maintained at 20 MPa and 300 °C. Subsequently superheated steam at 7 MPa and 850 °C is admitted into the vessel from a second main until finally the vessel contains dry saturated steam at 7.0 MPa.

a. Find the mass of steam that enters the vessel from the second main.
b. Find the pressure in the vessel before the steam was admitted.

6.38 Figure 6.24 shows an insulated experimental test chamber of $V = 40$ m^3. At 7 o'clock in the morning the air in the chamber was at the state of the surroundings, i.e. at $p_0 =$ 1.01 bars and $T_0 = 20$ °C. An electrical device, which consumes power at a rate of $W = 36$kW, is turned on together with a ventilating system that circulates outside air through the chamber at a constant rate of 2 kg/s. The incoming air mixes completely with the chamber air and the pressure in the chamber remains constant and equal to that of the surroundings.

a. Find an expression for the temperature change in the test chamber as a function of time.
b. Will the temperature reach a maximum value? If so, what will it be?

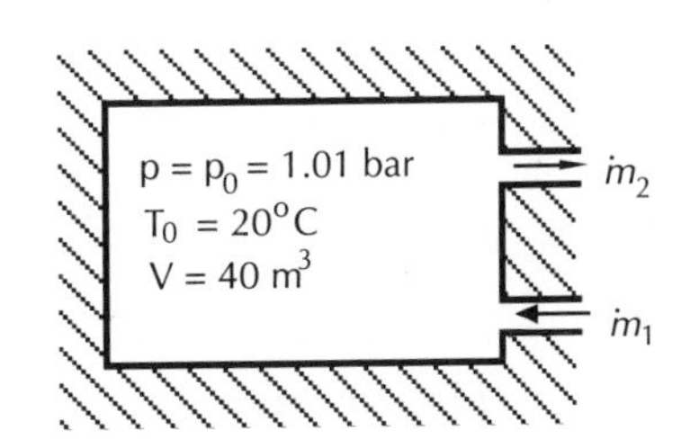

Figure 6.24
Experimental test chamber.

CHAPTER SEVEN

Heat engines and the second law of thermodynamics

In 1712 Thomas Newcomen invented the steam engine. James Watt took out a patent in 1769 for a separate condenser which greatly improved its performance. The development of the steam engine opened the way to the industrial revolution. The engine used steam raised in a boiler to produce work that was used to pump water. This invention pointed the way to converting heat into work. One of the first questions that arose with the invention of the heat engine was: how much work could an engine produce per unit heat input into the steam boiler? Another question was: could it be improved, and by how much?

In this chapter we consider these questions and develop the theory which is the basis for the operation of heat engines.

7.1 Heat engines

A heat engine is a closed system operating in a cycle while undergoing work and heat interactions.

We distinguish between two types of heat engines:

- those that use heat to produce work, $\oint \delta W > 0$, and,
- those that use work to produce cooling or heating, $\oint \delta W \leq 0$.

A steam power plant is an example of the first type while a household refrigerator is an example of the second type.

A work-producing engine is usually called a heat engine, while one for cooling or heating is called a refrigerator or a heat pump, respectively. The term *heat engine* has two

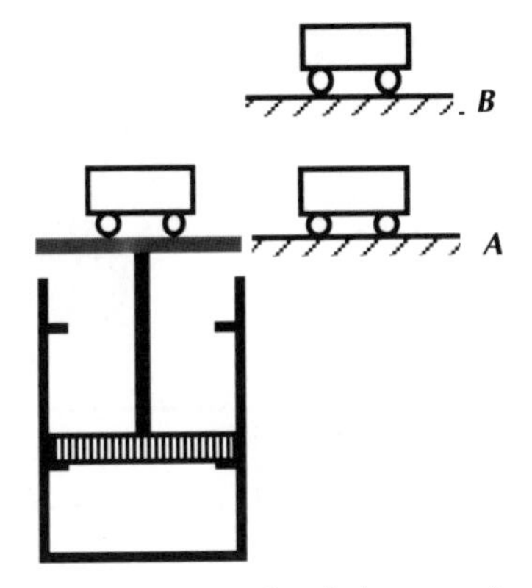

Figure 7.1 **A simple heat engine.**

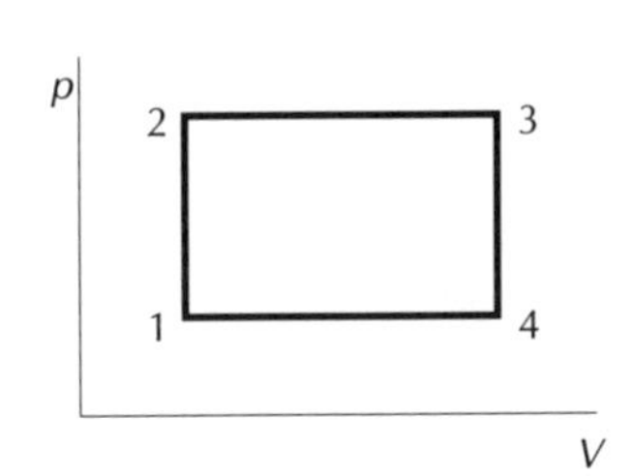

Figure 7.2 **A *p–V* diagram.**

meanings: that describing the entire class of cyclic devices that have heat and work interactions, and also a subclass of those devices that produce positive work*.

A simple example of a work-producing heat engine is a gas (the working fluid) contained in a cylinder–piston assembly, where the piston is limited in movement between two stops. Such a system is shown schematically in Fig. 7.1. This assembly can be used to lift carts, i.e. weights, from a low level A to a higher level B.

We begin the description of the heat engine at state 1 where the piston is at its lowest level, is not loaded, and is in equilibrium with the gas in the cylinder. A cart from level A is rolled onto the platform. The piston does not come down under the weight of the cart, because of the stops that carry the extra load. Next we begin to heat the gas. The temperature and the pressure of the gas increase, but the piston does not move as long as the gas pressure is below that of the equivalent pressure, p_e, of the loaded piston. This process continues until point 2 is reached, where $p_2 = p_e$. The process 1-2 is a constant-volume process represented by a vertical line on the p–V diagram, Fig. 7.2.

Further heating does not increase the pressure, but rather causes the piston to rise, thus doing work by lifting the cart. This process continues until the piston reaches the upper stop, at state 3. Process 2-3 is a constant-pressure process represented by a horizontal line on the p–V diagram. Now the cart is rolled off the platform onto the upper level, B, thus completing the cart lifting process. The state of the gas does not change, since the stop prevents the piston from rising further. In order to lift additional carts we have to bring the piston back to its initial state. This is done by cooling the gas under the unloaded piston. The cooling process consists of two steps. First the temperature and the pressure are reduced at constant volume, until the pressure is just sufficient to support the piston at point 4. Continued cooling results in a volume decrease until the initial state 1 is reached.

To summarize, the gas and the piston underwent a cycle, during which one cart was raised from level A to level B, while both heating and cooling interactions took place. This cycle may be repeated to raise any number of additional carts.

* This is somewhat misleading. It would be less confusing to use the term *heat machine* in the general sense, and reserve the term heat engine for devices producing positive work only.

The heat interactions can be accomplished by what is known as heat reservoirs.

A heat reservoir is defined as a closed system that passes through equilibrium states only, and its temperature does not change when it undergoes finite heat interactions.

A heat reservoir could be, for example, a very large system, such as the ocean or the atmosphere, provided it can be considered to be in equilibrium. Another example of a heat reservoir could be a system of liquid and vapor at a constant pressure. Finite heat interactions do not alter its temperature as long as the two phases coexist.

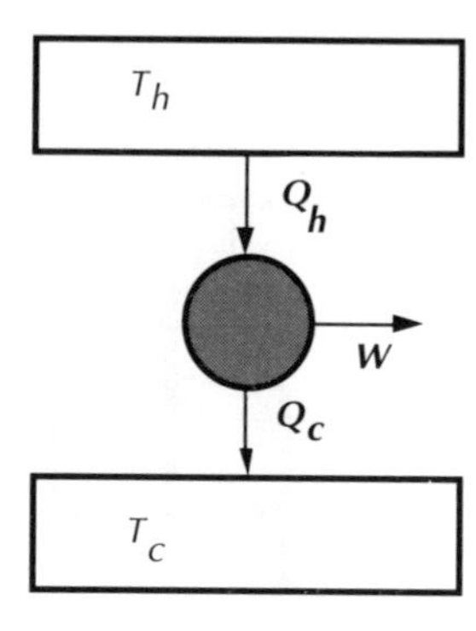

Figure 7.3

Figure 7.3 shows schematically a heat engine with two heat reservoirs used for heating and cooling, respectively, while performing work. The first law written for the heat engine undergoing a cyclic process is reduced to

$$\int \delta Q = \oint \delta W \tag{7.1}$$

since

$$\oint dE = 0 \tag{3.12}$$

The net work of the cycle given in Eq. (7.1) is equal to that required to lift a cart, while the net heat interaction is equal to the heat input into the engine from the hot reservoir minus the heat rejected by the engine into the cold reservoir:

$$W = Q_h - Q_c \tag{7.2}$$

where Q_h and Q_c are the absolute values of the heat interactions. Following the convention of denoting heat interactions as positive for heat input and negative for heat removal Eq. (7.2) can be rewritten as

$$W = Q_1 + Q_2 \tag{7.3}$$

where $Q_1 = Q_h$ and $Q_2 = -Q_c$.

7.2 Efficiency of heat engines

Generally, we define efficiency as the ratio of the output of an operation, *the product*, to its input, *the expense*.

The *product* of a heat engine is work. The input to a heat engine are heat interactions. Obviously, the ratio of the net work to the net heat of a cyclic process is unity as seen from Eq. (7.1). This ratio cannot be used to express the efficiency of a heat engine since it would result in the same efficiency for all engines. We note that in a cycle the total heat interaction is comprised of two parts, namely heat input into the engine from a hot reservoir and heat rejection from the engine into a cold reservoir. Usually, the hot reservoir is represented by burning fuel which costs money, while the cold reservoir is the ambient environment. Hence, the efficiency of a heat engine, η, can be defined as the ratio between the amount of work obtained to the amount of fuel consumed,

$$\eta = \frac{\text{product}}{\text{expense}} = \frac{W_{net}}{Q_h} \tag{7.4}$$

Using Eq. (7.2) the efficiency may be defined in terms of heat input and heat rejected:

$$\eta = 1 - \frac{Q_c}{Q_h} \tag{7.5}$$

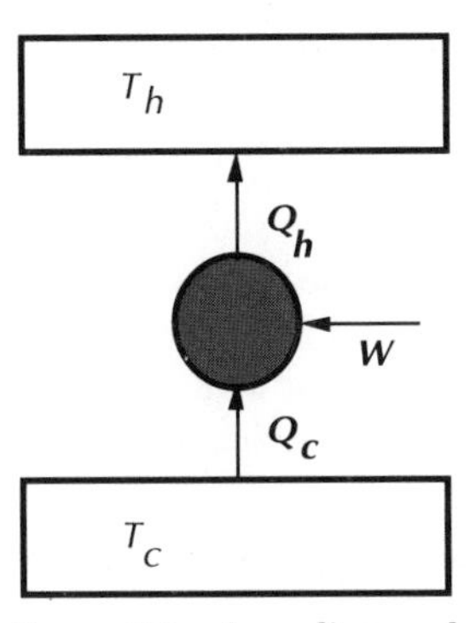

Figure 7.4 **A cooling cycle.**

We now turn to the performance of a refrigerator. Figure 7.4 shows a schematic of a refrigerator. It uses work, W, to remove heat, Q_c, from a cold reservoir at a temperature T_c and supply Q_h to a hotter reservoir at a temperature $T_h (T_h > T_c)$.

Consider now an air-conditioner that has both cooling and heating options. In the summer it removes heat from a cool room and transfers it to a warmer environment while using work to perform this task.

The performance of an air-conditioner or of a refrigerator can be measured by the amount of cooling obtained (the product) per unit work supplied (the expense). We define, therefore, a coefficient of performance, *COP*, of a refrigerator as

$$COP = \frac{\text{product}}{\text{expense}} = \left| \frac{Q_c}{W} \right| \tag{7.6}$$

Comparing Eqs (7.4) and (7.6) we note that the performance for both heat engines and refrigerators is defined as the ratio of the desired product to the required expense. However, the interpretation of the terms *product* and *expense* is different.

Substitution of Eq. (7.2) into Eq (7.6) gives the expression for the coefficient of performance of a refrigerator in terms of heat interactions:

$$COP = \frac{Q_c}{Q_h - Q_c} \tag{7.7}$$

During winter the operation of the air-conditioner is reversed. Now, the air conditioner uses work to remove heat from the colder surroundings and transfer it (together with the work) into the warmer room. An air-conditioner operating in this mode is referred to as a heat pump. The performance of a heat pump is taken as the ratio between the amount of heat supplied, Q_h (the product), to the amount of work consumed (the expense). Hence for a heat pump

$$COP = \frac{\text{product}}{\text{expense}} = \left| \frac{Q_h}{W} \right| \tag{7.8}$$

or in terms of heat interactions

$$COP = \frac{Q_h}{Q_h - Q_c} \tag{7.9}$$

Obviously, here $COP \geq 1$ with the limit of $COP \to 1$ being approached as the amount of heat removed from the cold surroundings approaches zero. In practice, this situation is approached as the temperature of the cold surroundings gets lower and lower. For that case the performance of the heat pump approaches that of a resistance heater.

EXAMPLE 7.1

The cylinder shown in Fig. 7.1 contains 0.35 kg of Freon-12 at 20 °C and 250 kPa. It is covered by a piston the weight of which is equivalent to a pressure of 250 kPa. At the beginning of the process the piston rests on the lower stop. A weight equivalent to 50 kPa is added to the piston and then the cylinder is heated by a heat reservoir at 150 °C raising the pressure of the gas until its temperature reaches 110 °C. At this point the piston reaches the upper stop. The extra weight is then removed and the cylinder is brought into contact with a cold reservoir at 10 °C. The heat removal is stopped when the gas temperature reaches 20 °C, completing a cycle. Find:

a. The heat and work interactions in the cycle.
b. The efficiency of the cycle.

SOLUTION

a. There are four states of the system that are of interest. These are marked as points 1, 2, 3, 4 in Fig. 7.2. We arrange the relevant properties of these states in the following table:

	p	T	v	h	$u = h - pv$
1	250	20.0	0.076218	201.322	182.267
2	300	72.06	0.076218	234.650	211.785
3	300	110.0	0.085566	260.391	234.721
4	250	50.32	0.085566	220.851	199.460

For the constant-volume processes 1–2 and 3–4: $W = 0$, $Q = m\Delta u$.
For the constant-pressure processes 2–3 and 4–1: $W = mp\Delta v$, $Q = m\Delta h$.

Thus,

$$W_{12} = 0$$

$$Q_{12} = m(u_2 - u_1) = 0.35(211.785 - 182.267) = 10.33 \text{ kJ}$$

$$W_{23} = mp_2(v_3 - v_2) = 0.35 \times 300\,(0.085566 - 0.076218) = 0.98 \text{ kJ}$$

$$Q_{23} = m(h_3 - h_2) = 0.35(260.391 - 234.650) = 9.01 \text{ kJ}$$

$$W_{34} = 0$$

$$Q_{34} = m(u_4 - u_3) = 0.35(199.460 - 234.721) = -1234 \text{ kJ}$$

$$W_{41} = mp_4(v_1 - v_4) = 0.35 \times 250(0.076218 - 0.085566) = -0.82 \text{ kJ}$$

$$Q_{41} = m(h_1 - h_4) = 0.35(201.322 - 220.851) = -6.84 \text{ kJ}$$

$$\oint \delta W = 0.98 - 0.82 = 0.16 \text{ kJ}$$

$$\oint \delta Q = 10.33 + 9.01 - 12.34 - 6.84 = 0.16 \text{ kJ}$$

$$Q_h = 10.33 + 9.01 = 19.34 \text{ kJ}$$

b. The efficiency is

$$\eta = \frac{\oint \delta W}{Q_h} = \frac{0.16}{19.34} = 0.0083 \quad (0.83\%)$$

7.3 The second law of thermodynamics

In the heat engine example discussed above, the heat engine interacted with two reservoirs. A positive heat interaction with a hot reservoir took place when the gas expanded and raised the weight. A negative heat interaction with a cold reservoir was used in order to restore the engine to its original state, by compressing the gas and thus completing a cycle.

The completion of a cycle allows the use of the heat engine to raise any number of weights again and again. One may ask whether it is possible to construct a heat engine that would complete a cycle, producing positive work, while interacting with one reservoir only. For such an engine the work interaction would be exactly equal to the heat input from the single reservoir and therefore its efficiency would be equal to unity. This would obviously be a very desirable heat engine. Many attempts have actually been made to construct such an ideal heat engine, but all have failed. To date no one has ever succeeded in demonstrating such an engine. This fact was generalized into the second law of thermodynamics. Kelvin and Planck expressed it as:

It is impossible to construct a device that operates in a cycle and produces positive work while interacting with one heat reservoir only.

A device that operates in a cycle and produces positive work while interacting with one heat reservoir only is called a perpetual motion machine of the second kind, or a PMM2. The statement of Kelvin and Planck essentially asserts that a PMM2 is impossible. Another statement of the second law of thermodynamics is that of Clausius:

It is impossible to devise a process the sole result of which is the transfer of heat from a cold reservoir to a hotter one.

Both versions state the impossibility of certain processes and can be proven to be equivalent, by showing that violation of one statement also violates the other, and vice versa.

Assume that the Kelvin–Planck statement is incorrect, i.e. it is *possible* to construct a heat engine that produces work while interacting with a single reservoir. Obviously, in this case $W = Q_h$. Let us use the work of this engine to drive a heat pump that extracts Q_c

from a cold reservoir and supplies an amount of heat $Q_c + W = Q_c + Q_h$ to the hot reservoir. Figure 7.5 shows schematically such an arrangement.

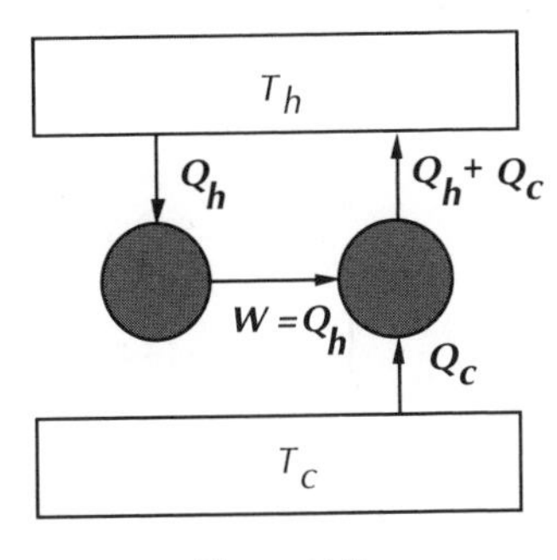

Figure 7.5

The work produced by the heat engine is consumed exactly by the heat pump, and there is no net work interaction with the surroundings. Hence, the net result of this process is the transfer of Q_c from the cold reservoir to the hot reservoir with no other net effects on the environment. This is, obviously, a violation of the Clausius statement of the second law.

To complete the proof of equivalence of the two statements of the second law, it is necessary to show that a violation of the Clausius statement constitutes a violation of the Kelvin–Planck statement also. This is left as an exercise for the student.

7.4 Reversibility

In mechanics for every process, in the absence of friction, one can find another process for which the motion at each point is exactly the same but in an opposite direction. For example, a pendulum swinging from left to right could, in the absence of friction, reverse its motion and swing from right to left with the same absolute velocities at each point, without any effect on the environment. This is just one example of a reversible process. In thermodynamics a reversible process is defined as follows:

A reversible process is one for which there exists a complementary process that brings the system and the environment back to their respective original states.

In the example above, the pendulum swinging from left to right executes a reversible process according to the definition, since there exists a complementary process of the pendulum swinging from right to left, which completes a cycle with no net effects on the environment. The reversibility of this process depends, obviously, on the absence of friction. If friction were present, the pendulum would not return to its original state without help from the environment. Friction is, therefore, one of the causes of irreversibility. There are other effects preventing processes from being reversible; these will be discussed later.

Let us call a complementary process that brings the system and its environment back to their original states, a *reverse process*.

The premise that a process is reversible means that a *reverse process* exists. If no *reverse process* exists, the process is irreversible. To show that a process is reversible it is sufficient to find at least one *reverse process* that exists in reality. This was done in the case of the pendulum described above.

To show that a process is irreversible, it is sufficient to prove that if a reverse process existed it would violate the second law of thermodynamics. Let us illustrate what has been said above by several examples.

EXAMPLE 7.2

Consider an insulated cylinder with a stopped piston that divides it into two parts, Fig. 7.6. One part contains a gas, say oxygen, and the other part is empty.

The stop is removed without applying an external load to the piston rod. The gas expands with no resistance till the piston hits the wall of the cylinder. Such a process is called a free expansion process.

Prove that free expansion of a gas is an irreversible process.

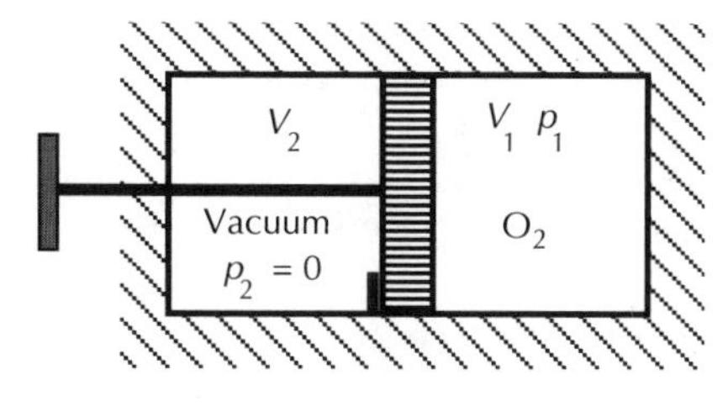

Figure 7.6

SOLUTION

Let us denote the free expansion process, described in the example as process "A". Now let us examine the effects of "process A" both on the system and on the environment. We note that no heat interaction took place, $Q_A = 0$, since the cylinder was insulated, and no work was done, $W_A = 0$, since the piston was not loaded. We therefore conclude that there were no effects whatsoever in the environment. Similarly, we note that in the system, the energy did not change, since $\Delta U_A = Q_A - W_A = 0$, and the volume of the gas increased, from V_1, the contracted volume, to V_2, the expanded volume, $\Delta V_A = V_2 - V_1 > 0$. (Other effects, such as $\Delta p_A < 0$, were also present, but these are not required for the analysis since they are not independent. Indeed, U and V are the two independent properties which are sufficient to determine the state of the system.)

In order to demonstrate that process "A" is not reversible, we consider its reverse process, RevA, which starts with the expanded state and causes the gas to contract back to its initial volume V_1 without changing the energy of the system and with no interactions with the environment. We can easily describe the effects of process RevA even though we may not be able to perform such a process in reality.

Let us now combine the *reverse process*, RevA, with two real processes: an expansion from the compressed state to the expanded volume, while imposing an appropriate load on the piston rod, thus producing positive work, W_B (call it process "B"); and process "C", a heat interaction with a single reservoir in the amount of $Q_C = W_B$, restoring the energy of the system to its original state.

The combination process (RevA + "B" + "C") constitutes a cycle. This cycle produces positive work while interacting with a single reservoir only. Obviously, it is a PMM2, which contradicts the second law. We know that both processes "B" and "C" are possible. Hence, it follows that the process RevA is impossible; that is, there exists no reverse process to process "A". Thus process "A" is irreversible.

It is not too difficult to arrive at the conclusion that any free expansion, or an expansion where the effective pressures on both sides of the piston are not equal, is an irreversible process.

EXAMPLE 7.3

Consider a system consisting of two parts, each in equilibrium, but at different temperatures, T_1 and T_2 ($T_1 > T_2$), respectively, as shown in Fig. 7.7. In process A, heat is transferred from part 1 to part 2.

Question: Is process A reversible?

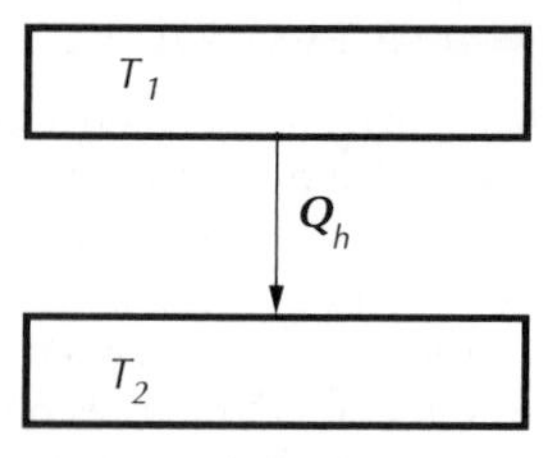

Figure 7.7

SOLUTION

Process A has no effects on the environment, while its effects in the system are

$$-\Delta U_1 = \Delta U_2 = Q_h > 0$$

$$\Delta V_1 = \Delta V_2 = 0$$

The *reverse process,* RevA, if it existed, would remove heat from a colder reservoir (2) and supply it to a hotter reservoir (1) with no other effects on the system nor on the environment. This is contradictory to the second law, according to the Clausius statement, and is therefore impossible.

Here again it is possible to generalize, and conclude that any heat transfer across a finite temperature difference is an irreversible process.

The examples described above indicate two effects that cause irreversibility. There are other effects that cause processes to be irreversible, such as:

- Friction.
- Free expansion.
- Expansion across a finite pressure difference.
- Heat transfer across a finite temperature difference.
- Mixing of substances of dissimilar states.
- Plastic deformation of solids.
- Flow of electric current through a resistance.
- Hysteresis.
- Spontaneous chemical reactions.

Since it is impossible completely to eliminate all these effects, truly reversible processes cannot occur in nature. In some processes, however, the effects causing irreversibility can be reduced to any desired degree. Such processes are called "reversible in principle." In the case of the swinging pendulum, for example, the friction can be reduced more and more by

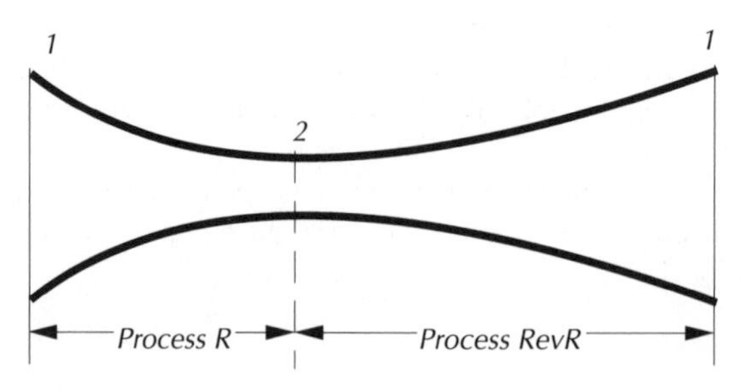

Figure 7.8

a careful design of the pendulum bearing. We shall refer to processes which are reversible in principle as reversible processes.

Another example of a reversible process (in principle) is the flow of a fluid through a nozzle. The properties of the fluid entering the nozzle can be restored by letting the fluid flow through an appropriate extension to the original nozzle, Fig. 7.8 opposite. The degree to which the properties can be restored depends on the extent to which friction is eliminated.

7.5 Internally reversible process

Sometimes an irreversible process can be made reversible, if allowed to interact with a different environment, even though the system follows the same path and the same interactions at its boundary. Such a process is called *internally reversible.*

Consider, for example, two systems shown in Fig. 7.9, each consisting of a gas enclosed in a cylinder–piston assembly. Each system undergoes a quasistatic adiabatic expansion.

One system interacts with a variable weight (such as fine sand). The expansion is achieved by removing a small grain of sand at a time. In the limit, this process is quasistatic, since the system goes through equilibrium states only. At any time the direction of the process can be reversed by adding, rather than subtracting, an infinitesimal grain of sand. This is a reversible process, by definition.

The second system interacts with friction pads that control the expansion. Here again, the process is quasistatic, since the system goes through equilibrium states only. However, this process is certainly irreversible, since there is no way the gas under the piston can be compressed by "undoing" the action of the friction pads. This can be proven formally by showing that a PMM2 would result, had the process been reversible. The proof is left as an exercise to the student.

To summarize, both systems go through identical paths and boundary interactions. Yet one process is reversible and the other is not. Obviously, the irreversibility in the second case cannot be attributed to whatever occurs within the system, since that is the same as

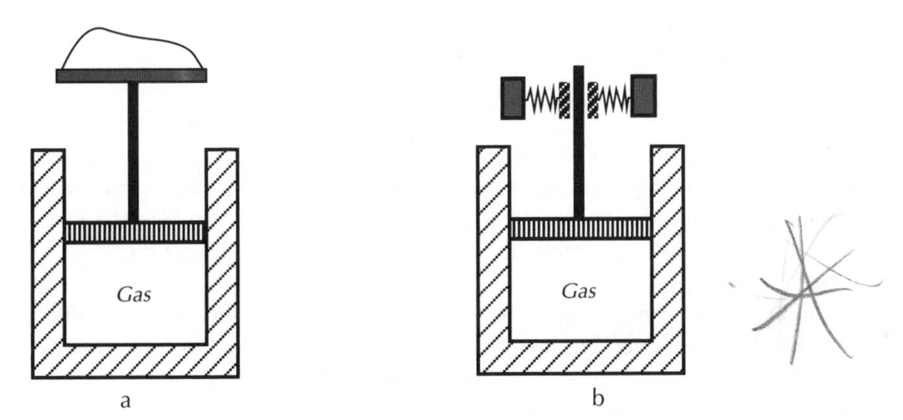

Figure 7.9 **Reversible and internally reversible processes.**

in the reversible process; it must therefore be attributed to what happened in the environment. We call such a process an *internally reversible process.*

A system is said to undergo an internally reversible process if the process can be made reversible by changing the environment only.

From the above discussion it follows that a quasistatic process is always *internally reversible* but not necessarily *reversible.*

7.6 The Carnot cycle

Let us now focus our attention on a class of cycles where all the processes are reversible. Such cycles, called reversible cycles, play an important role in thermodynamics.

One of the most important reversible cycles is associated with the name of Carnot. It is comprised of four distinct processes, two of which are adiabatic and two isothermal, at the temperatures of the hot and the cold reservoirs, respectively.

Consider an ideal gas enclosed in a cylinder–piston assembly undergoing a cycle shown in the *p–V* diagram of Fig. 7.10. The four reversible processes comprising the Carnot cycle are:

1–2: Isothermal compression, while interacting with the cold reservoir at $T_c = T_1 = T_2$. ($W_{12} < 0$.)
2–3: Adiabatic compression up to T_h. ($W_{23} < 0$.)
3–4: Isothermal expansion, while interacting with the hot reservoir at $T_h = T_3 = T_4$. ($W_{34} > 0$.)
4–1: Adiabatic expansion to T_c. ($W_{41} > 0$.)

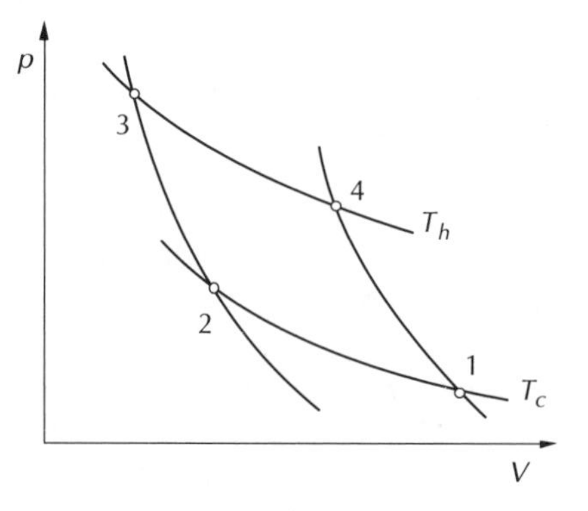

Figure 7.10 **Ideal gas Carnot cycle.**

As the cycle is reversible the net work is equal to the area enclosed by the lines in the *p–V* diagram.

$$W_{net} = \oint p dV \tag{7.10}$$

If the cycle were irreversible, the work would be less. The working fluid need not be an ideal gas. Indeed, any working substance, steam, Freon, or even a magnetic material, would do. The only condition is that the cycle be comprised of two isothermal processes, at the temperatures of the respective reservoirs with two adiabatic processes connecting them.

During the cycle the gas interacts with a cold and a hot reservoir and produces net positive work. It constitutes a heat engine, which is known as the *Carnot engine.* Since every part of the cycle is reversible, the whole cycle could be executed in the reverse direction, in which case it would be a *Carnot refrigerator.*

7.7 Efficiency and the reversible engine

The efficiency of a heat engine operating between two heat reservoirs was shown to be

$$\eta = 1 - \frac{Q_c}{Q_h} \tag{7.5}$$

It follows from the second law of thermodynamics that Q_c can never be zero and, therefore, the efficiency of a heat engine is always less than unity. A question can be raised: what is the highest efficiency of a heat engine operating between two given heat reservoirs? That is, given a hot and a cold heat reservoir, what is the maximum work per unit heat input that a heat engine can deliver? The answer to the question lies in two theorems, sometimes referred to as Carnot principles, which assert:

1. *The efficiency of a heat engine operating between two heat reservoirs cannot exceed that of a reversible heat engine operating between the same reservoirs.*

2. *All reversible heat engines operating between two given heat reservoirs have the same efficiency.*

The proof of these theorems is based on the premise that the second law of thermodynamics cannot be violated.

Assume that the first theorem is incorrect, namely that there exists a heat engine X, whose efficiency is higher than that of a reversible engine R, operating between the same heat reservoirs, as shown in Fig. 7.11. It follows that if both engines receive the same heat input Q_1 from the hot reservoir, the work of engine X will be greater than that of engine R, $W_X > W_R$.

Let us now reverse the operation of the reversible heat engine R, and operate it as a refrigerator, RevR. The combination of the two engines, X + RevR, will leave the hot reservoir unchanged, since it removes Q_1 into engine X and, at the same time, it returns Q_1 from RevR. The work of the combination is then

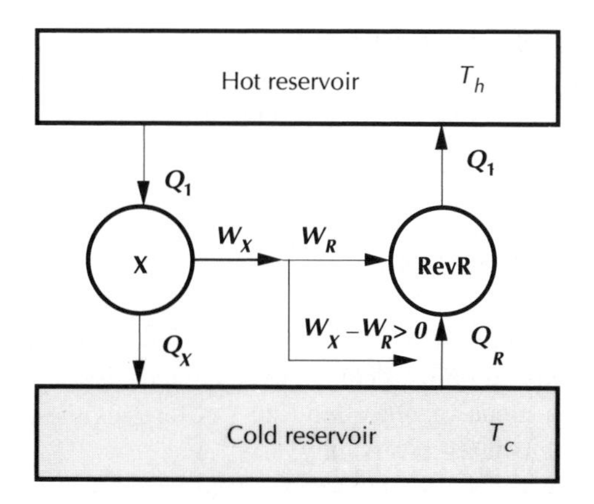

Figure 7.11

$$W_X + W_{RevR} = W_X - W_R > 0$$

This combination constitutes a PMM2, since it produces positive work while having heat interactions with a single reservoir only (the cold one). We must, therefore, conclude that it is incorrect to assume the existence of a heat engine, X, whose efficiency exceeds that of a reversible engine.

The second principle, stating that all reversible heat engines operating between two given reservoirs have the same efficiency, follows directly from the first principle. Indeed, if there are two reversible engines A and B, it follows from principle 1 that the efficiency of engine A cannot exceed that of B, since B is reversible, and at the same time the efficiency of B cannot exceed that of A, since A is reversible. Hence, both engines must have the same efficiency. Principle 2 is instrumental in defining a thermodynamic temperature scale discussed below.

Some real engineering cycles are presented later, and their thermal efficiencies come out lower than those of reversible engines operating between the same limit temperatures. This is, perhaps, not surprising, since the efficiency of a reversible engine emerged as the maximum possible for any heat engine. But is the lower thermal efficiency of a heat engine which is not reversible a direct result of its irreversibility? To answer this question we introduce a third theorem:

The thermal efficiency of an irreversible heat engine is lower than that of a reversible engine operating between the same reservoirs.

To prove this theorem we invoke the definition of reversibility, presented in section 7.4, and conclude that an irreversible cycle is one for which no complementary cycle exists such that the system and its environment return back to their respective original states. For if such a complementary cycle can be found the original cycle is, by definition, reversible.

Now consider Fig. 7.11, in which we identify the irreversible engine as X. Suppose it had the same thermal efficiency as the reversible one, the RevR engine. We now reverse the reversible engine, as shown in the figure, and use the work delivered by X to run RevR. If the two engines had identical efficiencies this work would be exactly enough to run the RevR engine, and cancel the effects of what the X engine had done. We have therefore found a complementary cycle which restores everything to its original state. But such a cycle does not exist and, hence is a contradiction, and the irreversible engine has a thermal efficiency lower than the reversible one.

7.8 Thermodynamic temperature scale

We have seen that the efficiency of all reversible engines operating between two given reservoirs is the same and does not depend on the details of the engines themselves such as: the design, the working fluid, the mode of operation, etc. As long as the engine is reversible its efficiency depends on the two reservoirs only.

The characteristic property of a reservoir is its temperature. Two reservoirs at the same temperature may be considered as the same reservoir. Therefore, the efficiency of a heat

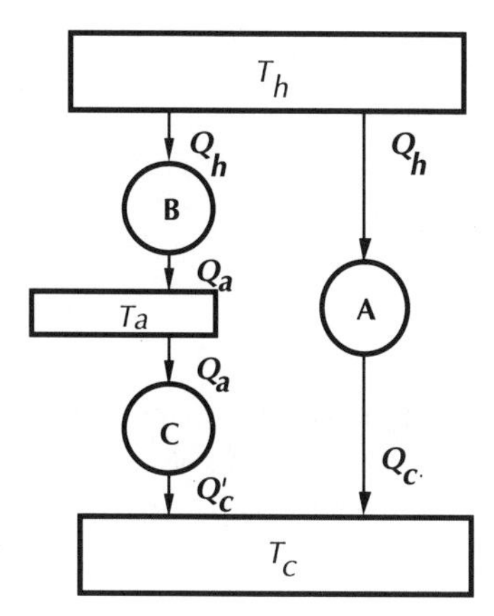

Figure 7.12

engine must depend on the temperatures of the reservoirs only:

$$\eta_{rev} = 1 - \frac{Q_c}{Q_h} = 1 - f(T_c, T_h) \tag{7.11}$$

or

$$\frac{Q_c}{Q_h} = f(T_c, T_h) \tag{7.12}$$

Let us now consider two heat reservoirs at temperatures T_h and T_c, and an auxiliary reservoir at T_a. Three reversible heat engines operate between these reservoirs, as shown schematically in Fig. 7.12.

Consider first heat engine A that draws Q_h from the hot reservoir at T_h, and rejects Q_c to the cold reservoir at T_c. Now consider the combination consisting of engine B that draws the same Q_h from the hot reservoir at T_h, and rejects Q_a into the auxiliary reservoir at T_a, and engine C that draws Q_a from the reservoir at T_a and rejects Q_c' to the cold reservoir at T_c. Since the heat rejected into the auxiliary reservoir is exactly equal to that drawn from it, no net change takes place in that reservoir. Considering the combination of B + C and the auxiliary reservoir as one reversible heat engine (it does go through a cycle and consists of reversible parts only), its efficiency must be equal to that of engine A, and therefore the heat rejected from the combination B + C must be equal to that rejected from engine A, namely $Q_c = Q_c'$. Now we rewrite Eq. (7.12) for engines A, B, and C, respectively:

$$Q_c / Q_h = f(T_c, T_h) \tag{7.13}$$

$$Q_a / Q_h = f(T_a, T_h) \tag{7.14}$$

$$Q_c / Q_a = f(T_c, T_a) \tag{7.15}$$

Since

$$\frac{Q_c}{Q_h} = \frac{Q_c / Q_a}{Q_h / Q_a} \tag{7.16}$$

it follows by substitution of Eqs (7.13)–(7.15) into Eq. (7.16) that

$$f(T_c, T_h) = \frac{f(T_c, T_a)}{f(T_h, T_a)} \tag{7.17}$$

The left hand side of Eq. (7.17) depends on T_c and T_h only; hence, the right hand side cannot be a function of T_a. The dependence on T_a must therefore cancel out. This occurs only if the function *f* has the form

$$f(T_i, T_j) = \frac{F(T_i)}{F(T_j)} \tag{7.18}$$

Substituting Eq. (7.18) into (7.17) does indeed remove the dependence of the right hand side of Eq. (7.17) on T_a. Equation (7.12) can now be rewritten with the help of Eq. (7.18) as

$$\frac{Q_c}{Q_h} = \frac{F(T_c)}{F(T_h)} \tag{7.19}$$

Since the ratio Q_c / Q_h is fixed for any two given reservoirs, the selection of the functional relationship $F(T)$ relates T_c to T_h. Strictly speaking, any function may satisfy mathematically Eq. (7.19). The form adopted in thermodynamics is

$$F(T) = T \tag{7.20}$$

Thus

$$\frac{Q_c}{Q_h} = \frac{T_c}{T_h} \tag{7.21}$$

This form was first suggested by Kelvin and is known as Kelvin's second temperature scale*.

Equation (7.21) defines a thermodynamic temperature scale that is completely independent of the properties of the materials from which the thermometer is made. It provides a means of measuring temperature without the need to resort to a "standard thermometer".

In order to complete the definition of the temperature scale it is necessary to assign arbitrarily a temperature to one reproducible state. This was done in the Tenth Conference on Weights and Measures, held in 1954, by assigning the exact temperature 273.16 K to the triple point of water. Under these conditions the approximate tempera-

* Kelvin also suggested another form for the function:

$F(T) = \exp(T)$

Thus

$Q_c/Q_h = \exp(T_c - T_h)$

where Q_c and Q_h are the absolute values of the heat interactions with the cold and hot reservoirs, respectively.

tures of the ice point and the steam point are 273.15 K and 373.15 K, respectively. In 1967 the Kelvin scale was used to redefine the Celsius scale as

$$T_{Celsius} = T_{Kelvin} - 273.15$$

In terms of the Kelvin temperature scale the efficiency of a Carnot engine, i.e. the efficiency of a reversible engine operating between two reservoirs is given by

$$\eta_{rev} = 1 - \frac{Q_c}{Q_h} = 1 - \frac{T_c}{T_h} \tag{7.22}$$

EXAMPLE 7.4

A heat engine operates between two reservoirs, one at 400 °C and the other at 50 °C. The engine produces 7.5 kW of power and rejects heat into the cold reservoir at a rate of 9.0 kW.

a. Find the efficiency of the heat engine.
b. Is the engine reversible?

SOLUTION

a. From the first law written for the heat engine we have

$$\dot{Q}_h = \dot{Q}_c + \dot{W} = 9.0 + 7.5 = 16.5 \text{ kW}$$

The efficiency is

$$\eta = \frac{\dot{W}}{\dot{Q}_h} = \frac{7.5}{16.5} = 0.455$$

b. The efficiency of a reversible engine between the same reservoirs is a function of their temperatures only, and is given by

$$\eta_{rev} = 1 - \frac{T_c}{T_h} = 1 - \frac{323.15}{673.15} = 0.520$$

and since $\eta < \eta_{rev}$ the engine is irreversible.

PROBLEMS

7.1 Air in a closed system undergoes the following cycle:

1–2 Heating at a constant pressure of 0.1 MPa, from 5 °C to 60 °C.
2–3 Cooling at a constant volume to 5 °C.
3–1 Isothermal compression to its initial state.

a. Show the cycle on a p–v diagram.
b. Calculate the heat and the work interactions in each stage, per kilogram of air.
c. Calculate the thermal efficiency of the cycle.

7.2 Indicate whether the following statements are true, sometimes true, or false.

a. A process that causes heat to be removed from one reservoir only is feasible.

b. A process that causes heat to be supplied to one reservoir only is feasible.
c. A process that causes heat to be transferred from reservoir A to reservoir B, as a single effect, is feasible.
d. For a heat pump $COP < 1$.
e. For a cooling cycle $COP < 1$.

7.3 A heat engine transfers 800 kJ from a heat reservoir at 500 °C and rejects 400 kJ to a heat reservoir at 27 °C. The engine is used to compress isothermally 2.0 kg of air at 0.1 MPa, 27 °C. Find:

a. Whether the engine is reversible.
b. The pressure of the compressed air.
c. The heat interaction of the air.

7.4 A heat engine operates between two reservoirs, one at 1000 °C and the other at 300 °C. For every heat interaction of 1 kJ with the high temperature reservoir it rejects 0.6 kJ to the low temperature reservoir.

a. Is such an engine feasible? If yes, is it reversible?
b. If it rejects 0.3 kJ to the low temperature reservoir, is it feasible?

7.5 An inventor claims to have a device that uses a solar water heater for air-conditioning, without the need for work input. The inventor states essentially that given a supply of hot water at 95 °C and an environment at 38 °C the device can remove heat at a rate of 3.4 kW from a room at 20 °C.

a. Is such a device feasible?
b. Assuming the device is feasible and ideal, find the rate of heat supply to the solar water heater.

7.6 A system undergoing a reversible cycle interacts with three reservoirs at temperatures $T_A = 120$ °C, $T_B = 20$ °C and $T_C = -20$ °C. No other systems are involved. The system receives 1000 kJ from reservoir A. Calculate the heat interactions of reservoirs B and C.

7.7 An ideal gas Carnot refrigerator operates between the temperatures $T_1 = 268$ K and $T_2 = 283$ K. The power consumption is 10 kW. Find the relative change (%) of the *COP* if the maximum temperature of the cycle increases by 2 K and the minimum temperature decreases by 2 K and draw the two cycles on the same p–v diagram.

7.8 A refrigerator extracts 291 kW from a cooled space at 253 K, while the ambient temperature is 293 K.

a. Find the maximum *COP*.
b. Find the minimum power consumption.
c. Find the heat interaction in the air cooler (hot source).

7.9

a. Define a PMM2.
b. State the second law.
c. Show by a logical procedure that mixing 9 kg of ice with 1 kg of steam at 1 bar to give 10 kg of water is an irreversible process.
d. Find the final water temperature and the entropy change in the mixing process.

7.10 A solar collector is used as a heat source for a Cornot engine with a heat sink at 300K. The efficiency of the solar collector, ε, is defined as the fraction of the energy reaching the collector which is actually absorbed. It is related to the temperature of the collector as:

$$\varepsilon = 0.75 - 1.75(T/300 - 1)$$

Determine the best operating temperature of the collector, i.e. the temperature that yields maximum power from the Carnot engine.

7.11 The cylinder shown in Fig. 7.1 contains 0.5 kg of H_2O at 40 °C and 150 kPa. It is covered with a piston of a weight equivalent to a pressure of 150 kPa. At the beginning of the process the pisto on the lower stop. A weight equivalent to 450 kPa is added to the piston and then the cylinder is hea by a heat reservoir at 250 °C raising the pressure of the system till its temperature reaches 200 °C. At this point the piston reaches the upper stop. The extra weight is then removed and the cylinder is brought in contact with a cold reservoir at 10 °C. The heat removal is stopped when the temperature in the system reaches 40 °C, thus completing a cycle. Find:

a. The heat and work interactions of the cycle.
b. The efficiency of the cycle.

7.12 A heat engine operates in a cycle consisting of two isotherms at T_1 and T_2, respectively, and two polytropic processes.

a. Plot the power output and thermodynamic efficiency of the engine versus the polytropic exponent, *n*.
b. Find the value of *n* resulting at maximum power and efficiency.

7.13 When one junction of a thermoelectric generator is in good contact with the environment at 25 °C and the other with a reservoir at 300 °C, the open circuit voltage is 0.95 V. An ideal 50 W electric motor connected to the generator draws 80 A. The rate of heat removal from the cold junction is 900 W.

a. Find the internal resistance of the generator.
b. Find the efficiency of the generator.
c. Is the cycle reversible?

7.14 A new thermodynamic temperature scale is proposed where the temperature on the Kelvin scale *T* is related to the temperature *X* on the new scale by

$$T = a \ln X + b$$

The temperatures on the new *X* scale have the same values as those of the Kelvin scale at two points: the ice point and the boiling point of water.

a. Find the value of *X* that corresponds to zero on the Kelvin scale.
b. Plot a graph of *X* vs *T*.

7.15 Kelvin first suggested a thermodynamic temperature scale defined by

$$\frac{Q_2}{Q_1} = e^{\mu_2 - \mu_1}$$

a. Plot a graph of μ vs *T*.
b. Derive an expression for the Carnot efficiency in terms of the first Kelvin scale.

EIGHT

Entropy

The second law of thermodynamics and the concepts of reversibility and irreversibility indicate that certain processes are possible in one direction but not in the reverse. For example, a cyclic machine that consumes work from the environment and delivers heat to a single reservoir can be built. On the other hand a machine cannot be built to do the opposite, namely, to receive heat from a single reservoir while producing positive work. The directionality in nature is obvious, yet we have no quantitative measure by which this can be evaluated.

In this chapter we show that a certain inequality, i.e. the Clausius inequality, must be true for any cycle. This inequality leads to the definition of a new property, called entropy, that can be quantitatively related to the measure of irreversibility.

8.1 Clausius inequality

The second law of thermodynamics states, in essence, that processes can proceed in certain directions while in other directions they cannot. For example, any device operating in a cyclic process, that interacts with a single heat reservoir, cannot deliver net work to its environment. It can, however, receive net work from the environment while rejecting heat into a single reservoir. This concept can also be expressed in terms of an inequality, known as the Clausius inequality, which states:

For any closed system undergoing a cyclic process, the integral of $\delta Q/T$ can never be positive:

$$\oint\left(\frac{\delta Q}{T}\right) \le 0 \tag{8.1}$$

The proof of Eq. (8.1) relies on the fact that the work of a system that goes through a cycle while interacting with a single heat reservoir is never positive, i.e.

$$\oint \delta W = \left[\oint \delta Q\right] \le 0 \text{ (single reservoir)} \tag{8.2}$$

Consider now system A in Fig. 8.1 that undergoes a cyclic process. The system may have heat interactions at various temperatures as well as work interactions. Let us now carry out all the heat interactions of system A through a Carnot engine and a single reservoir at T_R. Clearly, if the reversible engine accepts heat δQ_R from a reservoir at T_R and rejects δQ to system A at T, it follows from the efficiency of a reversible engine that

$$\frac{\delta Q_R}{\delta Q} = \frac{T_R}{T} \tag{8.3}$$

The last expression is correct for any temperature of the system and for any direction of heat flow, into or out of system A, since the engine between system A and the reservoir is reversible.

Now consider the combined system, consisting of A and the Carnot engine, enclosed by a control surface, shown in Fig. 8.1.

The work of a complete cycle of the combined system, which is equal to the heat in the cycle, is

$$\oint (\delta W + \delta W_{rev}) = \oint \delta Q_R \tag{8.4}$$

The combined system, contrary to the Carnot engine, interacts with a single reservoir. Thus the work of a cycle of the combined system cannot be positive, as this would constitute a PMM2. It can, however, be negative or zero:

$$\oint (\delta W + \delta W_{rev}) = \oint \delta Q_R \le 0 \tag{8.5}$$

Substituting δQ_R from Eq. (8.3) we obtain

$$T_R \oint \left(\frac{\delta Q}{T} \right) \le 0 \tag{8.6}$$

Since T_R is always positive, it follows that

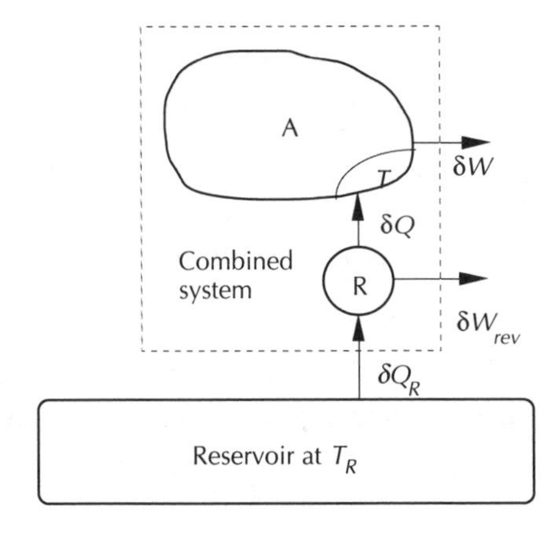

Figure 8.1

$$\oint\left(\frac{\delta Q}{T}\right) \leq 0 \tag{8.1}$$

This is the Clausius inequality which applies to all cyclic processes, whether reversible or irreversible. For irreversible processes the integral is less than zero:

$$\oint\left(\frac{\delta Q}{T}\right)_{irrev} < 0 \tag{8.7}$$

For reversible cycles the integral must be zero:

$$\oint\left(\frac{\delta Q}{T}\right)_{rev} = 0 \tag{8.8}$$

8.2 Entropy

Equation (8.8) indicates that for any reversible process the cyclic integral of $(\delta Q/T)_{rev}$ vanishes. Hence, the integrand must describe the change of a property, as defined in Chapter 2.

It can be shown that when different reversible processes connect state 1 to state 2, the integral of $\delta Q/T$ has the same value.

Consider two states, 1 and 2, of a system connected by two reversible processes A and B, as shown in Fig. 8.2. Since process B is reversible there exists a process RevB which goes from 2 to 1. Processes A and RevB constitute a cycle, for which Eq. (8.8) yields

$$\left(\int_1^2\left(\frac{\delta Q}{T}\right)_{rev}\right)_A + \left(\int_2^1\left(\frac{\delta Q}{T}\right)_{rev}\right)_{RevB} = 0 \tag{8.9}$$

But the effects of RevB are exactly opposite to those of B; thus

$$\left(\int_1^2\left(\frac{\delta Q}{T}\right)_{rev}\right)_A = \left(\int_1^2\left(\frac{\delta Q}{T}\right)_{rev}\right)_B \tag{8.10}$$

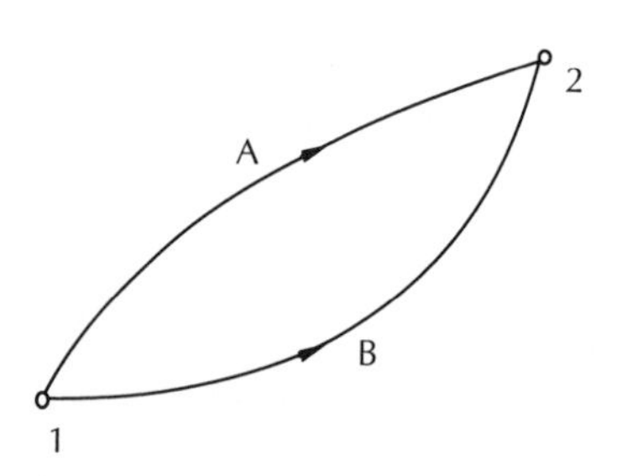

Figure 8.2

Equation (8.10) indicates that the integral of $(\delta Q/T)_{rev}$ between two points does not depend on the path. Therefore, it defines a property. This property is called *entropy* and is denoted by S,

$$dS = \left(\frac{\delta Q}{T}\right)_{rev} \tag{8.11}$$

The change in entropy between two states is given by

$$\Delta S = S_2 - S_1 = \int_1^2\left(\frac{\delta Q}{T}\right)_{rev} \tag{8.12}$$

Only the change of entropy between states can be defined. Thus, entropy is a derived property. Values of entropy may be given relative to an arbitrarily selected reference state. In the steam tables, for example, the state of the saturated liquid at the triple point is used as a reference point at which the specific entropy as well as the specific internal energy are set to zero.

Entropy is an extensive property. We define entropy per unit mass as the specific entropy and denote it by s. As in the case of energy and enthalpy, the entropy of a simple substance in the two-phase region is given by

$$s = (1-x)s_f + xs_g = s_f + xs_{fg} \tag{8.13}$$

8.3 Entropy change in an irreversible process

In an irreversible process, the change in entropy between two states, ΔS, cannot be calculated by integrating $\delta Q/T$ of the process. In fact we now show that for an irreversible process

$$\Delta S > \int_1^2 \left(\frac{\delta Q}{T}\right) \tag{8.14}$$

Let two processes, R and X, connect states 1 and 2, Fig. 8.3. Process R is reversible, while process X can either be reversible or not. The change of entropy between states 1 and 2 can be calculated from process R using Eq. (8.12)

$$\Delta S = S_2 - S_1 = \int_1^2 \left(\frac{\delta Q}{T}\right)_{rev} \tag{8.12}$$

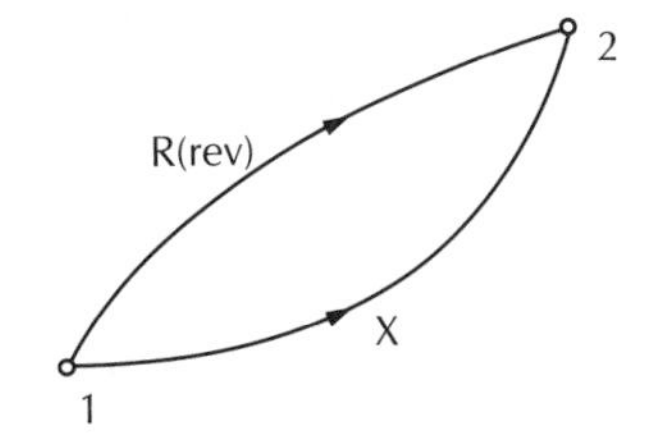

Figure 8.3

Now consider a cycle comprised of processes X and RevR (i.e. the reverse of process R). Applying the Clausius inequality to this cycle we obtain

$$\left(\int_1^2 \left(\frac{\delta Q}{T}\right)\right)_X + \left(\int_2^1 \left(\frac{\delta Q}{T}\right)_{rev}\right)_{RevR} \le 0 \tag{8.15}$$

Since both processes R and RevR are reversible

$$\left(\int_1^2 \left(\frac{\delta Q}{T}\right)_{rev}\right)_R + \left(\int_2^1 \left(\frac{\delta Q}{T}\right)_{rev}\right)_{RevR} = 0 \tag{8.16}$$

Combining Eqs (8.15) and (8.16) leads to

$$\left(\int_1^2 \left(\frac{\delta Q}{T}\right)_{rev}\right)_R \ge \left(\int_1^2 \left(\frac{\delta Q}{T}\right)\right)_X \tag{8.17}$$

and substituting Eq. (8.12) into Eq. (8.17) we obtain the relationship, which holds for any process between states 1 and 2,

$$S_2 - S_1 \geq \int_1^2 \left(\frac{\delta Q}{T} \right) \tag{8.18}$$

For an infinitesimal process Eq. (8.18) reads

$$dS \geq \frac{\delta Q}{T} \tag{8.19}$$

or, equivalently,

$$\delta Q \leq TdS \tag{8.20}$$

where the equality holds for reversible processes, while the inequality holds for irreversible processes.

It is important to keep in mind that entropy is a property, and thus a change in entropy between two end states does not depend on whether the process is reversible or not. If the process is reversible there is a direct connection between the change of entropy and $\delta Q/T$, while if the process is irreversible there is not.

8.4 Principle of increase of entropy

For an adiabatic process $\delta Q = 0$; thus Eqs (8.11) and (8.12) yield for this case

$$dS_{adiabatic} \geq 0 \qquad (S_2 - S_1)_{adiabatic} \geq 0 \tag{8.21}$$

Once again the equalities hold for a reversible adiabatic process while the inequalities apply to an irreversible adiabatic process.

Similar conclusions can be drawn for an isolated system, i.e. a system that has no interactions (heat or work) with its environment. Thus

$$dS_{isolated} > 0 \qquad (S_2 - S_1)_{isolated} > 0 \tag{8.22}$$

These equations indicate that no process occurring in an isolated system can result in a decrease of entropy. If the process is reversible the entropy does not change, and if the process is irreversible the entropy increases.

The fact that the entropy of an isolated system can never decrease is known as the principle of increase of entropy. The question may be raised; is there a limit to the increase of entropy in an isolated system? Obviously, when a system reaches a state of stable equilibrium no further changes can take place, and no further increase of entropy is possible. The entropy of a stable equilibrium state, therefore, attains a maximum value*.

* The principles of conservation of energy and increase of entropy were used by Clausius to state the first and second laws of thermodynamics, respectively, as

The energy of the world stays constant.

The entropy of the world tends to a maximum.

Such statements lead to the conclusion that the world is headed toward a thermal death, since when the entropy of the world reaches a maximum no further processes can take place. The concept of thermal death had philosophical and theological implications that resulted in long and heated discussions among philosophers and scientists. In reality, such statements may be over-ambitious. It is not possible to describe the world as a finite, closed, and isolated system. We certainly cannot define its boundaries and establish whether there are interactions at these boundaries.

Processes can take place in an isolated system only if they bring the system closer to equilibrium. When equilibrium is reached, no further processes can occur without interactions with the environment. Any process that brings an isolated system to equilibrium is an irreversible process, which results in an increase of the system's entropy.

8.5 Calculating entropy change in an irreversible process

The change in entropy between two given states is independent of the process. This fact may be used to find the entropy change in an irreversible process. The entropy change for an irreversible process between two states is found according to the following procedure:

1. A reversible process connecting these two states is found.
2. The entropy change, ΔS, is calculated for the reversible process using Eq. (8.12).
3. The entropy change, ΔS, found above applies also to the irreversible process.

EXAMPLE 8.1

The change in specific enthalpy during the melting of ice at 0 °C and 1.01 bars is $\Delta h = 333.39$ kJ/kg.

Given a system consisting of ice and water, both at 0 °C and 1.01 bars in thermal contact with an environment at 20 °C, find for the process of melting 2 kg of ice at 0 °C and 1.01 bars the change of entropy of:

a. The ice.
b. The environment.
c. The universe (i.e. ice + environment).

SOLUTION

This process is irreversible, since heat is transferred across a finite temperature difference between the environment and the ice.

a. We first consider the ice. This is an internally reversible process, where the irreversibility due to the temperature difference may be viewed as being in the environment. We now replace the environment with one at 0 °C. The system still goes through a process between the two original states. This time, however, the process is reversible. For this isobaric (and isothermal) process:

$$Q_{12} = \Delta H = m\Delta h = 2 \times 333.39 = 666.78 \text{ kJ}$$

and the entropy change of the ice is

$$\Delta S = \int_1^2 (\delta Q/T)_{rev} = \frac{1}{T}\int_1^2 \delta Q = \frac{Q_{12}}{T} = \frac{m\Delta h}{T}$$

$$\Delta S = \frac{2 \times 333.39}{273.15} = 2.4411 \text{ kJ/K}$$

b. To find the entropy change of the environment we replace the water- ice system at 0 °C with a reservoir at 20 °C to which the environment loses 666.78 kJ. The environment now undergoes a reversible isothermal process for which

$$\Delta S_{envir} = \left(\frac{Q}{T}\right)_{rev} = \frac{-666.78}{273.15+20} = -2.2745 \text{ kJ/K}$$

c. The entropy change of the universe is

$$\Delta S_{total} = \Delta S_{sys} + \Delta S_{envir} = 2.4411 - 2.2745 = 0.1666 \text{ kJ/K} > 0$$

As seen, for the isolated assembly comprised of the system and its environment, which undergoes an irreversible process, $\Delta S > 0$, as it should be.

An interesting question may be asked: given the system of Example 8.1 at 0 °C and the environment at 20 °C, could the ice melting process have been done reversibly? This question is addressed in the following example.

EXAMPLE 8.2

For the system and environment of Example 8.l suggest a reversible process for melting 2 kg of ice. Calculate for this process ΔS_{sys}, ΔS_{envir}, and ΔS_{total}.

SOLUTION

Given an environment at 20 °C and a reservoir containing ice and water at 0 °C, we put a Carnot engine between them, as shown in Fig. 8.4, and use the temperature difference between the system and the environment to produce work.

The amount of heat required to melt the ice is still $Q_c = 666.78$ kJ and

$$\Delta S_{sys} = \left(\frac{Q}{T}\right)_{rev} = \left(\frac{666.78}{273.15}\right) = 2.4411 \text{ kJ/K}$$

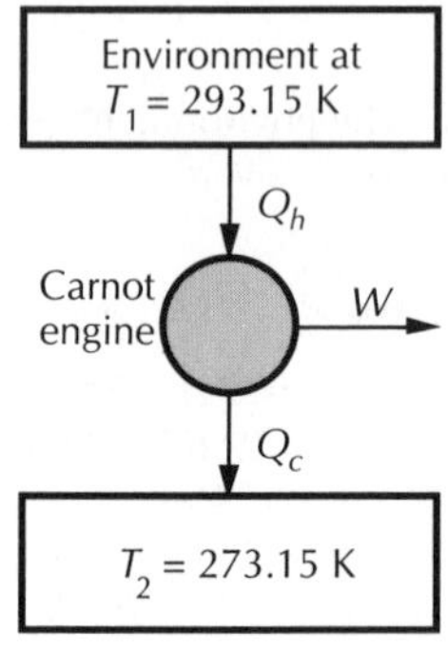

Figure 8.4

The environment, however, now loses more heat, part of which is used to produce work. We may now calculate Q_h from Eq. (7.21):

Thus

$$Q_h = Q_c\left(\frac{T_h}{T_c}\right) = \frac{666.78 \times 293.15}{273.15} = 715.60 \text{ kJ}$$

and the entropy change is now

$$\Delta S_{envir} = \frac{-715.60}{293.15} = -2.4411 \text{ kJ/K}$$

The total change in entropy is

$$\Delta S_{tot} = 2.4411 - 2.4411 = 0$$

as it should be for a reversible process.

8.6 Entropy equations

The calculation of entropy change on the basis of its definition may at times be difficult. It requires the performance of a reversible process and the measurement of the heat interaction along that same process, a task that is not always easy to perform.

It would be beneficial to relate the property of entropy to other properties of the system, since such a relation could facilitate easier calculation of entropy.

We note that for a simple system undergoing a reversible process

$$\delta Q_{rev} = TdS \tag{8.23}$$

and

$$\delta W_{rev} = pdV \tag{8.24}$$

Thus the first law for a reversible process may be written as

$$dU = TdS - pdV \tag{8.25}$$

Although Eq. (8.25) was derived for reversible processes only, it can also be applied to irreversible processes. Considering this expression, we note that it is a relationship between properties. Therefore, for a simple system between neighboring equilibrium states it depends on the end states only, and does not depend on the process, whether reversible or not. Hence, Eq. (8.25) applies to any process, reversible or irreversible!

In terms of specific properties, Eq. (8.25) is written as

$$du = Tds - pdv \tag{8.26}$$

The change of enthalpy is given by

$$dH = dU + pdV + Vdp \tag{8.27}$$

Substituting dU from Eq. (8.25) one obtains

$$dH = TdS + Vdp \tag{8.28}$$

and

$$dh = Tds + vdp \tag{8.29}$$

The differential change of specific entropy can be found from Eq. (8.26)

$$ds = \frac{1}{T}du + \frac{p}{T}dv \tag{8.30}$$

or from Eq. (8.29)

$$ds = \frac{1}{T}dh - \frac{v}{T}dp \tag{8.31}$$

8.7 Using entropy data from tables

The change of specific entropy between two given states can be found by integrating Eq. (8.30) or Eq. (8.31) along any path connecting these two states. Indeed, obtaining entropy data needed for property tables and diagrams is based on Eqs (8.30) and (8.31), rather than on the definition of entropy, Eq. (8.12). The steam tables list entropy data calculated in this fashion. These can be used directly in thermodynamic calculations, as demonstrated in the following examples.

EXAMPLE 8.3

A system consisting of 18 kg of steam expands from 9 MPa and 325 °C to 3 MPa and 250 °C.

a. Find the change in entropy of the steam.
b. Could the process be adiabatic?

SOLUTION

a. The change of entropy is $\Delta S = m(s_2 - s_1)$.
   From the table of superheated steam we find that the specific entropies for the initial and final states are 5.8712 kJ/kg K and 6.2872 kJ/kg K, respectively. Hence,

$$\Delta S = 18 \times (6.2872 - 5.8712) = 7.488 \text{ kJ/K}$$

b. Yes, the process could be adiabatic since $\Delta S > 0$.

EXAMPLE 8.4

A system consisting of 18 kg of steam expands from 9.0 MPa and 325 °C to 3.0 MPa and $x = 0.9$.

a. Find the change in entropy of the steam.
b. Could the process be adiabatic?

SOLUTION

a. We arrange the properties of the initial and final states in a table:

State	p	T	x	s
1	9.0	325	–	5.8712
2	3.0		0.90	5.8328

The change of entropy of the steam is

$$s_2 - s_1 = 5.8328 - 5.8712 = -0.03842 \text{ kJ/kg}$$

b. An adiabatic process must comply with $s_2 \geq s_1$. In this case $s_2 \leq s_1$; thus the process could not be adiabatic. Heat *must* be removed during the process.

EXAMPLE 8.5

An insulated cylinder contains, under a stopped weighted piston, 0.1 kg of steam at 10 bars and 260 °C. The stop is released and the piston bounces up until equilibrium is reached at a pressure of 3 bars.

a. Find the final temperature.
b. Is the process reversible?

SOLUTION

a. Using the first law for this adiabatic process

$$\Delta U = -W$$

or

$$U_2 - U_1 = -p_2(V_2 - V_1)$$

Substituting $U = H - pV$ leads to

$$H_2 = H_1 + (p_2 - p_1)V_1$$

and finally

$$h_2 = h_1 + (p_2 - p_1)v_1 = 2964.3 + (3 - 10)10^5 \times 0.2378 \times 10^{-3} = 2797.8 \text{ kJ/kg}$$

For p_2 = 3 bars and h_2 = 2797.8 kJ/kg we have T_2 = 167.5 °C.

We now summarize the data in the following table.

State	p	T	v	h	s
1	<u>10.0</u>	<u>260.0</u>	0.2378	2964.3	6.9641
2	<u>3.0</u>	167.5		<u>2797.8</u>	7.1619

b. $\Delta S = m(s_2 - s_1) = 0.1 \times (7.1619 - 6.9641) = 0.01978$ kJ/K

The process is irreversible since it is adiabatic and $\Delta S > 0$.

8.8 Entropy change in an ideal gas

Equations (8.30) and (8.31) are now used to calculate the entropy change between two states of an ideal gas. We substitute the ideal gas relationships

$$pv = RT \tag{8.32}$$

$$du = c_v dT \tag{8.33}$$

$$dh = c_p dT \tag{8.34}$$

into Eqs (8.30) and (8.31), respectively, and obtain

$$ds = c_v \frac{dT}{T} + R\frac{dv}{v} \tag{8.35}$$

$$ds = c_p \frac{dT}{T} - R\frac{dp}{p} \tag{8.36}$$

The entropy change of an ideal gas can also be expressed in terms of changes of volume and pressure, by eliminating T from Eq. (8.36) with the help of Eq. (8.32). This results in

$$ds = c_p \frac{dv}{v} + c_v \frac{dp}{p} \tag{8.37}$$

Equations (8.35)–(8.37) can be integrated if c_v and $c_p (= c_v + R)$ are known as functions of temperature. For the special case of an ideal gas with constant specific heat Eqs (8.35)–(8.37) can be integrated directly resulting in

$$s_2 - s_1 = c_v \ln\left(\frac{T_2}{T_1}\right) + R\ln\left(\frac{v_2}{v_1}\right) \tag{8.38}$$

$$s_2 - s_1 = c_p \ln\left(\frac{T_2}{T_1}\right) - R\ln\left(\frac{p_2}{p_1}\right) \tag{8.39}$$

$$s_2 - s_1 = c_v \ln\left(\frac{p_2}{p_1}\right) + c_p\ln\left(\frac{v_2}{v_1}\right) \tag{8.40}$$

For an adiabatic process between two states Eq. (8.21) leads to

$$s_2 - s_1 \geq 0$$

Substitution of $s_2 - s_1$ from Eq. (8.38) yields

$$c_v \ln\left(\frac{T_2}{T_1}\right) + R\ln\left(\frac{v_2}{v_1}\right) \geq 0 \tag{8.41}$$

or

$$c_v \left[\ln\left(\frac{T_2}{T_1}\right) + (k-1)\ln\left(\frac{v_2}{v_1}\right) \right] \geq 0$$

and

$$\ln \frac{T_2 v_2^{k-1}}{T_1 v_1^{k-1}} \geq 0$$

and finally

$$T_2 v_2^{k-1} \geq T_1 v_1^{k-1} \tag{8.42}$$

When the process is adiabatic and reversible, the equality holds, namely

$$Tv^{k-1} = \text{const.} \tag{8.43}$$

Equation (8.43) holds for an adiabatic constant-entropy (isentropic) process. This equation has been already derived as Eq. (5.35) for an adiabatic quasistatic process before the concepts of entropy and reversibility were introduced. Similarly, for any adiabatic process

$$\frac{p_2{}^{(k-1)/k}}{T_2} \leq \frac{p_1{}^{(k-1)/k}}{T_1} \tag{8.44}$$

and

$$p_2 v_2^k \geq p_1 v_1^k \tag{8.45}$$

Once again the equality holds for the isentropic process while the inequality holds for the irreversible process.

EXAMPLE 8.6

Nitrogen, at 5 bars and 80 °C, is contained on one side of a partition and occupies one-third of the volume of a 1.2 m³ container, Fig. 8.5. The other side is evacuated. The partition is ruptured and a new equilibrium state is reached. Find:

a. The final pressure and temperature.
b. The change of entropy within the container.

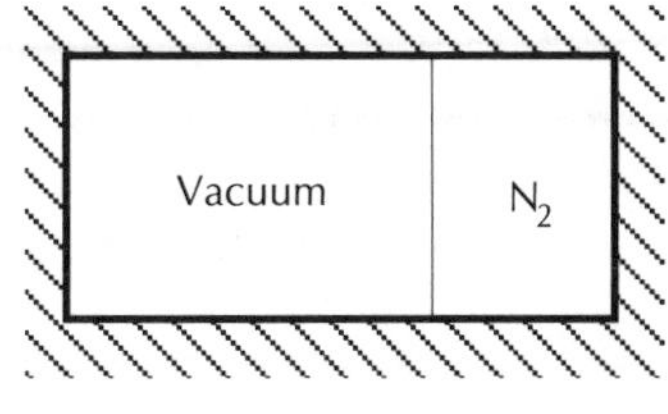

Figure 8.5

SOLUTION

a. For this isolated system:

$$Q = W = 0$$

and from the first law $\Delta U = 0$; hence

$$T_2 = T_1$$

and

$$p_2 = \frac{p_1 V_1}{V_2} = 5 \times \frac{0.4}{1.2} = 1.667 \text{ bars}$$

b. The change in specific entropy is calculated from Eq. (8.38) with $T_2 = T_1$:

$$\Delta s = R \ln \frac{V_2}{V_1} = \left(\frac{8.3143}{28}\right) \ln 3 = 0.3262 \text{ kJ/kg K}$$

and

$$\Delta S = m\Delta s = \frac{p_1 V_1}{RT_1} \Delta s = \frac{500 \times 0.4 \times 0.3262}{\left(\frac{8.3143}{28}\right) \times 353.15} = 0.6221 \text{ kJ/K}$$

EXAMPLE 8.7

A piston–cylinder assembly contains air at 400 K and 1 bar. The pressure is increased

isothermally to 1.6 bars. The environment is at 1 bar and 300 K. Determine:
a. The work and heat of the process.
b. The change of entropy of the system.
c. The change of entropy of the environment.

SOLUTION

a. For an isothermal process $\Delta u = 0$:

$$-q = w = RT\ln\left(\frac{p_2}{p_1}\right) = \left(\frac{8.3143}{29}\right) \times 400 \times \ln 1.6 = 53.9 \text{ kJ/kg}$$

b. From Eq. (8.39):

$$\Delta s = -R\ln\left(\frac{p_2}{p_1}\right) = -\left(\frac{8.3143}{29}\right)\ln 1.6 = -0.1348 \text{ kJ/kg K}$$

c. $\Delta S_{envir} = -\dfrac{q}{T_{envir}} = \dfrac{53.9}{300} = 0.1797$ kJ/K

Note that ΔS_{envir} is calculated per kilogram of system.

8.9 Entropy diagrams

It follows from Eq. (8.23) that for a reversible process

$$Q_{rev} = \int_1^2 TdS$$

Therefore, if one constructs a T–s diagram for a simple system, then the area under the curve for a reversible process is equal to the heat interaction of 1 kg of material, Fig. 8.6a. This is analogous to the work interaction of a reversible process described by the area under the curve of a p–v diagram.

When the process is irreversible, the areas under the curves in the respective diagrams in Fig. 8.6b are larger than the actual heat or work interactions. Still, even for these processes a T–s diagram is of importance, as it provides the upper bound on the heat interaction for a given path. Therefore, thermodynamic data are presented on T–s diagrams in parallel to p–v diagrams.

The area enclosed by a cycle on a p–v diagram is equal to the cyclic integral $\oint pdv$.

Similarly, the area enclosed by a cycle on a T–s diagram is equal to $\oint Tds$. For a given cycle the two areas must be equal, since

$$\oint dU = \oint TdS - \oint pdV = 0 \tag{8.46}$$

We recall that in a cycle the net work is equal to the net heat

$$\oint \delta Q = \oint \delta W \tag{7.1}$$

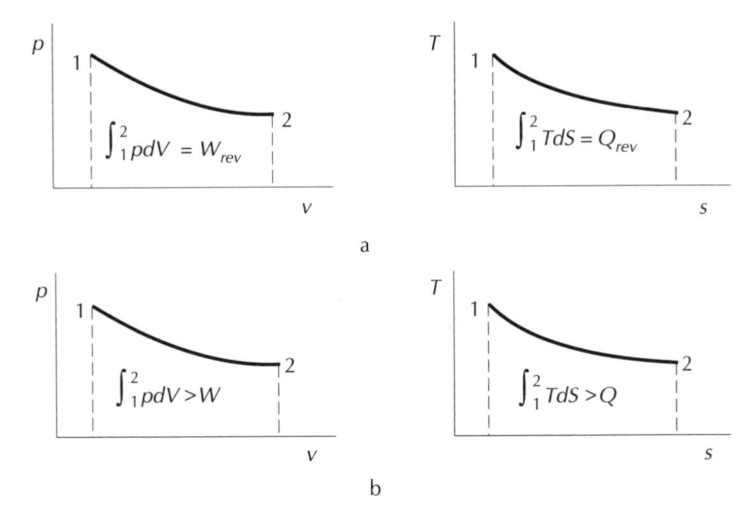

Figure 8.6 **Reversible (a) and irreversible (b) processes on *p–v* and *T–s* diagrams.**

However,

$$\oint \delta Q \le \oint TdS \tag{8.47}$$

and

$$\oint \delta W \le \oint pdV \tag{8.48}$$

It is useful to indicate on the *T–s* diagram certain characteristic lines, such as constant-pressure and constant-volume lines. The shape of the lines depends, of course, on the particular substance which the diagram represents. It is quite easy to construct these lines for an ideal gas by using the relationships between T and s as given by Eqs (8.38) and (8.39). Figure 8.7 shows schematically *p–v* and *T–s* diagrams for an ideal gas where the various characteristic curves are displayed.

The constant-pressure curve is constructed from Eq. (8.39), which after rearrangement yields

$$s = c_p \ln T + \left[s_0 - c_p \ln T_0 - R \ln\left(\frac{p}{p_0}\right)\right] \tag{8.49}$$

or

$$T = Ap^{\frac{k-1}{k}} \exp\left(\frac{s}{c_p}\right) \tag{8.50}$$

Thus the constant-pressure curve on a *T–s* diagram for an ideal gas is an exponential. Two curves, corresponding to two pressures, p_1 and p_2, are shifted horizontally relative to each other, where the higher pressure curve is located more to the left. The slope of the

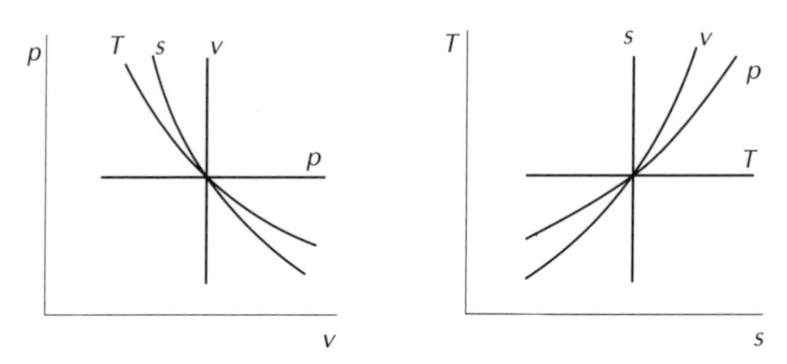

Figure 8.7 **p–v and T–s diagrams for an ideal gas.**

constant-pressure curve, at any point, is equal to

$$\left(\frac{\partial T}{\partial s}\right)_p = \frac{T}{c_p} \tag{8.51}$$

In a similar way, it can be shown from Eq. (8.38) that the equation for a constant-volume curve is given by

$$T = Av^{(1-k)} \exp\left(\frac{s}{c_v}\right) \qquad (v = \text{const.}) \tag{8.52}$$

and the slope is

$$\left(\frac{\partial T}{\partial s}\right)_v = \frac{T}{c_v} \tag{8.53}$$

Figure 8.8 shows schematically a T–s diagram of a real substance. The bell-shaped curve represents the saturation region. The top of the bell is the critical point. The left hand side corresponds to the saturated liquid while the right hand side corresponds to the

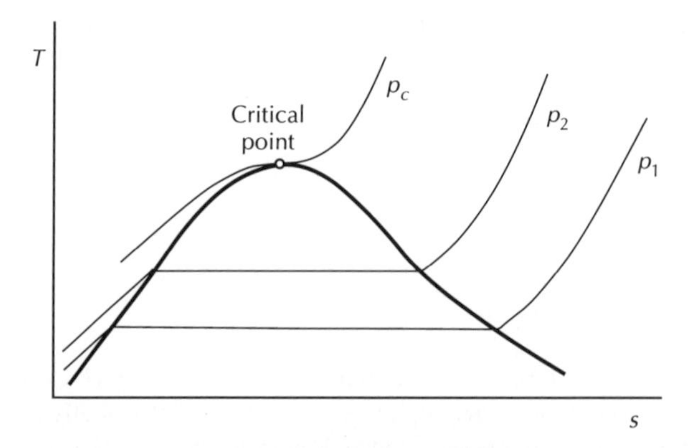

Figure 8.8 **A T–s diagram for a simple system.**

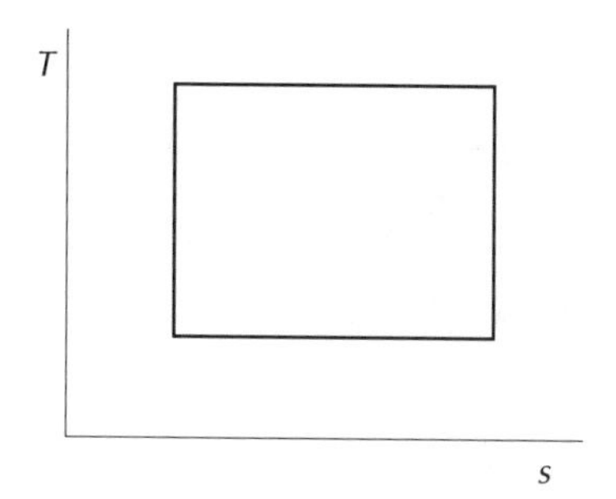

Figure 8.9 **A *T–s* diagram for a Carnot cycle.**

saturated vapor. Inside the bell, constant-pressure lines coincide with the constant-temperature lines, while outside the bell in the superheated region, the shape of a constant-pressure line approaches an exponential curve, as the vapor approaches ideal gas behavior.

A Carnot cycle is comprised of two isothermal processes connected by two reversible adiabatic (isentropic) processes. It is represented on a *T–s* diagram by a rectangle, Fig. 8.9.

Another useful diagram is the *h–s* diagram, also known as the Mollier diagram. On this diagram the work of an adiabatic steady state flow process is given by the vertical distance between the end points of the process, since $w_x = -\Delta h$.

The *h–s* diagram for an ideal gas has the same shape as the *T–s* diagram, because here the enthalpy is proportional to the temperature, $h = c_p T + \text{const.}$

A typical *h–s* diagram for a real substance is shown schematically in Fig. 8.10. Here the saturation curve is also bell shaped. However, it is skewed as compared to that of the

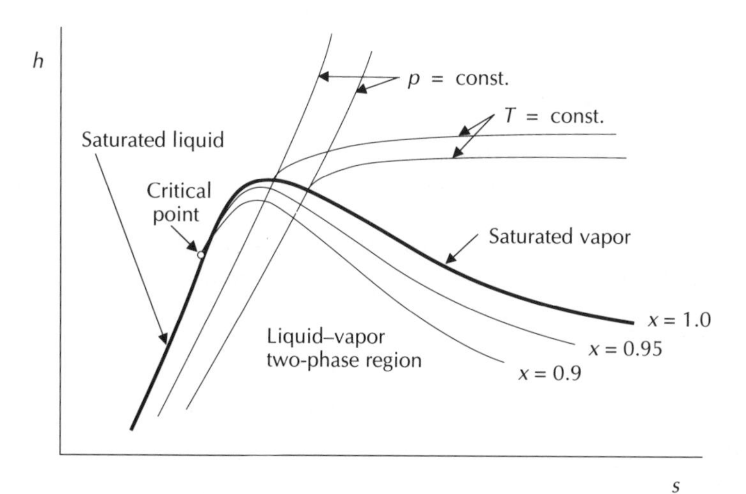

Figure 8.10 **An *h–s* diagram for a simple system.**

T–s diagram, and the critical point is not located at the highest point of the bell. The constant-pressure lines in the two-phase region are also constant-temperature lines. These are straight and their slopes are given by their temperature, since $(\partial h/\partial s)_p = T$. In the superheated region, for large increases in specific volume, the constant-pressure lines approach exponential curves, and the constant-temperature lines tend asymptotically to the horizontal, as in the case of the T–s diagram for an ideal gas.

8.10 Second-law analysis of control volumes

As a consequence of the second law of thermodynamics the relation between heat interactions and the change of entropy in a closed system was shown to be

$$S_2 - S_1 \geq \int_1^2 \left(\frac{\delta Q}{T}\right) \tag{8.18}$$

To derive an equivalent expression for a control volume we make use of Eq. (6.8) which holds for any extensive property B:

$$\Delta B_{cv} = \Delta B + \sum_{i=1}^{k} b_i m_i \tag{6.8}$$

Let $B = S$ and $b = s$ then

$$\Delta S_{cv} = \Delta S + \sum_{i=1}^{k} s_i m_i$$

Substituting ΔS from Eq. (8.18) we obtain

$$\Delta S_{cv} \geq \int_1^2 \left(\frac{\delta Q}{T}\right) + \sum_{i=1}^{k} s_i m_i \tag{8.54}$$

Equation (8.54) may be rewritten in terms of rates of change as

$$\left(\frac{dS}{dt}\right)_{cv} \geq \frac{\dot{Q}}{T} + \sum_{i=1}^{k} s_i \dot{m}_i \tag{8.55}$$

In Eqs (8.54) and (8.55) the left hand side is evaluated within the control volume, while the terms on the right hand side are evaluated at the boundary of the control volume.

For the case of a steady state process there are no changes of properties within the control volume; hence the left hand side of Eq. (8.55) vanishes resulting in

$$-\sum_{i=1}^{k} s_i \dot{m}_i \geq \frac{\dot{Q}}{T} \tag{8.56}$$

For an adiabatic control volume, $Q = 0$ and Eq. (8.56) simplifies to

$$-\sum_{i=1}^{k} s_i \dot{m}_i \geq 0 \tag{8.57}$$

or

$$\sum_{i=1}^{k}\left(s_i\dot{m}_i\right)_{out} \geq \sum_{i=1}^{k}\left(s_i\dot{m}_i\right)_{in} \tag{8.58}$$

Thus in a steady state adiabatic process the total entropy of the streams leaving the control volume is never less than the total entropy of the incoming streams.

Many engineering applications involve control volumes that operate at steady state, and have one inlet and one outlet. For such cases Eq. (8.56) yields

$$\dot{m}\left(s_{out} - s_{in}\right) \geq \frac{\dot{Q}}{T} \tag{8.59}$$

For an adiabatic process Eq. (8.59) simplifies to

$$s_{out} - s_{in} \geq 0 \tag{8.60}$$

Table 8.1 summarizes the governing equations for open and closed systems.

Table 8.1 **Summary of the governing equations.**

Control volume	System	Conservation law
$\left(\frac{dm}{dt}\right)_{cv} = \sum_{i=1}^{k}\dot{m}_i$	$dm = 0$	Conservation of mass
$\left(\frac{dE}{dt}\right)_{cv} = \dot{Q} - \dot{W}_x + \sum_{i=1}^{k} h_i^0\dot{m}_i$	$dE = \delta Q - \delta W$	First law of thermodynamics (energy equation)
$\left(\frac{dS}{dt}\right)_{cv} \geq \frac{\dot{Q}}{T} + \sum_{i=1}^{k} s_i\dot{m}_i$	$dS \geq \frac{\delta Q}{T}$	Second law of thermodynamics (entropy equation)
Inside On the boundary		

PROBLEMS

8.1 Indicate whether the following statements are true, false, or sometimes true.
For a reversible process:

a. $Q = 0$.
b. Work may be calculated using the equation of state.
c. The entropy change of the system is zero.
d. The total entropy change for the system and the surroundings is zero.

For a reversible adiabatic process:

e. $W = 0$.
f. $Q = 0$.
g. The entropy change of the system is always zero.
h. The total entropy change for the system and the surroundings is zero.

For a simple compressible system the work is

i. $W = \int c_p \, dV$ for a reversible process.

j. $\delta W \leq TdS - dU$.

k. $W = 0$ for a constant-volume process.

l. Independent of path.

The heat absorbed by a system in a reversible constant-pressure process is

m. $Q = \int c_p \, dT$.

n. $Q = \int (c_p/T) dT$.

o. $Q = \Delta U + W$.

p. $Q = \int TdS$.

q. $Q = \int dS$.

8.2 Indicate whether the following statements are true, false, or sometimes true. For a reversible process:

a. $\Delta S = 0$.

b. $\Delta S = \int (\delta Q/T)$.

c. $\Delta S = -\Delta S_{envir}$.

d. $\Delta S > 0$.

For a reversible isothermal process:

e. $Q = T\Delta S$.

f. $Q = 0$.

g. $\Delta U = 0$.

8.3 Indicate whether the following statements are true, false, or sometimes true. In a simple compressible system:

a. $\delta W = TdS - dU$.

b. $\delta W > pdV$.

c. The work in a reversible adiabatic process does not depend on the path.

d. The work in an irreversible adiabatic process does not depend on the path.

e. In an isothermal process, $\delta Q = dU + \delta W$.

f. In an isothermal process, $\delta Q = TdS$.

g. In an isothermal process, $\delta Q > TdS$.

h. In an isothermal process, $Q = W$.

i. In an isothermal process, $\delta W = TdS$.

j. In a process from state 1 to state 2, $\Delta S_{rev} < \Delta S_{irrev}$.

8.4 Indicate whether the following statements are true, false, or sometimes true. For a reversible process in a closed system:

a. The entropy change of the environment is negative.

b. The entropy change of the system is negative.

c. The entropy change of the environment and the system is negative.

d. The temperature does not change.

e. $\oint pdv = \oint Tds$.

f. $\oint pdV = \oint TdS$.

g. $\oint \delta W = \oint TdS$.

h. $\oint \frac{\delta Q}{T} = 0$.

i. $\oint \frac{\delta Q}{T} = 1\,\text{kJ/K}$.

j. $\oint \frac{\delta Q}{T} = -1\,\text{kJ/K}$.

8.5 Determine which of the following cases are feasible:

a. A compressor where the inlet and outlet entropies are equal.
b. A non-ideal compressor where the inlet and outlet entropies are equal.
c. The entropy of steam decreases when it passes through a turbine.
d. A heat exchanger where the specific entropy of the cooling fluid decreases.
e. A heat engine that operates in a cycle and interacts with one reservoir only.
f. Steam passing through a throttling valve undergoes no enthalpy change.
g. Steam passing through a throttling valve undergoes no entropy change.
h. An isothermal process in a system the entropy of which decreases.
i. An adiabatic process in a system the entropy of which decreases.

8.6 Consider a system consisting of 10 kg of saturated steam at 200 °C.

a. If the steam can reject heat to the surroundings at 25 °C, suggest a way of condensing the steam to saturated water at 200 °C, *reversibly*.
b. What is the entropy change of the steam in the reversible process in part a?
c. What is the amount of heat absorbed by the surroundings (the cold reservoir) in the reversible process?
d. What is the entropy change of the surroundings in the reversible process?
e. If the steam were condensed by a direct heat interaction with the surroundings, i.e. by an irreversible process, what would be its entropy change?
f. What would be the entropy change of the surroundings for part e?
g. If the steam were condensed by mixing it in an isobaric process with a large amount of water at 25 °C, what would be the entropy change of the universe?

8.7 A refrigeration system removes 100 kJ/min from a cooling station held at a temperature of –5 °C and rejects 125 kJ/min to the surroundings at 30 °C.

a. Calculate the coefficient of performance of the system.
b. Is the process reversible? Support your answer by appropriate calculations.

8.8 Steam at 3 MPa and 160 °C is produced from water at 2.5 MPa and 40 °C in an irreversible process at a rate of 5.6 kg/s. Find the rate of entropy change of the process.

8.9 A reservoir at 20 °C receives 800 kJ of heat from the surroundings at 30 °C.

a. What is the entropy change of the reservoir?
b. Could the process be performed reversibly? If not, why? If so, how?

8.10 Steam at 0.1 MPa and $x = 0.8$ enters a compressor at a rate of 14.3 kg/s. The compressor power input is 2.5 MW and its effectiveness is 0.9.

a. Determine the pressure and temperature at the outlet of the compressor.
b. Calculate the specific entropy change of the steam that passes through the compressor.

8.11 In an adiabatic vessel 20 kg of water at 20 °C and 100 kPa are separated by a partition from 1 kg of saturated steam at 100 °C. The partition is ruptured and the contents of the vessel mix. Find the entropy change in the mixing process.

8.12 In an adiabatic vessel 20 kg of air at 20 °C and 100 kPa are separated by a partition from 1 kg of air at 500 °C and 20 MPa. The partition is ruptured and the contents of the vessel mix. Find the entropy change in the mixing process.

8.13 A heat engine receives 700 kJ of heat from a hot reservoir at T_h = 1000 °C and provides 300 kJ of work while exchanging heat with a cool reservoir at T_c = −100 °C.

a. Is the heat engine reversible?
b. Find the entropy change of everything involved in the process.

8.14 A system goes through a cycle having interactions with three reservoirs. The work of the cycle is 1000 kJ:

Q_1 = 1500 kJ at 580 °C
Q_2 = 875 kJ at 210 °C

a. Find the magnitude of Q_3.
b. What must be the temperature of the third reservoir if the cycle is reversible?
c. What can be the range of temperatures of the third reservoir?

8.15 A 5 kg metal block at 100 °C is brought into thermal contact with a 2 kg metal block at −50 °C. The specific heat capacity of each is the same, equal to 0.45 kJ/kg K.

a. What is the final temperature?
b. What is the total entropy change?

8.16 An adiabatic cylinder covered by a weighted piston contains 0.03 kg of steam at 0.4 MPa and 160 °C. The weight is removed from the piston and the steam expands to 0.13 MPa.

a. Find the final state of the steam.
b. Find the change of entropy of the steam during the process. Is the process reversible? Explain.

8.17 Steam is compressed from 80 °C and 20 kPa to 0.06 MPa.

a. Find the work and heat interactions for a reversible isothermal compression.
b. What are the conditions for the compression to be reversible, and what other systems are required for that purpose? Explain.

8.18 Steam at 2 MPa, 500 °C expands in a well-insulated cylinder to 1 MPa, 440 °C.

a. Find the work of the process.
b. Is the process internally reversible? If so, why? If not, is it possible to perform a reversible process between these states?

8.19 In a refrigeration cycle, saturated water vapor at 5 °C is compressed reversibly and adiabatically to the pressure corresponding to saturated vapor at 26 °C. Find the temperature, enthalpy, and specific volume of the vapor at the end of the compression.

8.20 Three kilograms of liquid A at 15 °C with c_p = 4 kJ/kg K are mixed with 5 kg of liquid B at 120 °C which has a heat capacity of c_p = 2.5 kJ/kg K. Determine:

a. The final equilibrium temperature of the mixture.
b. The change in entropy of the system.

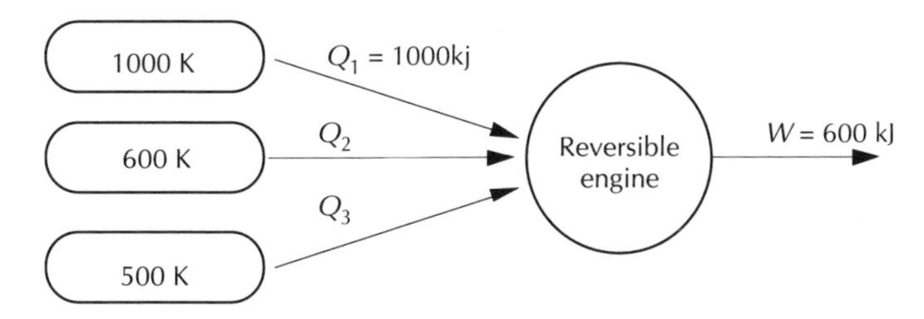

Figure 8.11

8.21 The circle in Fig. 8.11 represents a reversible engine. During some integral number of complete cycles, the engine absorbs 1000 kJ from the reservoir at 1000 K and performs 600 kJ of mechanical work

a. Find the quantities of heat exchanged with the other reservoirs and state whether the reservoirs give up or absorb heat.
b. Find the change in entropy of each reservoir.
c. What is the change in entropy of the universe?

8.22 A simple system at a state A of 140 °C and 0.3 MPa undergoes an isothermal and reversible process to a state B. The work of the system during this process is –300 kJ. Then the system undergoes an adiabatic process from B to A, during which the work is 150 kJ.

a. Find the change of entropy during the process from A to B.
b. Find the change of entropy during the process from B to A.
c. Is process BA reversible?

8.23 A system goes from a state A to a state B reversibly and isothermally at 500 °C having a work interaction of 1000 kJ. The system then goes back from B to A along a different path having a work interaction of 500 kJ and a heat interaction of 1000 kJ. Find the change in entropy of the system in the second process.

8.24 One kmol of an ideal gas with constant heat capacity c_p = 20 kJ/kmol K is compressed adiabatically from 10 kPa and 10 °C to 0.5 MPa. The process is irreversible and requires twice the work than a reversible adiabatic compression from the initial to the final state.
a. How much work is required?
b. What is the entropy change of the gas?

8.25 A reversible engine absorbs 1000 kJ of heat from a reservoir at 500 K and performs 600 kJ of mechanical work.

a. Find the amount of heat exchanged with the other reservoir.
b. Find the change in entropy of each reservoir.
c. What is the change in entropy of the universe?

8.26 An engine comprising a piston–cylinder assembly uses argon (k = 5/3, M = 40) as the working material. The piston has an area of 200 cm^2 and a stroke of 12 cm. The engine turns at 1500 rpm, and the ratio between the maximum and the minimum volume in the cylinder is 9.0. The engine operates on a closed cycle having three internally reversible steps:

1–2 Isobaric expansion at 2.8 MPa, from minimum volume till the volume triples.
2–3 Adiabatic expansion till maximum volume is reached.
3–1 Return to initial state by a polytropic process.

a. Show the cycle on a p–v and on a T–s diagram.
b. Calculate the engine efficiency and the power.

8.27 A system goes from a state A to a state B reversibly and isothermally at a temperature $T = 250$ °C, while having a work interaction of 1000 kJ. The system then goes from B back to A along a different path, having a work interaction of 500 kJ and a heat interaction of 1000 kJ. Find the change in entropy of the system in the second process.

8.28 A system of 2 kg of H_2O undergoes a reversible process that can be described by a straight line in the T–s diagram from an initial state of $T_1 = 95$ °C and $v_1 = 1.25\text{m}^3/\text{kg}$ to a final state of $T_2 = 250$ °C and $p_2 = 0.7$ MPa. Find the heat and work interactions for this process.

8.29 Two identical systems in rigid boundaries have the same properties and the same initial state. The two systems together are surrounded by adiabatic walls, as shown in Fig. 8.12. A refrigerator is interposed between the two systems. Find:

a. The minimum work required to change the temperature of one system to $T_1 (T_1 < T_2)$.
b. The range of temperatures the second system can assume when the first system reaches T_1.
c. The work as a function of T_1 and T_2.
d. The entropy as a function of the work and T_1.

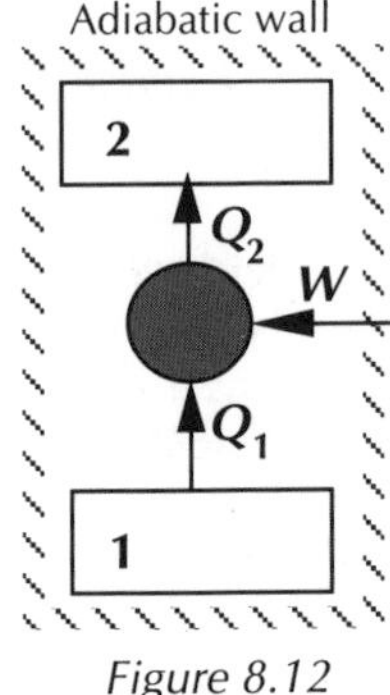

Figure 8.12

8.30 Two insulated masses are brought into thermal contact with each other and allowed to attain mutual equilibrium. Initially the temperature of mass A is greater than the temperature of mass B.

a. Does the entropy of mass A increase or decrease?
b. Does the entropy of mass B increase or decrease?
c. How does the total entropy (A + B) change?

8.31 Two identical systems in rigid boundaries are initially at temperatures T_1 and T_2 respectively. The temperatures are allowed to reach a common value while work may be performed on another system. Assume c_v to be constant and the same for both systems. Find:

a. The work as a function of the final temperature.
b. The entropy as a function of the final temperature.
c. In what range can the final temperature be?
d. What is the maximum work?

8.32 A system of 1 kg of H_2O at an initial condition of $p_1 = 0.15$ MPa and $v_1 = 0.6\text{m}^3/\text{kg}$ undergoes a reversible process that can be described by a straight line on the p–v diagram to a final state of $p_2 = 15$ MPa, $T_2 = 250$ °C. Find:

a. The heat and work interactions of this process.
b. The entropy change of the system.

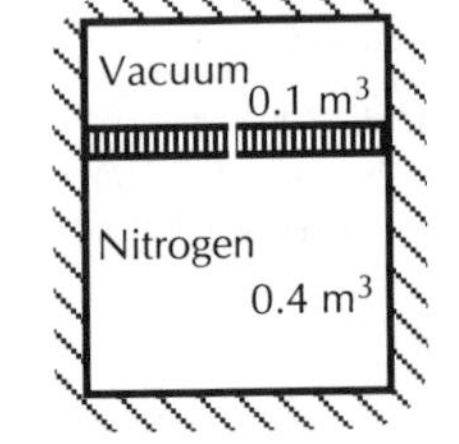

Figure 8.13

8.33 An adiabatic cylinder contains 0.4 m³ nitrogen (ideal gas, $M = 28$, $k = 1.4$) at 40 °C under a floating piston which exerts a pressure equal to 1.2 MPa (Fig. 8.13). Above the piston is 0.1 m³ of vacuum. A small orifice is opened in the piston and the nitrogen leaks slowly through until the flow stops and equilibrium is reached. Find the entropy change of the nitrogen.

8.34 The lower part of a cylinder under a heavy and frictionless piston, shown in Fig. 8.14 contains 0.4 m³ steam at 0.2 MPa and 150 °C. The part above the piston is evacuated. The cylinder is kept at 150 °C by a thermostatic bath.

At a certain moment a hole is punctured in the piston and the steam leaks slowly to the upper part until the flow stops and equilibrium is reached.

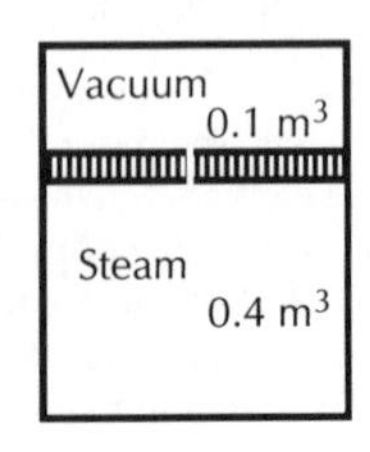

Bath at 150° C

Figure 8.14

a. Find the final pressure of the steam.
b. Find the entropy change in the process.

8.35 Air is to be compressed from the atmospheric condition of p_1 = 100 kPa, T_1 = 20 °C, to a final state of p_2 = 0.8 MPa and T_2 = 150 °C. Find:

a. The work if the compression is done first isentropically to the final pressure and then cooled to the final state.
b. The work if the process is done polytropically.

8.36 Dry saturated steam at 20 °C is compressed reversibly by an adiabatic compressor to a pressure of 150 kPa. Subsequently it is cooled through a heat exchanger at constant pressure to a saturated liquid. It is then expanded through an adiabatic throttle valve to a pressure equal to the inlet pressure of the compressor, and heated at constant pressure back to its initial state. A diagram of the process is shown in Fig. 11.20. Calculate

a. The coefficient of performance of the refrigeration cycle.
b. The power in kW required to remove 30000 kJ/h from the cold reservoir.

8.37 One kg of air at 300 °C and 150 kPa is contained in an adiabatic cylinder. The cylinder is covered with a piston which is held by a stop. The stop is removed and the piston falls, compressing the air to a new equilibrium state where the pressure of the air, which is equal to 1.5 MPa, balances the weight of the piston. Assuming air to be an ideal gas prove that the process is irreversible and calculate the increase in entropy.

8.38 A constant-volume storage battery at state 1 has a temperature of T_1 = 250 °C and voltage $\varepsilon_1 = 6\,V$. When this battery is discharged reversibly and isothermally till the voltage is $\varepsilon_2 = 0$, the work and the heat are Q_0 = 200Wh and W_0 = 1000 Wh, respectively. The specific heat at constant volume and constant zero voltage is constant and equal to C_v =1.6 Wh/K. Find the amount of work that can be obtained in a reversible adiabatic discharge from state 1 to a state where $\varepsilon = 0$.

Hint: Draw the appropriate *T–s* diagram, and try to identify a line corresponding to all states of zero voltage.

8.39 An empty elastic and adiabatic balloon is connected through a valve to a main supply line in which air flows at 327 °C, 8 MPa, as shown in Fig. 8.15. The pressure in the balloon is proportional to its volume. The valve is opened and 3 kg of air enter the balloon, and the pressure reaches 0.8 MPa. Determine:

a. The volume of the balloon at the end of the process.
b. The entropy change of the air that entered the balloon.

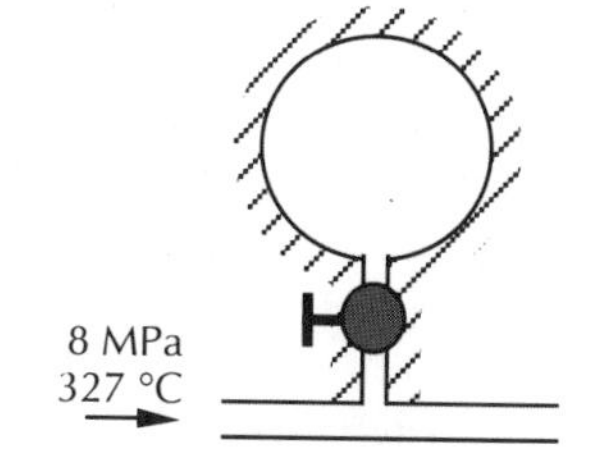

Figure 8.15

8.40 An elastic envelope is connected through a valve to a main containing saturated liquid water at 6 MPa. The envelope exerts a pressure proportional to its volume. Initially the volume of the envelope was V_1= 0. The valve was opened, flow started till the pressure in the envelope reached 0.6 MPa, and the valve was closed again. Assuming that the envelope is adiabatic find:

a. The final state of the water inside the envelope.
b. The change of entropy of everything involved in the process.

8.41 A reversible heat pump absorbs heat from a reservoir at 5 °C and rejects heat into a closed tank of 30 m^3 that contains steam. At the beginning of the process the steam in the tank was saturated at 100 °C. The heat pump operates until the pressure in the tank reaches 0.4 MPa. Find the heat and work interactions of the engine.

8.42 A heat engine receives 1000 kJ during a cycle from a heat reservoir at T_H = 1000 °C. The engine is internally reversible and provides 690 kJ of work, while reversibly exchanging heat at T_c = 300 K with a cool reservoir.

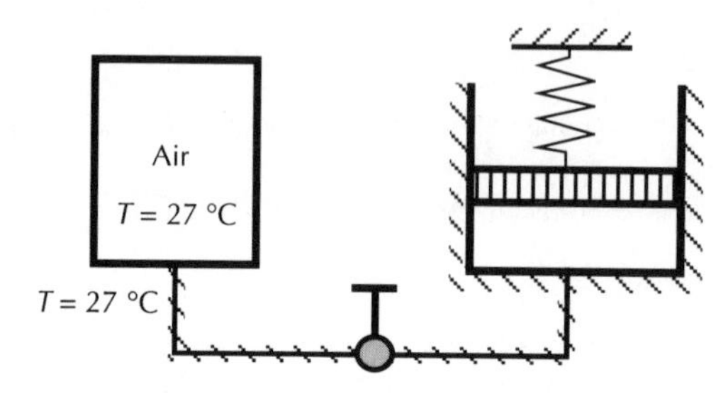

Figure 8.16

a. Find the temperature at which the heat engine isothermally absorbs heat from the hot reservoir.
b. Find the total entropy change during the cycle.

8.43 A vessel of 0.03 m^3 containing air (ideal gas, M = 29, k = 1.4) at p = 3.5 MPa is maintained at a constant temperature of T = 27 °C. The vessel is joined via a duct and a valve to an insulated cylinder covered by a 0.03 m^2 weightless piston, which is held by a linear spring of k = 40 kN/m (Fig. 8.16). Initially the volume under the piston was V = 0 and the spring was unloaded. The valve is opened and air flows into the cylinder till its pressure reaches 1.5 MPa. Then the valve is closed.

a. Find the final temperature and volume of the air in the cylinder.
b. Find the final pressure and mass in the vessel.
c. Find the heat interaction of the vessel.

8.44 Calibration measurements for a defective throttling calorimeter show that for every kilogram of steam flowing through the instrument 30 kJ are lost to the surroundings. When the calorimeter was connected to a pipeline containing wet steam at 3.0 MPa, the conditions at the exit were found to be 115 °C and 100 kPa.

a. Determine the quality of the steam in the pipeline.
b. If this steam line were used to feed a reversible adiabatic turbine with an exhaust pressure of 100 kPa how much work could have been done per kilogram of steam?

8.45 A 10 m^3 tank contains air at 2.5 MPa and 600 °C. The tank is connected to a turbine which exhausts to the atmosphere. The processes in the tank, pipes, and turbine are reversible and adiabatic and the atmosphere is at 100 kPa, 15 °C. Neglect the volume of the pipes and turbine.

a. Find the total mass flow through the turbine until the flow stops.
b. Find the work delivered to the turbine shaft.
c. Is the exhaust air in equilibrium with the atmosphere?

8.46 A 10 m^3 tank contains steam at 2.5 MPa and 600 °C. The tank is connected to a turbine which exhausts to the atmosphere. The processes in the tank, pipes, and turbine are reversible and adiabatic and the atmosphere is at 100 kPa, 15 °C. Neglect the volume of the pipes and turbine.

a. Find the total mass flow through the turbine until the flow stops.
b. Find the work delivered to the turbine shaft.

8.47 A reversible heat engine absorbs heat from a reservoir at 600 °C and rejects heat into a closed tank of constant volume that contains 100 kg of Freon-12. At the beginning of the process the matter in the tank was at 0 °C and 0.3 MPa. The engine operates until the temperature in the tank reaches 80 °C. Find the work of the engine.

8.48 A technical report describes a steady state process in which H_2O at 1.0 MPa and 200 °C enters an insulated experimental set-up at a rate of 4.0 kg/min. Half the amount leaves the set-up at 4.0 MPa and 350 °C while the other half leaves at 0.3 MPa, $x = 0.888$. Given that no work interactions are involved, determine if the process is possible.

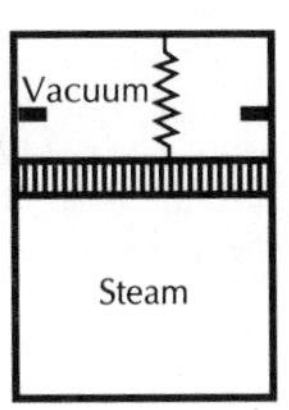

Figure 8.17

8.49 A large cylinder contains 10 kg of steam at 300 °C and 3.5 MPa (state 1) under a piston with an area $A = 0.1$ m^2 attached to a linear spring ($k = 123.6$ kN/m), as shown in Fig. 8.17. At the beginning the pressure of the steam is balanced by the weight of the piston and there is no stress on the spring. Now heat is transferred to the steam until the piston reaches the stops at which point the volume is $V_2 = 0.765$ m^3 (state 2). The heat interaction continues until the pressure reaches $p_3 = 7.0$ MPa (state 3).

a. Sketch processes 1→2 and 2→3 on a p–v diagram.
b. Find the work interaction of the steam during the 1→3 process.
c. Find the heat interaction of the steam during the 1→3 process.
d. Find the change of entropy of the steam during the 1→3 process.

8.50 A storage battery at state A_1 is discharged reversibly and isothermally at a temperature of 50 °C to an equilibrium state A_2 of a different chemical composition than A_1.

Measurements of the heat and the work yield

$$Q = 0.2 \text{ kWh}, \ W = 1.0 \text{ kWh}.$$

In an alternative process the battery at state A_1 is fully discharged adiabatically and reversibly. The heat capacity at constant volume of the battery at the discharged state is $C_v = 35$ kJ/K. Assume that the volume remains constant in both processes. Find the work of the adiabatic discharge.

CHAPTER NINE

Applications of the second law of thermodynamics

In this chapter we consider the application of the second law of thermodynamics and the property entropy to the analysis of closed and open systems.

The second law is most useful in solving problems of internally reversible processes. For these processes heat and work can be calculated from Eqs (8.23) and (8.24), respectively. The analysis of reversible processes can be extended to irreversible processes where the deviation from reversibility can be assessed.

The second law of thermodynamics can also be used to determine whether a given process is possible or not, and if possible, whether it is reversible or not. We begin this chapter with an example demonstrating how the notion of reversibility provides an additional condition required for solving problems in thermodynamics.

EXAMPLE 9.1

Container A of volume 0.6 m^3, Fig. 9.1, contains nitrogen at 3.0 MPa and 400 °C. It is connected through a pipe with a valve to container B of volume 1.0 m^3, which contains nitrogen at 0.2 MPa and 150 °C. The containers and the piping are well insulated. The valve is opened, and nitrogen flows slowly from A to B until the pressures equalize, at which time the valve is closed. Find:

a. The final temperature in each container.
b. The final mass in each container.
c. The total change of entropy.

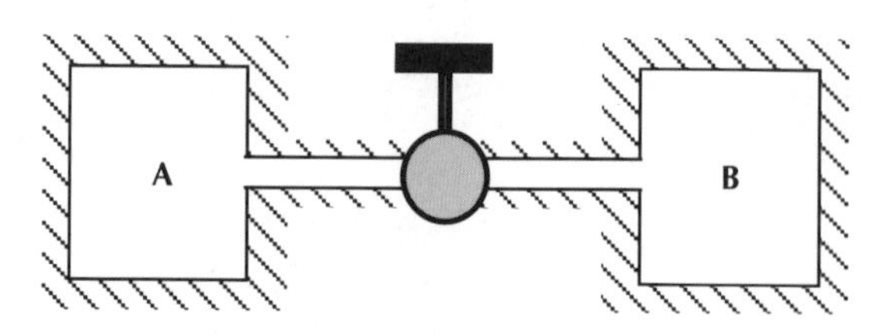

Figure 9.1

SOLUTION

a. There are four relevant states in this problem: the initial and the final states in A and in B. Let us denote them as follows:

1 – initial state in A
2 – final state in A
3 – initial state in B
4 – final state in B

States 1 and 3 are completely defined by their known pressures and temperatures. States 2 and 4 are not known and need to be calculated.

The initial mass in each container is

$$m_1 = \left(\frac{pV}{RT}\right)_1 = \frac{3000 \times 0.6}{(8.3143/28) \times 673.15} = 9.005 \text{ kg}$$

and

$$m_3 = \left(\frac{pV}{RT}\right)_3 = \frac{200 \times 1.0}{(8.3143/28) \times 423.15} = 1.592 \text{ kg}$$

The combined closed system, consisting of A and B, is rigid and adiabatic. Thus

$$\Delta U = Q - W = 0$$

Nitrogen can be considered an ideal gas ($M = 28$, $k = 1.4$). Using Eq. (5.20) we get

$$\Delta U = \frac{(p_2V_2 + p_4V_4) - (p_1V_1 + p_3V_3)}{k-1} = 0$$

Substitution of $p_4 = p_2$, $V_2 = V_1$, and $V_4 = V_3$ results in

$$p_4 = p_2 = \frac{(p_1V_1 + p_3V_3)}{V_1 + V_3} = \frac{3.0 \times 0.6 + 0.2 \times 1.0}{0.6 + 1.0} = 1.25 \text{ MPa}$$

We still need to find T_2 and T_4 (which are not necessarily equal). To do this, we assume that the process of discharging nitrogen from container A is sufficiently slow that the state within the container is uniform at any instant of time.

Let us now define a system comprised of the gas that by the end of the process will have filled container A completely, as shown in Fig. 9.2. This system is expanding while doing work on the environment which is at the same pressure and temperature as the system. Hence, this expansion is reversible and since it is also adiabatic, its specific entropy does not change:

$$s_2 = s_1$$

The final temperature T_2 in vessel A can now be calculated using one of the relationships for this constant-entropy process:

$$\frac{T_2}{T_1} = \left(\frac{p_2}{p_1}\right)^{\frac{k-1}{k}} = \left(\frac{1.25}{3.0}\right)^{\frac{1}{3.5}} = 0.7787$$

and

$$T_2 = 673.15 \times 0.7787 = 524.2 \text{ K}$$

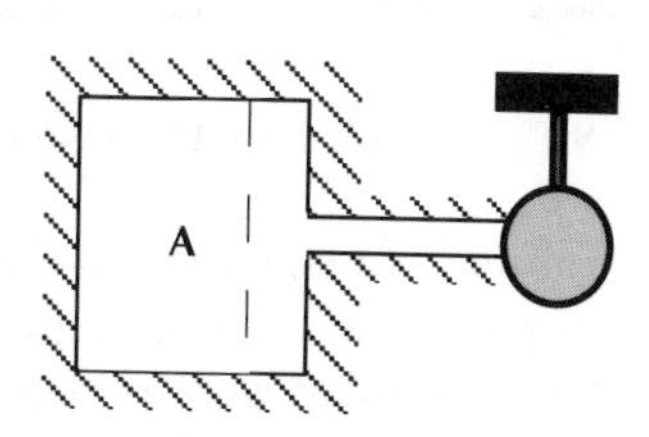

Figure 9.2

b. The mass that is left in A at the final state is

$$m_2 = \left(\frac{pV}{RT}\right)_2 = \frac{1250 \times 0.6}{(8.3143/28) \times 524.2} = 4.818 \text{ kg}$$

The mass transferred from A to B, Δm, is

$$\Delta m = m_1 - m_2 = 9.005 - 4.818 = 4.187 \text{ kg}$$

and

$$m_4 = m_3 + \Delta m = 1.592 + 4.187 = 5.779 \text{ kg}$$

The temperature T_4 is then

$$T_4 = \left(\frac{pV}{mR}\right)_4 = \frac{1250 \times 1.0}{(8.3143/28) \times 5.779} = 728.4 \text{ K}$$

The properties are summarized in the following table:

State	p MPa	T K	v m³/kg	m kg
A 1	3.00	673.15	0.06663	9.005
2	1.25	524.2	0.1245	4.818
B 1	0.20	423.15	0.08901	1.592
2	1.25	728.4	0.1475	5.779

c. The total change of entropy is

$$\Delta S = m_2 s_2 + m_4 s_4 - m_1 s_1 - m_3 s_3 = m_3(s_4 - s_3) + \Delta m(s_4 - s_1)$$

$$= m_3\left[c_p \ln\left(\frac{T_4}{T_3}\right) - R\ln\left(\frac{p_4}{p_3}\right)\right] + \Delta m\left[c_p \ln\left(\frac{T_4}{T_1}\right) - R\ln\left(\frac{p_4}{p_1}\right)\right]$$

$$\Delta S = R\left[m_3\left(\frac{k}{k-1}\ln\frac{T_4}{T_3} - \ln\frac{p_4}{p_3}\right) + \Delta m\left(\frac{k}{k-1}\ln\frac{T_4}{T_1} - \ln\frac{p_4}{p_1}\right)\right]$$

$$= \frac{8.3143}{28}\left[1.592\left(3.5\ln\frac{728.4}{423.15} - \ln\frac{1.25}{0.2}\right) + 4.187\left(3.5\ln\frac{728.4}{673.15} - \ln\frac{1.25}{3.0}\right)\right]$$

$$= 1.4640 \text{ kJ/K}$$

9.1 Work in expansion and compression processes

Expansion and compression processes play an important role in engineering. *Expansion* takes place in turbines, nozzles, etc., where the pressure of the fluid is reduced in order of either performing work or accelerating the fluid. *Compression* is the process that takes place in compressors, pumps, diffusers, etc. Here the goal is to increase the pressure of the working fluid either by doing work on the system or by reducing its kinetic energy.

We now consider the application of the laws of thermodynamics to work-producing and work-consuming devices, such as turbines, pumps, and compressors. These devices usually operate in steady state where the first law simplifies to

$$\dot{Q} - \dot{W}_x = \dot{m}\left(h_2^0 - h_1^0\right) \tag{6.34}$$

When the changes in velocity and elevation are small,

$$\dot{Q} - \dot{W}_x = \dot{m}\left(h_2 - h_1\right) \tag{9.1}$$

Division of Eq. (9.1) by $\dot{m}$ results in an equation written per unit mass flow through the control volume:

$$q - w_x = h_2 - h_1 \tag{9.2}$$

On the other hand we may write for this unit mass

$$dh = Tds + vdp \tag{8.29}$$

which upon integration yields

$$h_2 - h_1 = \int_1^2 Tds + \int_1^2 vdp \tag{9.3}$$

Substituting Eq. (9.3) into Eq. (9.2) yields the work of the device:

$$w_x = \left(q - \int_1^2 Tds\right) - \int_1^2 vdp \tag{9.4}$$

Reviewing Eq. (8.54) written for a two-port steady state control volume, we note that the quantity in parentheses is never positive and vanishes for a reversible process. Hence, for a reversible process we obtain

$$\left(w_x\right)_{rev} = -\int_1^2 vdp \tag{9.5}$$

Integration of Eq. (9.5) requires knowledge of the change of v along an isentropic path. For the special case of an ideal gas, it follows from the table in Chapter 5 that

$$v = v_1\left(\frac{p_1}{p}\right)^{\frac{1}{k}} \tag{9.6}$$

which, when substituted into Eq. (9.5), yields

$$\left(w_x\right)_{rev} = \frac{k}{k-1}p_1 v_1\left[1 - \left(\frac{p_2}{p_1}\right)^{\frac{k-1}{k}}\right] = \frac{kRT_1}{k-1}\left[1 - \left(\frac{p_2}{p_1}\right)^{\frac{k-1}{k}}\right] \tag{9.7}$$

For a general process, reversible or irreversible, the work is

$$w_x \le -\int_1^2 v dp \tag{9.8}$$

Equation (9.8) provides a bound on the amount of work of an open system in steady state, in terms of the pressure change. It applies to expansion (turbines) as well as to compression (pumps, compressors), regardless of the presence of heat interactions. It is obvious from Eq. (9.5) that the work is positive when the pressure is reduced (expansion) and negative when the pressure is raised (compression). Furthermore, the absolute value of the work depends strongly on the specific volume of the working fluid. The work associated with liquids, which have low specific volumes, is much smaller than that associated with gases, which have high specific volumes.

Equation (9.8) is especially useful in calculating the work of pumping liquids. In this case the specific volume changes very little and can be taken as constant. Hence, the integration is straightforward and yields

$$w_x \le -v(p_2 - p_1) \tag{9.9}$$

For a reversible process in a liquid the equality holds:

$$w_x = -v(p_2 - p_1) \tag{9.10}$$

EXAMPLE 9.2

In an industrial plant, water at 25 °C and 1 bar is pumped, at a rate of 10000 kg/h, into a boiler where the pressure is 25 bars. Find the work of the pump assuming it is reversible.

SOLUTION

From Eq. (9.8) the reversible work required to pump water is

$$\dot{W}_x = -\dot{m}v(p_2 - p_1) = -\frac{10000}{3600} \times 0.001003 \times (2500 - 100) = -6.687 \text{ kW}$$

In this problem the specific volume was assumed to be constant and was taken as corresponding to that of the initial state of 25 °C and 1 bar.

We now turn our attention to compressors. A compressor is used in industry to raise the pressure of a gas to a desired value; the final temperature of the gas is of lesser importance. Now a question may be asked: in which process is the fluid compressed most effectively? That is, which process requires the least amount of work?

Now consider four representative reversible processes for compressing a fluid from p_1 to p_2.

a. Adiabatic compression
b. Isothermal compression
c. Polytropic compression ($1 < n < k$)
d. Two-stage adiabatic compression with intercooling at the intermediate pressure p_i.

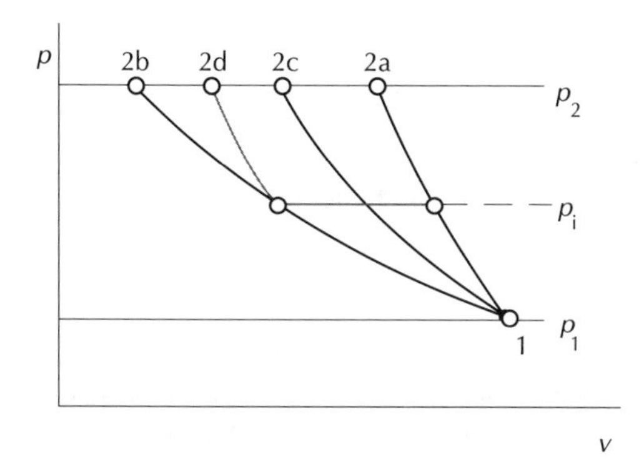

Figure 9.3

Figure 9.3 depicts schematically the four processes on a p–v diagram. All start at the same initial state 1; however, each ends up at a different state: 2a, 2b, 2c, 2d, respectively.

The work input during compression can be calculated for all four processes using Eq. (9.5):

$$-w_x = \int_1^2 v dp \tag{9.5}$$

This work is given by the area bounded by the p-axis and the respective curve. The smallest area in the p–v diagram, corresponding to the lowest work input, is required for the isothermal compression process (1–2b), while the most work is required by the adiabatic compression (1–2a).

In practice it is difficult to cool the compressor itself during the compression process, owing to lack of heat transfer surfaces. Hence it is customary to break up the compression into several stages; the higher the pressure ratio, the larger the number of stages. When the gas passes from one stage to the next, it is cooled in an intercooler by a cooling fluid, usually air or water, at the temperature of the environment. The work of a reversible, adiabatic two-stage compressor with intercooling between the stages at the intermediate pressure p_i is given for an ideal gas as

$$w_x = (w_x)_{1i} + (w_x)_{i2} = \frac{kRT_1}{k-1}\left[1-\left(\frac{p_i}{p_1}\right)^{\frac{k-1}{k}}\right] + \frac{kRT_1}{k-1}\left[1-\left(\frac{p_2}{p_i}\right)^{\frac{k-1}{k}}\right] \tag{9.11}$$

The optimal intermediate pressure, p_i, results in a minimum work input into the two-stage compressor. This is found by differentiating w_x with respect to p_i and equating the result to zero, resulting in an optimal intermediate pressure

$$(p_i)_{opt} = \sqrt{p_1 p_2} \tag{9.12}$$

which is the geometric mean of the initial and final pressures. The corresponding compression work is

$$w_x = \frac{2kRT_1}{k-1}\left[1-\left(\frac{p_2}{p_1}\right)^{\frac{k-1}{2k}}\right] \tag{9.13}$$

Similarly, for a compressor with r stages the optimal work is

$$w_x = \frac{rkRT_1}{k-1}\left[1-\left(\frac{p_2}{p_1}\right)^{\frac{k-1}{rk}}\right] \tag{9.14}$$

In principle, isothermal compression can be approached if the compression is done in an infinite number of stages, with intercooling between them. The number of stages to be selected in practice is an engineering compromise between the reduction of the work and the complexity and cost of the compressor.

EXAMPLE 9.3

Air at 105 kPa, 27 °C, is compressed to 1800 kPa at a rate of 4 kg/s. Find the power of the compressor and the rate of heat removal for:

a. Reversible isothermal compression.
b. Reversible adiabatic compression.
c. Reversible polytropic compression, $n = 1.22$.
d. Reversible adiabatic compression in two stages with intercooling.
   Air may be considered as an ideal gas for which $k = 1.4$ and $M = 29$.

SOLUTION

a. For reversible isothermal compression

$$T_2 = T_1 = 300.15 \text{ K}$$

$$\dot{W}_x = -\dot{m}\int_1^2 v dp = -\dot{m}RT_1 \ln\frac{p_2}{p_1} = -4\times\frac{8.3143}{29}\times 300.15\times \ln\frac{1800}{105} = -978.1 \text{kW}$$

The rate of heat interaction is found from the first law:

$$\dot{Q} = \dot{W}_x + \dot{m}(h_2 - h_1) = \dot{W}_x = -978.1 \text{kW}$$

b. For reversible adiabatic compression

$$T_2 = T_1\left(\frac{p_2}{p_1}\right)^{\frac{k-1}{k}} = 300.15\left(\frac{1800}{105}\right)^{\frac{0.4}{1.4}} = 676.0 \text{ K}$$

$$\dot{W}_x = -\dot{m}\int_1^2 v dp = \dot{m}\frac{kRT_1}{k-1}\left[1-\left(\frac{p_2}{p_1}\right)^{\frac{k-1}{k}}\right]$$

$$= \frac{4\times 1.4\times\frac{8.3143}{29}\times 300.15}{(1.4-1)}\left[1-\left(\frac{1800}{105}\right)^{\frac{0.4}{1.4}}\right] = -1508.5 \text{kW}$$

c. For the polytropic process

$$T_2 = T_1\left(\frac{p_2}{p_1}\right)^{\frac{n-1}{n}} = 300.15\times\left(\frac{1800}{105}\right)^{\frac{0.22}{1.22}} = 501.0 \text{ K}$$

$$\dot{W}_x = -\dot{m}\int_1^2 vdp = \dot{m}\frac{n}{n-1}RT_1\left[1-\left(\frac{p_2}{p_1}\right)^{\frac{n-1}{n}}\right]$$

$$= 4\times\frac{1.22\times(8.3143/29)\times 300.15}{(1.22-1)}\left[1-\left(\frac{1800}{105}\right)^{\frac{0.22}{1.22}}\right] = -1277.6 \text{ kW}$$

$$\dot{Q} = \dot{m}c_n(T_2 - T_1) = \frac{\dot{m}R(n-k)}{(n-1)(k-1)}(T_2 - T_1)$$

$$= 4\times\frac{8.3143}{29}\times\frac{1.22-1.4}{0.22\times 0.4}(501.0 - 300.15) = -471.1\text{kW}$$

d. The work is found from Eq. (9.13) as

$$\dot{Q} = \dot{m}c_n(T_2 - T_1) = \frac{\dot{m}R(n-k)}{(n-1)(k-1)}(T_2 - T_1)$$

$$= 4\times\frac{8.3143}{29}\times\frac{1.22-1.4}{0.22\times 0.4}(501.0 - 300.15) = -471.1\text{kW}$$

Here, heat is removed during intercooling from T_i back to T_1, where

$$T_i = T_1\left(\frac{p_i}{p_1}\right)^{\frac{k-1}{k}} = T_1\left(\frac{p_2}{p_1}\right)^{\frac{k-1}{2k}} = 300.15\left(\frac{1800}{105}\right)^{\frac{0.4}{2.8}} = 450.44 \text{ K}$$

Hence,

$$\dot{Q} = \dot{m}c_p(T_1 - T_i) = \dot{m}\frac{kR}{k-1}(T_1 - T_i)$$

$$= 4\frac{1.4\times 0.2867}{0.4}(300.15 - 450.44) = -603.2 \text{ kW}$$

9.2 Effectiveness of adiabatic processes

We now focus our attention on the question of evaluating the work in irreversible processes where the degree of irreversibility can be estimated.

Calculating the work of reversible, adiabatic steady state processes between two given pressures is quite straightforward. In this case the entropy does not change, and hence the final state is determined by the given pressure p_2 and by the entropy $s_2 = s_1$.

The work per unit mass in an isentropic process is

$$(w_x)_s = -(h_{2s} - h_1) \tag{9.15}$$

where the subscript s indicates that state 2 has the same entropy as state 1.

The reversible adiabatic work, as calculated by Eq. (9.15), is positive for expansion processes and negative for compression processes. In irreversible adiabatic processes

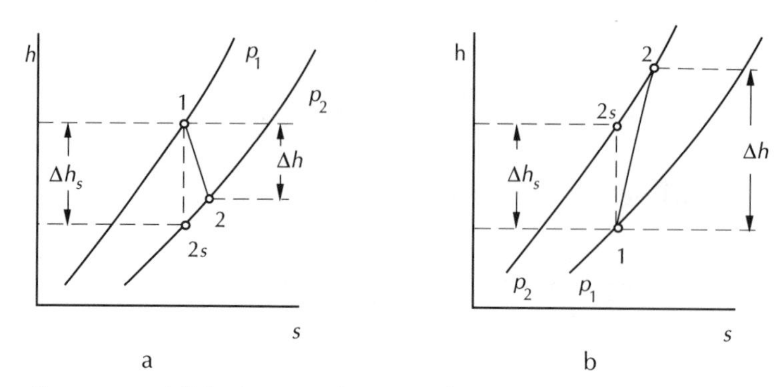

Figure 9.4 **Adiabatic expansion (a) and compression (b) processes, isentropic vs actual.**

between the same pressures, the entropy does not stay constant but rather increases from state 1 to state 2:

$$s_2 > s_1$$

These processes can be conveniently depicted on an h–s diagram, Fig. 9.4. We see that in both cases point 2, which is at pressure p_2 but at a higher entropy relative to state $2s$, is also at a higher enthalpy h_2, i.e. $h_2 > h_{2s}$.

Thus for an expansion process the work of the system, undergoing an adiabatic irreversible process, is less than that of a reversible process. The ratio of the real work to that of the reversible process is called the isentropic efficiency of the expansion and is denoted by ε_e:

$$\varepsilon_e = \frac{W_x}{(W_x)_s} = \frac{h_1 - h_2}{h_1 - h_{2s}} \tag{9.16}$$

The isentropic efficiency is a measure of the effectiveness of a real adiabatic process, relative to the best possible adiabatic process, i.e. the isentropic process. It is never higher than 1. Turbines and other expansion devices are usually characterized by their isentropic efficiency. The isentropic efficiencies of modern power plant turbines is in the range of 0.92–0.96, while the efficiencies of small industrial turbines are substantially lower, in the range of 0.7–0.9.

For a compression process the work input in a real irreversible process is larger than that of the corresponding reversible constant-entropy process. The ratio of the reversible compression work to that of the real irreversible compression is called the isentropic efficiency of the compression; it is denoted by ε_c, and given by

$$\varepsilon_c = \frac{-(W_x)_s}{-W_x} = \frac{h_{2s} - h_1}{h_2 - h_1} \tag{9.17}$$

Here also ε_c is never larger than 1. Note that ε_c and ε_e are not identically defined. The difference in the definition stems from the desire to denote the effectiveness of the "best" adiabatic process as 1, and less than 1 for all others.

The concept of isentropic efficiency can also be extended to flow in nozzles and diffusers. In these cases no work interaction is present, but a change in kinetic energy takes place.

We define the isentropic efficiency for nozzles, where the pressure is reduced and the velocity is increased, in the same way as for expansion processes:

$$\varepsilon_e = \frac{h_1 - h_2}{h_1 - h_{2s}} = \frac{(\mathrm{v}_2)^2 - (\mathrm{v}_1)^2}{(\mathrm{v}_{2s})^2 - (\mathrm{v}_1)^2} \tag{9.18}$$

For diffusers, on the other hand, where the pressure is raised at the expense of the kinetic energy, the definition of the isentropic efficiency is

$$\varepsilon_c = \frac{h_{2s} - h_1}{h_2 - h_1} = \frac{(\mathrm{v}_{2s})^2 - (\mathrm{v}_1)^2}{(\mathrm{v}_2)^2 - (\mathrm{v}_1)^2} \tag{9.19}$$

EXAMPLE 9.4

Steam enters a turbine at a rate of 8 kg/s. The conditions at the inlet are p_1= 6.0 MPa and T_1 = 500 °C, and the pressure at the exit is p_2 = 0.1 MPa. The isentropic efficiency is 0.8. Find:

a. The power delivered by the turbine.
b. The change in the specific entropy of the steam passing through the turbine.

SOLUTION

We first find the exit state 2*s* for an isentropic expansion through the turbine. Then we compute the actual final state, state 2, using Eq. (9.16). The following table summarizes the data for states 1 and 2*s*.

State	*p* MPa	*T* °C	*x*	*h* kJ/kg	*s* kJ/kg K
1	6.0	500	–	3422.2	6.8803
2*s*	0.1	(99.63)	0.9209	2496.8	6.8803

h_2 is found from Eq. (9.16):

$$h_2 = h_1 + \varepsilon(h_{2s} - h_1) = 3422.2 + 0.8 \times (2496.8 - 3422.2) = 2681.9 \text{ kJ/kg}$$

The properties of state 2 are found from p_2 and h_2. The complete table of data is as follows:

State	*p* MPa	*T* °C	*x*	*h* kJ/kg	*s* kJ/kg K
1	6.0	500	–	3422.2	6.8803
2*s*	0.1	(99.63)	0.9209	2496.8	6.8803
2	0.1	102.8	–	2681.9	7.3755

a. The power output of the turbine is

$$\dot{W}_X = \dot{m}(h_1 - h_2) = 8 \times (3422.2 - 2681.9) = 5922.4 \text{ kW}$$

b. The change in the specific entropy of the steam is

$$s_2 - s_1 = 7.3755 - 6.8803 = 0.4952 \text{ kJ/kg K}$$

9.3 Work and heat in isothermal processes

Entropy can be used, together with the first law of thermodynamics, conveniently to calculate the heat and work interactions of reversible isothermal processes for both closed and open systems. The heat interaction of a reversible process in a closed system is

$$\delta Q = TdS \tag{8.23}$$

which can be easily integrated for an isothermal process. Since T = const.,

$$Q = T\Delta S = T(S_2 - S_1) \tag{9.20}$$

The work can now be calculated from the first law:

$$W = Q - (U_2 - U_1) \tag{4.18}$$

We could also calculate the work, without resorting to the use of entropy, directly from

$$W = \int_1^2 pdV \tag{3.6}$$

This, however, would require us to *plot p* vs *v* along the isotherm and integrate graphically; or use an appropriate numerical integration procedure. It is clear that the use of entropy simplifies these calculations significantly.

EXAMPLE 9.5

A system of 0.2 kg of steam, at 200 kPa and 200 °C, is compressed isothermally and reversibly in a piston–cylinder assembly to one-tenth of its original volume.

a. Show the process on a *p–v* diagram and a *T–s* diagram.
b. Find the volumes at the beginning and the end of the process.
c. Find the heat and work interactions.

SOLUTION

The initial state is defined by the given temperature and pressure, while the final state is defined by the given temperature and the volume, which is one-tenth of the original volume. Other relevant properties for the two states are summarized in the table below:

State	p MPa	T °C	x	v m³/kg	u kJ/kg	h kJ/kg	s kJ/kg K
1	0.200	200	–	1.0803	2654.4	2870.5	7.5066
2	1.554	200	0.8468	0.10803	2328.1	2495.9	5.8041

a. The isothermal process is depicted on the *p–v* and the *T–s* diagrams in Fig. 9.5.
   Since the process is reversible the areas under the curves in the *p–v* and the *T–s* diagrams are equal to the work and the heat interactions, respectively. These quantities are both negative; that is, there is a work input, shown by the hatched area on the *p–v* diagram, and there is heat removal, shown by the hatched area on the *T–s* diagram.

b. $V_1 = mv_1 = 0.2 \times 1.0803 = 0.2161\text{m}^3$

   $V_2 = 0.1 \times V_1 = 0.02161\text{m}^3$

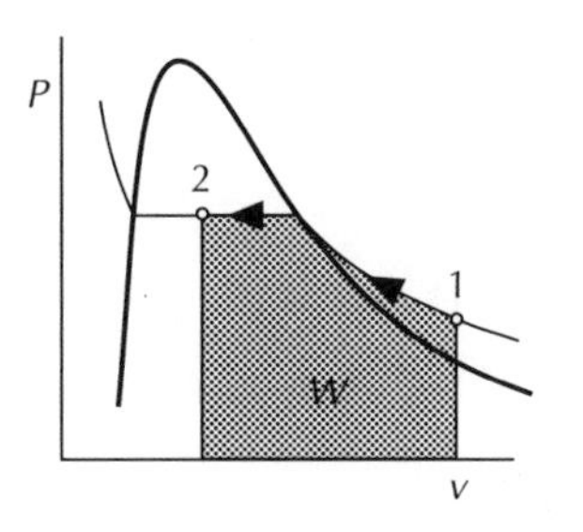

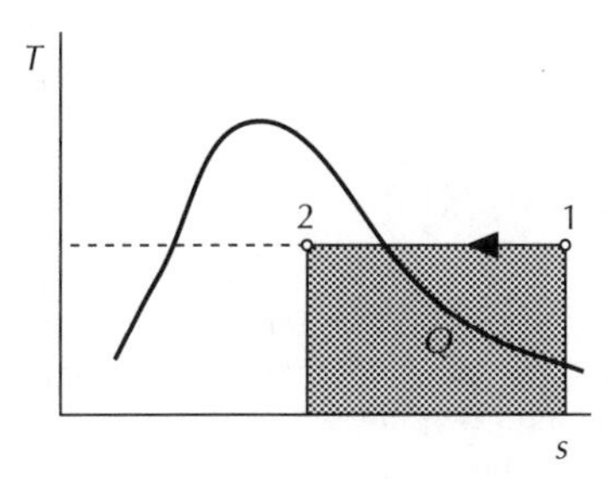

Figure 9.5

c. The heat interaction for the reversible isothermal process is calculated from Eq. (8.23), noting that T is constant:

$$Q = \int_1^2 TdS = T\int_1^2 dS = mT(s_2 - s_1)$$
$$= 0.2 \times 473.15 \times (5.8041 - 7.5066) = -161.1 \text{kJ}$$

The work interaction is found using the first law

$W = Q - \Delta U = -161.1 - 0.2 \times (2328.1 - 2654.4) = -95.8$ kJ

Note that before entropy was introduced, the work of an isothermal reversible process had to be calculated numerically, by integrating the area under the curve in the p–v diagram:

$$W = \int_1^2 pdV = m\int_1^2 pdv$$

For an open system in steady state, the heat in a reversible isothermal process can be calculated from

$$\dot{Q} = -T\sum s_i \dot{m}_i \tag{9.21}$$

and for the case of a two-port open system

$$\dot{Q} = -\dot{m}T(s_1 - s_2) \tag{9.22}$$

and

$$q = \dot{Q}/\dot{m} = -T(s_1 - s_2) \tag{9.23}$$

The work, $\dot{W}_x$, is calculated from the first law for an open system as

$$\dot{W}_x = \dot{Q} + \sum h_i \dot{m}_i = \sum \dot{m}_i (h_i - Ts_i) \tag{9.24}$$

which simplifies for a two-port open system to

$$\dot{W}_x = \dot{m}[(h_1 - h_2) - T(s_1 - s_2)] \tag{9.25}$$

or

$$w_x = \dot{W}_x / \dot{m} = (h_1 - h_2) - T(s_1 - s_2) \tag{9.26}$$

EXAMPLE 9.6

Steam, at 200 kPa and 200 °C, is compressed reversibly and isothermally at a rate of 0.2 kg/s in a steady state process to one-tenth of its original specific volume.

a. Show the process on a *p–v* diagram and on a *T–s* diagram.
b. Find the volume flowrates into and out of the compressor.
c. Find the rates of heat and work interactions.

SOLUTION

The conditions of the steam at the inlet and at the outlet are the same as in the initial and the final states of Example 9.5, respectively. Therefore:

a. The *p–v* and *T–s* diagrams for the process are the same as in Fig. 9.5.

b. $\dot{V}_1 = \dot{m}_1 v_1 = 0.2 \times 1.0803 = 0.2161 \text{m}^3/\text{s}$

$\dot{V}_2 = 0.1 \times \dot{V}_1 = 0.2161 \text{m}^3/\text{s}$

c. The rate of heat interaction is

$$\dot{Q} = \dot{m}T(s_2 - s_1)$$
$$= 0.2 \times 473.15 \times (5.8041 - 7.5066) = -161.1 \text{kW}$$

The work interaction is

$$\dot{W}_x = \dot{m} \times [(h_1 - h_2) - T(s_1 - s_2)]$$
$$= 0.2 \times [(2870.5 - 2495.9) - 473.15 \times (7.5066 - 5.8041)] = -86.2 \text{ kW}$$

9.4 Effectiveness of heat exchangers

Consider a counter-flow heat exchanger as shown in Fig. 9.6 and described in section 6.4.4. A first-law analysis of the heat exchanger yields

$$\dot{m}_c(h_2 - h_1) = \dot{m}_h(h_3 - h_4) \tag{9.27}$$

The first law only provides a balance between the cooling of the hot stream and the heating of the cold stream. It does not provide information as to the extent of the heat transfer between the streams. The answer to that question can be supplied by the second law of thermodynamics. A corollary to the second law is that heat cannot be transferred from a stream at a low temperature to a stream at a higher temperature. This holds true for any point along the heat exchanger. Obviously, the temperature of the cold stream, exiting from the heat exchanger, cannot exceed that of the hot stream entering it. At the same time the temperature of the hot stream exiting from the heat exchanger cannot be less than that of the incoming cold stream. Thus, there is a thermodynamic limit to the

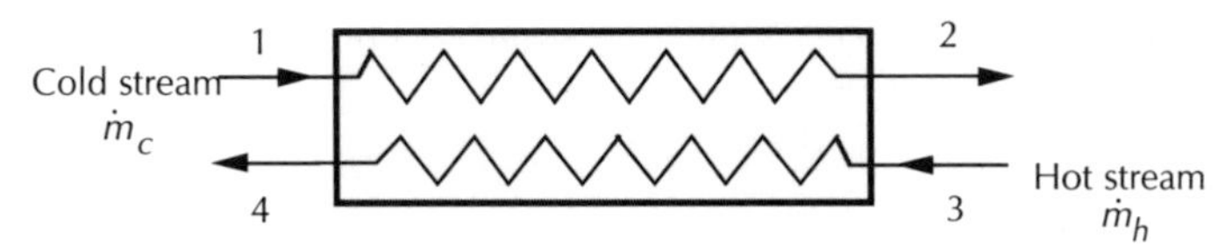

Figure 9.6 **Schematic of a heat exchanger.**

heating of the cold stream and to the cooling of the hot stream. This limit can be expressed mathematically by the following inequalities:

$$T_2 \leq T_3 \text{ and } T_1 \leq T_4 \tag{9.28}$$

Both conditions must be satisfied simultaneously regardless of the design of the heat exchanger.

We now consider the special case of isobaric operation and constant c_p streams and evaluate the maximum amount of heat that can be transferred between the two streams. Equation (9.27) can now be rewritten as

$$(\dot{m}c_p)_c(T_2 - T_1) = (\dot{m}c_p)_h(T_3 - T_4) \tag{9.29}$$

When the heat capacities of the two streams are equal, i.e.

$$(\dot{m}c_p)_c = (\dot{m}c_p)_h \tag{9.30}$$

the exchanger is called "balanced". For this case Eq. (9.27) yields

$$T_2 - T_1 = T_3 - T_4 \tag{9.31}$$

or

$$T_2 - T_3 = T_1 - T_4 \tag{9.32}$$

The most effective balanced exchanger is one for which the equalities in Eq. (9.28) hold true, i.e. the exiting cold stream attains the temperature of the incoming hot stream and vice versa:

$$T_2 = T_3 \text{ and } T_1 = T_4 \tag{9.33}$$

If the heat exchanger is not balanced, only one stream, specifically the one that has the lower heat capacity, can at best exit at the inlet temperature of the other stream. In that case, at the other end of the exchanger the inequality holds, i.e.

$$T_2 = T_3 \text{ and } T_1 < T_4 \tag{9.34}$$

or

$$T_2 < T_3 \text{ and } T_1 = T_4 \tag{9.35}$$

A real heat exchanger operates even less effectively.

The effectiveness of a heat exchanger, ε, is defined by the ratio of the actual heat transferred to the maximum possible under the thermodynamic constraints:

$$\varepsilon = \frac{Q}{Q_{max}} = \frac{\text{actual heat transfer}}{\text{maximum possible heat transfer}} \tag{9.36}$$

For a heat exchanger with flowrates of equal heat capacities (a balanced heat exchanger) the effectiveness can be expressed as

$$\varepsilon = \frac{Q}{Q_{max}} = \frac{T_2 - T_1}{T_3 - T_1} = \frac{T_3 - T_4}{T_3 - T_1} \tag{9.37}$$

For the general case of variable c_p the effectiveness is determined in terms of the lower heat capacity stream. If stream 1–2 has the lower heat capacity then

$$\varepsilon = \frac{Q}{Q_{max}} = \frac{h_2 - h_1}{h(T_3) - h_1} \tag{9.38}$$

where $h(T3)$ is the exit enthalpy of stream 1–2 at temperature T_3. If stream 3–4 has the smaller heat capacity then

$$\varepsilon = \frac{Q}{Q_{max}} = \frac{h_3 - h_4}{h_3 - h(T_1)} \tag{9.39}$$

where $h\ (T_1)$ is the exit enthalpy of stream 3–4 at temperature T_1.

EXAMPLE 9.7

Hot exhaust gases, coming out of a gas turbine, are used to preheat an equal amount of compressed air. Given that the flowrates of the streams are 5.0 kg/s and the inlet temperatures are 450 °C and 200 °C, respectively, find the rate of heat transfer if the effectiveness of the heat exchanger is $\varepsilon = 0.82$. Assume that the properties of the exhaust gases are identical to those of air.

SOLUTION

We refer to Fig. 9.6 where the cold stream and the hot stream are labeled 1–2 and 3–4, respectively. In the present case the flows and the properties of the two streams are equal; hence the exchanger is balanced. The actual heat transfer is found from Eq.(9.37):

$$\dot{Q} = \varepsilon \dot{Q}_{max} = \varepsilon \dot{m}(h_3 - h_1) = \varepsilon \dot{m} c_p (T_3 - T_1)$$
$$= 0.82 \times 5.0 \times 1.0035 \times (450 - 200) = 1028.6 \text{ kW}$$

EXAMPLE 9.8

Saturated liquid Freon-12 at 40 °C is cooled by an equal amount of saturated Freon-12 vapor at –30 °C in a counter-flow heat exchanger shown in Fig. 9.6. The flowrate of each stream is 0.8 kg/s. Find the exit temperature of each stream and the rate of heat transfer for:

a. An ideal heat exchanger.

b. A heat exchanger whose effectiveness is 0.85.

SOLUTION

a. The properties of the streams at the respective inlets are the underlined quantities in the following table.

State	p kPa	T °C	x	h kJ/kg
1	10.04	$\underline{30}$	$\underline{1.00}$	174.076
2	$\underline{10.04}$	$\underline{40}$	–	216.104
3	96.07	$\underline{40}$	$\underline{0.00}$	74.527
4	$\underline{96.07}$	$\underline{-4}$	–	32.498

In order to find the exit temperatures we use either Eq. (9.34) or Eq. (9.35). Let us begin by testing Eq. (9.35). That is, we assume that the exit temperature of the hot stream attains that of the cold stream, $T_4 = T_1$. Then the enthalpy at $T_4 = -30$ °C (and $p_4 = 0.9607$ bars) is $h_4 = 8.854$ kJ/kg.

It follows from Eq. (9.27) that for equal mass flowrates

$$h_2 = h_1 + h_3 - h_4 = 174.076 + 74.527 - 8.854 = 239.749 \text{ kJ/kg}$$

The temperature that corresponds to $p_2 = 0.10$ MPa and $h_2 = 239.749$ kJ/kg is

$$T_2 = 78\ ^{\circ}\text{C} > T_3$$

which, obviously, violates Eq. (9.35). Thus we must assume that Eq. (9.34) holds, i.e. $T_2 = T_3 = 40$ °C. T_4 is then found from Eq. (9.27). Now we can find the properties at the other ports and add the respective values to the above table (the non-underlined quantities).

The rate of heat transfer is

$$\dot{Q} = \dot{Q}_{max} = \dot{m}_1(h_2 - h_1) = -\dot{m}_3(h_4 - h_3) = 0.8 \times (216.104 - 174.076) = 33.62 \text{ kW}$$

b. In this case the rate of heat transfer is lower and is calculable from Eq. (9.36):

$$\dot{Q} = \varepsilon \dot{Q}_{max} = 0.85 \times 33.62 = 28.58 \text{ kW}$$

9.5 A test for the impossibility of a process

The second law of thermodynamics allows us to identify processes that could never occur, irrespective of the details of the system. A PMM2 is an example of such a process.

A general test for an *impossible process* is to find whether it violates the second law of thermodynamics or any of its corollaries. A process that violates the second law is obviously impossible.

EXAMPLE 9.9

An inventor claims to have built an adiabatic superturbine that requires 2 kg/s of steam at 2 MPa and 300 °C, exhausts it at 0.1 MPa, and produces 2000 kW of power. Is such a device possible?

SOLUTION

From the first law for an open system the work of an adiabatic turbine is

$$\dot{W}_x = \dot{m}(h_1 - h_2)$$

where the subscripts 1 and 2 refer to the inlet and outlet, respectively. This equation is used to calculate h_2 from

$$h_2 = h_1 - (\dot{W}_x/\dot{m}) = h_1 - 2000/2 = h_1 - 1000$$

We now arrange the data for states 1 and 2 in the following table.

State	p kPa	T °C	x	h kJ/kg	s kJ/kg K
1	2.0	300	–	3023.5	6.7664
2	0.1	(99.63)	0.7113	2023.5	5.6106

From the table we note that $s_2 - s_1 = 5.6106 - 6.7664 = -1.1558$ kJ/kg K < 0, which for an adiabatic process violates the second law. Hence, the inventor's claim must be rejected.

It should be noted that no details of the device were required in order to arrive at our conclusion.

EXAMPLE 9.10

An inventor filed for a patent for a device called an injector, Fig. 9.7. According to the inventor's claims the device is adiabatic and operates at steady state. It uses steam at 3 bars and 250 °C to pump liquid water at 1 bar and 20 °C. The claimed mass ratio between the streams is $m_2/m_1 = 10$. The two streams mix and exit the device as a single stream at 5 bars.

a. Find the state of the exiting stream, assuming that the device can actually operate as claimed.
b. The patent clerk took one glance at the claim and pronounced that it is impossible to mix two streams, both at low pressures, and come up with a stream at a much higher pressure, without resorting to external work input. Being a cautious and experienced bureaucrat, however, the patent clerk decided to hire you as a consultant before rejecting the patent. What would be your advice?

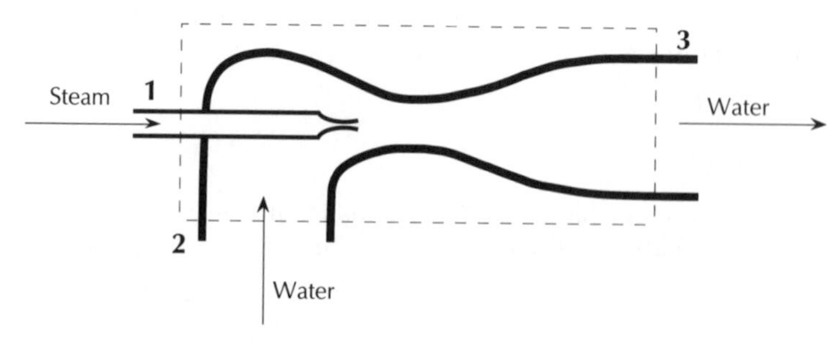

Figure 9.7 **An injector.**

SOLUTION

a. Assuming that the device works, it follows from the mass conservation principle and the first law for the open system in steady state with $W_x = Q = 0$ that

$$\sum \dot{m}_i = 0 \qquad \dot{m}_3 = -(\dot{m}_1 + \dot{m}_2)$$

$$\sum \dot{m}_i h_i = 0 \qquad \dot{m}_3 h_3 = -(\dot{m}_1 h_1 + \dot{m}_2 h_2)$$

Combining these two equations we obtain

$$h_3 = \frac{m_1 h_1 + m_2 h_2}{m_1 + m_2} = \frac{1 \times 2967.6 + 10 \times 83.96}{1 + 10} = 346.11 \text{ kJ/kg}$$

This value, together with p_3 = 5 bars, is used to find the other properties of state 3, which turns out to be in the compressed liquid region. The original data and results of the calculations are shown in the following table.

State	p kPa	T °C	h kJ/kg	s kJ/kg K	m kg/s
1	300	250	2967.6	5.5166	1.0
2	100	20	83.96	0.2966	10.0
3	500	82.7	346.11	1.1654	11.0

b. A process is impossible if it violates the second law. The injector is adiabatic and operates at steady state, and therefore the second law requires that

$$-\sum \dot{m}_i s_i \geq 0 \tag{8.57}$$

and indeed we obtain

$$-\sum \dot{m}_i s_i = -1 \times 7.5166 - 10 \times 0.2966 + 11 \times 1.1654 = 2.3368 \text{ kJ/K} > 0$$

Since the total change of entropy is positive, i.e. the entropy of the exiting stream is higher than the entropy of the two incoming streams, the device does not violate the second law of thermodynamics. Hence, we cannot reject the idea on the basis of thermodynamic arguments. As a matter of fact, devices like the one proposed, which are called condensing injectors, can actually be designed and operated.

PROBLEMS

9.1 A cylinder in constant contact with a bath at a temperature of 260 °C is divided by a stopped piston into two compartments. Compartment A contains 0.1 m^3 of H_2O at a pressure of 20 MPa. Compartment B contains 9.0 m^3 of H_2O at a pressure of 70 kPa. At a certain moment the stop is removed and the piston moves until a new equilibrium is reached.

a. Determine the final state. (Give sufficient properties.)
b. Calculate the heat interaction and the work of the cylinder.
c. Calculate the entropy change of everything involved in the process.

9.2 The pneumatic jack in Fig. 9.8 uses air (ideal gas, M = 29, k = 1.4) from a supply line at p_0 = 1.5MPa, T_0 = 30 °C. At state 1 (T_1= 30 °C, p_1 = 0.5 MPa, V_1 = 0.006 m^3) the piston is supported by a stop. At state 2 p_2 = 0.8 MPa and V_2 = 0.018 m^3. All the elements of the system are completely insulated. Calculate

a. The mass of the air that entered the cylinder.
b. The entropy change of everything involved in the process.

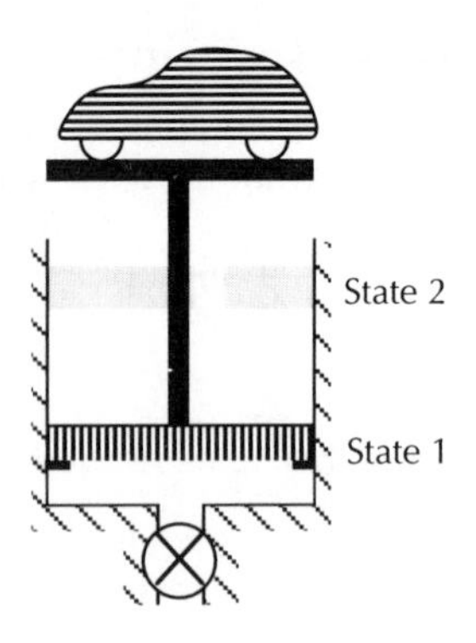

Figure 9.8

9.3 An insulated vessel containing air at 3.0 MPa and 27 °C has a volume of 0.5 m^3. It is necessary to fill the vessel with more air taken from the surroundings at 27 °C, 0.1 MPa, until the pressure in the vessel reaches 10 MPa. An inventor claims to have a single-stage adiabatic compressor that can fulfil this task, while consuming 6500 kJ of work.

Is the inventor's claim possible from a thermodynamic point of view? Explain and justify your explanation with appropriate calculations.

Note: The volume of the compressor may be neglected in the calculations.

9.4 A vessel containing H_2O at a pressure of 0.1 MPa and quality $x = 0.01$ has a volume of 0.2 m^3. At the upper part of the vessel is a pressure valve that prevents a pressure rise over 2 MPa by releasing steam to the environment at 0.1 MPa. Heat is transferred to the vessel from a reservoir at 250 °C. When the pressure reaches 2 MPa, the valve opens and steam is released so that the pressure in the vessel remains at 2 MPa. The valve remains open until a state of $x = 0.90$ is reached in the vessel, at which point the process is stopped. Find:

a. The mass of steam that was released through the valve.
b. The heat interaction during the process.
c. The entropy change of everything involved in the process.

9.5 An insulated vessel containing steam at a pressure of 50 bars and a temperature of 300 °C, has a volume of 2 m^3. The vessel is connected through an insulated pipe to a reversible adiabatic turbine which is connected to a cylinder loaded by a piston, as shown in Fig.9.9. The piston exerts on the cylinder an effective pressure of 10 bars. At the beginning of the process the cylinder is empty and the valve closed. At a certain moment the valve is opened, and steam flows through the turbine. The process ends when the pressure in the vessel reaches 10 bars. It can be assumed that there is no pressure drop in the pipes, and that during the process the state of the vessel is uniform. Also, the mass of the steam in the turbine and in the pipes can be neglected. Find:

a. The mass of the steam that remained in the vessel at the end of the process.
b. The work of the turbine.
c. The entropy change of everything involved in the process.

9.6 A compressor is an adiabatic device that increases a fluid's pressure by consuming work. Steam at 0.1 MPa and 150 °C, enters a compressor with an isentropic efficiency of 0.9 at a speed of 60 m/s. The cross-sectional area of the inlet pipe to the compressor is 300 cm^2. The speed at the compressor discharge is 60 m/s. The power consumption of the compressor is 1 MW. Determine the pressure and temperature (or quality) of the steam at the discharge from the compressor.

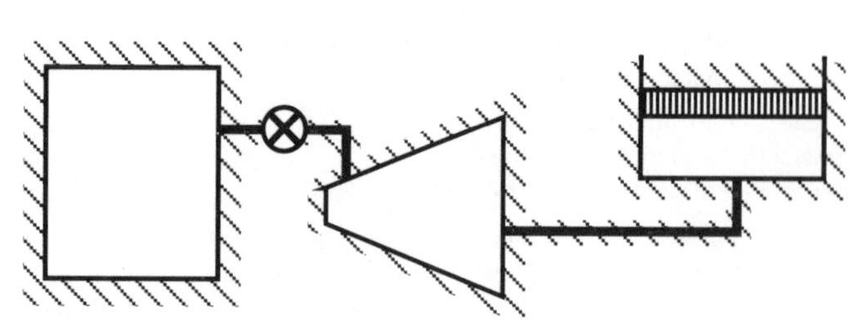

Figure 9.9

9.7 A salesperson claims to have a 100 kW steam turbine. Steam enters the turbine at 0.8 MPa and 250 °C and leaves the turbine at 0.2 MPa and 200 °C. The temperature of the surroundings is 25 °C.

a. Can this turbine be adiabatic? Explain.
b. After further explanation of the device, the salesperson states that the steam flowrate through the turbine is 0.3 kg/s. Is such a turbine possible, i.e. does not violate the second law of thermodynamics?

9.8 A salesperson claims to have a 50 kW steam compressor. Steam enters the compressor at a pressure of 0.1 MPa and a temperature of 100 °C and leaves at a pressure of 1.2 MPa and a temperature of 350 °C. The temperature of the surroundings is 25 °C.

a. Can this compressor be adiabatic? Explain.
b. After further explanation of the device, the salesperson states that the steam flowrate through the compressor is 0.3 kg/s. Is such a compressor possible, i.e. does not violate the second law of thermodynamics?

9.9 Exhaust gases at 0.19 MPa and 725 °C (assume ideal gas, $M = 29$, $k = 1.4$) from a jet engine turbine enter an adiabatic nozzle at a rate of 200 kg/s, and a speed of 60 m/s. The pressure in the environment is 0.06 MPa.

a. What is the maximum speed that can be obtained at the nozzle outlet?
b. Calculate the exit speed at the above conditions for a nozzle of isentropic efficiency 0.9.
c. What is the rate of the entropy change of the exhaust gases as they pass through the nozzle at the conditions of parts a and b?

9.10 An insulated cylinder shown in Fig. 9.10 is divided by an adiabatic frictionless piston into two equal compartments of 25 L each. The pressure in both compartments is 100 kPa. Compartment A contains air at 25 °C and compartment B contains saturated steam. The valve opens to a supply line at 700 kPa and 25 °C and air flows slowly into the cylinder. When the pressures in the system become equal to that of the supply line the valve is closed.

a. Calculate the air mass that entered the cylinder.
b. Calculate the entropy change of everything involved in the process.

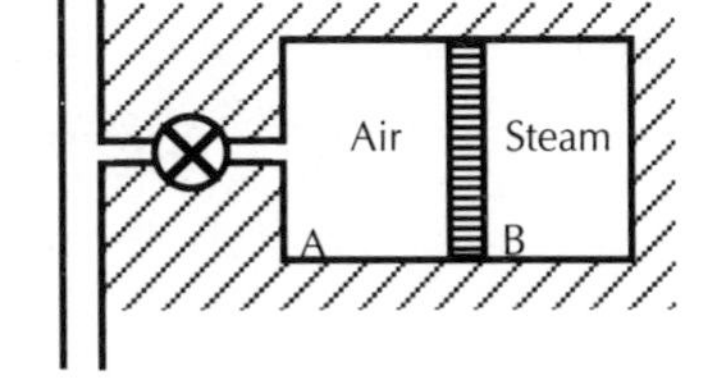

Figure 9.10

9.11 Two adiabatic tanks are interconnected through a valve. Tank A contains 0.2 m^3 of air at 40 bars and 90 °C. Tank B contains 2.0 m^3 of air at 1 bar and 30 °C. The valve is opened and the pressure in A drops slowly. When the pressure in A is 15 bars the valve is closed. Find:

a. The pressures and temperatures in both tanks at the end of the process.
b. The mass that transferred from tank A to tank B.

9.12 An adiabatic rigid tank of 2 m^3 contains helium (an ideal gas, $M = 4.0$, $k = 1.667$) at 25 °C and 2 MPa. The tank is connected through a closed valve to a vertical and adiabatic cylinder covered by an adiabatic piston, as shown in Fig. 9.11. Initially the cylinder contains 2 m^3 helium at 25 °C and 1 MPa. The valve is opened and helium flows slowly from the tank to the cylinder. The process stops when the pressures in the tank and in the cylinder equalize. Find:

a. The final volume and temperature of the gas in cylinder A.
b. The work and heat interactions of the system.
c. The energy change of the system.
d. The entropy change of everything involved in the process.

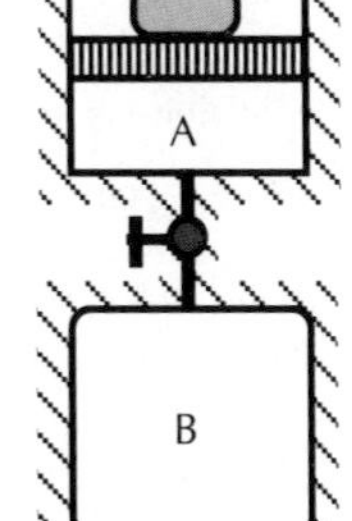

Figure 9.11

9.13 Two adiabatic containers are interconnected through a valve, as shown in Fig. 9.1. Container A has a volume of 0.6 m^3 and contains steam at 3.0 MPa,

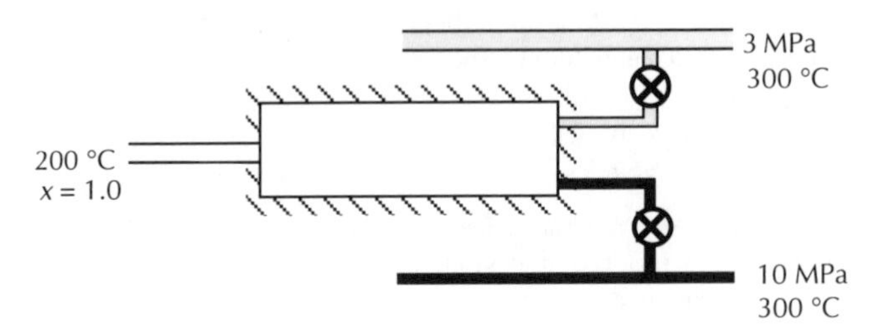

Figure 9.12

400 °C. Container B has a volume of 1.0 m^3 and contains steam at 0.2 MPa, 150 °C. The valve is partially opened, and the pressure in A drops slowly to 2.0 MPa. Find:

a. The final pressures and temperatures in the containers.
b. The mass that moved from A to B.
c. The total change of entropy.

9.14 A pump with an adiabatic efficiency of 0.7 pumps water at 0.1 MPa and 25 °C and discharges it at 5 MPa.

a. Find the enthalpy change of the water upon passing through the pump.
b. Find the entropy change of the water upon passing through the pump.

9.15 In a certain plant 2.5 kg/s of saturated steam at 200 °C are needed. In that plant there are two supply lines, one of steam at 300 °C, 3.0 MPa, and the other of water at 300 °C, 10 MPa. It is suggested that an adiabatic mixing chamber with suitable pressure reducing valves, as shown in Fig. 9.12, should be used in order to generate the required saturated steam. Find:

a. The flowrates of the water and the steam.
b. The specific entropy of the water passing through the reduction valve.
c. The rate of entropy change of everything involved in the process.

9.16 A pneumatic jack consisting of a piston–cylinder assembly, shown in Fig. 9.13 is used to lift a 2000 kg car by means of an adiabatic compressor that compresses air from the environment at 20 °C, 100 kPa. At the beginning the piston was at the bottom of the cylinder while at the end the piston was raised by 1.8 m. The isentropic efficiency of the compressor is 0.8, the piston area is 0.04 m^2, and the whole system is insulated. Find:

a. The temperature at the outlet of the compressor.
b. The final temperature in the cylinder.
c. The work of the compressor.
d. The entropy of everything involved in the process.

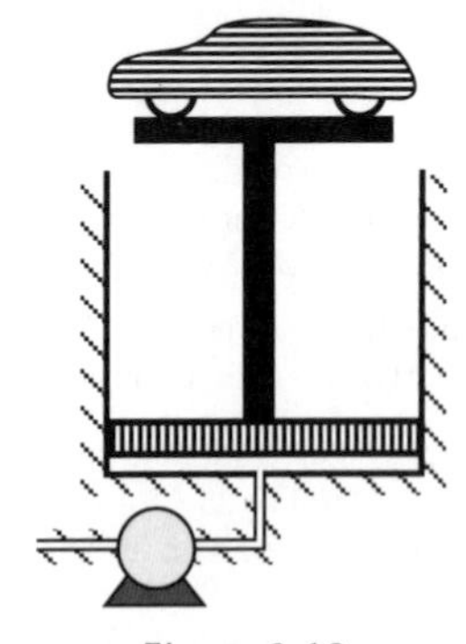

Figure 9.13

9.17 An empty insulated container is connected through a valve to a main of saturated steam at 16 MPa. The valve is opened and steam flows into the vessel. When the pressure in the container reaches 7.0 MPa, the valve is closed. Calculate:

a. The final temperature in the container.
b. The specific entropy change of the steam that entered the vessel.

9.18 A cylinder 0.6 m in diameter is divided by a piston into two parts, as shown in Fig. 9.14. The left side contains 10 g of helium at 2.0 bars and 77 °C. Air from a main, at 6.0 bars and 27 °C, enters slowly into the right side of the cylinder until the flow stops; then the valve is closed. The cylinder, the piston, the pipes, and the valve are well insulated. Neglect friction between the piston and the cylinder. Find:

a. The final temperature of the helium.
b. The final temperature of the air in the cylinder.
c. The amount of air that entered the cylinder.
d. The entropy change of the helium.
e. Is the overall process reversible? Explain.

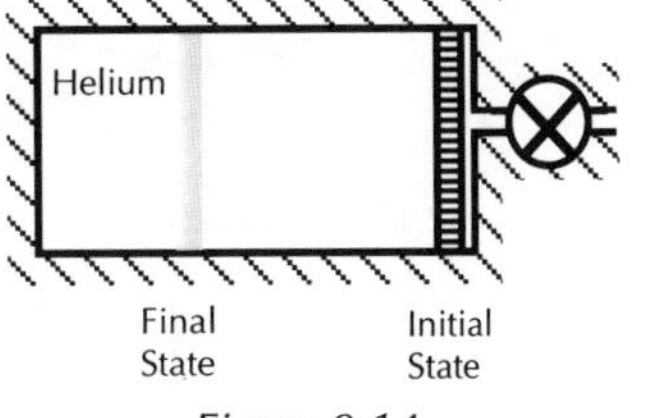

Figure 9.14

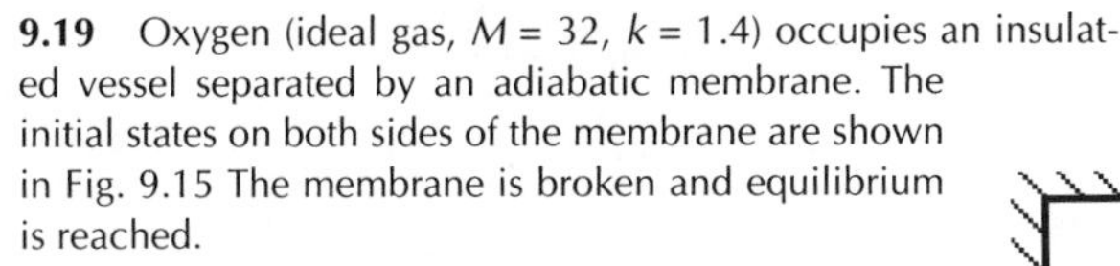

9.19 Oxygen (ideal gas, $M = 32$, $k = 1.4$) occupies an insulated vessel separated by an adiabatic membrane. The initial states on both sides of the membrane are shown in Fig. 9.15 The membrane is broken and equilibrium is reached.

a. Find the final pressure and temperature.
b. Find the entropy change.
c. Is the process reversible? Explain.

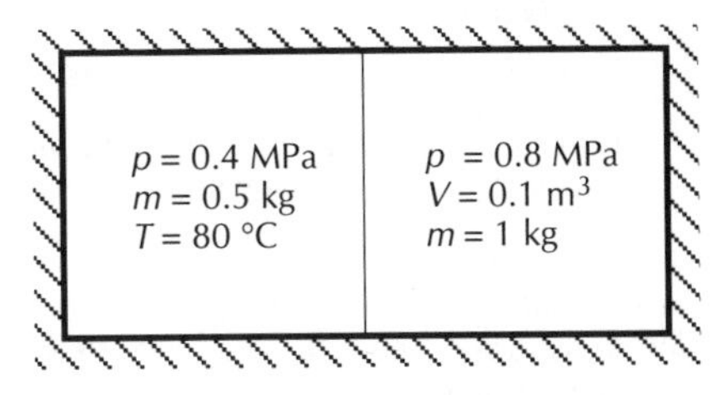

Figure 9.15

9.20 Air (an ideal gas, $k = 1.4$, $M = 29$) at 100 kPa and 5 °C is compressed in a reversible, adiabatic two-stage compressor to 1.6 MPa. Between the two stages the air is cooled in an intercooler at constant pressure to 5 °C, as shown in Fig. 9.16.

a. What intermediate pressure is required in order to produce the minimum power input to the compressor?
b. Calculate the horsepower required to compress 1 kg/s if the intermediate pressure is that determined in part a.
c. What is the rate of heat removal in the intercooler?
d. Repeat the problem for a compressor with an isentropic efficiency of 0.8.

9.21 Show that the work of a multistage adiabatic compressor with intercooling approaches the work of an isothermal compressor as the number of stages goes to infinity.

9.22 A 2 m^3 tank contains air at $p = 1.8$ MPa and $T = 500$ °C. The tank is connected to a turbine which exhausts into the atmosphere, Fig. 9.17. Assume:

(i) The atmosphere is at $p_a = 100$ kPa, $T_a = 5$ °C.
(ii) The processes in the tank, pipes, and turbine are reversible and adiabatic.
(iii) The volumes of pipes and turbine are negligible.

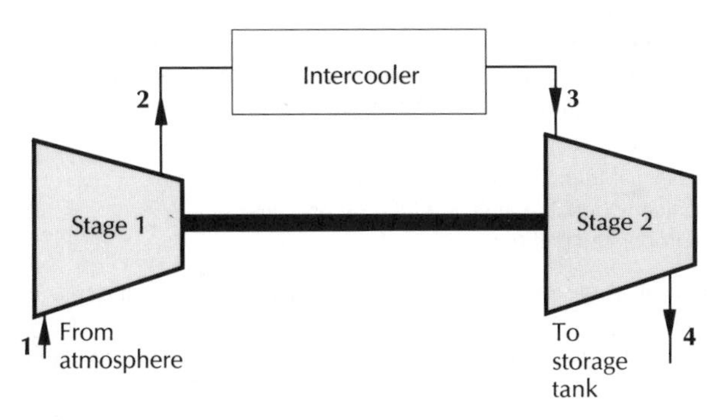

Figure 9.16

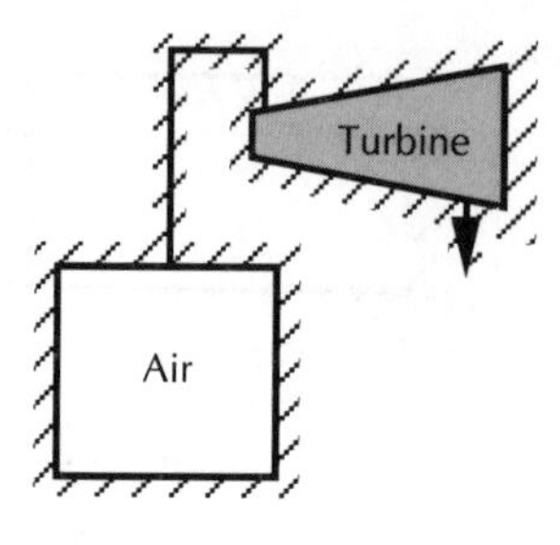

Figure 9.17

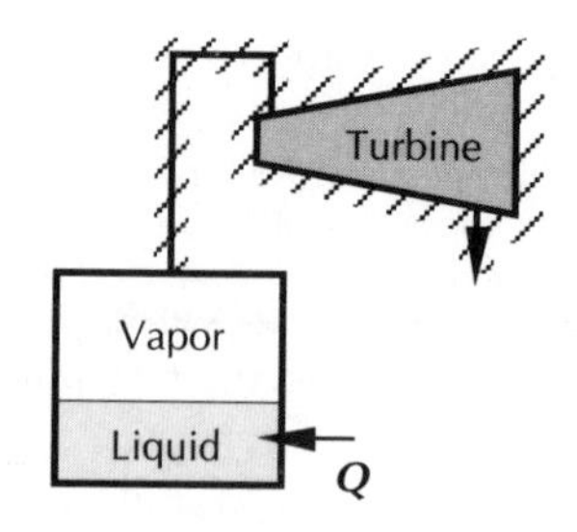

Figure 9.18

a. Find the total mass flowrate through the turbine until the flow stops.
b. Calculate the work delivered to the turbine shaft.

9.23 A 1.5 m^3 tank contains 50% by volume of liquid water in equilibrium with its vapor at 150 kPa. The container is heated at constant volume until the pressure reaches 6.0 MPa. As heating continues the pressure is maintained at 6 MPa while steam is fed from the container to an adiabatic turbine whose isentropic efficiency is 80% (see Fig.9.18).

The pressure at the exhaust of the turbine is 100 kPa. The process ends at the point where all of the liquid water in the tank has evaporated. Determine:

a. The temperature of the water when the pressure reaches 6.0 MPa.
b. The total mass of steam that passed the turbine.
c. The temperature of the steam at the turbine exhaust.
d. The work output of the turbine.

9.24 Extremely high speed flows may be obtained by expanding high pressure, high temperature gases through a suitable nozzle. (Examples: rocket and jet engines.) You can use as a working gas to expand in the nozzle either air or helium at p_1 = 6.5 MPa and T_1 = 900 °C with negligible initial velocity. The properties of these gases may be found in *Gas Tables.*

a. You need to design a system that will produce a flowrate of 1.0 kg/s with an exit velocity of 1000 m/s for a mission in an environment with a very low pressure. Determine, for each of the gases, the pressure and temperature at the nozzle exit.
b. If the mission environment is at 12 kPa and 220 K, determine the exit velocity that each of the gases will produce.
c. Which gas would you select for the mission?

9.25 A chemical plant requires large quantities of steam of low quality (approximately 10%) at 175 °C. High pressure boilers are quite expensive.

An inventor suggests that saturated atmospheric pressure steam (cheap boiler) could be mixed with high pressure water (7 MPa, 17 °C) in an adiabatic steady flow process to produce the desired feed water. The inventor claims that the requirements could be satisfied by mixing two parts (by mass) of water with one part of steam.

a. Are the inventor's figures reasonable in view of the first law?
b. Is the process thermodynamically possible in view of the second law?
   Support your answer with proper calculations.

9.26 Water must be pumped at a rate of 20 kg/s from a river where the conditions are 0.10 MPa, 10 °C, to a pressure of 1.5 MPa.

An inventor suggests an adiabatic device that will do the job provided it is supplied with 2.0 kg/s of saturated steam at 0.30 MPa. A single mixed stream exits the device.

a. If the inventor is right, determine the final conditions at the exit of the device in view of the first law.

b. Is the process thermodynamically possible in view of the second law?

9.27 0.075 kg/s of helium (ideal gas, $M = 4$, $k = 1.667$) enter a nozzle at 240 kPa, 82 °C, and a velocity of 150 m/s. The pressure at the exit is 0.05 MPa. The nozzle is maintained at a constant temperature by a reservoir at 82 °C. Assume a reversible process.

a. Determine the velocity of the helium at the exit.
b. Determine the cross-sectional areas at the inlet and exit.
c. Find the rate of heat interaction of the nozzle.

9.28 An adiabatic engine nozzle, whose adiabatic efficiency is 90%, receives 200 kg/s of gas (properties are same as air) at 200 kPa, 720 °C, and 60 m/s. The gas exits at 70 kPa. The environment is air at 102 kPa, 20 °C. Determine the exit velocity of the gas.

9.29 Steam at 0.8 MPa, 460 °C, and 80 m/s enters an adiabatic nozzle at a rate of 0.04 kg/s. The pressure at the exit of the nozzle is 0.14 MPa. Find:

a. The exit velocity assuming a reversible process.
b. The exit velocity assuming an isentropic efficiency of 0.75.
c. The inlet and exit cross-sectional areas for cases a and b.

CHAPTER TEN

Availability, exergy, and irreversibility

The first law of thermodynamics may be considered as a balance equation between the change of energy and work and heat interactions. This law makes no distinction between the two interactions. There is no inherent loss mechanism associated with the first law, so one cannot determine on the basis of the first law alone whether a process is efficient or not.

In previous chapters we have seen that reversible processes perform better, thermodynamically, than irreversible processes. We have introduced the concept of isentropic efficiency to compare a real, adiabatic steady state process, such as expansion in a turbine, with a reversible adiabatic process between the same pressures. The deviation of the isentropic efficiency from unity was considered a measure of the relative loss of shaft work.

It may be questioned whether this is a good way of measuring losses. For example, consider a steam turbine operating adiabatically between two given pressures, p_1 and p_2. The lower the effectiveness, the higher the loss. One could think that if the effectiveness is zero, such as in a throttling process, the loss is complete; that is, all the energy is lost and a turbine could produce no more work from the steam at the exit. We shall show in this chapter that such a statement is too trivial and does not consider all the real loss aspects. Indeed the steam at the exit of a throttling device could still be useful to produce work albeit not directly in a turbine.

In this chapter we deal with the thermodynamic limits of performance of a system between given end states, and introduce an alternative, more exact method, based on the second law of thermodynamics, for evaluating losses in real processes. We define new concepts, namely those of availability, exergy, and irreversibility, that describe the ability of a system to produce work, and provide a measure for the loss of this capability in real processes. We also offer a method for analyzing the performance of a system based on exergy analysis. This analysis, which is based on the second law of thermodynamics, offers some engineering advantages in locating the larger contributors to losses and in indicating the absolute limits of a process.

10.1 Available work

Consider a system, shown in Fig. 10.1, that undergoes a process between states 1 and 2, in which the heat interactions are limited to those with the environment at T_0.

The work of the system, associated with the change of its state, is given by the first law of thermodynamics:

$$W = -(U_2 - U_1) + Q_0 \tag{10.1}$$

where Q_0 is the heat supplied to the system from the environment. The heat interaction of the environment, Q_E, is obviously $Q_E = -Q_0$.

Since energy is a property, its change between two given states does not depend on the process connecting them. Hence, the term $(U_2 - U_1)$ that appears in Eq. (10.1) is fixed by the end states. The heat interaction, however, is not a property, and therefore its magnitude depends on the particular process between these end states. Inspection of Eq. (10.1) leads to the conclusion that a process between two end states that consumes more heat also produces more work.

Now let us relate the heat interaction, Q_0 to changes in the properties of the system. Since the environment is in equilibrium and undergoes only internally reversible processes, its heat interaction, Q_E, can be related to its change in entropy by

$$\Delta S_E = \frac{Q_E}{T_0} = -\frac{Q_0}{T_0} \tag{10.2}$$

The combination of the system and the environment constitutes an adiabatic system. In general, its entropy change cannot be negative:

$$(S_2 - S_1) + \Delta S_E \geq 0 \tag{10.3}$$

Substitution of Eq. (10.2) into Eq. (10.3) yields

$$(S_2 - S_1) - \frac{Q_0}{T_0} \geq 0$$

or

$$Q_0 \leq T_0(S_2 - S_1) \tag{10.4}$$

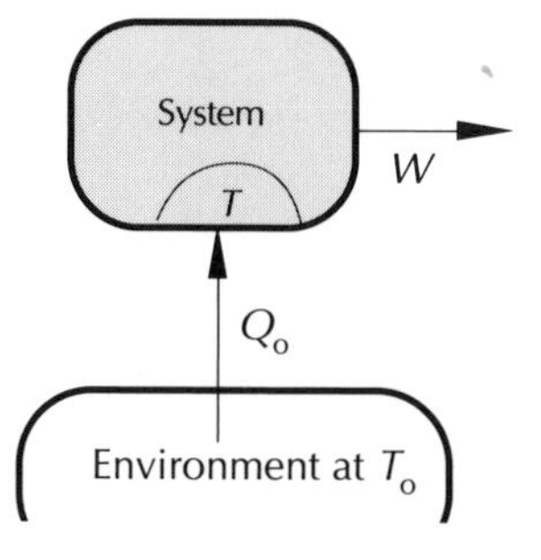

Figure 10.1 **A system interacting with the environment.**

Thus, the heat interaction has a maximum which is given by the right hand side of the inequality (10.4). The limit on the work of a system is obtained by substituting Eq. (10.4) into Eq. (10.1):

$$W \le -(U_2 - U_1) + T_0(S_2 - S_1)$$

which may be rewritten as

$$W \le -[(U_2 - T_0S_2) - (U_1 - T_0S_1)] \tag{10.5}$$

Equation (10.5) applies for any process, reversible or irreversible, between states 1 and 2 of a simple system interacting with an environment at T_0. The inequality holds for an irreversible process, while the equality holds for a reversible process. Equation (10.5) indicates that of all the processes that a system may undergo between two end states, while interacting with an environment at T_0, the reversible process produces maximum work:

$$W_{rev} = -[(U_2 - T_0S_2) - (U_1 - T_0S_1)] \tag{10.6}$$

Figure 10.2 shows the work of such a reversible system.

Each term in the parentheses of Eq. (10.6) represents a property of the system relative to a given temperature of the environment. This property is called the available energy and is denoted by Ω:

$$\Omega = U - T_0S \tag{10.7}$$

The *specific available energy,* i.e. the available energy per unit mass, is

$$\omega = u - T_0s \tag{10.8}$$

Combining Eqs (10.5) and (10.7), we obtain

$$W \le -\Delta\Omega \tag{10.9}$$

and Eqs (10.6) and (10.7) yield

$$W_{rev} = -\Delta\Omega \tag{10.10}$$

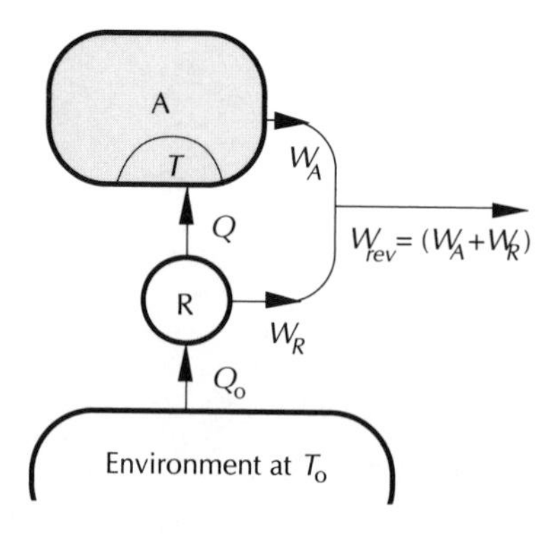

Figure 10.2 **A system interacting reversibly with the environment.**

Equations (10.9) and (10.10) indicate that the maximum work a system can perform between two given states, while interacting with the environment only, is the reversible work, which is equal to the decrease of the available energy of the system between these end states*.

Available energy is an extensive property; namely, the available energy of two or more systems relative to the environment is the sum of the available energies of each system separately.

A special case worth noting is that of a system which is a reservoir at a temperature T_R, that undergoes a heat interaction with the environment at T_0. The work of the reservoir is zero, and the first law yields

$$Q_R = \Delta U_R$$

The entropy change of the reservoir is

$$\Delta S_R = \frac{\Delta U_R}{T_R} = \frac{Q_R}{T_R}$$

and the change of the available energy of the reservoir is then

$$\Delta\Omega_R = \Delta U_R - T_0 \Delta S_R = Q_R\left(1 - \frac{T_0}{T_R}\right) \tag{10.11}$$

If $Q_R > 0$, i.e. heat is added to the reservoir, the available energy of the reservoir increases and if $Q_R < 0$, i.e. heat is removed from the reservoir, then the available energy is reduced. The maximum work associated with such a process is equal to the reduction in the available energy of the reservoir:

$$W_{rev} = -\Delta\Omega = -(\Delta U - T_0\Delta S) = -\left(Q_R - T_0\frac{Q_R}{T_R}\right) = -Q_R\left(1 - \frac{T_0}{T_R}\right) \tag{10.12}$$

Indeed, Eq. (10.12) states that the maximum work that can be obtained when a reservoir at T_R has a heat interaction Q_R is by operating a reversible heat engine between the reservoir and an environment at T_0.

Another property, the *available enthalpy*, B, may be defined in a similar way to the definition of available energy:

$$B = H - T_0 S \tag{10.13}$$

The available enthalpy is also known as the *exergy*. The *specific available enthalpy*, or *specific exergy*, b, is

$$b = h - T_0 s \tag{10.14}$$

The significance of this property will be better understood when applications to control volumes in steady state processes are discussed later on in this chapter.

* In some books energy is defined as the ability to perform work. This definition, obviously, does not describe that property, but rather it is more suitable for the property available energy.

EXAMPLE 10.1

A cylinder and piston assembly which contains 2 kg of water at 200 kPa, 20 °C, is heated at a constant pressure till the temperature of the water reaches 150 °C. A single reservoir at the lowest possible temperature is used for this purpose. The environment is at 100 kPa and 20 °C. Find:

a. The work of the water.
b. The heat interaction of the water.
c. The maximum work of the process between the two end states.

SOLUTION

We first find the properties of the water in the initial and final states as follows:

	p	T	x	v	u	h	s
1	200	20	–	0.001002	83.95	83.96	0.2966
2	200	150		0.9596	2576.90	2768.80	7.2795

State 1 is found by interpolation between saturation at 20 °C and the closest compressed liquid state at 20 °C.

a. The work in a constant-pressure process is

$$W = mp(v_2 - v_1) = 2 \times 200 \times (0.9596 - 0.001) = 383.4 \text{ kJ}$$

b. The process is isobaric; therefore the heat interaction is

$$Q = m(h_2 - h_1) = 2 \times (2768.8 - 83.96) = 5369.7 \text{ kJ}$$

c. The lowest reservoir temperature is 150 °C. The maximum work between the two given states of the system is the reversible work, which is equal to the negative change of the available energy of the system and the reservoir. Hence, for the system

$$\Delta\Omega = m\left[(u_2 - u_1) - T_0(s_2 - s_1)\right]$$
$$= 2\left[(2576.9 - 83.9) - 293.15(7.2795 - 0.2966)\right] = 891.8 \text{ kJ}$$

and for the reservoir

$$\Delta\Omega_R = -Q_R\left(1 - \frac{T_0}{T_R}\right) = -5369.7\left(1 - \frac{293.15}{423.15}\right) = -1649.6 \text{ kJ}$$

The maximum work between the two given states of the system is, therefore,

$$W_{rev} = -\left(\Delta\Omega + \Delta\Omega_R\right) = -891.8 + 1649.7 = 757.9 \text{ kJ}$$

The actual work is indeed much less than the maximum possible work between the end states of the process.

Is it possible to describe a process that would yield that work? In principle there is always such a process. For example, one way to obtain the maximum work from the process described in Example 10.1 is to introduce a reversible heat engine between the reservoir and the environment that would use heat from the reservoir, produce work, and reject heat to the environment. The heat to the system would be supplied by means of a reversible heat pump that uses work to supply heat from the environment to the system.

10.2 Useful work

In most cases of interest, the system is surrounded by an environment at pressure p_0 and temperature T_0. When the system undergoes a process that involves a change in volume, part of the work interaction of the system is done on the environment. The work on the environment is given by

$$W_0 = p_0(V_2 - V_1)$$

which is positive when the system expands, and negative when it contracts. That part of the work is usually of no interest. We define *useful work* as the work done by the system in excess of that on the environment:

$$W^u = W - p_0\Delta V \tag{10.15}$$

The maximum useful work of a system is then the reversible useful work:

$$W^u_{rev} = W_{rev} - p_0\Delta V \tag{10.16}$$

or

$$W^u_{rev} = -\Delta(U + p_0V - T_0S) \tag{10.17}$$

The quantity in parentheses is a property of the system relative to a given environment. It is called the available work and is denoted by Λ:

$$\Lambda = U + p_0V - T_0S \tag{10.18}$$

and the corresponding specific property is

$$\lambda = \Lambda/m = u + p_0v - T_0s \tag{10.19}$$

10.3 Irreversibility

We have seen that in real processes the system produces less work than could have been obtained under ideal conditions. The difference between the maximum work, i.e. the work that is obtained for a reversible process, and the actual work represents a loss that cannot be recovered. This difference is called the irreversibility of the process and is denoted by I:

$$I = W_{rev} - W \tag{10.20}$$

Substitution of W_{rev} from Eq. (10.6) into Eq. (10.20) yields

$$I = -[(U_2 - U_1) - T_0(S_2 - S_1)] - W \quad (10.21)$$

and by using the first law, Eq. (10.1), we obtain

$$I = T_0(S_2 - S_1) - Q_0 \quad (10.22)$$

Expressing Q_0 in terms of the entropy change of the environment, Eq. (10.2), leads to

$$I = T_0[(S_2 - S_1) + \Delta S_E] \quad (10.23)$$

Equation (10.23) shows that the total change of entropy of everything involved in the process is an indicator of the irreversibility of the process. We may note that "everything involved in the process" constitutes an adiabatic system. We know that an increase of entropy in an adiabatic process is associated with irreversibility. Equation (10.23) assigns a quantitative measure to that irreversibility. It should be noted that irreversibility is not a property of the system, since its value depends on the whole process and not just on the end states. Indeed, for reversible processes the irreversibility is zero.

Irreversibility was defined in Eq. (10.20) as the difference between reversible and actual work. An equivalent expression, in terms of useful work, can be obtained by substituting into Eq.(10.20) W_{rev} and W from Eqs. (10.16) and (10.15), respectively, leading to

$$I = W^u_{rev} - W^u \quad (10.24)$$

EXAMPLE 10.2

Find the irreversibility of the process of Example 10.1.

SOLUTION

Irreversibility is calculated using Eq. (10.20):

$$I = W_{rev} - W = 757.8 - 383.4 = 374.4 \text{ kJ}$$

Irreversibility can also be calculated on the basis of Eq. (10.23) as follows:

The change of entropy of the water is

$$\Delta S = m(s_2 - s_1) = 2 \times (7.2795 - 0.2966) = 13.966 \text{ kJ/K}$$

The change of entropy of the reservoir is

$$\Delta S_R = \frac{Q_R}{T_R} = -\frac{5369.7}{423.15} = -12.689 \text{ kJ/K}$$

The environment was not involved in the process; therefore

$$\Delta S_E = 0$$

Now, combining

$$I = T_0(\Delta S + \Delta S_R + \Delta S_E) = 293.15(13.966 - 12.689) = 374.4 \text{ kJ}$$

10.4 Availability

In a previous section we dealt with the work of a reversible process between given end states of a system when heat interactions are allowed with the environment only. A question may be raised: what is the absolute maximum work that can be obtained from a system at a given state in conjunction with a given environment? We allow any changes in the state of the system and we look for the one that yields the most work. Obviously, if the system is in mutual equilibrium with the environment, no work can be obtained from the system (see Chapter 5); such a state is sometimes called a *dead state*. In order to do work, the system must start from a state which is not in equilibrium with the environment. Maximum work can then be obtained by a reversible process that would bring the system to mutual equilibrium with the environment.

The maximum work can be calculated, without referring to a specific process, from Eq. (10.9), where the final state is the dead state, or the state of mutual equilibrium with the environment. We denote that state by the subscript 0.

$$W_{max} = \Omega - \Omega_0 = (U - U_0) - T_0(S - S_0) \tag{10.25}$$

The equivalent expression in terms of useful work, i.e. the maximum work in excess of that done on the environment, is

$$W^u_{max} = \Lambda - \Lambda_0 = (U - U_0) - T_0(S - S_0) + p_0(V - V_0) \tag{10.26}$$

For a given environment W^u_{max} depends on the initial state of the system only and thus it is a property. This property is called the availability and is denoted by Φ:

$$\Phi = \Lambda - \Lambda_0 = (U - U_0) - T_0(S - S_0) + p_0(V - V_0) \tag{10.27}$$

and the specific availability is

$$\phi = \lambda - \lambda_0 = (u - u_0) - T_0(s - s_0) + p_0(v - v_0) \tag{10.28}$$

Thus the availability of a system at a given state describes the maximum useful work that the system can perform in conjunction with the environment. Note that the availability can have a different value, if a different environment is considered.

The maximum useful work that a system can perform between two given states, while having heat interactions with the environment only, is equal to the decrease of the availability of the system between these end states. This maximum work is, obviously, the same as the reversible useful work between the two states:

$$\begin{aligned} W^u_{max} &= W^u_{rev} = -(\Phi_2 - \Phi_1) \\ &= -m\left[\left(u_2 - u_1\right) - T_0\left(s_2 - s_1\right) + p_0\left(v_2 - v_1\right)\right] \end{aligned} \tag{10.29}$$

The availability, Eq. (10.27), differs from the available work of the system, Eq. (10.18), by a constant, and therefore the change in availability between two given end states is also the change in available work between these states:

$$\Delta\Phi = \Delta\Lambda \tag{10.30}$$

While the available work may attain both positive and negative values, depending on the selection of the reference state, the availability is never negative. It is equal to zero only when the system is in a state of mutual equilibrium with the environment.

EXAMPLE 10.3

A system consists of a very long cylinder covered by a piston containing 0.032 m^3 of compressed air at 20 MPa and 25 °C. The environment is air at 101 kPa and 25 °C. Assuming that there are no limitations on the expansion of the piston find the maximum useful work that may be obtained from the system.

SOLUTION

The maximum work will be obtained when the final state of the air in the cylinder is that of the environment. The maximum work between the initial and final states is calculated from Eq. (10.26):

$$W^u_{max} = \Lambda - \Lambda_0 = (U - U_0) - T_0(S - S_0) + p_0(V - V_0)$$
$$= m\left[(u - u_0) - T_0(s - s_0) + p_0(v - v_0)\right]$$

$$m = \frac{pV}{RT} = \frac{20000 \times 0.032}{(8.3143/29) \times 298.15} = 7.487 \text{ kg}$$

$$u_1 - u_0 = c_v(T_1 - T_0) = 0$$

$$T_0(s - s_0) = c_p T_0 \ln\frac{T}{T_0} - RT_0 \ln\frac{p}{p_0} = -RT_0 \ln\frac{p}{p_0}$$

$$p_0(v - v_0) = p_0 v_0\left(\frac{v}{v_0} - 1\right) = RT_0\left(\frac{p_0 T}{pT_0} - 1\right) = RT_0\left(\frac{p_0}{p} - 1\right)$$

$$W^u_{max} = W^u_{rev} = mRT_0\left[(0) + \ln\frac{p}{p_0} + \frac{p_0}{p} - 1\right] = pV\left[\ln\frac{p}{p_0} + \frac{p_0}{p} - 1\right]$$
$$= 20000 \times 0.032\left[\ln\frac{20}{0.101} + \frac{0.101}{20} - 1\right] = 2747.8 \text{ kJ}$$

EXAMPLE 10.4

Find the maximum work and the maximum useful work that can be done with respect to an environment at 0.1 MPa, 27 °C, by:

a. 5 kg of steam at 360 °C and 0.5 MPa.
b. 5 kg of steam at 360 °C and 0.1 MPa.
c. 5 kg of steam at 360 °C and 10.0 MPa.
d. 5 kg of steam at 360 °C and 30.0 MPa.

SOLUTION

$$W_{max} = \Omega - \Omega_0 = m[(u - u_0) - T_0(s - s_0)$$

$$W^u_{max} = \Lambda - \Lambda_0 = \Phi = m[(u - u_0) - T_0(s - s_0) + p_0(v - v_0)]$$

We solve the problem by summarizing the relevant data for steam at the state of equilibrium with the environment and at the four initial states (a)–(d).

We calculate $\Omega - \Omega_0$ and $\Phi = \Lambda - \Lambda_0$, noting that $T_0 = 27 + 273.15 = 300.15$ K and $p_0 = 100$ kPa. The calculated values are entered into the table below.

State	p kPa	T °C	v m³/kg	u kJ/kg	s kJ/kg K	Ω–Ω_0 kJ	Φ kJ
0	100	27	0.0010035	113.25	0.3952	0.0	0.0
a	500	360	0.5796	2898.72	7.6651	3017.1	3306.4
b	100	360	2.9174	2904.90	8.4124	1926.4	3384.6
c	10000	360	0.023218	2725.84	5.9978	4654.8	4665.9
d	30000	360	0.0016265	1675.40	3.7494	2532.9	2533.2

In this example we compared the maximum work and maximum useful work of a fixed amount of steam at a given temperature but various pressures. We note that the highest value of the maximum work is not necessarily obtained at the highest pressure. Steam at (d), for example, could produce less work than that at (c) or even at (b). At high pressure the steam is compressed liquid and has substantially less energy.

We also note that the maximum useful work is different from the maximum work since it depends strongly on the initial volume of the steam. Thus steam at 0.1 MPa can produce more useful work (but less work) than steam at a higher pressure of 0.5 MPa.

EXAMPLE 10.5

A water heater tank contains 150 kg of water at 6.0 bar, 15 °C. The water is to be heated to 6.0 bar, 75 °C. (Assume that the pressure is maintained constant by an internal diaphragm.) The environment is at 1.0 bar, 10 °C. Find:

a. The change in the availability of the water.
b. The total change in availability when heated electrically.
c. The total change in availability when heated by condensing steam at $p = 1.0$ bar.
d. The irreversibility in (b).
e. The irreversibility in (c).

SOLUTION

We list the data in a table. The state of the system in equilibrium with the environment is denoted by 0, and the initial and final states are denoted by 1 and 2, respectively.

State	p MPa	T °C	v m³/kg	u kJ/kg	h kJ/kg	s kJ/kg K
0	0.1	10	0.0010004	42.01	42.11	0.1510
1	0.6	15	0.0010009	62.99	63.59	0.2245
2	0.6	75	0.0010259	313.90	314.52	1.0155

a. The change in the availability of the water is found from Eq.(10.40)

$$\Delta\Phi = m\,\Delta\phi = m[(u_2 - u_1) - T_0(s_2 - s_1) + p_0(v_2 - v_1)]$$
$$= 150[(313.90 - 62.99) - 283.15(1.0155 - 0.2245)$$
$$+100(0.0010259 - 0.0010009)] = 150 \times 26.94 = 4040 \text{ kJ}$$

b. In this case there is no heat interaction. The work interaction is the sum of volume work and electric work. The change in the energy of the system is given by the first law as

$$\Delta U = U_2 - U_1 = -W = -W_{el} - p\Delta V$$

from which the electric work of the system W_{el} can be calculated as

$$W_{el} = -m(h_2 - h_1) = -150 \times (314.52 - 63.59) = -37640 \text{ kJ}$$

The change in the availability of the water is $\Delta\Phi = 4040$ kJ.

The work of the electric source W_{source} is equal in magnitude and opposite in sign to the electric work of the system. Hence, the change in the availability of the source of the electricity is

$$\Delta\Phi_{source} = -W_{source} = W_{el} = -37640 \text{ kJ}$$

The total change in availability is then

$$\Delta\Phi_{total} = \Delta\Phi_{source} + \Delta\Phi = -37640 + 4040 = -33600 \text{ kJ}$$

c. In this case the heat interaction with the steam is

$$Q = U_2 - U_1 + p(V_2 - V_1) = H_2 - H_1 = m(h_2 - h_1) = 37640 \text{ kJ}$$

The change in the availability of the water is $\Delta\Phi = 4040$ kJ.

The change in the availability of the steam is the same as the change in the availability of a reservoir at $T_R = 372.78$ K:

$$\Delta\Phi_{steam} = Q(1 - T_0/T_R) = -37640 \times (1 - 283.15/372.78) = -9050 \text{ kJ}$$

$$\Delta\Phi_{total} = 4040 - 9050 = -5010 \text{ kJ}$$

d. The irreversibility in process (b) is found from Eq. (10.23):

$$I = T_0(\Delta S + \Delta S_E)$$

In this process there is no change of entropy in the environment; hence,

$$I = mT_0(s_2 - s_1) = 150 \times 283.15 \times (1.0155 - 0.2245) = 33600 \text{ kJ}.$$

e. In this case the change of entropy of the system plus the steam must be considered:

$$I = T_0(\Delta S + \Delta S_{steam}) = T_0(m\Delta s + (-Q)/T_R)$$
$$= 283.15 \times [150 \times (1.0155 - 0.2245) - 37640/372.78] = 5007 \text{ kJ}$$

Comparing the results of (d) and (e) we note that using electrical work for heating resulted in a higher degree of irreversibility than in steam heating. Moreover, since no work was performed in process (c) the total reduction in the availability of this process is equal to its irreversibility.

10.5 Control volume analysis – exergy

The analysis of a control volume differs considerably from that of a closed system. In general, the control volume may have work and heat interactions, its state may change, and there may be changes in the streams that flow across the boundary.

Consider a control volume, Fig. 10.3, having any number of incoming and outgoing flows. All the required heat interactions are done with a single reservoir, say the environment. If the respective temperatures of the system and the environment cannot permit the required heat interaction, a heat engine or a heat pump is employed to facilitate that interaction. The total power, including that of the heat engine, is calculated from the first law as

$$\dot{W}_x = \dot{Q}_0 - \left(\frac{dU}{dt}\right)_{cv} + \sum_{i=1}^{k} h_1^0 \, \dot{m}_i \tag{10.31}$$

where $\dot{Q}_0$ is the rate of heat transfer from the environment (possibly via a heat engine).

Here again, for given inlet and outlet fluxes and a given rate of change within the control volume, the last two terms in Eq. (10.31) are fixed and are independent of the process that takes place within the control volume. On the other hand, the rate of heat transfer, Q_0 does depend on the process. The higher the rate of heat transfer into the control volume, the higher the power that is obtained from it. The rate of heat input into the control volume, which equals the rate of heat loss by the environment, may be expressed in terms of the rate of change of entropy of the environment:

$$\dot{Q}_0 = -\dot{Q}_E = -T_0\left(\frac{dS_E}{dt}\right) \tag{10.32}$$

We note that the combination of the control volume and the environment is adiabatic; hence

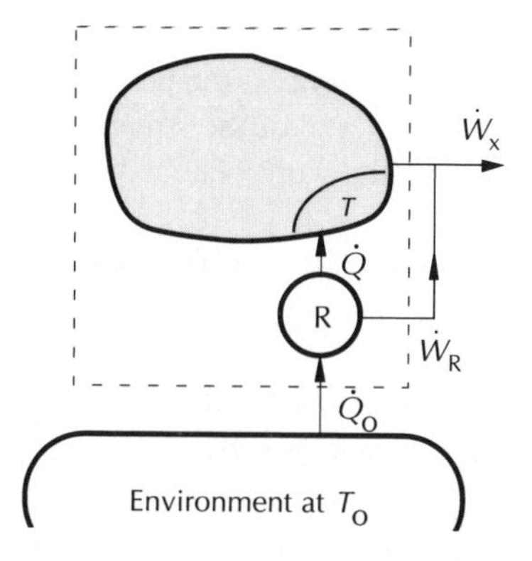

Figure 10.3 **Control volume interacting with the environment.**

$$\frac{d}{dt}\left(S_{cv}+S_E\right)-\sum_{i=1}^{k} s_i\dot{m}_i \geq 0 \tag{10.33}$$

Substituting Eqs (10.32) and (10.33) into Eq. (10.31) yields

$$\dot{W}_x \leq -\left[\frac{d(U-T_0S)}{dt}\right]_{cv}+\sum_{i=1}^{k}\left(h_i^0-T_0s_i\right)\dot{m}_i \tag{10.34}$$

The right hand side of Eq. (10.34) can be expressed in terms of the property specific available enthalpy, or specific exergy, defined by Eq. (10.14):

$$b = h - T_0 s \tag{10.35}$$

The specific stagnation exergy is then

$$b^0 = h^0 - T_0 s \tag{10.36}$$

Thus Eq. (10.34) becomes

$$\dot{W}_x \leq -\left(\frac{d\Omega}{dt}\right)_{cv}+\sum_{i=1}^{k} b_i^0\,\dot{m}_i \tag{10.37}$$

The inequality applies to irreversible processes within the control volume. For reversible processes the equality holds, resulting in maximum power output:

$$\left(\dot{W}_x\right)_{max}=\left(\dot{W}_x\right)_{rev}=-\left(\frac{d\Omega}{dt}\right)_{cv}+\sum_{i=1}^{k} b_i^0\,\dot{m}_i \tag{10.38}$$

At steady state there are no changes in properties within the control volume. Hence,

$$\left(\dot{W}_x\right)_{rev}=\sum_{i=1}^{k} b_i^o\dot{m}_i \tag{10.39}$$

and for cases where potential and kinetic energy effects are negligible

$$\left(\dot{W}_x\right)_{rev}=\sum_{i=1}^{k} b_i\dot{m}_i \;=\; \dot{B}_{in}-\dot{B}_{out} \tag{10.40}$$

Equation (10.40) indicates that in a steady state reversible process the power output of the control volume is equal to the rate of decrease of the exergy of the streams crossing the control volume. Obviously, for an irreversible process the work obtained is less than the loss of exergy of the streams.

For a steady state process in a two-port control volume Eq. (10.40) is modified as

$$\left(\dot{W}_x\right)_{rev}=\dot{m}\left(b_1-b_2\right) \tag{10.41}$$

The maximum work in a steady state process is directly related to the change of the exergy of the fluid crossing the control volume. Steady state processes are quite common in practical applications. These include flows in pumps, compressors, turbines, heat exchangers, chemical reactors, etc. Second-law, or exergy, analysis has gained in importance in recent years, since it can provide information on the maximum possible performance in such processes, and also point out where losses occur and how extensive they are.

The *useful work of a control volume* is defined in the same manner as for a closed system, i.e. as the work done by the control volume on all other systems excluding the environment. Thus,

$$W_x^u = W_x - p_0 \Delta V_{cv} \tag{10.42}$$

and the useful power is

$$\dot{W}_x^u = \dot{W}_x - p_0 \left(\frac{dV}{dt} \right)_{cv} \tag{10.43}$$

Substitution of Eq. (10.34) into Eq. (10.43) yields

$$\dot{W}_x^u \le -\left[\frac{d(U + p_0 V - T_0 S)}{dt} \right]_{cv} + \sum_{i=1}^{k} \left(h_i^0 - T_0 s_i \right) \dot{m}_i \tag{10.44}$$

or

$$\dot{W}_x^u \le -\left[\frac{d\Lambda}{dt} \right]_{cv} + \sum_{i=1}^{k} \left(h_i^o - T_0 s_i \right) \dot{m}_i \tag{10.45}$$

Using the property exergy we rewrite Eqs (10.44) or (10.45) as

$$\dot{W}_x^u \le -\left[\frac{d(U + p_0 V - T_0 S)}{dt} \right]_{cv} + \sum_{i=1}^{k} b_i^o \dot{m}_i \tag{10.46}$$

and

$$\dot{W}_x^u \le -\left[\frac{d\Lambda}{dt} \right]_{cv} + \sum_{i=1}^{k} b_i^o \dot{m}_i \tag{10.47}$$

Of course the maximum useful power of a control volume is given by the right hand side of Eqs (10.46)–(10.47) for the case of a reversible process. Hence, for a reversible process

$$\left(\dot{W}_x^u \right)_{rev} = -\left[\frac{d(U + p_0 V - T_0 S)}{dt} \right]_{cv} + \sum_{i=1}^{k} b_i^o \dot{m}_i \tag{10.48}$$

$$\left(\dot{W}_x^u \right)_{rev} = -\left[\frac{d\Lambda}{dt} \right]_{cv} + \sum_{i=1}^{k} b_i^o \dot{m}_i \tag{10.49}$$

It is obvious, from Eq. (10.30), that the term $d\Lambda/dt$ in Eqs (10.45), (10.47), and (10.49) can be replaced by $d\Phi/dt$.

For a control volume with a single port that exhausts to the environment, Eq. (10.49) may be modified with the help of Eq. (6.48) to yield

$$\left(\dot{W}_x^u \right)_{max} = \left(\dot{W}_x^u \right)_{rev} = -\left[\frac{d\Lambda}{dt} \right]_{cv} + b_0 \left(\frac{dm}{dt} \right)_{cv} \tag{10.50}$$

where b_0 is the exergy of the matter that leaves the control volume and attains equilibrium with the environment, when it reaches its temperature and pressure. For a finite change between two states Eq. (10.50) reads

$$W_{rev}^{u} = -\Delta\Lambda_{cv} + b_0 \Delta m_{cv} \tag{10.51}$$

At steady state there are no changes in the properties within the control volume. Therefore, the first term on the right hand side of each of Eqs (10.44)–(10.49) vanishes, and the useful power is exactly equal to the power of the control volume. The maximum power in steady state is then

$$\left(\dot{W}_x\right)_{max}^{u} = \left(\dot{W}_x\right)_{rev}^{u} = \left(\dot{W}_x\right)_{rev} = \sum_{i=1}^{k} b_i^0 \dot{m}_i = \left(\dot{B}^0\right)_{in} - \left(\dot{B}^0\right)_{out} \tag{10.52}$$

while the actual power is

$$\dot{W}_x^u = \dot{W}_x \leq \sum_{i=1}^{k} b_i^0 \dot{m}_i = \left(\dot{B}^0\right)_{in} - \left(\dot{B}^0\right)_{out} \tag{10.53}$$

The irreversibility of a process within a control volume is again defined as the difference between the reversible work and the actual work. In terms of rate processes the expression for the rate of irreversibility is given as

$$\dot{I} = (\dot{W}_x)_{rev} - \dot{W}_x \tag{10.54}$$

Substitution of Eqs (10.38) and (10.31) into Eq. (10.54) results in

$$\dot{I} = T_0\left[\left(\frac{dS}{dt}\right)_{cv} - \sum_{i=1}^{k} s_i \dot{m}_i\right] - \dot{Q}_0 \tag{10.55}$$

Replacing $\dot{Q}_0$ from Eq. (10.32) one obtains

$$\dot{I} = T_0\left[\left(\frac{dS}{dt}\right)_{cv} + \left(\frac{dS}{dt}\right)_{E} - \sum_{i=1}^{k} s_i \dot{m}_i\right] \tag{10.56}$$

Once again the total change of entropy is an indicator of the irreversibility of the process. Note that the negative sign in the summation of Eq. (10.56) indicates that the entropy of the incoming streams should be subtracted, and that of the outgoing streams added.

EXAMPLE 10.6

A system consists of 0.032 m^3 of compressed air at 20 MPa and 25 °C inside a rigid tank with a control valve. The environment is air at 101 kPa and 25 °C.

Find the maximum useful work that may be obtained from the system.

SOLUTION

This problem is similar to Example 10.3. The difference is that here air is allowed to leave the tank and mix with the air outside. It is obvious that the compressed air will attain equilibrium with the environment when it reaches its temperature and pressure. The maximum work between the initial state and that of the environment may be obtained by installing a reversible work-producing device (say, a turbine) between the tank and the environment. This work is calculated from Eq. (10.51):

$$W^u_{rev} = -\Delta\Lambda_{cv} + b_0 \Delta m_{cv}$$

Now

$$-\Delta\Lambda_{cv} = m(u - T_0 s + p_0 v) - m_0(u_0 - T_0 s_0 + p_0 v_0)$$

where m_0 is the mass remaining in the control volume at the final state:

$$b_0 \Delta m = (h_0 - T_0 s_0)(m_0 - m)$$

Hence

$$\begin{aligned} W^u_{rev} &= -\Delta\Lambda_{cv} + b_0 \Delta m \\ &= m(u - T_0 s + p_0 v) - m_0(u_0 - T_0 s_0 + p_0 v_0) + (h_0 - T_0 s_0)(m_0 - m) \\ &= m\left[(u - T_0 s + p_0 v) - (h_0 - T_0 s_0)\right] \\ &= m\left[(u - T_0 s + p_0 v) - (u_0 + p_0 v_0 - T_0 s_0)\right] \\ &= m\left[(u - u_0) - T_0(s - s_0) + p_0(v - v_0)\right] \end{aligned}$$

We obtained an identical expression for the maximum useful work as the one in Example 10.3. Therefore, the answer is also the same, namely

$$W^u_{max} = W^u_{rev} = mRT_0\left[(0) + \ln\frac{p_0}{p} + \frac{p_0}{p} - 1\right] = pV\left[\ln\frac{p_0}{p} + \frac{p_0}{p} - 1\right]$$

$$= 20000 \times 0.032\left[\ln\frac{20}{0.101} + \frac{0.101}{20} - 1\right] = 2747.8 \text{ kJ}$$

EXAMPLE 10.7

A plant that has two supply lines, one of steam at 300 °C, 3.0 MPa, and another of water at 300 °C, 10 MPa, requires saturated steam at 200 °C at a rate of 2.5 kg/s. It was suggested that an adiabatic mixing chamber with suitable pressure reducing valves, as shown in Fig. 10.4, could be used to generate the required saturated steam. The environment is at 25 °C and 101 kPa. Find:

a. The flowrates of the water and the steam.
b. The absolute exergy entering and exiting the mixing chamber.

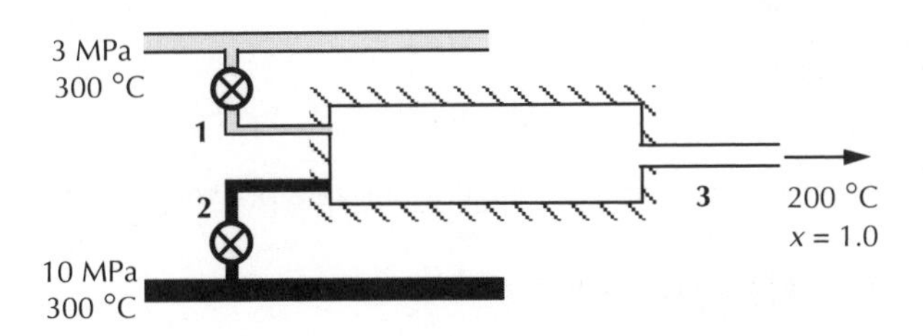

Figure 10.4 **Adiabatic mixing chamber.**

c. The maximum useful work of the process.
d. The irreversibility of the process.

SOLUTION

We arrange the properties of the steam at ports 1–3 and also its properties (it turns out to be compressed liquid) when it is in pressure and temperature equilibrium with the environment (state 0). The underlined properties are known a priori and the properties h and s are taken from the steam tables.

State	p MPa	T °C	x	h kJ/kg	s kJ/kg K	b kJ/kg	$\underline{b}=b-b_0$ kJ/kg
0	$\underline{0.101}$	$\underline{25}$	–	104.89	0.3674	−4.65	0.00
1	$\underline{3.000}$	$\underline{300}$	–	2993.5	6.5390	1043.90	1048.55
2	$\underline{10.000}$	$\underline{300}$	–	1342.3	3.2469	374.24	378.89
3	(1.554)	$\underline{200}$	$\underline{1.00}$	2793.2	6.4323	875.41	880.06

The available enthalpy is calculated by Eq. (10.18): $b = h - T_0 s$
The absolute available enthalpy, or exergy, is: $\underline{b} = b - b_0$

a. The mass flowrate at the exit is given as: $\dot{m}_3 = 2.5$ kg/s
The other mass flowrates are calculated from the continuity equation and the first law equation for a control volume in steady state:

$$\dot{m}_1 + \dot{m}_2 + \dot{m}_3 = 0$$
$$\dot{m}_1 h_1 + \dot{m}_2 h_2 + \dot{m}_3 h_3 = 0$$

Thus,

$$\dot{m}_1 = -\dot{m}_3 \frac{h_3 - h_2}{h_1 - h_2} = 2.5 \frac{2793.2 - 1342.3}{2993.5 - 1342.3} = 2.197 \text{ kg/s}$$

$$\dot{m}_2 = -\dot{m}_3 \frac{h_3 - h_1}{h_2 - h_1} = 2.5 \frac{2793.2 - 2993.5}{1342.3 - 2993.5} = 0.303 \text{ kg/s}$$

b. The absolute exergy entering the chamber is

$$\dot{\underline{B}}_{in} = \dot{m}_1 \underline{b}_1 + \dot{m}_2 \underline{b}_2 = 2.197 \times 1048.55 + 0.303 \times 378.89 = 2418.5 \text{ kW}$$

$$\dot{\underline{B}}_{out} = \dot{m}_3 \underline{b}_3 = 2.5 \times 880.06 = 2188.5 \text{ kW}$$

The rate of exergy decrease for the process is

$$\dot{\underline{B}}_{in} - \dot{\underline{B}}_{out} = 2406.7 - 2188.5 = 218.2 \text{ kW}$$

c. The maximum useful power of the process is equal to the rate of exergy decrease of the streams:

$$\dot{W}_{max} = \dot{W}_{rev} = \dot{\underline{B}}_{in} - \dot{\underline{B}}_{out} = 218.2 \text{ kW}$$

d. The irreversibility is equal to the difference between the maximum work and the actual work. The latter is zero for this case. Thus, the irreversibility is exactly equal to the maximum work:

$$\dot{I} = \dot{W}_{rev} - \dot{W} = 218.2 \text{ kW}$$

In other words, the irreversibility is equal to work that could have been done, but was actually lost.

Note that from the standpoint of the first law there was no loss whatsoever, since the enthalpy going out was the same as that coming in.

Table 10.1 **Summary table.**

	Closed system	**Open system**
First law	$dU = dQ - dW$	$\left(\frac{dU}{dt}\right)_{cv} = \dot{Q} - \dot{W}_x + \sum h_i^{o} \dot{m}_i$
Second law	$dS \geq \frac{dQ}{T}$	$\left(\frac{dS}{dt}\right)_{cv} = \frac{\dot{Q}j}{Tj} + \sum s_i \dot{m}_i$

Concept	**Property**	**Specific property**
Available energy	$\Omega = U - T_0 S$	$\omega = u - T_0 s$
Exergy	$B = H - T_0 S$	$b = h - T_0 s$
Available work	$\Lambda = U - T_0 S + p_0 V$	$\lambda = u - T_0 s + p_0 v$
Availability	$\Phi = \Lambda - \Lambda_0$ $= (U - U_0) - T_0(S - S_0)$ $+ p_0(V - V_0)$	$\phi = \lambda - \lambda_0$ $= (u - u_0) - T_0(s - s_0)$ $+ p_0(v - v_0)$

Table 10.1 **Summary table** (continued)

Quantity	Reversible process	Irreversible process
Work of system	$W_{rev} = -\Delta\Omega$	$W < -\Delta\Omega$
	$\Delta\Omega = m[(u_2 - u_1) - T_0(s_2 - s_1)]$	
Useful work of system	$W^u_{rev} = -\Delta\Lambda$	$W^u = W - mp_0(v_2 - v_1)$
	$\Delta\Lambda = m[(u_2 - u_1) - T_0(s_2 - s_1) + p_0(v_2 - v_1)]$	
Maximum work of system	$W_{max} = W_{rev} = \Omega - \Omega_0 = m[(u - u_0) - T_0(s - s_0)]$	
Maximum useful work of system	$W^u_{max} = W^u_{rev} = \Phi = m[(u - u_0) - T_0(s - s_0) + p_0(v - v_0)]$	
Irreversibility for system	$I = 0$	$I = W_{rev} - W = W^u_{rev} - W^u$ $= T_0(\Delta S_{sys} + \Delta S_{envir}) \geq 0$
Work of control volume	$\left(\dot{W}_x\right)_{rev} = -\left(\frac{d\Omega}{dt}\right)_{cv} + \sum b_i^0 \dot{m}_i$	$\dot{W}_x < -\left(\frac{d\Omega}{dt}\right)_{cv} + \sum b_i^0 \dot{m}_i$
Useful work of control volume	$\left(\dot{W}_x\right)^u_{rev} = -\left(\frac{d\Phi}{dt}\right)_{cv} + \sum b_i^0 \dot{m}_i$	$\left(\dot{W}_x\right)^u < -\left(\frac{d\Phi}{dt}\right)_{cv} + \sum b_i^0 \dot{m}_i$
Irreversibility for control volume	$\dot{I} = 0$	$\dot{I} = (\dot{W}_x)_{rev} - \dot{W}_x \geq 0$ $\dot{I} = T_0\left[\left(\frac{dS}{dt}\right)_{cv} - \sum s_i \dot{m}_i\right] - \dot{Q}_0$

PROBLEMS

10.1 The environment is air at 300 K and 102 kPa. Determine the availability of a closed system containing:

a. Air at 102 kPa, 300 K.
b. Air at 200 kPa, 300 K.
c. Air at 102 kPa, 600 K.
d. Air at 50 kPa, 600 K.
e. Air at 50 kPa, 300 K.
f. Air at 50 kPa, 150 K.
g. Repeat parts a–f for water instead of air.

10.2 A completely evacuated container has a volume of 0.16 m^3. The environment is air at 300 K and 102 kPa.

a. Determine the maximum work that can be obtained from the system.
b. Determine the maximum useful work that can be obtained from the system.

10.3 A mass of 2.0 kg of oxygen (O_2) in a cylinder and piston assembly is compressed by an internally reversible isothermal process at 438 K from 0.18 MPa to 3.2 MPa. Assume the surroundings to be air at 300 K and 1.02 bar.

a. Discuss the requirements for additional reservoirs to accomplish the process.
b. Determine the work and heat interactions of the oxygen.
c. Determine the maximum work of the process.

10.4 A mass of 2 kg of water (H_2O) in a cylinder and piston assembly is compressed by an internally reversible isothermal process at 438 K from 0.18 MPa to 3.2 MPa. Assume the surroundings to be air at 300 K and 1.02 bar.

a. Discuss the requirements for additional reservoirs to accomplish the process.
b. Determine the work and heat interactions of the water.
c. Determine the maximum work of the process.

10.5 A mass of 2 kg of oxygen (O_2) in a cylinder and piston assembly expands by an internally reversible isothermal process at 438 K from 3.2 MPa to 0.18 MPa. Assume the surroundings to be air at 300 K and 1.02 bar.

a. Discuss the requirements for additional reservoirs to accomplish the process.
b. Determine the work and heat interactions of the oxygen.
c. Determine the maximum work of the process.

10.6 A mass of 2 kg of water (H_2O) in a cylinder and piston assembly expands by an internally reversible isothermal process at 438 K from 3.2 MPa to 0.18 MPa. Assume the surroundings to be air at 300 K and 1.02 bar.

a. Discuss the requirements for additional reservoirs to accomplish the process.
b. Determine the work and heat interactions of the water.
c. Determine the maximum work of the process.

10.7 A well-insulated tank contains 1.5 kg of air, initially at 100 kPa, 47 °C. An impeller inside the tank is operated by an external mechanism till the pressure inside reaches 125 kPa. The environment is air at 300 K and 1.02 bar. Determine:

a. The useful work of the system.
b. The maximum useful work (minimum input) for the same change of state.
c. The irreversibility of the process.

10.8 Steam at 16 MPa and 400 °C enters a throttling valve, and exits at 0.3 MPa. Assume negligible inlet and exit velocities. The environment is air at 300 K and 102 kPa. Determine the irreversibility for each of the following process conditions:

a. The valve is adiabatic.
b. A heat reservoir maintains the air at 400 °C throughout the valve.

10.9 A reservoir at 500 °C receives 1000 kJ of heat. The environment is air at 102 kPa, 20 °C.

a. Determine the change of availability of the reservoir.
b. Could heat be added to the reservoir reversibly? Explain briefly.

10.10 Given an environment at 300 K and 101 kPa determine the change in availability for the following processes:

a. A heat interaction of 750 kJ between a reservoir at 75 °C and the environment.
b. A heat interaction of 750 kJ between a reservoir at (–75)°C and the environment.
c. A heat interaction of 750 kJ between the two reservoirs.

10.11 Find the availability of empty space relative to an environment at 300 K and 101 kPa.

10.12 Given an environment at 300 K and 101 kPa:

a. Determine the availability of 1 kg of air (ideal gas, $k = 1.4$, $M = 29$) at 0.4 MPa and 0.4 m^3.
b. Determine the change in availability of the air upon doubling its volume in a reversible adiabatic process.
c. Determine the change in availability of the air upon doubling its volume in a reversible isothermal process.
d. Determine the change in availability of the air upon doubling its volume in an adiabatic process without work.

10.13 Given an environment at 300 K and 101 kPa, find the maximum useful work in the following processes:

a. Two kg of air at 300 °C expand quasistatically from 200 kPa to 50 kPa, while having a heat interaction with a reservoir at 360 °C.
b. Water at 20 °C and 101 kPa is converted into vapor at 100 °C.

10.14 Given an environment at 300 K and 101 kPa, find the maximum useful work when a 100 L vessel, containing oxygen at 500 °C and 1 MPa, is brought into contact with a reservoir at 200 °C and allowed to come to mutual equilibrium with it.

10.15 Steam at 5 MPa and 400 °C expands through an adiabatic turbine at a rate of 0.1 kg/s and an isentropic efficiency of 0.8. At the outlet of the turbine the pressure is 10 kPa. The environment is at 300 K and 101 kPa. Find:

a. The state of the steam at the outlet of the turbine.
b. The power developed by the turbine.
c. The maximum power the turbine could develop for the same inlet and outlet conditions.

10.16 For an environment at 300 K and 101 kPa find:

a. The availability of 1 kg of saturated water at 3 MPa.
b. The availability of 1 kg of saturated steam at 3 MPa.
c. The availability of 1 kg of superheated steam at 3 MPa and 400 °C.

10.17 One kmol of an ideal gas with constant heat capacity, c_p = 20 kJ/kmol K, is compressed adiabatically from 100 kPa and 10 °C to 0.5 MPa. The process is irreversible and requires twice the work than a reversible adiabatic compression from the initial to the final state.

a. How much work is required?
b. What is the entropy change of the gas?
c. What is the irreversibility of the process?

10.18 An adiabatic cylinder contains 0.15 m^3 of air (ideal gas, M = 29, k = 1.4) at 40 °C under a floating piston which exerts a pressure equal to 1.2 MPa (Fig.10.5). The volume above the piston is 0.05 m^3 and it is completely evacuated. At a certain moment the piston breaks up and falls to the bottom of the cylinder.

a. Find the entropy change of the air.
b. Find the change in availability of the entire system if the environment is air at 102 kPa, 22 °C.

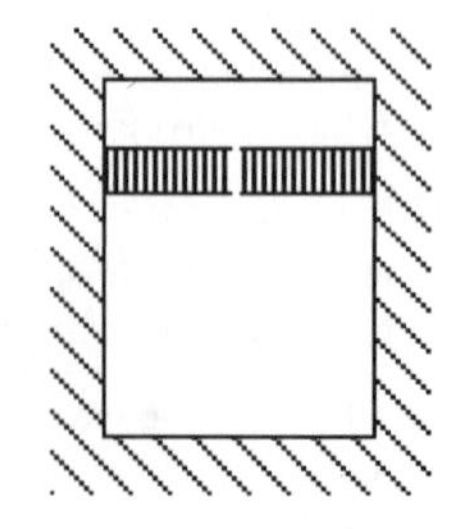

Figure 10.5

10.19 An adiabatic turbojet engine nozzle receives 100 kg/h of gas, that may be considered as air, at 200 kPa, 700 °C, and 60 m/s. The gas leaves the nozzle at 80 kPa. The nozzle efficiency is 90%. The environment is air at 300 K and 102 kPa. Determine:

a. The exit velocity.
b. The irreversibility of the process.

10.20 A 30 L can of compressed air is suspended in a large atmosphere the pressure of which is p_0 = 0.5 MPa and the temperature is T_0 = 40 °C. Initially the pressure of the air in the can is 1.5 MPa. A small hole is made in the can allowing air to escape slowly to the atmosphere. The process is carried out slowly enough so that the temperature of the air in the can is always the same as in its environment.

a. Determine the heat interaction of the can during the process.
b. What is the irreversibility of the process?

10.21 Compressed air (ideal gas, k = 1.4, M = 29) at a pressure of 1.5 MPa and temperature of 80 °C contained in a 0.4 m^3 tank is used to operate machinery on Pyke's Peak where the barometric pressure is 70 kPa and the temperature is 5 °C.

a. What is the maximum work that can be delivered to the machinery if the air can undergo no heat interactions?
b. What is the maximum work that can be delivered to the machinery without any restriction on heat transfer?

10.22 One kmol of an ideal gas with constant heat capacity, c_p = 20 kJ/kmol K, is compressed adiabatically from 10 kPa and 10 °C to 0.5 MPa. The process is irreversible and requires twice the work than a reversible adiabatic compression from the initial to the final state. The environment is air at 300 K and 102 kPa.

a. How much work is required?
b. What is the entropy change of the gas?
c. What is the irreversibility of the process?

10.23 What is the maximum electric power (per kilogram of water) that can be obtained from the hydroelectric power station located at the foot of a 300 m dam in Fig. 10.6? Water at 15 °C and 101 kPa enters the pipe at the top of the dam and flows downward, passing through a turbine and then out into a river. Assume that the pipe diameter is constant throughout, both inlet and outlet, and that the pressure and the temperature of the water at the outlet are approximately equal to those at the inlet, i.e. 101 kPa and 15 °C. The turbine drives a generator which produces the electric power output.

a. Derive an expression for the maximum power output; clearly state any additional assumptions which you may make.
b. Using this expression calculate the magnitude of the maximum power (per kilogram of water).

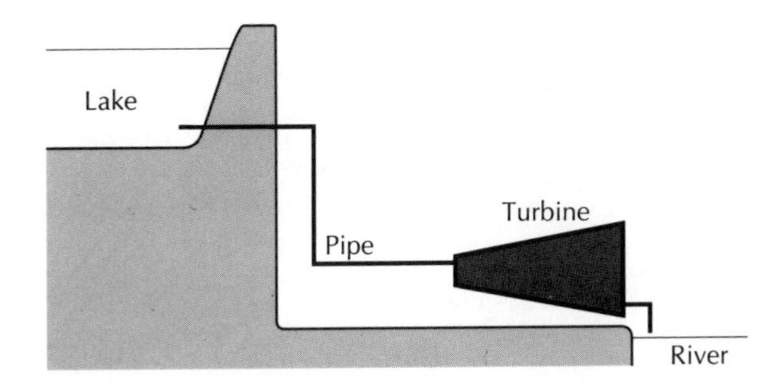

Figure 10.6

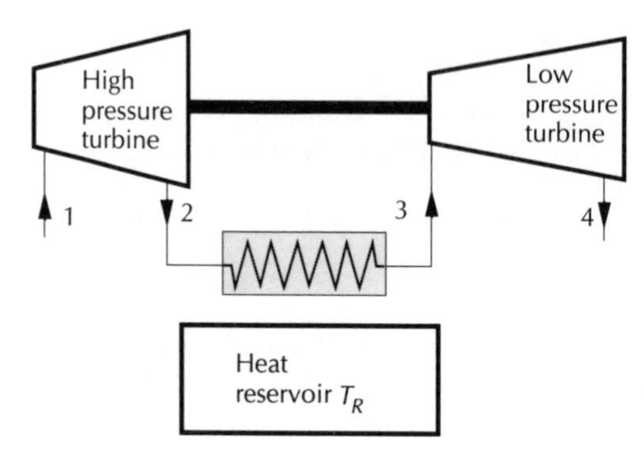

Figure 10.7

10.24 Figure 10.7 shows a two-stage steam turbine with reheat. Both stages may be considered adiabatic. Steam at p_1 = 20.0 MPa, T_1 = 500 °C, is supplied at a rate of 10^5 kg/h to the high pressure turbine and comes out of it saturated at p_2 = 3.0 MPa. Then it is reheated at a constant pressure by means of a heat reservoir at T_R = 560 °C until its temperature reaches T_3 = 450 °C, and finally after passing through the low pressure turbine it is exhausted saturated at p_4 = 0.24 MPa. The environment is air at p_a = 0.1 MPa, T_a = 5 °C. Find:

a. The power supplied by the turbine.
b. The heat flux.
c. The maximum power that can be obtained from the steam and the reservoir.
d. The irreversibility of the process.

10.25 An adiabatic vessel is divided by a partition into two parts. One part contains 20 kg of air at 20 °C and 100 kPa and the other 1 kg of air at 500 °C and 20 MPa. The environment is air at 100 kPa and 20 °C. The partition is ruptured and the contents of the vessel mix. Find the irreversibility of the mixing process.

10.26 An adiabatic vessel is divided by a partition into two parts. One part contains 20 kg of H_2O at 20 °C and 100 kPa and the other 1 kg of H_2O at 500 °C and 20 MPa. The environment is air at 100 kPa and 20 °C. The partition is ruptured and the contents of the vessel mix. Find the irreversibility of the mixing process.

10.27 Consider the following descriptions of a number of processes that take place in a closed system which contains 1 kg of water (H_2O) at 250 °C and 0.8 MPa. The surroundings are at 300 K and 1.02 bars and there are no other reservoirs, unless otherwise stated.

1. The volume of the system is doubled at a constant pressure by heating with the help of a reservoir at the lowest temperature allowable to complete the process.
2. The volume of the system is doubled at a constant pressure by rapid stirring of the system.
3. The volume of the system is doubled in an adiabatic and quasistatic process.
4. The volume of the system is doubled in an isothermal and quasistatic process by heating with the help of a reservoir at the lowest temperature allowable to complete the process.
5. The volume of the system is doubled by expansion into an empty vessel connected to the system by a pipe.

For each of the above processes find:

a. The final state of the system.
b. The work and heat interactions of the system.
c. The useful work of the system.

d. The maximum work for the same extreme states of the system and of the additional reservoir (if one is used).
e. The change in the availability of the system and of the reservoir (if one is used).
f. The irreversibility of the process.

10.28 A tank of 0.3 m^3 containing helium (ideal gas, $M = 4$, $k = 1.667$) at 1.5 MPa, 90 °C, is used to inflate slowly a large adiabatic research balloon that is unable to sustain a pressure difference, from zero volume till the pressures equalize. The environment is at 0.1 MPa, 25 °C.

a. Determine the volume of the balloon when the flow stops.
b. Find the change of availability associated with the process.

10.29 A piston–cylinder assembly contains 0.02 kg of steam at 3.0 MPa and a volume of 0.002 m^3. The state is changed by a process that may be described by a straight line on a T–s diagram to 0.2 MPa, 0.014 m^3. The environment is at 0.1 MPa, 25 °C.

a. Without asking whether this process is actually useful determine the heat and work interactions associated with the process.
b. If only one reservoir is used in what range could its temperatures be?
c. Select a reasonable temperature for the reservoir and find the maximum work associated with the process.

10.30 A vessel in good contact with a bath at 400 °C is divided by a stopped piston into two equal parts, Fig. 10.8. One side contains 2.0 kg of nitrogen at 5.0 MPa and the other side is empty. The stop is removed and the piston moves until a new equilibrium state is attained. The environment is air at 102 kPa, 20 °C.

a. Find the heat interaction of the nitrogen.
b. Find the maximum work associated with the process.

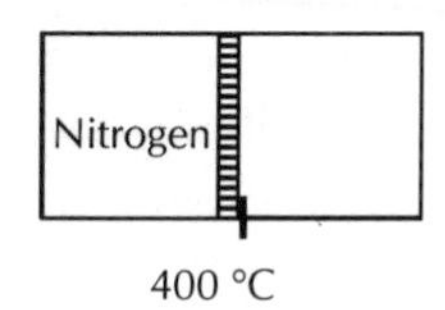

Figure 10.8

10.31 A vessel in good contact with a bath at 400 °C is divided by a stopped piston into two equal parts, Fig. 10.9. One side contains 2.0 kg of steam at 5.0 MPa and the other side is empty. The stop is removed and the piston moves until a new equilibrium state is attained. The environment is air at 102 kPa, 20 °C.

a. Find the heat interaction of the steam.
b. Find the maximum work associated with the process.

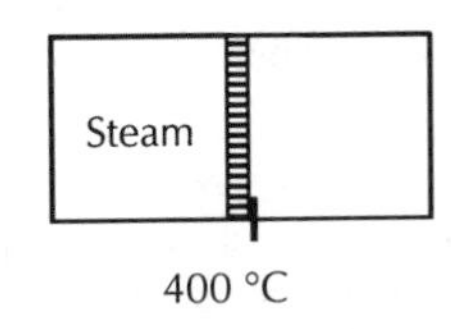

Figure 10.9

10.32 A cylinder, divided by a stopped piston into two parts, is placed on the surface of Venus, where the environment is at 70 kPa, 260 °C. Part A contains 0.01 m^3 water at 30 MPa and part B contains 2.49 m^3 steam at 0.2 kPa, Fig. 10.10. The stop is removed and a new equilibrium state is reached.

a. Determine the final state in the cylinder.
b. Find the work and heat interactions.
b. Find the maximum work associated with the process.

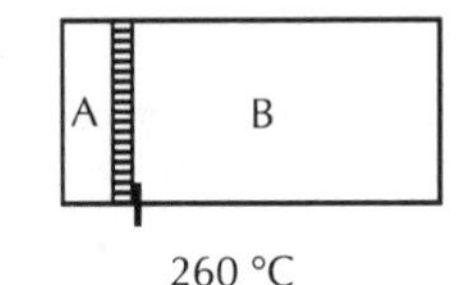

Figure 10.10

10.33 A cylinder maintained at 260 °C by a bath is divided by a stopped piston into two parts. Part A contains 0.01 m^3 water at 30 MPa and part B contains 2.49 m^3 steam at 0.2 kPa, Fig 10.10. The stop is removed and a new equilibrium state is reached. The environment is air at 102 kPa, 20 °C.

a. Determine the final state in the cylinder.
b. Find the work and heat interactions.
c. Find the maximum work associated with the process.

10.34 A light adiabatic envelope contains 30 g of nitrogen (ideal gas, $M = 28$, $k = 1.4$) at 0.4 MPa, 240 K. The envelope exerts an additional pressure on its contents proportional to the enclosed volume. The nitrogen is heated by a reservoir at 400 °C till the temperatures equalize. The environment is at 0.1 MPa, 300 K.

a. Determine the final state of the nitrogen.
b. Find the heat and work interactions of the nitrogen.
c. Find the change of availability of the nitrogen.
d. Find the irreversibility of the process.

10.35 An industrial plant requires a steady supply of 3.0 kg/s of steam at 0.2 MPa, 180 °C. The plant is located next to a river whose water is suitable for steam production and also has a reservoir at 400 °C. The environment is air at 102 kPa, 20 °C.

a. Find the least amount of heat that must be taken from the reservoir to produce the required steam.
b. Describe schematically a physical system that may perform the task.

10.36 Air (ideal gas, $M = 29$, $k = 1.4$) is compressed by an adiabatic compressor, whose adiabatic efficiency is 0.75, from 100 kPa, 25 °C, to 600 kPa. Then the air is cooled in a heat exchanger to 600 kPa, 45 °C, by cooling water that enters the heat exchanger at 101 kPa, 25 °C, and leaves at 100 kPa, 30 °C. The environment is air at 100 kPa, 25 °C.

a. Find the power of the compressor.
b. Find the maximum power (minimum power input) associated with the process.
c. Find the irreversibility of the process.

10.37 A thin elastic balloon contains 30 g of nitrogen (ideal gas, $M = 28$, $k = 1.4$) at 200 K and 0.4 MPa. The balloon exerts on its contents a pressure difference which is proportional to its volume. The pressure of the surroundings outside the balloon is 1 bar and the temperature 300 K. The nitrogen undergoes a heat interaction with a reservoir at 400 K until mutual equilibrium is attained. Find:

a. The final pressure of the nitrogen.
b. The work and heat interactions during the process.
c. The change in availability of everything involved in the process.

10.38 Air from the environment, where the conditions are 100 kPa, 25 °C, is compressed at a rate of 0.3 kg/s to 600 kPa by an adiabatic compressor with an adiabatic efficiency of 75%, Fig. 10.11. The compressed air is then cooled at a constant pressure to 45 °C in a heat exchanger by water that enters at 101 kPa, 25 °C, and exits at 100 kPa, 40 °C. The air may be treated as an ideal gas ($M = 29$, $k = 1.4$).

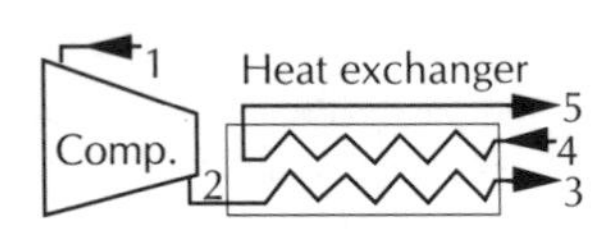

Figure 10.11

a. Determine the power of the compressor.
b. Find the maximum power associated with the process.
c. Determine the irreversibility of the process.

10.39 A steady rate of 5.6 kg/s of steam at 300 kPa, 160 °C, is generated from water at 400 kPa, 40 °C. The environment is air at 102 kPa, 20 °C.

a. Determine the rate of entropy change.
b. Determine the maximum power associated with the process (minimum power input).

10.40 An adiabatic engine nozzle, whose adiabatic efficiency is 90%, receives 200 kg/s of gas (properties the same as air) at 200 kPa, 720 °C and 60 m/s. The gas exits at 70 kPa. The environment is air at 102 kPa, 20 °C.

a. Determine the exit velocity of the gas.
b. Determine the rate of irreversibility of the process.

CHAPTER ELEVEN

Power and refrigeration cycles

In Chapters 7 and 8 it was established that to generate power by a heat engine at least two heat reservoirs at different temperatures are needed. The efficiency of power generation was shown to depend on the temperatures of the reservoirs, and on the type of engine that operates between them.

In Chapter 7 we also introduced the concept of a Carnot engine which used an ideal gas as a working fluid. It was shown that the efficiency of that engine is the highest possible for an engine operating between two given reservoirs. In reality, an ideal gas Carnot engine is not a practical engine. Firstly it is difficult to build an engine that alternates between adiabatic and isothermal processes. Furthermore, the net work of this engine is obtained as a difference between two large quantities, the expansion work and the compression work. The isentropic efficiencies of expansion and compression in real engines are less than one. The net work is, therefore, considerably reduced and the efficiency of the cycle becomes quite low.

A Carnot engine with condensable vapor can overcome some of the problems mentioned above. A T–s diagram for such an engine is shown in Fig. 11.1.

The isotherms in the two-phase region describe constant-pressure processes which can be more easily accomplished in a practical system. Moreover, the work of compression is much lower than that of expansion, and thus the net work is less affected by the reduced isentropic efficiency. An example of a physical system that accomplishes such a cycle is shown schematically in Fig. 11.2.

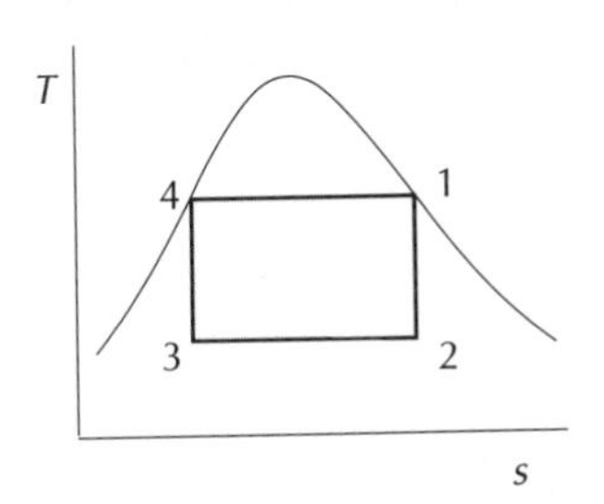

Figure 11.1 **Carnot cycle.**

There are, however, some practical difficulties associated with the vapor Carnot cycle. The pumping process 3–4 is problematic, since at the inlet to the pump the fluid is composed of two phases, liquid and vapor. Pumps do not operate well under these conditions. The expansion

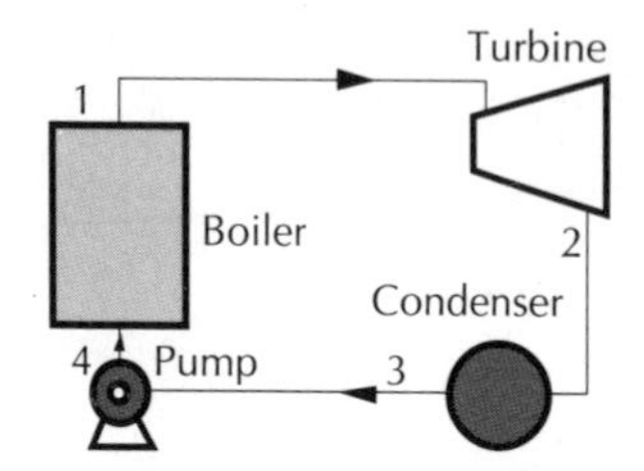

Figure 11.2 **Vapor cycle engine.**

process 1–2 also has complications, since at the later part of the expansion a liquid phase, in the form of droplets, is created. These droplets, which move at high speed, may cause accelerated erosion of the turbine blades.

Cycles that overcome the difficulties of the Carnot cycle have been devised and are being used in practice. In this chapter we describe the more important of these cycles. In each case, we first present the basic concept of the ideal cycle. We then discuss some of the practical limitations of the cycle, and show how the major parameters are calculated.

We start with vapor cycles, i.e. cycles in which the working fluid undergoes a liquid–vapor phase change. We then proceed with gas cycles, where the working fluid can be approximated by an ideal gas. Cycles for internal combustion engines are described next, followed by refrigeration cycles.

11.1 Rankine cycle

The Rankine* cycle is a practical modification of the Carnot vapor cycle. Several configurations are classified under the general heading of Rankine cycles; we shall discuss the more important ones.

The basic Rankine cycle, shown on a T–s diagram in Fig. 11.3, consists essentially of the same elements as the Carnot vapor cycle of Fig. 11.2. All the processes in the basic Rankine cycle are internally reversible. Superheated steam (point 1) expands through a turbine to the lower pressure at point 2, where it is condensed. The saturated liquid, point 3, is pumped into the boiler, point 4, where it is heated at constant pressure to point 1.

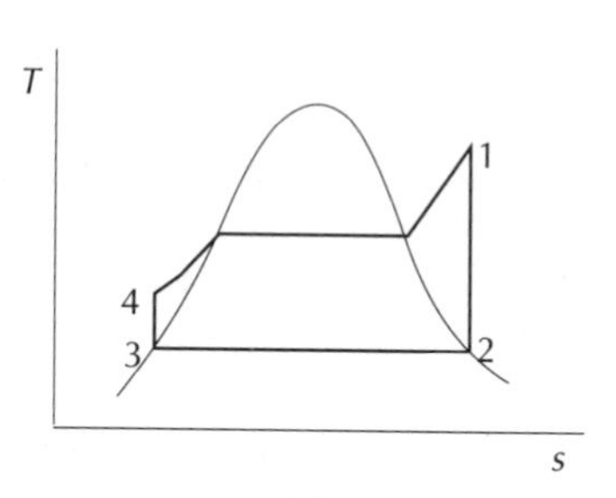

Figure 11.3 **Basic Rankine cycle.**

The problems encountered in the Carnot vapor cycle are solved in the Rankine cycle. The problem of expansion into the two-phase region is solved by superheating the vapor so that after the expansion there is no moisture in the last stages of the turbine. The vapor is completely condensed, entering the pump as a saturated liquid. This allows for the use of a simple pump for reduced power consumption.

* William J.M. Rankine (1820–1872), Scottish engineer. He suggested an absolute temperature scale, similar to the Kelvin scale, but where the degree size is equal to that of Fahrenheit. This scale is known as the Rankine scale.

EXAMPLE 11.1

In a standard Rankine cycle steam enters the turbine at 20 bars and 400 °C. The pressure in the condenser is 0.2 bars, and the liquid leaves the condenser saturated. Assuming the turbine and the pump to be adiabatic and reversible:

a. Find all the end points of the cycle.
b. Draw a *T–s* diagram for the cycle.
c. Calculate the heat and work interactions.
d. Calculate the efficiency of the cycle.
e. Compare with the Carnot efficiency between two reservoirs.

SOLUTION

a. We arrange the data for the Rankine cycle in the following table:

State	p	T	x	h	s	Remark
1	20.0	400.0	–	3247.6	7.1271	
2	0.2	60.06	0.8896	2349.3	7.1271	$s_2 = s_1$
3	0.2	60.06	0.0	251.4	0.8320	
4	20.0	~60.6	–	253.4	0.8320	$s_4 = s_3$

We calculated h_4 with the help of Eq. (9.10) which holds for the reversible compression of a liquid:

$$h_4 = h_3 - w_x = h_3 + v_3(p_4 - p_3) = 251.4 + 0.001017 \times (2000 - 20) = 253.4 \text{ kJ/kg}$$

b. The *T–s* diagram is drawn schematically in Fig. 11.3.

c. The respective heat and work interactions are

$$q_{12} = 0 \qquad (w_x)_{12} = h_1 - h_2 = 898.3 \text{ kJ/kg}$$

$$q_{23} = h_3 - h_2 = -2097.9 \text{ kJ/kg} \qquad (w_x)_{23} = 0$$

$$q_{34} = 0 \qquad (w_x)_{34} = h_3 - h_4 = -2.0 \text{ kJ/kg}$$

$$q_{41} = h_1 - h_4 = 2994.2 \text{ kJ/kg} \qquad (w_x)_{41} = 0$$

$$q_{net} = \sum q = 896.3 \text{ kJ/kg} \qquad (w_x)_{net} = \sum w_x = 896.3 \text{ kJ/kg}$$

d. The cycle efficiency is

$$\eta = \frac{(w_x)_{net}}{q_{in}} = \frac{896.3}{2994.2} = 0.299$$

e. The efficiency of a Carnot cycle between the maximum and minimum temperatures of the present cycle is

$$\eta_{Carnot} = 1 - \frac{T_c}{T_h} = 1 - \frac{(273.15 + 60.06)}{(273.15 + 400)} = 0.505$$

In a real heat engine the expansion and compression processes are not isentropic. Instead, the entropy increases in these processes. Thus, the end point of the expansion

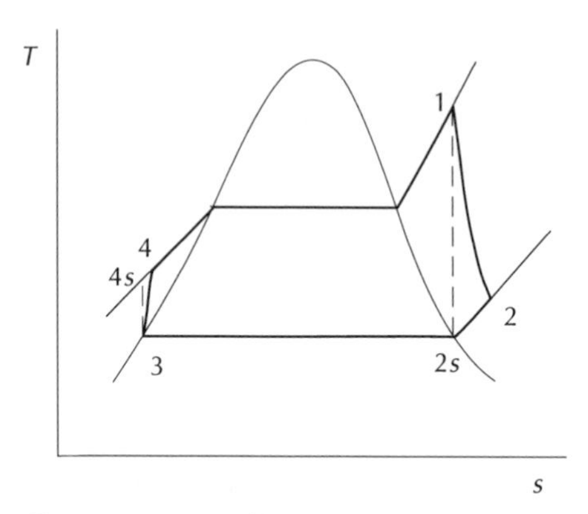

Figure 11.4 **Rankine cycle with non-isentropic expansion and compression.**

(state 2) has a higher entropy than that of the isentropic expansion (state 2*s*). Similarly, point 4 has higher entropy than point 4*s*. Figure 11.4 shows the *T–s* diagram of a real, basic Rankine cycle.

The efficiency of a basic Rankine cycle depends on several factors. These are boiler pressure and temperature, condenser pressure, and the isentropic efficiency of the turbine and the pump.

The reduction of condenser pressure results in a higher cycle efficiency. The pressure in the condenser depends on the availability of a suitable coolant. The lower the coolant temperature, the lower the pressure that can be maintained in the condenser. Usually water from the ocean or from a river is used for cooling. Occasionally, where water is unavailable, atmospheric air is used as the coolant. Hence, we have little control over the temperature of the coolant.

Higher steam temperatures, at the inlet to the turbine, are associated with higher cycle efficiencies as well as with the reduction of the moisture content at the turbine exit. There are, however, material limitations to higher steam temperatures. The strength of most regular boiler materials drops drastically at elevated temperatures. A typical steam temperature range of large, modern power stations is 530–560 °C. For smaller industrial plants a lower steam temperature of 350–500 °C is typical.

The cycle efficiency also depends on steam pressure in the boiler. Higher pressures result in higher efficiencies, since at a higher pressure the heat is received at a higher average temperature. At the same time, higher pressures have a negative effect by increasing moisture at the turbine exit. The boiler pressure is a design parameter that can be selected over a wide range. It is usually selected as a compromise between the desire to obtain high efficiencies and the need to reduce initial installation costs. High pressure boilers are considerably more expensive. A typical range of pressures in power plants is 10–20 MPa. In industrial boilers, which are also used for electric power generation, the range of pressures is 1–10 MPa.

EXAMPLE 11.2

In a Rankine cycle steam enters the turbine at 20 bars and 400 °C. The pressure in the condenser is 0.2 bars and the liquid coming out of the condenser is saturated. The isentropic efficiency of the turbine is 0.9 and that of the pump is 0.8.

a. Draw a *T–s* diagram for the cycle.
b. Find all the end points of the cycle.
c. Calculate the heat and work interactions.
d. Calculate the efficiency of the cycle.
e. Compare with the Carnot efficiency.
f. Find the steam mass flowrate for a 100 MW power plant.

SOLUTION

a. The *T–s* diagram is as shown in Fig. 11.5.

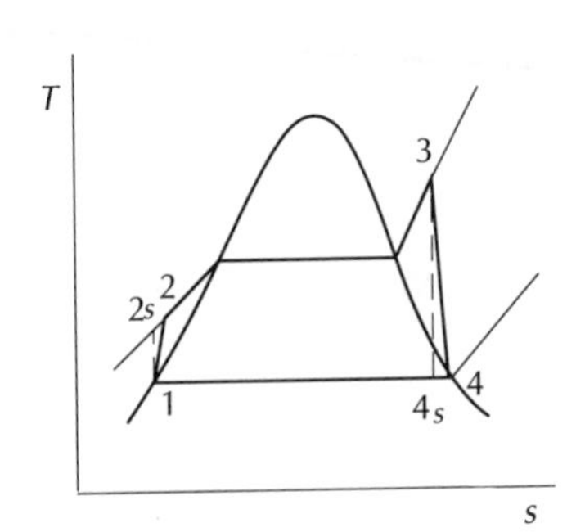

Figure 11.5

b. The relevant data for the cycle are arranged as follows:

State	p bar	T °C	x	h kJ/kg	s kJ/kg K	Remark
1	0.2	60.06	0.0	251.4	0.8320	$v_f = 0.001017$
2s	20.0	~60.06	–	253.4	0.8320	$h_{2s} = h_1 + v_f(p_2 - p_1)$
2	20.0		–	253.9	–	$h_2 = h_1 + (h_{2s} - h_1)/\varepsilon_c$
3	20.0	400.0	–	3247.6	7.1271	
4s	0.2	60.06	0.8896	2349.3	7.1271	$s_{4s} = s_3$
4	0.2	60.06	0.9277	2439.1	7.3973	$h_4 = h_3 + \varepsilon_t(h_3 - h_{4s})$

c. The net work is

$$w_{net} = w_{turb} + w_{pump} = (h_3 - h_4) + (h_1 - h_2)$$
$$= (3247.6 - 2439.1) + (251.4 - 253.9) = 808.5 - 2.5 = 806.0 \text{ kJ/kg}$$

The heat interactions are

$$q_h = h_3 - h_2 = 2993.7 \text{ kJ/kg}$$
$$q_c = h_1 - h_4 = -2187.7 \text{ kJ/kg}$$

d. The cycle efficiency is

$$\eta = w_{net} / q_h = 806.0 / 2993.7 = 0.2692$$

e. The Carnot efficiency is the same as in Example 11.1, i.e.

$$\eta_{Carnot} = 0.505 > 0.2692$$

f. The power output is given by

$$P = \dot{m} w_{net}$$

Hence,

$$\dot{m} = P / w_{net} = \frac{100000 \text{ kW}}{806.0 \text{ kJ/kg}} = 124.07 \text{ kg/s}$$

11.2 Rankine cycle modifications

Several modifications on the basic Rankine cycle are used in practice for the purpose of alleviating some of the drawbacks of the basic cycle. We shall now describe a few of these modifications.

11.2.1 The reheat cycle

We have already seen that higher efficiencies can be obtained by raising the boiler pressure, but that it is also accompanied by a higher moisture content in the last stages of the turbine. An improvement on the basic cycle can be achieved by breaking the expansion into two (or more) stages and reheating the steam after each intermediate expansion.

The heat input is carried out at a higher average temperature which leads to a higher efficiency and a lower moisture content at the exit of the turbine. Figure 11.6 shows a

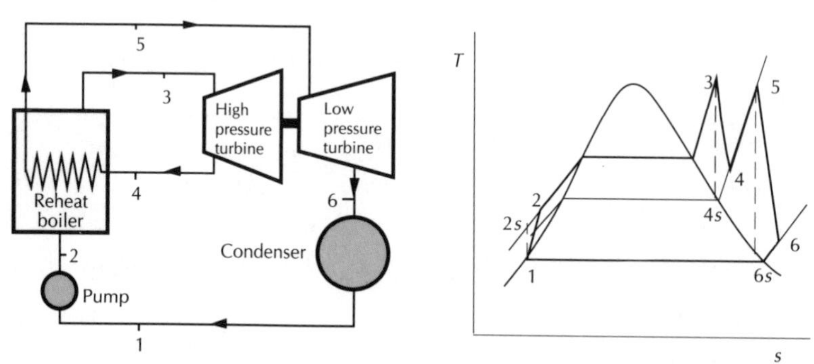

Figure 11.6 **Reheat cycle.**

schematic of a reheat cycle and the corresponding T–s diagram. The steam from the boiler enters the high pressure turbine where it expands to an intermediate pressure. The steam is then returned to the reheat coils in the boiler, where its temperature is raised before it enters the low pressure turbine and expands to the condenser pressure.

11.2.2 The regenerative cycle

Further improvement of the cycle efficiency can be achieved by preheating the boiler feed water with bleed steam for the last stages of the turbine. There is some loss of work associated with the reduction in steam flow but in most cases it is well compensated by the reduction of heat in the boiler.

Two general types of feed water preheaters are used. One is a closed preheater, which is a heat exchanger in which the bleed steam does not mix with the water. The steam pressure can therefore be different from that of the feed water. Figure 11.7 is a schematic of a shell-and-tube closed preheater.

Feed water enters the preheater at state w_1 and exits at w_2, where the temperature is raised to a value somewhat below the saturation temperature of the condensing steam. The temperature differential, which is usually 1 to 5 °C, is a design parameter. Smaller temperature differences are associated with higher efficiencies but also with larger heat exchangers, resulting in higher initial costs.

We now compute the ratio of steam flow to feed water flow. The preheater is analyzed as an open system operating at steady state. The energy equation is for this case

$$m_s\left(h_{s1} - h_{s2}\right) = m_w\left(h_{w2} - h_{w1}\right) \tag{11.1}$$

$$\left(\frac{m_s}{m_w}\right) = \left(\frac{h_{w2} - h_{w1}}{h_{s1} - h_{s2}}\right) \tag{11.2}$$

Equation (11.2) gives the ratio of the bleed steam flow required to preheat the feed water. It is usually in the range of a few percent.

Another type of preheater is an open heater where bleed steam is brought into direct contact with the feed water. The result is a single stream of liquid water at a temperature

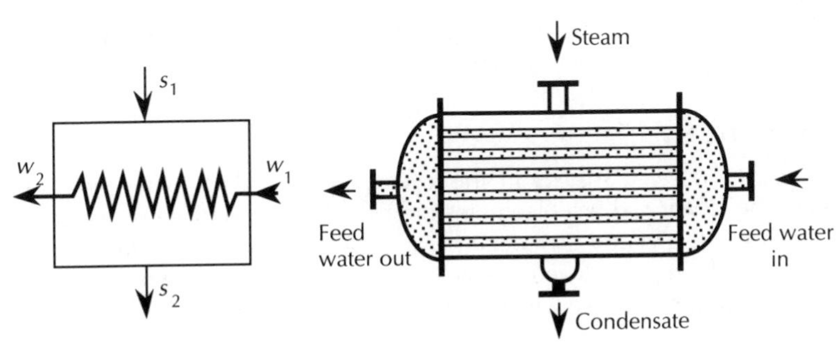

Figure 11.7 **Closed feed water preheater.**

somewhat below saturation. Obviously, since the two streams mix, they must be at the same pressure. Figure 11.8 shows, schematically, an open feed water preheater.

An open preheater usually serves also as a deaerator where the non-condensables (O_2, N_2, CO_2, etc.) that leak into the steam, are removed.

The analysis of an open heater is similar to that of a closed one and is based on the same equations, so that

$$m_s h_s + m_{w1} h_{w1} = m_{w2} h_{w2} \tag{11.3}$$

All the enthalpies are known and thus the ratio m_s/m_w can be solved:

$$\left(\frac{m_s}{m_{w1}}\right) = \left(\frac{h_{w2} - h_{w1}}{h_s - h_{w2}}\right) \tag{11.4}$$

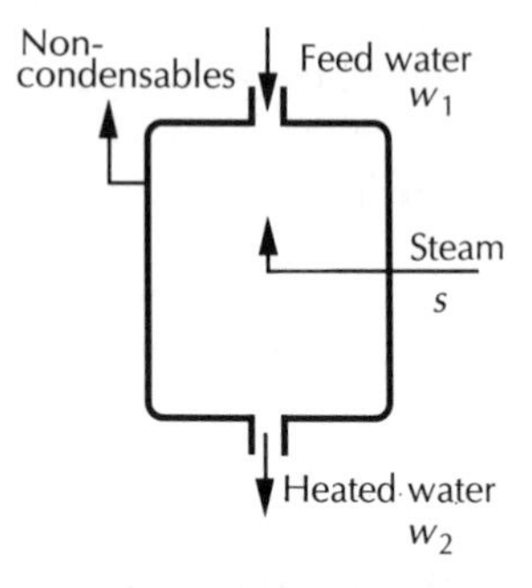

Figure 11.8 **Open feed water preheater.**

Because the pressure in the open preheater is lower than that in the boiler, an additional pump is required to pump the liquid from the preheater to the boiler. Example 11.3 incorporates all the modifications described in this section.

EXAMPLE 11.3

In a 150 MW power station, Fig. 11.9, steam enters the high pressure turbine at 150 bars and 550 °C, where it expands to 10 bars. Most of the steam is reheated to 500 °C followed by expansion in the low pressure turbine to 0.075 bars which is the condenser pressure. The system includes two closed feed water preheaters which are heated by bleed steam at 10 bars and 0.5 bars, and an open preheater (deaerator) which is supplied with bleed steam at 1.5 bars.

The isentropic efficiency of the turbine is 90% and that of the pumps is 85%. A temperature difference of 3 °C is required in the closed heaters between the condensing steam and the feed water exit temperature. A 1 °C subcooling is maintained at the deaerator.

a. Show the cycle on a *T–s* diagram.
b. Calculate the flowrate percentage for each bleeding point.
c. Calculate the efficiency of the cycle.
d. Calculate the steam flowrate into the high pressure turbine.
e. Calculate the diameter of the main steam pipe into the high pressure turbine, given that the steam velocity at that point is 40 m/s.

SOLUTION

a. There are five relevant isobars in this cycle, corresponding to the boiler pressure at 150 bars: the reheat and first bleed pressure of 10 bars; two bleed points at 1.5 bars and 0.5 bars, respectively; and the condenser pressure, 0.075 bars. Figure 11.10 depicts the *T–s* diagram for the process and the table that follows lists all the relevant data. The two independent properties, from which each state was found, are underlined in the table.

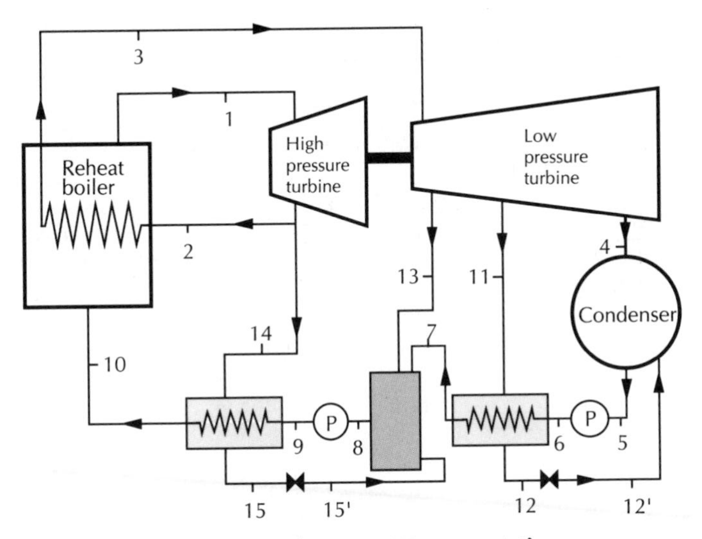

Figure 11.9 **Schematic of a 150 MW power station.**

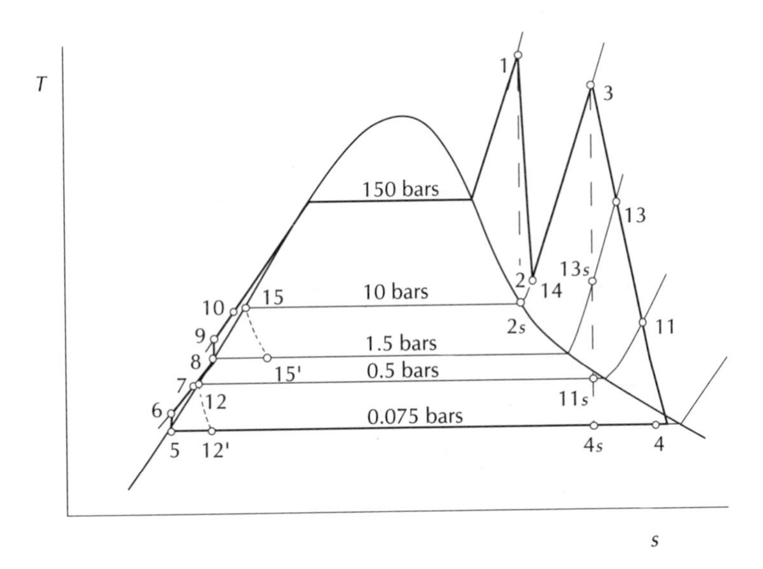

Figure 11.10 **T–s diagram for the cycle of the 150 MW power plant.**

State	p bar	T °C	x	v m³/kg	h kJ/kg	s kJ/kg K	Remark
1	150.00	550	–	0.02293	3448.6	6.5199	Table A.1.3
2s	10.00	(179.91)	0.9850		2747.9	6.5199	Table A.1.2
2	10.00	196	–	0.2037	2818.0	6.6726	Table A.1.3
3	10.00	500	–	0.3541	3478.5	7.7622	Table A.1.3
4s	0.075	(40.24)	0.9362		2421.4	7.7622	Table A.1.2
4	0.075	(40.24)	0.9802		2527.1	8.0993	Table A.1.2
5	0.075	(40.24)	0.0	0.001008	168.8	0.5764	Table A.1.2
6	1.50	40.3	–		169.0		Note A
7	1.50	78.33	–		327.9		Note B
8	1.50	110.37	–	0.001052	462.7	1.4224	Note C
9	150.0	112.1	–		480.9		Note D
10	150.0	176.91	–		756.7		Note E
11s	0.50	113.8	–		2709.3	7.7622	Table A.1.3
11	0.50	153	–		2786.2		Table A.1.3
12	0.50	(81.33)	0.0	0.001030	340.5	1.0910	Table A.1.2
13s	1.50	222.9	–		2918.5	7.7622	Table A.1.3
13	1.50	250	–		2974.5		Table A.1.3
14	10.00	196	–	0.2037	2818.0	6.6726	Same as 2
15	10.00	(179.91)	0.0	0.001127	762.8	2.1387	Table A.1.2

Note A: $h_6 = h_5 + v_5 (p_6 - p_5)/\varepsilon_c$ Note B: $T_7 = T_{12} - 3$ °C Note C: $T_8 = T_{sat} - 1$ °C

Note D: $h_9 = h_8 + v_8 (p_9 - p_8)/\varepsilon_c$ Note E: $T_{10} = T_{15} - 3$ °C

b. The amounts of bleed steam per kilogram of feed steam are found from mass and enthalpy balances on the respective preheater:

$$y_1 = \frac{m_{14}}{m_1} = \frac{h_{10} - h_9}{h_{14} - h_{15}} = \frac{756.7 - 480.9}{2818.0 - 762.8} = 0.1342$$

$$y_2 = \frac{m_{13}}{m_1} = \frac{(h_8 - h_7) - y_1 (h_{15} - h_7)}{h_{13} - h_7}$$

$$= \frac{(462.7 - 327.9) - 0.1342 \times (762.8 - 327.9)}{2974.5 - 327.9} = 0.0288$$

$$y_3 = \frac{m_{11}}{m_1} = \frac{(h_7 - h_6) \times (1 - y_1 - y_2)}{h_{11} - h_{12}}$$

$$= \frac{(327.9 - 169.0) \times (1 - 0.1342 - 0.0288)}{2786.2 - 340.5} = 0.0544$$

c. The heat interactions in the boiler and the condenser, respectively, are

$$q_{in} = q_{10\text{-}1} + q_{2\text{-}3} = (h_1 - h_{10}) + (1 - y_1)(h_3 - h_2)$$
$$= (3448.6 - 756.7) + (1 - 0.1342) \times (3478.5 - 2818.0) = 3263.8 \text{ kJ/kg}$$

$$q_{out} = (h_5 - h_4)(1 - y_1 - y_2 - y_3) + y_3(h_5 - h_{12})$$
$$= (h_5 - h_4)(1 - y_1 - y_2) + y_3(h_4 - h_{12})$$
$$= (168.8 - 2527.1) \times (1 - 0.1342 - 0.0288) + (2527.1 - 340.5) \times 0.0543$$
$$= -1854.9 \text{ kJ/kg}$$

The net work per kilogram of steam that passes the boiler is

$$w_{net} = q_{in} + q_{out} = 3263.8 - 1854.9 = 1408.8 \text{ kJ/kg}$$

The efficiency is

$$\eta = \frac{w_{net}}{q_{in}} = \frac{1408.8}{3263.8} = 0.4316 \quad \rightarrow \quad 43.16\%$$

d. The mass flow through the boiler is

$$\dot{m}_1 = \frac{P}{w_{net}} = \frac{150000}{1408.8} = 106.47 \text{ kg/s}$$

where P is the power.

e. The cross-sectional area of the main steam pipe is

$$A_1 = \frac{\dot{m}_1 v_1}{\mathbf{v}_1} = \frac{106.47 \times 0.02293}{40} = 0.0610 \text{ m}^2$$

and the diameter is $D_1 = 0.279$ m.

11.3 Brayton cycle

The standard Brayton cycle is similar to the Rankine cycle in that it consists of two constant-pressure processes connected by two steady flow adiabatic processes. All processes are internally reversible. It differs from the Rankine cycle in that the working fluid is a non-condensable gas.

The Brayton cycle constitutes the basis of the operation of a gas turbine. A schematic of the physical elements involved in a Brayton cycle is given in Fig. 11.11.

In the ideal cycle gas at state 1 is compressed adiabatically to pressure p_2 and then it is heated at a constant pressure to temperature T_3. The hot pressurized gas expands in the turbine back to the initial pressure and is then cooled isobarically to the initial state, thus completing the cycle. The cycle is shown on the p–v and T–s diagrams in Fig. 11.12.

For an ideal Brayton cycle, where the working fluid is an ideal gas, the heat and work interaction per kilogram of gas can be calculated as follows:
In the isentropic compression 1–2

$$(w_x)_{12} = h_1 - h_2 = c_p(T_1 - T_2) \qquad q_{12} = 0 \tag{11.5}$$

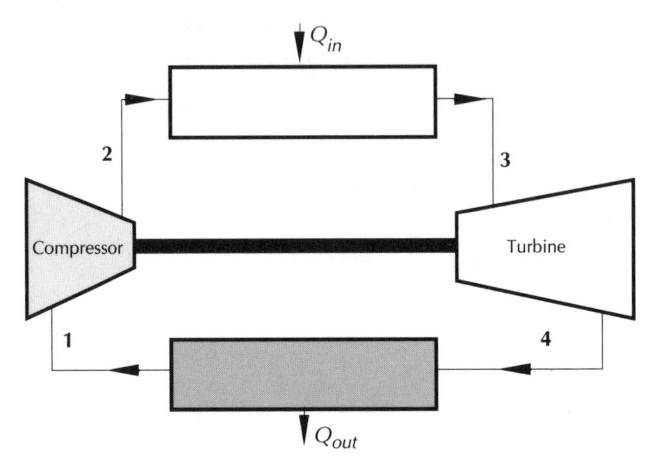

Figure 11.11 **Schematic of Brayton cycle.**

During isobaric heating 2–3

$$(w_x)_{23} = 0 \qquad q_{23} = c_p(T_3 - T_2) \tag{11.6}$$

During isentropic expansion

$$(w_x)_{34} = c_p(T_3 - T_4) \qquad q_{34} = 0 \tag{11.7}$$

and during the isobaric cooling

$$(w_x)_{41} = 0 \qquad q_{41} = c_p(T_1 - T_4) \tag{11.8}$$

The net work of the cycle is

$$(w_x)_{net} = c_p(T_1 - T_2 + T_3 - T_4) \tag{11.9}$$

The efficiency of the cycle is

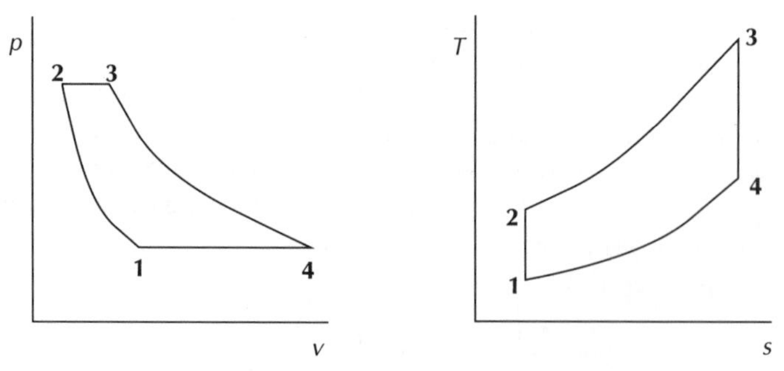

Figure 11.12 **Brayton cycle on *p*–*v* and *T*–*s* diagrams.**

$$\eta = \frac{w_{net}}{q_{in}} = \frac{T_1 - T_2 + T_3 - T_4}{T_3 - T_2} = 1 - \frac{T_4 - T_1}{T_3 - T_2} \tag{11.10}$$

This expression can be simplified for isentropic processes, since

$$\frac{T_2}{T_1} = \left(\frac{p_2}{p_1}\right)^{\frac{k-1}{k}} = \frac{T_3}{T_4}$$

resulting in

$$\eta = 1 - \frac{T_1}{T_2} = 1 - \left(\frac{p_1}{p_2}\right)^{\frac{k-1}{k}} = 1 - \frac{1}{r^{(k-1)/k}} \tag{11.11}$$

where $r = p_2/p_1 = p_3/p_4$ is the pressure ratio of the cycle.

Equation (11.11) indicates that the efficiency of an ideal Brayton cycle increases with the pressure ratio. It should be noted that while the efficiency calculated from Eq. (11.10) holds for any cycle with ideal gas, that calculated from Eq. (11.11) holds for a reversible cycle only.

The cycle described above is a closed cycle in which the working fluid circulates between the components of the system. In practice if the working fluid is air, it is possible to "save" the cooler by expelling the air to the atmosphere, at point 4, and admitting fresh air at point 1. It is also possible to replace the high temperature heat exchanger with a combustion chamber where fuel, injected into the air, is burned. Such a cycle is called an open cycle. Strictly speaking it does not constitute a heat engine; however, what happens in each component is equivalent to what would have happened had the cycle been closed. Most gas turbines work in an open cycle.

The analysis of real cycles must be modified to account for deviations from the ideal. Compression and expansion, though very close to being adiabatic, are not reversible and therefore not isentropic. In fact the entropy increases in these processes resulting in a reduction of the expansion work and an increase in the work required for compression. Furthermore, there is a pressure drop in the combustion chamber and the turbine exhausts at a somewhat higher pressure than that of the compressor inlet. In general these pressure drops are quite small and for the sake of simplicity will be neglected from the analysis in this book.

All the above effects reduce the efficiency of the gas turbine as compared with that of the standard cycle. Figure 11.13 shows a *T–s* diagram on which a cycle with real expansion and compression is compared with the ideal standard cycle.

EXAMPLE 11.4

Air at 300 K and 100 kPa enters the compressor of a gas turbine engine that operates on a Brayton cycle. The air mass flowrate is 5 kg/s and the maximum air temperature in the engine is 1200 K. If the pressure ratio of the cycle is $r = p_2/p_1 = 4$, find:

a. The efficiency of the engine, assuming ideal compression and expansion.
b. The power output for case a.

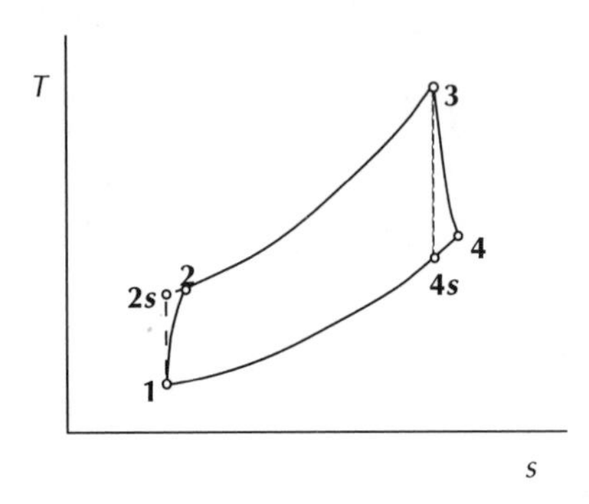

Figure 11.13 **T–s diagram for an actual Brayton cycle.**

c. If the compressor and turbine were not ideal, what would be the isentropic efficiency of each device that would result in no work output from the engine?
d. What are the exit temperatures from the turbine and the compressor for that case?

SOLUTION

The ideal and the non-ideal cycles are shown in Fig. 11.13.
a. The unknown temperatures T_{2s} and T_{4s} are found from

$$T_{2s} = T_1\left(\frac{p_2}{p_1}\right)^{\frac{k-1}{k}} = 300 \times 4^{\frac{0.4}{1.4}} = 300 \times 1.4860 = 445.8 \text{ K}$$

$$T_{4s} = T_3\left(\frac{p_4}{p_3}\right)^{\frac{k-1}{k}} = 1200 \times \frac{1}{1.4860} = 807.5 \text{ K}$$

The efficiency of the ideal cycle is found from Eq. (11.11):

$$\eta = 1 - \frac{T_1}{T_2} = 1 - \frac{300}{445.8} = 0.3271$$

b. The power output is given by

$$P = \dot{m}w_{net}$$

where

$$w_{net} = (h_3 - h_{4s}) + (h_1 - h_{2s}) = \frac{kR}{k-1}(T_3 - T_{4s} + T_1 - T_{2s})$$

$$= 3.5 \times \left(\frac{8.3143}{29}\right)(1200 - 807.5 + 300 - 445.8) = 247.6 \text{ kJ/kg}$$

Hence,

$$P = 5 \times 247.6 = 1238 \text{ kW}$$

c. For zero net work output the work of the turbine equals the work input to the compressor, i.e.

$$(h_3 - h_{4s})\varepsilon_e = \frac{(h_{2s} - h_1)}{\varepsilon_c}$$

Thus

$$\varepsilon_e \varepsilon_c = \frac{h_{2s} - h_1}{h_3 - h_{4s}} = \frac{T_{2s} - T_1}{T_3 - T_{4s}} = \frac{445.8 - 300}{1200 - 807.5} = 0.3715$$

and if the isentropic efficiencies are equal

$$\varepsilon_e = \varepsilon_c = \sqrt{0.3715} = 0.6095$$

d. T_2 and T_4 are found from

$$T_2 = T_1 + \frac{(T_{2s} - T_1)}{\varepsilon_c} = 300 + \frac{(445.8 - 300)}{0.6095} = 539.2 \text{ K}$$

$$T_4 = T_3 + \varepsilon_e (T_{4s} - T_3) = 1200 + (807.5 - 1200) \times 0.6095 = 960.8 \text{ K}$$

Taking into account the deviations from the ideal, the important parameters and the efficiency are calculated below. The compressor inlet conditions are usually known since they are dictated by the environment. The pressure ratio in the cycle is a design parameter and so is the maximum temperature at the turbine inlet. The latter is set as high as possible for given turbine structural materials.

Let us calculate the properties of the cycle assuming that p_1, T_1, p_2/p_1, T_3, ε_c, ε_e are known. For the compression process we have

$$\frac{T_{2s}}{T_1} = \left(\frac{p_2}{p_1}\right)^{\frac{k-1}{k}} \equiv \lambda \qquad (11.12)$$

where

$$\lambda = r^{(k-1)/k} \qquad (11.13)$$

The actual compressor exit temperature, T_2, is calculated from the isentropic efficiency, Eq. (9.17):

$$T_2 = T_1 + \frac{(T_{2s} - T_1)}{\varepsilon_c} = T_1 \left[1 + \frac{(\lambda - 1)}{\varepsilon_c}\right] \qquad (11.14)$$

Similarly for the expansion in the turbine

$$\frac{T_{4s}}{T_3} = \left(\frac{p_4}{p_3}\right)^{(k-1)/k} = \frac{1}{\lambda}$$

The turbine exit temperature is found using Eq. (9.16):

$$T_4 = T_3 + \varepsilon_e (T_{4s} - T_3) = T_3 \left[1 + \varepsilon_e \left(\frac{1}{\lambda} - 1 \right) \right] \tag{11.15}$$

The work and heat interactions for this case are calculated by the same equations as for the ideal case, Eqs (11.5)–(11.9), using the appropriate temperatures. The efficiency of the real cycle is calculated from Eq. (11.10):

$$\eta = 1 - \frac{T_4 - T_1}{T_3 - T_2} \tag{11.10}$$

which can be rewritten in terms of the known quantities as

$$\eta = 1 - \frac{(T_3 T_4 / T_1 T_3) - 1}{(T_3 T_1 / T_1 T_2) - 1} = 1 - \frac{(T_3/T_1)[1 - \varepsilon_e (1 - 1/\lambda)] - 1}{(T_3/T_1) - 1 - (\lambda - 1)/\varepsilon_c}$$

or

$$\eta = \frac{\varepsilon_c \varepsilon_e (T_3/T_1) - \lambda}{\varepsilon_c (T_3/T_1) + (1 - \varepsilon_c) - \lambda} \left(1 - \frac{1}{\lambda} \right) \tag{11.16}$$

The term $(1 - 1/\lambda)$ in Eq. (11.16) is the efficiency of the ideal Brayton cycle given in Eq. (11.11), while the term preceding it expresses the reduction in cycle efficiency due to non-idealities in the compressor and the turbine.

Let us find the lowest possible isentropic efficiency, if the cycle work remains non-negative. This condition requires that the numerator of the first term in Eq. (11.16) be non-negative, which is met when

$$\varepsilon_e \varepsilon_c \geq \lambda \frac{T_1}{T_3} \tag{11.17}$$

In Example 11.4, where $T_1 / T_3 = 300/1200 = 0.25$ and $\lambda = T_{2s} / T_1 = 1.486$, a positive cycle efficiency is obtained, by Eq. (11.17), only if

$$\varepsilon_c \varepsilon_e = 1.486 \times 0.25 \geq 0.3715$$

which is equivalent to the result obtained in part c of that example.

Regenerative Brayton cycle

At times, especially for lower pressure ratios, the temperature of the gases leaving the turbine exceeds that of the air leaving the compressor. An improvement of the cycle efficiency can be achieved if the hot exhaust gases are used to heat the compressed air by means of a regenerator. Figure 11.14 shows such an arrangement, together with the corresponding *T–s* diagram.

The regenerator is essentially a counter-flow heat exchanger in which the hot exhaust gases emerging from the turbine at state 4 are used to heat the colder compressed air from state 2 to 2*. In that process the hot gases are cooled from state 4 to 4*.

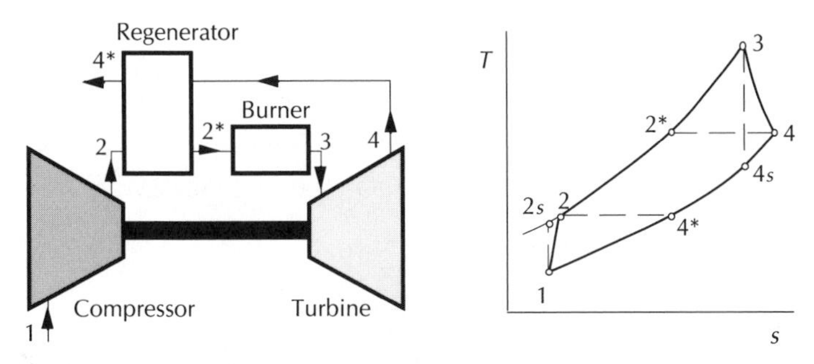

Figure 11.14 **Regenerative Brayton cycle.**

Exchanging heat, as described above, does not change the net power of the cycle, since the turbine and the compressor work under the same conditions, but it reduces the required heat input in the combustion chamber.

EXAMPLE 11.5

Air enters the compressor of a regenerative gas turbine, as shown in Fig. 11.14, at 100 kPa and 300 K. The pressure ratio is $p_2/p_1 = 4$ and the maximum allowed temperature is 1200 K. The flowrate through the engine is 8 kg/s. The isentropic efficiencies of the compressor and the turbine are 0.85 and 0.9, respectively, while the regenerator is ideal. Find:

a. The net power output.
b. The efficiency of the cycle.

SOLUTION

We first calculate the pressures and temperatures at each point of the cycle, shown in the *T–s* diagram of Fig. 11.14:

$$p_4 = p_1 = 100 \text{ kPa} \qquad p_2 = p_3 = 4p_1 = 400 \text{ kPa}$$

$$T_{2s} = T_1\left(\frac{p_2}{p_1}\right)^{\frac{k-1}{k}} = 300 \times 4^{\frac{1}{3.5}} = 445.80 \text{ K}$$

$$T_{4s} = T_3\left(\frac{p_4}{p_3}\right)^{\frac{k-1}{k}} = 1200 \times 0.25^{\frac{1}{3.5}} = 807.54 \text{ K}$$

$$T_2 = T_1 + \frac{T_{2s} - T_1}{\varepsilon_c} = 300 + \frac{445.80 - 300}{0.85} = 471.53 \text{ K}$$

$$T_4 = T_3 + (T_{4s} - T_3)\varepsilon_e = 1200 + (807.54 - 1200) \times 0.9 = 846.79 \text{ K}$$

Since the mass flows at states 2 and 4 are the same and the gases are considered ideal, and since the heat exchanger is also ideal, the hot stream exits at the temperature of the cold stream and the cold stream emerges at the temperature of the hot stream. Thus,

$$T_{4*} = T_2 = 471.53\ \text{K} \ \text{and} \ T_{2*} = T_4 = 846.79\ \text{K}$$

a. The net power is

$$P = \dot{m}[(h_3 - h_4) - (h_2 - h_1)] = \dot{m}c_p[(T_3 - T_4) - (T_2 - T_1)]$$
$$= 8 \times 1.0035 \times [(1200 - 846.79) - (471.53 - 300)] = 1458.5\ \text{kW}$$

b. The efficiency of the cycle is:

$$\eta = \frac{(h_3 - h_4) - (h_2 - h_1)}{h_3 - h_{2*}} = \frac{(T_3 - T_4) - (T_2 - T_1)}{T_3 - T_{2*}} = 0.514$$

11.4 Cycles for internal combustion engines

Up to now we have described cycles consisting of elements each of which is a steady flow control volume. The working fluid completes a cycle after it has passed through all the elements. We now consider another class of heat engines, where the working fluid undergoes a cyclic change within the same physical element.

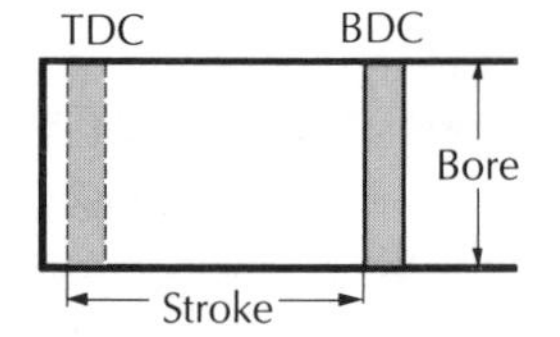

Figure 11.15

The cycle comprises processes that take place in a cylinder–piston assembly as shown in Fig. 11.15. The following terms are usually used in connection with internal combustion engines, with the notation corresponding to Figs. 11.15 and 11.16.

Bore	piston diameter
Stroke	maximum movement of the piston
Top dead center (TDC)	piston position where the volume is at minimum, V_2
Bottom dead center (BDC)	piston position where the volume is at maximum, V_1
Clearance volume	the volume at TDC
Compression ratio (r)	ratio of maximum to minimum volumes, $r = V_1/V_2$
Mean effective pressure (MEP)	the average pressure in the cylinder for a full cycle, $\oint pdV/(V_2 - V_1)$

We first describe the so-called air standard cycle, which is a theoretical idealized cycle. Then we cover the corresponding practical cycle and its deviations from the air-standard cycle.

In most cases, the practical cycle is not really a heat engine in the thermodynamic sense. The working fluid is usually air and the heat interactions of the air-standard cycle are replaced by the combustion of fuel that is added to the air or by rejecting the burned gases and admitting fresh portions of air. Thus the real engine is not even a closed system and could not be strictly considered a heat engine. Still, the air-standard cycle is quite helpful in the analysis of the corresponding engine since it contains many of its main characteristics.

11.5 The Otto cycle*

The air-standard Otto cycle uses air (assumed to be an ideal gas) as its working fluid. The air is enclosed in a piston–cylinder assembly and undergoes four internally reversible processes, described below. Figure 11.16 depicts the cycle on a p–v and a T–s diagram.

Air is compressed adiabatically (from state 1 to 2) while consuming work. Then heat is added at a constant volume (2 to 3). An adiabatic expansion follows (3 to 4) producing work, in excess of that consumed during compression, and finally the air is cooled at constant volume (4 to 1) to complete the cycle.

The efficiency of the Otto cycle is calculated by Eq. (7.5):

$$\eta = 1 - \frac{q_c}{q_h} \tag{7.5}$$

Since the working fluid is ideal gas

$$q_c = -q_{41} = -c_v(T_1 - T_4) \tag{11.18}$$

$$q_h = q_{23} = c_v(T_3 - T_2) \tag{11.19}$$

Processes 1–2 and 3–4 are reversible adiabatic and therefore isentropic. Thus from Eq. (5.34) we obtain

$$\frac{T_2}{T_1} = \frac{T_3}{T_4} = r^{k-1} \tag{11.20}$$

where $r = v_1/v_2$ is the compression ratio.

Inserting Eqs (11.18)–(11.20) into Eq. (7.5) yields, after some simple algebraic manipulation,

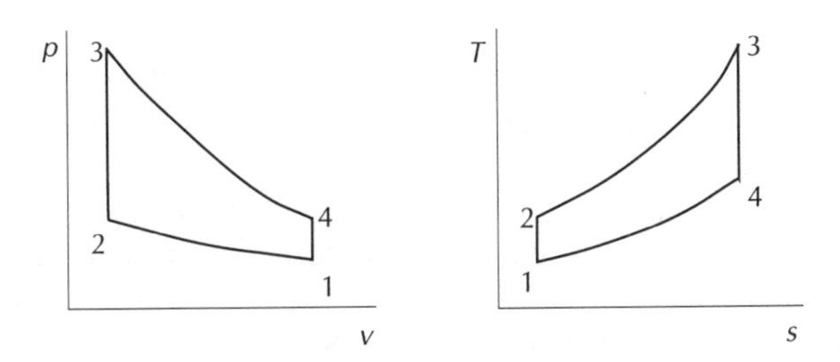

Figure 11.16 **The air-standard Otto cycle.**

* Nikolaus August Otto, 1832–1891. A travelling salesman and inventor. He came upon the idea of the four-stroke internal combustion engine through reading in a newspaper of an earlier invention by Lenoir.

$$\eta = 1 - \frac{T_1}{T_2} = 1 - \frac{1}{r^{k-1}} \tag{11.21}$$

The efficiency of the air-standard Otto cycle depends on the compression ratio. The higher the compression ratio, the higher the efficiency.

In a real automobile engine, the working fluid is not pure air, and it is replaced in each cycle. A mixture of air and fuel is admitted into the cylinder, the intake valve is closed, and the cycle begins by first compressing the mixture and then igniting it and raising its temperature. This process corresponds to the heating process in the air-standard cycle. Since the combustion process is not instantaneous, it does not occur at constant volume. The burned gases expand; toward the end of the expansion the exhaust valve opens and the pressure is reduced owing to gas discharge. This last process corresponds to the cooling process in the air-standard cycle. Finally, all the gases are expelled by the piston in preparation for a new cycle. There are four motions of the piston for each cycle; hence the origin of the name for the four-stroke engine. Figure 11.17 shows the p–v diagram of a real cycle, superimposed on an air-standard cycle.

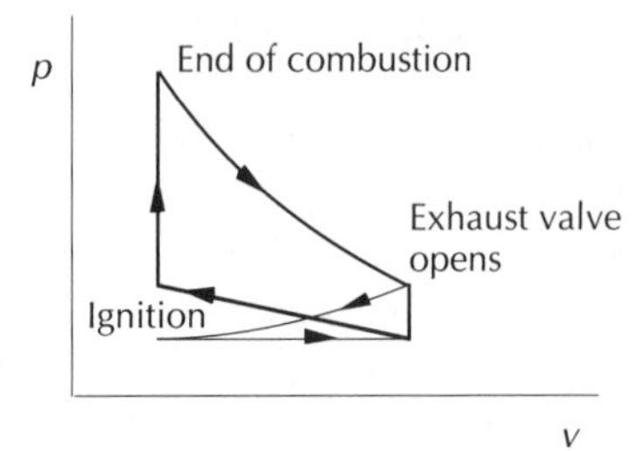

Figure 11.17

The efficiency of a real engine, like that of the air-standard cycle, depends strongly on the compression ratio, but not exclusively. Other parameters, such as resistance to flow in the valves, friction, leakage, heat loss, etc., greatly reduce efficiency.

As the compression ratio increases the temperature rises substantially. This may cause premature ignition of the mixture. Therefore, the compression ratio cannot be increased above a certain limit which depends on the ignition point of the fuel. A compression ratio of 10–12 is considered the upper limit for today's gasolines, while normally only 8–9.5 is used.

11.6 Diesel cycle*

The air-standard Diesel cycle is a variation on the Otto cycle in which the heating step is done at a constant pressure instead of a constant volume. Figure 11.18 shows the p–v and T–s diagrams of a Diesel cycle.

In the theoretical cycle air is compressed adiabatically from state 1 to 2 while consuming work. Heat is added at a constant pressure (2 to 3), followed by an adiabatic expansion (3 to 4) in which work is produced, in excess of that consumed during compression, and finally the air is cooled at constant volume (4 to 1) to complete the cycle.

In a real diesel engine air is admitted into the cylinder, the intake valve is closed, and

* Rudolf Diesel, 1858–1913, a German engineer.

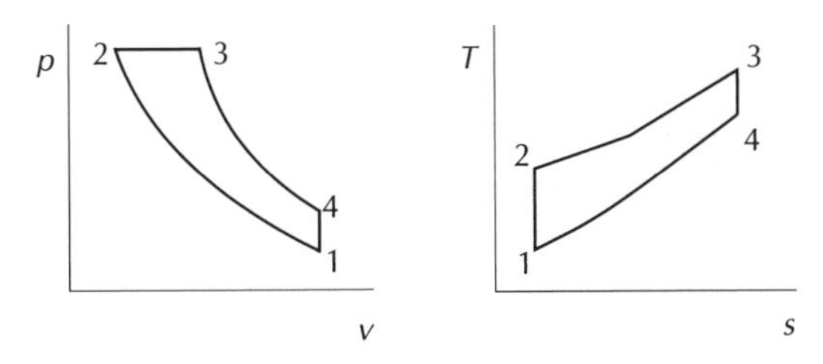

Figure 11.18 **The air-standard Diesel cycle.**

the air is compressed under conditions which are close to adiabatic, resulting in a rise in its temperature. The isobaric heating process is simulated in practice by injecting fuel into the hot compressed air, resulting in self-ignition and combustion of the air–fuel mixture. The burning mixture expands isobarically until the fuel supply is shut off. From this point on the expansion is adiabatic. Toward the end of the expansion the exhaust valve opens and the gas exhausts to the environment. This last process corresponds to the cooling process in the theoretical cycle. When all the gases have been expelled by the piston the exhaust valve is closed, the intake valve is opened, and fresh air is admitted into the cylinder for a new cycle.

The cycle is characterized by two parameters, the compression ratio, r, and the cut-off ratio, r_c, where

$$r = v_1 / v_2 \qquad \text{(compression ratio)}$$

and

$$r_c = v_3 / v_2 \qquad \text{(cut-off ratio)}$$

The efficiency is derived using Eq. (7.5), where

$$q_{out} = q_{41} = c_v(T_1 - T_4) \tag{11.22}$$

$$q_{in} = q_{23} = c_p(T_3 - T_2) \tag{11.23}$$

$$T_2 / T_1 = r^{k-1} \tag{11.24}$$

$$T_3 / T_2 = r_c \tag{11.25}$$

$$\frac{T_3}{T_4} = \left(\frac{r}{r_c}\right)^{k-1} \tag{11.26}$$

Substituting Eqs (11.22)–(11.23) into Eq. (7.5) and using Eqs (11.24)–(11.26) yields

$$\eta = 1 - \frac{1}{r^{k-1}} \frac{r_c^k - 1}{k(r_c - 1)} \tag{11.27}$$

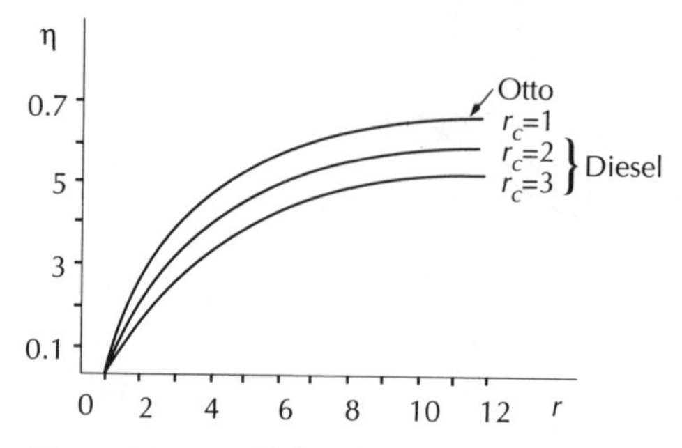

Figure 11.19 **Efficiencies of Otto and Diesel cycles.**

We see that Diesel efficiency becomes equal to Otto efficiency as r_c approaches unity, while when $r_c > 1$ the efficiency is reduced. A comparison between the efficiencies of Otto and Diesel cycles is shown in Fig. 11.19.

For any given compression ratio, the efficiency of the Diesel cycle is lower than that of the Otto cycle. Diesel engines compress air rather than an air–fuel mixture, which allows the use of much higher compression ratios (of the order of 20–30) with a corresponding increase in efficiency.

11.7 The dual cycle

The air-standard dual cycle is a combination of Otto and Diesel cycles. Figure 11.20 shows the p–v and the T–s diagrams for the dual cycle.

Three parameters affect performance:

$r = v_1 / v_2$ compression ratio

$r_p = p_3 / p_2$ pressure ratio

$r_c = v_4 / v_3$ cut-off ratio

The efficiency is given by

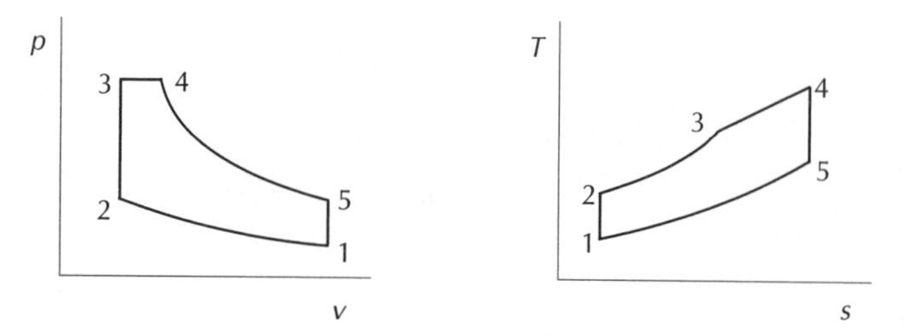

Figure 11.20 **Diagrams for the dual cycle.**

$$\eta = 1 - \frac{1}{r^{k-1}} \frac{r_p r_c^k - 1}{kr_p(r_c - 1) + (r_p - 1)} \tag{11.28}$$

When $r_c = 1$, the efficiency becomes that of the Otto cycle, and, when $r_p = 1$, the efficiency becomes that of the Diesel cycle.

11.8 Refrigeration cycles

In Chapter 7 we briefly described refrigeration cycles. These cycles consume work in order to provide cooling or heating, as required. The net work in refrigeration cycles is never positive

$$\oint dQ = \oint dW \leq 0 \tag{11.29}$$

The performance of refrigeration cycles is evaluated through a parameter called the coefficient of performance (*COP*), which is the ratio of the desired effect, cooling or heating, to the work that is consumed. For a refrigerator the desired effect is cooling, and *COP* is defined as

$$COP_{cooling} = \left| \frac{Q_c}{W} \right| = \frac{Q_c}{Q_h - Q_c} \tag{11.30}$$

while for a heat pump, that is to produce a heating effect,

$$COP_{heating} = \left| \frac{Q_h}{W} \right| = \frac{Q_h}{Q_h - Q_c} \tag{11.31}$$

11.9 Basic refrigeration cycle

The basic refrigeration cycle is a modification of the reverse Rankine cycle. It consists of four elements, a compressor, a condenser, a throttling valve, and an evaporator, as shown in Fig. 11.21.

Vapor of a refrigerant is compressed from state 1 to a pressure whose saturation temperature is above the temperature of the hot reservoir, state 2. It is then condensed completely to a liquid (state 3) and throttled to a lower pressure (state 4) so that the corresponding saturation temperature is lower than the temperature of the cold reservoir. At that low pressure, the refrigerant enters the evaporator where it evaporates while absorbing heat from the low temperature reservoir. The vapor that emerges from the evaporator (state 1) enters the compressor, thus completing a cycle.

The working fluid in a refrigeration cycle is called a refrigerant. A good refrigerant should have a high latent heat of vaporization, h_{fg}, a vapor pressure above atmospheric at the lowest temperature of the cycle, and not too high a pressure in the condenser. It

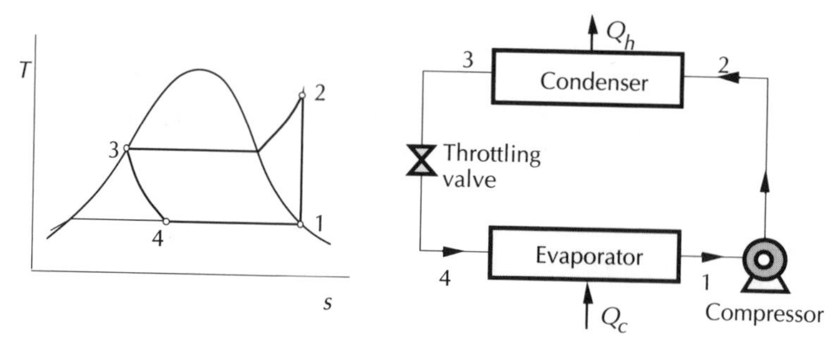

Figure 11.21 **Basic refrigeration cycle.**

should be non-toxic, non-corrosive, and, preferably, environmentally non-polluting. Typical refrigerants used in industry are ammonia for large refrigeration plants and fluorinated and chlorinated hydrocarbons, known as freons, for smaller units. Recently, it was found that the more common freons, such as R12, used in home refrigerators and car air-conditioners, have a detrimental effect on the ozone layer in the atmosphere. Efforts are under way to replace them with environmentally more friendly refrigerants.

The net effect of a refrigeration cycle is the removal of heat from a reservoir at a low temperature and the supply of heat to a reservoir at a higher temperature. This, of course, is accomplished by consuming work.

The rate of heat removal at the cold end is called the capacity of the cooling system. It is measured by units of power, e.g. kW, kcal/h, Btu/h, etc. A commonly used unit for the capacity of a cooling system is the *ton refrigeration*, which is defined as

$$1 \text{ ton refrigeration} = 12000 \text{ Btu/h} \cong 3.516 \text{ kW} \tag{11.32}$$

It is equal to the heat removal required to produce 1 short ton of ice from liquid water at freezing point, within 24 hours, i.e. 288000 Btu per 24 hours.

Practical refrigeration cycles, even though they consume work and produce heat interactions, are not exactly the reverse of power cycles. They employ throttling, shown as process 3–4 in Fig. 11.21, as a means of pressure reduction, instead of a turbine or an expander. This process is inherently irreversible but has economic advantages. The enthalpy change in this process is, obviously, zero. It is customary to describe refrigeration cycles on a p–h diagram, where the ordinate is the pressure (actually, log p) and the abscissa is the enthalpy.

Figure 11.22 shows a schematic of a typical p–h diagram, on which the refrigeration cycle of Fig. 11.21 is drawn.

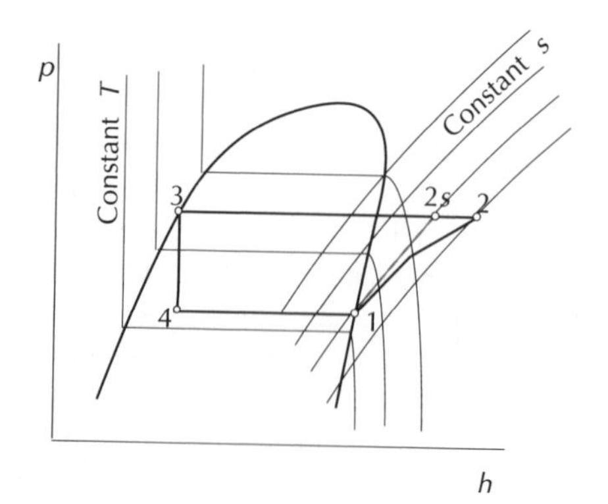

Figure 11.22 **A p–h diagram.**

The two-phase liquid–vapor region is depicted by the enclosed area of the bell-shaped curve. In this region pressure and temperature lines are parallel. To the left is the liquid region, where temperature lines are almost parallel to the enthalpy lines. To the right (larger enthalpies) the constant-temperature lines are curved but, as the degree of superheat increases, the temperature lines become more and more parallel to the enthalpy lines; for an ideal gas they are exactly parallel. The constant-entropy lines are oblique lines where the slope decreases slowly with enthalpy.

The refrigeration cycle is comprised of three straight lines: 2–3 (condenser), 3–4 (throttle), and 4–1 (evaporator). The compression line is not straight. It follows the entropy line if the process is reversible and deviates more to the right if the process is irreversible.

EXAMPLE 11.6

A refrigeration unit, shown in Fig. 11.21, uses Freon-12 to remove 10^6 kJ/h from a cold storage room at –5 °C. The environment is at 32 °C. The evaporator operates at 0.2 MPa, while the condenser is at 1 MPa. The refrigerant enters the compressor as a saturated vapor and is compressed to 1 MPa and 60 °C. Find:

a. The *COP* of the unit.
b. The power requirement.
c. The *COP* of a Carnot cycle operating between the same temperatures.

SOLUTION

The following table summarizes the operating conditions of the cycle.

State	p bar	T °C	x	h kJ/kg	s kJ/kg K
1	0.2	(–12.53)	1.0	182.07	0.7035
2s	1.0	~50.4	–	210.70	0.7035
2	1.0	60.0	–	217.97	0.7259
3	1.0	(41.64)	0.0	76.26	0.2770
4	0.2	(–12.53)	0.3282	76.26	0.2975

a. $$COP = \left|\frac{Q_c}{W}\right| = \frac{h_1 - h_4}{h_2 - h_1} = \frac{182.07 - 76.26}{217.97 - 182.07} = 2.95$$

b. The power is

$$\dot{W} = \frac{\dot{Q}}{COP} = \frac{10^6}{3600 \times 2.95} = 94.\dot{2}\text{ kW}$$

c. The efficiency of a Carnot refrigerator depends on the temperatures of the reservoirs only. Hence

$$COP_{Carnot} = \frac{T_c}{T_h - T_c} = \frac{268.15}{32 - (-5)} = 7.243$$

11.10 Internal heat exchanger

The liquid that emerges from the condenser is at the temperature of the environment or slightly higher while the vapor that comes out of the evaporator is at low temperature. It is, therefore, possible to add a heat exchanger to the system to use the vapor to cool the liquid further.

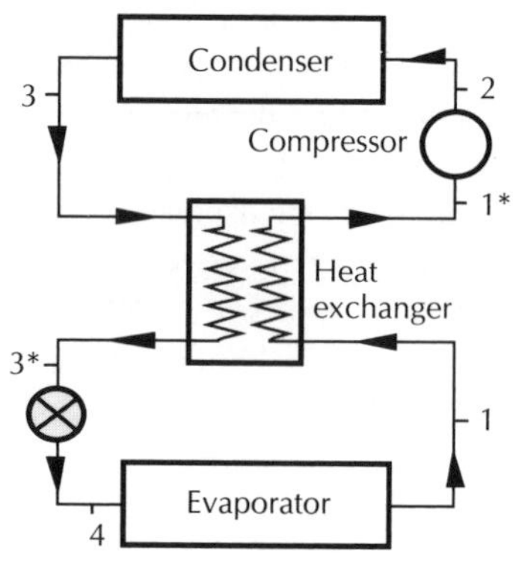

Figure 11.23

Figure 11.23 shows schematically a cooling cycle in which a counter-flow heat exchanger is used. The corresponding *p–h* and *T–s* diagrams are shown in Fig. 11.24.

The advantage of introducing an internal heat exchanger is that the range of evaporation is increased and with it the heat removal from the cold reservoir, namely

$$Q_c^* > Q_c \quad \text{or} \; h_1 - h_{4*} > h_1 - h_4$$

Another advantage to be considered is the assurance that the compressor receives dry vapor. There is, however, a price to be paid. The work of the compressor is increased when the internal heat exchanger is used since the volume of the vapor that enters the compressor at a higher temperature is now larger.

The net effect on the coefficient of performance (*COP*) of using a heat exchanger depends on the cooling fluids that are used in the cycle. For some fluids such as ammonia, the *COP* is actually reduced by an internal heat exchanger, while for Freons the *COP* increases.

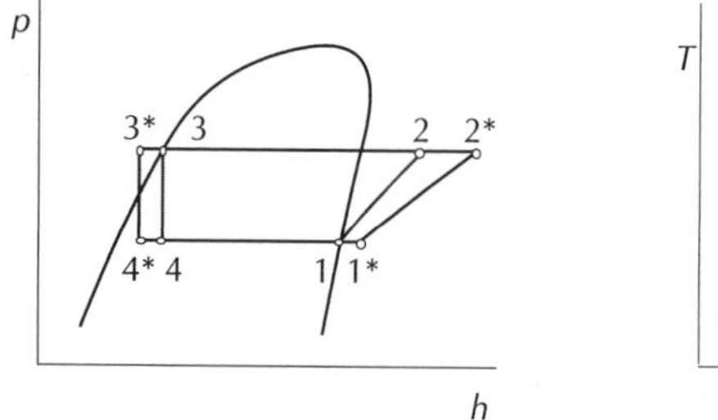

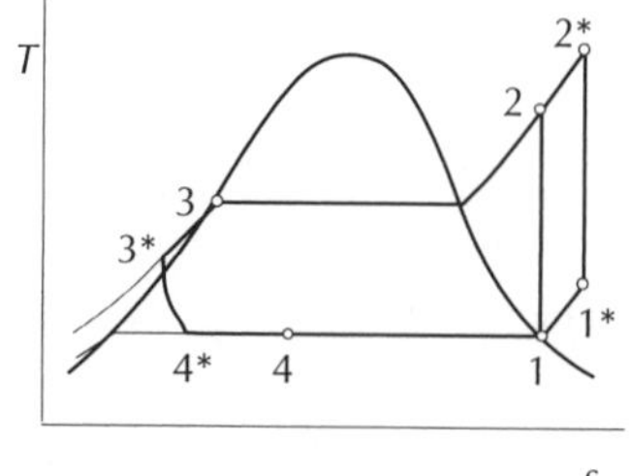

Figure 11.24 **Refrigeration cycle with internal heat exchanger.**

EXAMPLE 11.7

A refrigeration cycle that uses Freon-12 is to remove 6 kW from a cold reservoir at –7 °C while the temperature of the environment is 38 °C. A temperature difference of 3 °C is required both in the evaporator and in the condenser. The isentropic efficiency of the compressor is 75% and its mechanical efficiency is 94%.

a. Describe the cycle on a *p–h* diagram.
b. Find the *COP*.
c. Find the power required to run the compressor.
d. Repeat parts a–c for a modified cycle where an internal heat exchanger is introduced between the vapor from the evaporator and the liquid from the condenser.

SOLUTION

a. Since a 3 °C temperature difference is required in the heat exchangers, the evaporation temperature is –10 °C and the condensation temperature is +41 °C. Note that when heat is removed from the cold reservoir the working fluid must be at a lower temperature, while in the condenser when heat is transferred from the working fluid to the environment the temperature of the fluid must be higher than that of the environment.

   The high pressure of the cycle is found from the condensation temperature of 41 °C to be 1.00 MPa. The low pressure is determined by the evaporation temperature to be 0.2194 MPa.

   We assume that state 1 is that of a saturated vapor and state 3 is a saturated liquid. The properties are shown in the following table.

	p	*T*	*x*	*h*	*s*
1	0.2191	–10	1.0	183.058	0.7014
2*s*	50		–	210.000	0.7014
2	1.00		–	218.981	
3	1.00	41	0.0	75.551	
4	0.2191	–10	–	75.551	

b. The coefficient of performance (*COP*) is given by

$$COP = \frac{Q_c}{W/\eta_m} = \frac{h_1 - h_4}{h_2 - h_1}\eta_m = \frac{183.058 - 75.551}{218.981 - 183.058}0.94 = 2.813$$

c. The introduction of the heat exchanger does not change the pressure levels of the cycle. Thus points 1 and 3 are not changed.
d. Since the heat capacity of the liquid stream into the heat exchanger is larger than that of the vapor, the temperature of the vapor at the exit is 3 °C below that of the entering liquid, namely 41 – 3 = 38 °C. This allows us to calculate points 1*, 2_s^*, and 2*. The state at point 3* is determined from the enthalpy balance for the heat exchanger, Eq.(6.47):

$$h_{3*} = h_3 - (h_{1*} - h_1) = 45.327 \text{ kJ/kg}$$

	p	T	x	h	s
1	0.2191	−10	1.0	183.058	0.7014
1*	0.2191	38	–	213.282	0.8072
2^*_s	1.00	98.9	–	246.634	0.8072
2*	1.00	114.1	–	257.751	
3	1.00	41	0.0	75.551	
3*	1.00	10	–	45.327	
4*	0.2191			45.327	

Now we are ready to calculate the *COP*:

$$COP = \frac{Q_c}{W/\eta_m} = \frac{h_1 - h_3{}^*}{h_2{}^* - h_1{}^*}\eta_m = \frac{183.058 - 45.327}{257.751 - 213.282}0.94 = 2.911$$

The *COP* is improved compared with the previous case.

The power input is

$$\dot{W} = \frac{\dot{Q}_c}{COP} = \frac{6}{2.911} = 2.06 \text{ kW}$$

11.11 Refrigeration with two-stage compression

The compressor work of a refrigeration system may be reduced without reducing the heat removal rate by dividing the compression process into two or more stages, and intercooling the working fluid between stages to the temperature of the environment. This procedure is, of course, possible only if the intermediate temperature of the working fluid is higher than that of the environment, a situation that is not always realistic. A situation where two-stage compression may be employed is given in the following example.

EXAMPLE 11.8

Ammonia is the working fluid of a refrigeration system that removes 100 kW of heat at – 30 °C while the environment is at 30 °C. The isentropic efficiency of the compressor is 0.8. Find the *COP* of the refrigeration system:

a. If compression is performed in a single stage.
b. If the compression is in two stages, and the ammonia is cooled at the intermediate pressure of 400 kPa to the temperature of the environment.

SOLUTION

a. The relevant properties for a single-stage compression are given in the table

	T	p	x	h	s
1	-30	(199.55)	1.00	1404.6	5.7815
2s	115.7	1166.49	–	1748.9	5.7815
2		1166.49		1835.0	
3	30	1166.49	0.00	322.9	
4		119.55		322.9	

where

$$h_2 = h_1 + (h_{2s} - h_1)/\varepsilon_c$$
$$= 1404.6 + (1748.9 - 1404.6)/0.8 = 1835.0 \text{ kJ/kg.}$$

Thus

$$COP = \frac{h_1 - h_4}{h_2 - h_1} = \frac{1404.6 - 322.9}{1835.0 - 1404.6} = 2.513$$

and the power required for the compressor is

$$\dot{W} = \frac{\dot{Q}}{COP} = \frac{100}{2.513} = 39.8 \text{ kW}$$

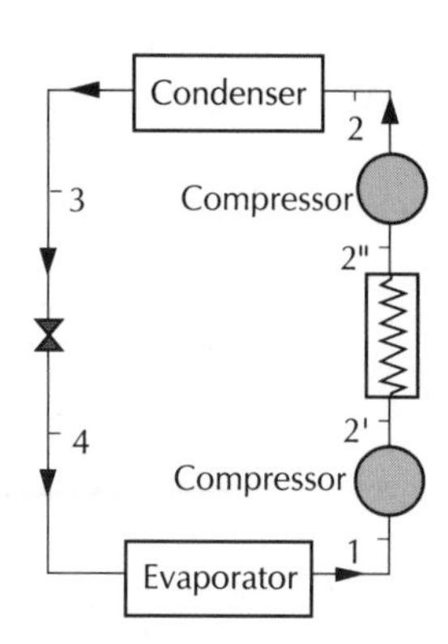

Figure 11.25

b. The two-stage compression system is shown in Fig. 11.25. The relevant properties are given in the following table:

	T	p	x	h	s
1	-30	(199.55)	1.00	1404.6	5.7815
2′s	65.6	500	–	1600.3	5.7815
2′		500	–	1649.2	
2″	30	500	–	1515.0	5.5157
2s	94.4	1166.49	–	1646.0	5.5157
2		1166.49		1678.8	
3	30	1166.49	0.00	322.9	
4		119.55		322.9	

$$COP = \frac{h_1 - h_4}{h_{2'} - h_1 + h_2 - h_{2''}} = \frac{1404.6 - 322.9}{(1649.2 - 1404.6) + (1678.8 - 1515)} = 2.649$$

$$\dot{W} = \frac{\dot{Q}}{COP} = \frac{100}{2.649} = 37.8 \text{ kW}$$

We note that in the case of ammonia as a coolant an improvement of the order of 5% of the *COP* is possible. Had we used Freon-12 as the refrigerant such an improvement would not be possible. Problem 11.41 illustrates this fact.

11.12 Exergy analysis

In Chapter 9 we introduced the concept of isentropic efficiency as a measure of loss of work in steady state adiabatic processes in turbines, compressors, pumps, and fans. The lower the isentropic efficiency the higher the loss. Hence, a zero isentropic efficiency implies complete loss of work. As that analysis is meaningful only for adiabatic processes, losses in other steady state processes cannot be evaluated by this method. In Chapter 10 we have shown that exergy analysis is a more suitable tool to evaluate real losses associated with steady state processes.

We have found that the work of a control volume is limited by

$$\dot{W}_x \le -\left(\frac{d\Omega}{dt}\right)_{cv} + \sum_{i=1}^{k} b_i^0 \dot{m}_i \tag{10.37}$$

The inequality applies to irreversible processes within the control volume. For reversible processes the equality holds, resulting in maximum power output:

$$\left(\dot{W}_x\right)_{max} = \left(\dot{W}_x\right)_{rev} = -\left(\frac{d\Omega}{dt}\right)_{cv} + \sum_{i=1}^{k} b_i^0 \dot{m}_i \tag{10.38}$$

At steady state there are no changes in properties within the control volume, and for cases where potential and kinetic energy effects are negligible the maximum work is

$$\left(\dot{W}_x\right)_{rev} = \sum_{i=1}^{k} b_i \dot{m}_i = \dot{B}_{in} - \dot{B}_{out} \tag{11.33}$$

where $\dot{B}_{out}$ and $\dot{B}_{in}$ are the rates at which the total exergies exit and enter the control volume, respectively. Equation (11.33) states that the work can never exceed the decrease in total exergy in the process.

The difference between the maximum work and the actual work is the real thermodynamic loss, which represents the extra work that could have been done if all the processes were reversible. For a steady state process it can be expressed in terms of irreversibility:

$$\dot{I} = \left(\dot{W}_x\right)_{rev} - \dot{W}_x = \sum_{i=1}^{k} b_i \dot{m}_i - \dot{W}_x = \left(\dot{B}_{in} - \dot{B}_{out}\right) - \dot{W}_x \tag{11.34}$$

The following example illustrates the application of exergy analysis to power cycles.

EXAMPLE 11.9

The power station of Example 11.3 operates in an environment which is at 101 kPa and 25 °C. It is also given that the steam in the boiler is heated by flue gases that have the properties of air (ideal gas, M = 29, k = 1.35), entering at 102 kPa, 1500 °C, and leaving at 101 kPa, 400 °C. The condenser is cooled by water entering at 105 kPa, 25 °C, and leaving at 102 kPa, 30 °C.

a. Find the specific exergy input and output and the rate of irreversibility in the high pressure turbine.
b. Find the specific exergy input and output and the rate of irreversibility in the low pressure

turbine, compared to the maximum work.

c. Find the specific exergy input and output and the rate of irreversibility of each preheater.
d. Find the specific exergy input and output and the rate of irreversibility of the condenser.
e. Find the specific exergy input and output and the rate of irreversibility of the boiler.

SOLUTION

To solve this example we need to know the properties at each state point. Most of these properties were calculated in Example 11.3. The entropies for some state points were not needed for the calculations of Example 11.3 and were not given in that table. Here we must know the entropies of all the states; thus we copy the table and add the missing entropy values. The properties of the cooling water in the condenser are included at the bottom of the table.

State	p bar	T °C	x	v m³/kg	h kJ/kg
1	150.00	550	–	0.02293	3448.6
2s	10.00	(179.91)	0.9850		2747.9
2	10.00	196	–	0.2037	2818.0
3	10.00	500	–	0.3541	3478.5
4s	0.075	(40.24)	0.9362		2421.4
4	0.075	(40.24)	0.9802		2527.1
5	0.075	(40.24)	0.0	0.001008	168.8
6	1.50	40.3	–		169.0
7	1.50	78.33	–		327.9
8	1.50	110.37	–	0.001052	462.7
9	150.0	112.1	–		480.9
10	150.0	176.91	–		756.7
11s	0.50	113.8	–		2709.3
11	0.50	153	–		2786.2
12	0.50	(81.33)	0.0	0.001030	340.5
13s	1.50	222.9	–		2918.5
13	1.50	250	–		2974.5
14	10.00	196	–	0.2037	2818.0
15	10.00	(179.91)	0.0	0.001127	762.8
w_1	1.05	25	–		104.9
w_2	1.02	30	–	0.2037	125.8

In Example 11.3 we found the mass flows through each component. The mass flow into the high pressure turbine was found to be m_1 = 106.47 kg/s. All the bleed ratios were also found in that example. We shall use these values here.

a. The high pressure turbine has one inlet and one outlet. The specific exergies at the inlet and outlet are, respectively,

$$b_1 = h_1 - T_0\, s_1 = 3448.6 - 298.15 \times 6.5199 = 1504.7 \text{ kJ/kg}$$

$$b_2 = h_2 - T_0\, s_2 = 2818.0 - 298.15 \times 6.6726 = 828.6 \text{ kJ/kg}$$

The incoming and outgoing exergies are, respectively,

$$\dot{B}_{in} = \dot{m}_1 b_1 = 106.47 \times 1504.7 = 160205.4 \text{ kW}$$

$$\dot{B}_{out} = \dot{m}_2 b_2 = 106.47 \times 828.6 = 88221.0 \text{ kW}$$

The rate of exergy decrease (which is equal to the maximum thermodynamic work) in the high pressure turbine is

$$\dot{B}_{in} - \dot{B}_{out} = (\dot{W}_x)_{rev} = \dot{m}_1 (b_1 - b_2) = 106.47 \times (1504.7 - 828.6) = 71984.4 \text{ kW}$$

The power output of the high-pressure turbine is:

$$\dot{W}_x = \dot{m}_1 (h_1 - h_2) = 106.47 \times (3448.6 - 2818.0) = 67140.0 \text{ kW}$$

The rate of irreversibility in the high pressure turbine is, therefore,

$$\dot{I} = \left(\dot{B}_{in} - \dot{B}_{out}\right) - \dot{W}_x = 71984.4 - 67140.0 = 4844.4 \text{ kW}$$

The ratio of the actual work of the high pressure turbine to the rate of exergy decrease (i.e. the maximum thermodynamic work) is

$$\frac{\dot{W}_x}{\dot{B}_{in} - \dot{B}_{out}} = \frac{67140.0}{71984.4} = 0.933$$

Note that this ratio is higher than the isentropic efficiency of the turbine $(\varepsilon_T = 0.90)$, meaning that the loss is not really that bad.

b. The low pressure turbine has one inlet and three outlets. The specific exergies at the inlet and outlets are, respectively,

$$b_3 = h_3 - T_0 s_3 = 3478.5 - 298.15 \times 7.7622 = 1164.2 \text{ kJ/kg}$$

$$b_4 = h_4 - T_0 s_4 = 2527.1 - 298.15 \times 8.0993 = 112.3 \text{ kJ/kg}$$

$$b_{11} = h_{11} - T_0 s_{11} = 2786.2 - 298.15 \times 7.9540 = 414.7 \text{ kJ/kg}$$

$$b_{13} = h_{13} - T_0 s_{13} = 2974.5 - 298.15 \times 7.8446 = 635.6 \text{ kJ/kg}$$

The incoming and outgoing exergies for the low pressure turbine are

$$\dot{B}_{in} = \dot{m}_3 b_3 = (1 - y_1)\dot{m}_1 b_3 = 0.8658 \times 106.47 \times 1164.2 = 107318.0 \text{ kW}$$

$$\dot{B}_{out} = \dot{m}_1 \left[(1 - y_1 - y_2 - y_3) b_4 + y_2 b_{13} + y_3 b_{11}\right]$$
$$= 106.47 \times [0.7826 \times 112.3 + 0.0288 \times 635.6 + 0.0544 \times 414.7] = 13708.1 \text{ kW}$$

The rate of exergy decrease in the low pressure turbine is

$$\dot{B}_{in} - \dot{B}_{out} = 107318.0 - 13708.1 = 93609.9 \text{ kW}$$

The power output of the low pressure turbine is

$$\dot{W}_x = \dot{m}_1 \left[(1 - y_1) h_3 - y_2 h_{13} - y_3 h_{11} - (1 - y_1 - y_2 - y_3) h_4\right]$$
$$= 106.47 \times [0.8658 \times 3478.5 - 0.0288 \times 2974.5 - 0.0544 \times 2786.2 - 0.7826 \times 2527.1]$$
$$= 84829.1 \text{ kW}$$

The rate of irreversibility in the low pressure turbine is, therefore,

$$\dot{I} = \left(\dot{B}_{in} - \dot{B}_{out}\right) - \dot{W}_x = 93609.9 - 84829.1 = 8780.8 \text{ kW}$$

The ratio of the actual work of the low pressure turbine to the rate of exergy decrease (which is equal to the maximum thermodynamic work) is

$$\frac{\dot{W}_x}{\dot{B}_{in} - \dot{B}_{out}} = \frac{84829.1}{93609.9} = 0.906$$

Again this ratio is higher than the isentropic efficiency of the turbine.

c. Each of the closed preheaters have four ports, two inlets and two outlets, while the open preheater (deaerator) has three inlets and one outlet.

The specific exergies for the low pressure closed preheater are

$$b_6 = h_6 - T_0 s_6 = 169.0 - 298.15 \times 0.5765 = -2.9 \text{ kJ/kg}$$

$$b_7 = h_7 - T_0 s_7 = 327.9 - 298.15 \times 1.0554 = 13.2 \text{ kJ/kg}$$

$$b_{11} = h_{11} - T_0 s_{11} = 2786.2 - 298.15 \times 7.9540 = 414.7 \text{ kJ/kg}$$

$$b_{12} = h_{12} - T_0 s_{12} = 340.5 - 298.15 \times 1.0910 = 15.2 \text{ kJ/kg}$$

$$\dot{B}_{in} = \dot{m}_1\left[(1 - y_1 - y_2)b_6 + y_3 b_{11}\right]$$
$$= 106.47 \times \left[0.8370 \times (-2.9) + 0.0544 \times 414.7\right] = 2143.5 \text{ kW}$$

$$\dot{B}_{out} = \dot{m}_1\left[(1 - y_1 - y_2)b_7 + y_3 b_{12}\right]$$
$$= 106.47 \times \left[0.8370 \times 13.2 + 0.0544 \times 15.2\right] = 1264.4 \text{ kW}$$

The rate of exergy decrease in the low pressure preheater is

$$\dot{B}_{in} - \dot{B}_{out} = 2143.5 - 1264.4 = 879.1 \text{ kW}$$

The preheater has no work interaction, so the whole reduction of the exergy is a loss; hence, $\dot{I} = 879.1 \text{ kW}$.

The specific exergies for the high pressure closed preheater are

$$b_9 = h_9 - T_0 s_9 = 480.9 - 298.15 \times 1.4417 = 51.1 \text{ kJ/kg}$$

$$b_{10} = h_{10} - T_0 s_{10} = 756.7 - 298.15 \times 2.1098 = 127.7 \text{ kJ/kg}$$

$$b_{14} = b_2 = 828.6 \text{ kJ/kg}$$

$$b_{15} = h_{15} - T_0 s_{15} = 762.8 - 298.15 \times 2.1387 = 125.1 \text{ kJ/kg}$$

$$\dot{B}_{in} = \dot{m}_1\left[b_9 + y_1 b_{14}\right] = 106.47 \times \left[51.1 + 0.1342 \times 828.6\right] = 17279.9 \text{ kW}$$

$$\dot{B}_{out} = \dot{m}_1\left[b_{10} + y_1 b_{15}\right] = 106.47 \times \left[127.7 + 0.1342 \times 125.1\right] = 15383.7 \text{ kW}$$

The rate of exergy decrease in the low pressure preheater is

$$\dot{B}_{in} - \dot{B}_{out} = 17279.9 - 15383.7 = 1896.2 \text{ kW}$$

The preheater has no work interaction. Thus the total decrease in exergy is a loss; hence, $\dot{I} = 1896.2 \text{ kW}$.

We include the throttling valve (between 15 and 15′) in the open preheater. The specific exergies for the open preheater ports are then

$$b_7 = h_7 - T_0 s_7 = 327.9 - 298.15 \times 1.0554 = 13.2 \text{ kJ/kg}$$

$$b_8 = h_8 - T_0 s_8 = 462.7 - 298.15 \times 1.4224 = 38.6 \text{ kJ/kg}$$

$$b_{13} = h_{13} - T_0 s_{13} = 2974.5 - 298.15 \times 7.8446 = 635.6 \text{ kJ/kg}$$

$$b_{15} = h_{15} - T_0 s_{15} = 762.8 - 298.15 \times 2.1387 = 125.1 \text{ kJ/kg}$$

$$\begin{aligned} \dot{B}_{in} &= \dot{m}_1[(1-y_1-y_2)b_7 + y_2 b_{13} + y_1 b_{15}] \\ &= 106.47 \times [0.8370 \times 13.2 + 0.0288 \times 635.6 + 0.1342 \times 125.1] \\ &= 4912.7 \text{ kW} \end{aligned}$$

$$\dot{B}_{out} = \dot{m}_1 b_8 = 106.47 \times 38.6 = 4109.7 \text{ kW}$$

The rate of exergy decrease in the low pressure preheater is

$$\dot{B} = \dot{B}_{in} - \dot{B}_{out} = 4912.7 - 4109.7 = 803.0 \text{ kW}$$

The preheater has no work interaction. Thus the total decrease in exergy is a loss; hence, $\dot{I} = 803.0$ kW.

d. We include the throttling valve (between 12 and 12′) in the condenser. The condenser has three working-fluid ports, two inlets and one outlet, and two cooling-water ports, one inlet and one outlet.

We first find the required quantity of cooling water. The heat removed in the condenser, calculated in Example 11.3, is $q_{out} = -1854.9$ kJ/kg. The heat interaction of the cooling water is then

$$\dot{Q}_w = -\dot{m}_1 q_{out} = 106.47 \times 1854.9 = 197491.2 \text{ kW}$$

The relevant properties of the cooling water were added to the table. The flowrate of the cooling water is

$$\dot{m}_w = \frac{\dot{Q}_w}{h_{w2} - h_{w1}} = \frac{197491.2}{125.8 - 104.9} = 9449.3 \text{ kg/s}$$

The specific exergies for the condenser ports are

$$b_4 = h_4 - T_0 s_4 = 2527.1 - 298.15 \times 8.0993 = 112.3 \text{ kJ/kg}$$

$$b_5 = h_5 - T_0 s_5 = 168.8 - 298.15 \times 0.5764 = -3.0 \text{ kJ/kg}$$

$$b_{12} = h_{12} - T_0 s_{12} = 340.5 - 298.15 \times 1.0910 = 15.2 \text{ kJ/kg}$$

$$b_{w1} = h_{w1} - T_0 s_{w1} = 104.8 - 298.15 \times 0.3672 = -4.681 \text{ kJ/kg}$$

$$b_{w2} = h_{w2} - T_0 s_{w2} = 125.8 - 298.15 \times 0.4367 = -4.402 \text{ kJ/kg}$$

$$\begin{aligned} \dot{B}_{in} &= \dot{m}_1[(1-y_1-y_2-y_3)b_4 + y_3 b_{12}] + \dot{m}_{cw} b_{w1} \\ &= 106.47 \times [0.7826 \times 112.3 + 0.0544 \times 15.2] + 9449.3 \times (-4.681) \\ &= -34786.9 \text{ kW} \end{aligned}$$

$$\begin{aligned} \dot{B}_{out} &= \dot{m}_1[(1-y_1-y_2)b_5] + \dot{m}_{cw} b_{w2} \\ &= 106.47 \times [0.8370 \times (-3.0)] + 9449.3 \times (-4.402) \\ &= -41863.2 \text{ kW} \end{aligned}$$

The rate of exergy decrease in the boiler is

$$\dot{B} = \dot{B}_{in} - \dot{B}_{out} = -34786.9 - (-41863.2) = 7076.3 \text{ kW}$$

The condenser has no work interaction, so the whole reduction of the exergy is a loss; hence,

$$\dot{I} = \dot{B}_{in} - \dot{B}_{out} - 0 = 7076.3 \text{ kW}$$

e. The boiler has four ports for the working fluid, two inlets and two outlets, and two ports for the flue gas, one inlet and one outlet.

We first find the required quantity of flue gas. The heat input into the steam, calculated in Example 11.3, is $q_{in} = 3263.8$ kJ/kg. The heat interaction of the flue gas is then

$$\dot{Q}_{gas} = -\dot{m}_1 q_{in} = -106.47 \times 3263.8 = -347496.8 \text{ kW}$$

The flowrate of the flue gas is calculated from

$$\dot{m}_g = \frac{\dot{Q}_{gas}}{c_p\left(T_{g2} - T_{g1}\right)}$$

where

$$c_p = \frac{k\overline{R}}{(k-1)M} = \frac{1.35 \times 8.3143}{0.35 \times 29} = 1.1058 \text{ kJ/kg K}$$

Hence,

$$\dot{m}_g = \frac{\dot{Q}_{gas}}{c_p\left(T_{g2} - T_{g1}\right)} = \frac{-347496.8}{1.1058 \times (400 - 1500)} = 285.68 \text{ kg/s}$$

The specific exergies for the boiler ports were calculated before:

$b_1 = 1504.7 \quad b_2 = 828.6 \quad b_3 = 1164.2 \quad b_{10} = 127.7$ kJ/kg

We select the initial state of the flue gas (102 kPa, 1500 °C) as the reference state. Thus,

$$b_{g1} = h_{g1} - T_0 s_{g1} = 0.0 - 298.15 \times 0.0 = 0.0 \text{ kJ/kg}$$

$$b_{g2} = h_{g2} - T_0 s_{g2} = c_p\left[T_2 - T_1 - T_0\left(\ln\frac{T_2}{T_1} - \frac{k-1}{k}\ln\frac{p_2}{p_1}\right)\right]$$

$$= 1.1058 \times \left[400 - 1500 - 298.15 \times \left(\ln\frac{673.15}{1773.15} - \frac{0.35}{1.35}\ln\frac{101}{102}\right)\right]$$

$$= -897.9 \text{ kJ/kg}$$

$$\dot{B}_{in} = \dot{m}_1\left[(1-y_1)b_2 + b_{10}\right] + \dot{m}_g b_{g1}$$

$$= 106.47 \times \left[0.8658 \times 828.6 + 127.7\right] + 285.68 \times 0.0 = 89978.0 \text{ kW}$$

$$\dot{B}_{out} = \dot{m}_1\left[(1-y_1)b_3 + b_1\right] + \dot{m}_g b_{g2}$$

$$= 106.47 \times \left[0.8658 \times 1164.2 + 1504.7\right] + 285.68 \times (-897.9)$$

$$= 11011.7 \text{ kW}$$

The rate of exergy decrease in the boiler is

$$\dot{B}_{in} - \dot{B}_{out} = 89978.0 - 11011.7 = 78966.3 \text{ kW}$$

The boiler has no work interaction, and the total exergy decrease is a loss; hence, $\dot{I} = 78966.3$ kW.

We found that the biggest loss occurs in the boiler. The main loss is due to the large temperature difference between the flue gas and the steam. It is worth while to note that the first law does not show any loss in the boiler since all the heat that was taken from the gas went into the steam.

PROBLEMS

11.1 State whether the following statements are true, sometimes true, or false.

A. In an ideal Rankine cycle:

a. All the processes are internally reversible.
b. Efficiency equals that of a Carnot cycle.
c. The pressure at the turbine outlet depends on the condenser temperature.
d. Cycle efficiency increases as condenser pressure decreases.
e. Cycle efficiency increases as boiler pressure decreases.
f. The lowest pressure in the cycle is atmospheric.
g. In the condenser $\Delta S_{steam} > 0$.
h. In the turbine $\Delta S_{steam} > 0$.
i. The entropy of steam passing through the boiler increases.
j. The entropy of the boiler remains constant.
k. The efficiency increases along with the pressure in the boiler.

B. In an ideal Otto cycle:

a. All processes are internally reversible.
b. The efficiency increases with the maximum temperature.
c. There is a constant ratio between the work and the mean effective pressure.
d. The gas temperature after compression is higher than after expansion.
e. The efficiency depends on the temperature ratio during compression.

C. In an ideal Diesel cycle:

a. The efficiency increases with the maximum temperature.
b. The efficiency depends on the compression ratio only.

D. In an ideal cooling system consisting of a compressor, an evaporator, a valve, and a condenser:

a. All the processes are internally reversible.
b. The coefficient of performance equals that of the Carnot cycle.
c. The coefficient of performance increases with the evaporation temperature.
d. The coefficient of performance increases with the condensation temperature.
e. The pressure at the compressor outlet depends on the evaporation temperature.
f. The minimum pressure is the atmospheric pressure.
g. The entropy change of the refrigerant across the evaporator is negative.
h. The entropy of the refrigerant increases upon passing through the throttle.
i. The evaporator temperature is higher than that of the surroundings.
j. The temperature in the condenser is lower than that of the surroundings.
k. In a heat pump $COP = 1.9$.
l. In a heat pump $COP = 0.9$.

11.2 It is desired to study the effect of boiler and condenser pressures on the efficiency of a Rankine cycle. Given a temperature of 350 °C at the boiler outlet, calculate the efficiency and the steam quality at the turbine exhaust for the following two sets of data:

a. Boiler pressure: 35 bars.
   Condenser pressures: 5 kPa, 10 kPa, 50 kPa, 100 kPa.

b. Condenser pressure: 5 kPa.
   Boiler pressures: 10 bars, 35 bars, 60 bars, 100 bars.

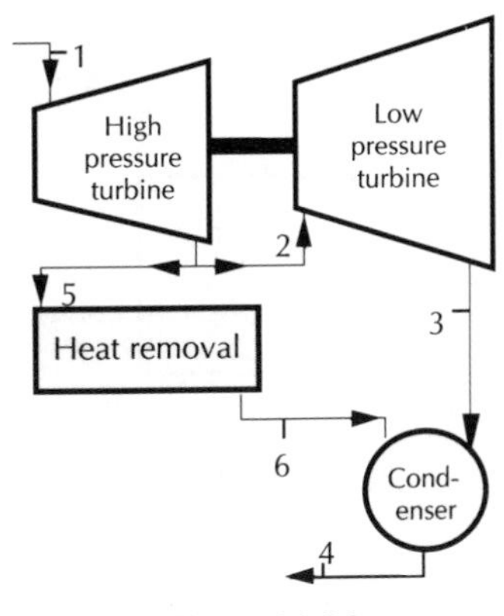

Figure 11.26

11.3 Steam at 3 MPa, 350 °C enters the high pressure turbine, Fig. 11.26, and expands to 0.4 MPa. At that point, 0.5 kg/s of steam are extracted for heating purposes and then returned as condensate at 140 °C to the condenser. The rest of the steam expands in the low pressure turbine to 7 kPa. The isentropic efficiency values of the turbines and the pump are 0.82 and 0.73, respectively, and the mechanical efficiencies are 0.96. The net power of the system is 1500 kW.

a. Show the processes on a *T–s* diagram.
b. Calculate the mass flowrate of the steam in the turbines.
c. Calculate the heat supply of the extracted steam.

11.4 A 16 MW steam turbine with an isentropic efficiency of $\eta_e = 0.82$ receives steam at $p_1 = 35$ bars, $T_1 = 600$ °C and discharges at $p_2 = 0.05$ bars.

a. Draw the process on an *h–s* diagram.
b. Find the specific fuel consumption per kilojoule of power output, if the mechanical efficiency is $\eta_m = 0.92$, the generator efficiency is $\eta_g = 0.98$, and the fuel heating value is 42000 kJ/kg.
c. Find the steam flowrate in the turbine.

11.5 In a Rankine cycle with reheat steam leaves the boiler at 17.5 MPa and 500 °C, and then it is isentropically expanded through a high pressure turbine to 3 MPa. It is reheated at constant pressure to 500 °C and isentropically expanded through a low pressure turbine to 70 kPa. The steam is then condensed to saturated liquid at 70 kPa and isentropically compressed to 17.5 MPa to repeat the cycle.

a. Draw the cycle on a *T–s* diagram.
b. Determine the heat added.
c. Determine the heat rejected.
d. Determine the thermal efficiency of the cycle.

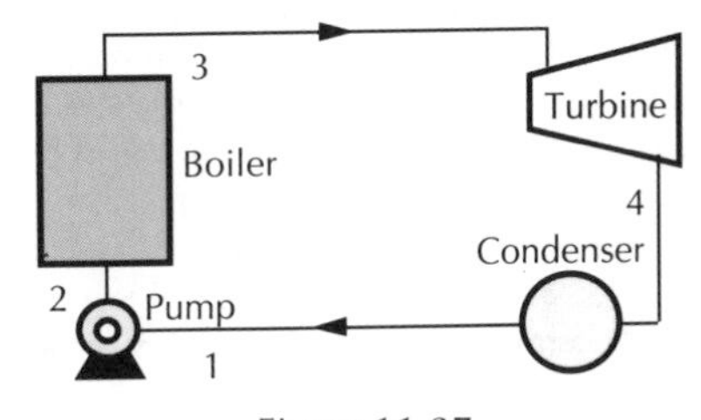

Figure 11.27

11.6 Steam circulates through the following steady state reversible cycle in a power plant consisting of a steam boiler, a turbine, a condenser, and a boiler feed pump (Fig. 11.27):

1–2 Saturated liquid at 2 psia is pumped adiabatically to 700 psia by the feed pump.
2–3 Constant-pressure heating in the steam boiler at 700 psia to 600 °F.
3–4 Reversible adiabatic expansion in the turbine from 700 psia to 2 psia.
4–1 Constant pressure cooling in the condenser at 2 psia to saturated liquid.

Neglect changes in velocity and elevation and find:

a. The efficiency of the power plant.
b. The flowrate for a power output of 1000 hp.

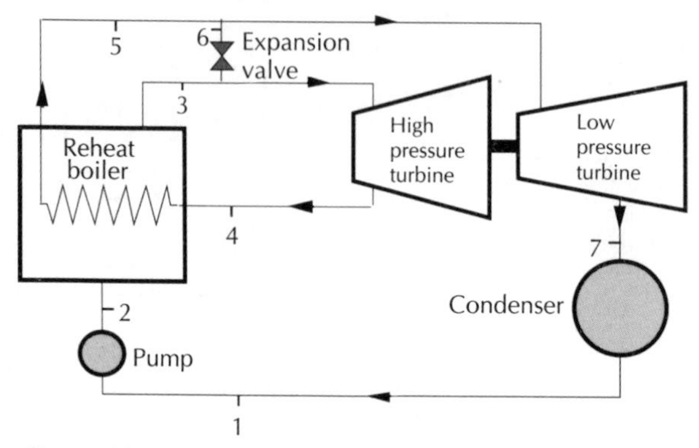

Figure 11.28

11.7 In the ordinary operating mode of a 75 kW power plant, shown in Fig. 11.28, the expansion valve is closed, and the steam from the boiler passes through the high pressure turbine to the superheater and into the low pressure turbine (1→2→3→4 →5→7→1).

When the high pressure turbine is out of service the plant is operated in an emergency mode in which the steam from the boiler is passed through the expansion valve directly into the low pressure turbine. The modified cycle is now 1→2→3→6 →7→1.

Data:	p_1 = 5 kPa	p_2 = 10 MPa	p_5 = 0.5 MPa
	x_1 = 0	T_3 = 500 °C	T_5 = 480 °C

The isentropic efficiency of the pump and the turbines is 0.90.

a. Describe the two cycles on a *T–s* diagram.
b. Calculate the efficiency of each cycle.
c. Calculate the mass flowrate of the steam in the ordinary operating mode.
d. Calculate the output power in the emergency cycle for the same mass flowrate.

11.8 The basic thermodynamic cycle for a steam power plant is a Rankine cycle with reheat. Steam leaves the boiler at 17.5 MPa and 550 °C, and then it is isentropically expanded through a high pressure turbine to 3 MPa. It is reheated at constant pressure to 500 °C and isentropically expanded through a low pressure turbine to 50 kPa. The steam is then condensed to saturated liquid at 50 kPa and isentropically compressed to 17.5 MPa to repeat the cycle.

a. Draw the cycle on a *T–s* diagram.
b. Determine the heat added.
c. Determine the heat rejected.
d. Determine the thermal efficiency of the cycle.

11.9 Steam is generated in a boiler at 4 MPa and 600 °C. It is fed to an adiabatic turbine which has an isentropic efficiency of 80%. The turbine exhausts at 7 kPa. Condensate is then pumped, as a liquid, back to the boiler. Assume no subcooling of the condensate occurs in the condenser, and negligible pump work.

For a power generation of 500 MW calculate:

a. The rate of steam circulation.
b. The amount of heat supplied to the steam by the boiler.
c. The thermal efficiency of the cycle.

11.10 In an industrial plant, in order to meet a heating requirement at a rate of 11.5 MW in addition to an electrical load, steam is generated in a boiler at 6.0 MPa, 600 °C. The steam is supplied to a turbine of 85% adiabatic efficiency. The steam leaves the turbine at 0.2 MPa and is fed to the heating loop. It emerges from the loop as a saturated liquid at 0.16 MPa and is pumped back to the boiler.

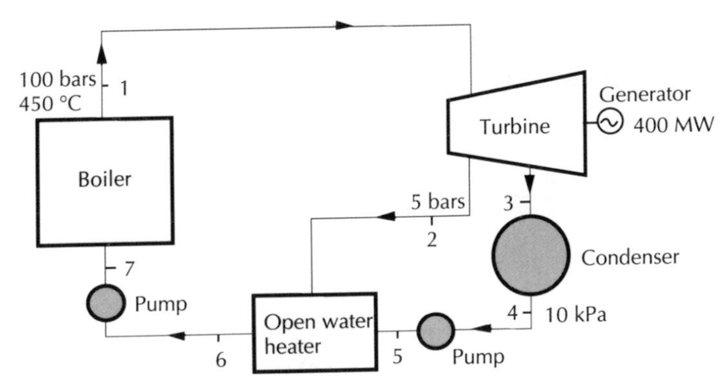

Figure 11.29

a. Show schematically the main parts of the system and their relative location.
b. Show the process on a *T–s* diagram.
c. Calculate the power of the turbine.

11.11 The profitability of a 2 MW Rankine power cycle driven by solar energy is to be investigated. The working fluid is Freon-12. Freon enters the turbine at 90 °C, 2.5 MPa, and exits the condenser as a saturated liquid at 25 °C. The adiabatic efficiency of the turbine is 0.8 and of the pump is 1.0.

Assume a temperature difference of 5 °C for heat transfer in the evaporator (which receives heat from a solar collector) and in the condenser.

a. Describe the cycle on a *T–s* diagram and calculate the points in the cycle (point 1 is at the entrance to the turbine).
b. Calculate the efficiency of the cycle and compare with Carnot efficiency.
c. Calculate the Freon mass flowrate.
d. Estimate the hourly saving in fuel, if the thermodynamic efficiency of a conventional power plant is 40%, and the caloric value of the fuel is 42000 kJ/kg.

11.12 A power plant operates according to the Rankine cycle, as shown in Fig. 11.29. The efficiencies of the turbine and pump are 0.9.

a. Draw the cycle on a *T–s* diagram.
b. Find the efficiency of the cycle.
c. Find the steam flowrate.
Note: Assume any data that are missing and justify your assumptions.

11.13 A compressor cycle is comprised of the following processes: 1–2 adiabatic compression, 2–3 isobaric air discharge, 3–4 isochoric pressure reduction, and 4–1 isobaric air intake. Air at 1 bar and 290 °C enters the compressor at a rate of 900 m3/h and is discharged at 8 bars. The mechanical efficiency of the compressor is 0.92, and the theoretical compression ratio is infinite (no dead volume).

a. Draw the cycle on the *p–v* and *T–s* diagrams.
b. Find the power needed to operate the compressor.
c. Find the final temperature of the compressed air.

11.14 Air at 280 K and 1 bar enters a compressor having a compression ratio r. The compressor cycle is made up of the following processes: 1- 2 polytropic compression with $n = 1.25$, 2- 3 isobaric air discharge, 3- 4 isochoric pressure reduction, and 4- 1 isobaric air intake.

a. Plot the maximum (discharge) pressure versus *r*.
b. Plot the discharge temperature versus *r*.

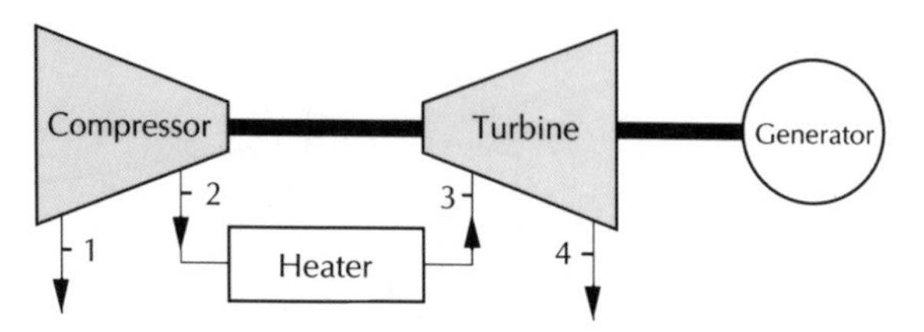

Figure 11.30

11.15 A gas turbine, Fig. 11.30, operates a 1000 kW generator. Air at 1.0 bar and 30 °C enters the compressor and is compressed to 7.0 bars. The exhaust gas temperature is 665 K. The isentropic efficiencies of the compressor and the turbine are 0.88 and 0.92, respectively.

a. Describe the cycle schematically on a T–s and on a p–v diagram.
b. Calculate the temperature at the inlet of the turbine.
c. Calculate the efficiency of the cycle.
d. Calculate the volumetric flowrate at the compressor inlet.
e. Calculate the entropy change between the compressor's inlet and outlet.

11.16 A gas turbine operates a 1000 kW generator. Air at 1.0 bar and 30 °C enters the compressor and is compressed to 7.0 bars. The gas leaves the turbine at 665 K and enters an ideal regenerator. The isentropic efficiencies of the compressor and the turbine are 0.88 and 0.92, respectively.

a. Show the cycle schematically on a T–s and on a p–v diagram.
b. Find the temperature at the inlet of the turbine.
c. Find the cycle efficiency.
d. Calculate the volumetric flowrate at the inlet to the compressor.
e. Find the entropy change between the inlet and the outlet of the compressor.

11.17 Air from the surroundings enters the compressor of a gas turbine at 100 kPa, 290 K, and a rate of 5 kg/s. The pressure ratio is $p_2/p_1 = 5$ and the maximum allowed temperature in the cycle is 1200 K.

a. If that cycle is used to run an electric generator and the compressor and the turbine are ideal, find the cycle efficiency and the electrical power supplied.
b. If the compressor and the turbine are not ideal, for what isentropic efficiencies will the cycle efficiency be equal to zero?
c. If the system is used as a jet engine (isentropic efficiency of 100%) exhausting air to the surroundings, determine the velocity of the jet.

11.18 Air at 1 bar, 300 K, and a rate of 40 kg/s enters the compressor of a gas turbine operating on a Brayton cycle, as shown in Fig. 11.13. The discharge pressure of the compressor is 6 bars, the temperature at the turbine intake is 1073 K, the isentropic efficiencies of the compressor and the turbine are, respectively, $\eta_c = 0.84$ and $\eta_t = 0.87$, and the mechanical efficiencies are $\eta_m = 0.98$.

a. Find the net power output.
b. Find the thermodynamic efficiency.
c. Find the fuel consumption for a burner efficiency of $\eta_b = 0.98$, a fuel heating value of 41900 kJ/kg, and $c_p = 1.01$ kJ/kg K, $c_v = 0.715$ kJ/kg K.

11.19 A regenerative gas turbine is shown in Fig. 11.31. Air from the surroundings (ideal gas, $M = 29$, $k = 1.4$) enters the compressor at 1 bar and 27 °C. The compression has an adiabatic efficiency of 80% and a pressure ratio of 6.0. The gas temperature at the burner outlet is 750 °C. The expansion in the turbine is polytropic at $n = 1.3$.

The exhaust gas temperature (at point 6) is 10 °C higher than that at the compressor outlet. Neglect pressure losses through the heat exchanger. The calculations are to be made per unit mass of flowing gas.

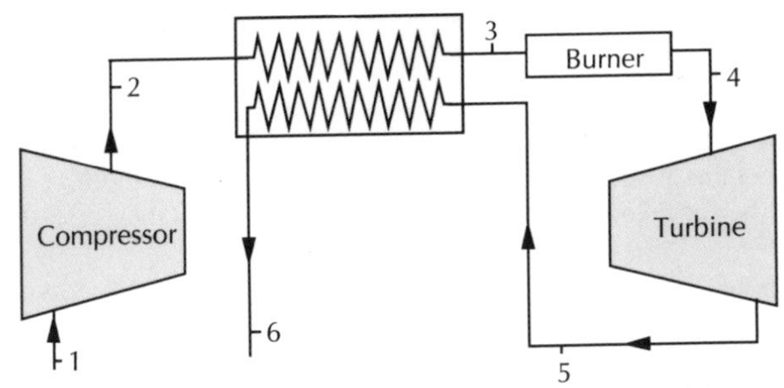

Figure 11.31 **Schematic of a regenerative gas turbine.**

a. Describe the process in a p–v and a T–s diagram.
b. Calculate the amount of heat transferred in the heat exchanger.
c. Calculate the amount of heat supplied to the burner.
d. Calculate the cycle efficiency.

11.20 A nuclear-powered gas turbine, shown in Fig. 11.32, is used to propel a naval vessel. The working gas is CO_2 (ideal gas, $M = 44$, $k = 4/3$). The required power output at the propeller is 50 MW. The cycle includes a regenerative heat exchanger and the cooling is done by sea water, the temperature of which increases by 10 °C. The table below lists the points of the cycle.

a. Draw the T–s and p–v diagrams for the cycle.
b. Fill in the table; list your assumptions and show the details of your calculations.
c. Find the isentropic efficiency of the turbine.
d. Find the entropy change of the gas across the compressor.
e. Find the thermodynamic efficiency of the cycle.
f. Find the water inflow to the cooler. Assume for water $c_p = 4.2$ kJ /kg K.

	1	2s	2	3	4	5s	5	6
T (K)	310		540		920		610	
p (bar)	0.95			6.0				

11.21 An engine working according to the ideal Otto cycle is designed for a 120 kW output using a compression ratio of $r = 9$ and a combustion temperature of 2400 K. The heating value of gasoline is 42000 kJ/kg. Owing to wear, the compression ratio of this ideal cycle is reduced to $r = 8$. The ambient temperature is $T_1 = 300$ K.

a. Draw the original cycle and the new cycle on the same diagram.

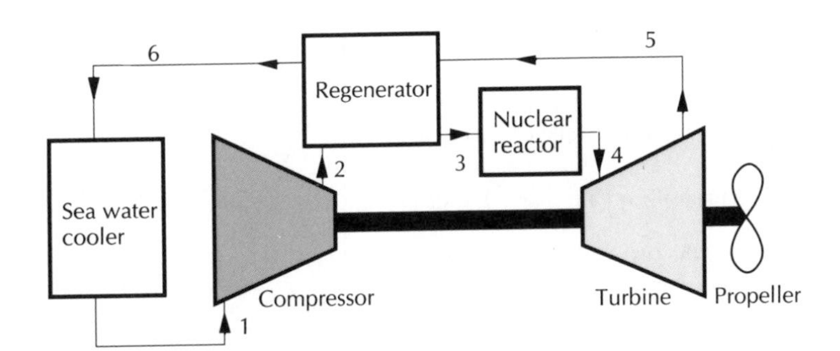

Figure 11.32

b. Find the fuel consumption of the worn engine, operating at the same power output and rpm as in the original design.
c. Find the maximum temperature in the worn engine.

11.22 Nitrogen (ideal gas, $M = 28$, $k = 1.4$) is the working fluid in an imaginary four-cylinder engine, with compression ratio 8.0, that turns at 3000 rpm. The cross-sectional area of each piston is $A = 80\ \text{cm}^2$ and its stroke is $L = 10.5$ cm. The engine operates in a closed cycle, consisting of three reversible stages, as follows:

1–2 Isothermal compression from $p_1 = 100$ kPa, $T_1 = 27$ °C, to minimum volume.
2–3 Isobaric heating.
3–1 Adiabatic expansion.

a. Describe the cycle on p–v and T–s diagrams.
b. Determine the power of the engine and its efficiency.
c. Determine the irreversibility of the total process relative to an environment at $p_0 = 100$ kPa, $T_0 = 300$ K.
d. Determine the irreversibility of the total process relative to an environment at $p_0 = 200$ kPa, $T_0 = 350$ K.

11.23 An internal combustion engine works according to an ideal Otto cycle. At the beginning of compression the conditions are 0.1 MPa, 27 °C, and the volume of the cylinder is 0.002 m^3. The pressure at the end of compression is 1.2 MPa. Heat is added at a rate of 4.2 kJ per cycle.

a. Show the cycle schematically on a p–v and T–s diagram.
b. Determine the pressure, temperature, and volume at each point of the cycle.
c. Find the work and heat interactions of each process of the cycle.
d. Find the thermal efficiency of the cycle.

11.24 Consider a cycle similar to that of the previous problem except that the gas continues to expand till it reaches the initial pressure. It is then cooled at a constant pressure to the initial state.

a. Show the cycle schematically on a p–v and T–s diagram.
b. Determine the maximum volume in this cycle.
c. Find the thermal efficiency of the cycle.

11.25 A diesel engine is designed such that in a standard cycle the compression ratio is 14 and the cut-off ratio is 3.2. The conditions at the engine inlet are 27 °C and 105 kPa. From measurements done on the engine it became clear that the pressure at the end of the expansion process was 95% of the expected pressure. The assumption is that the only reason for the error in the designed cycle is the incomplete combustion of the fuel that produces less heat from the combustion process than expected.

a. Show the two cycles on a p–v and a T–s diagram.
b. Calculate the points of the designed and the actual cycles.
c. Calculate the heat interactions in both cycles.
d. Calculate the efficiency of the two cycles. Explain your answer, and compare the actual cycle to the designed cycle.

11.26 A Diesel cycle has a compression ratio of 18. The conditions at the beginning of compression are 0.1 MPa, 15 °C, and the maximum temperature is 2500 K. Assume that the working gas has the same properties as air.

a. Show the cycle schematically on a p–v and T–s diagram.
b. Determine the states of the gas at all the cycle points.
c. Find the work and heat interactions of each process of the cycle.
d. Find the thermal efficiency of the cycle.

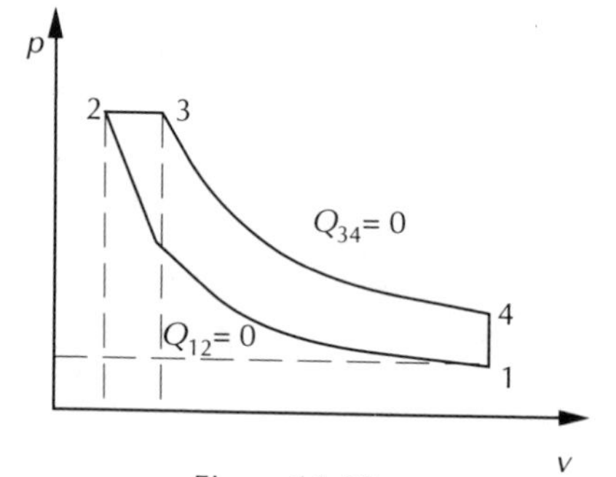

Figure 11.33

11.27 A four-stroke diesel engine, Fig. 11.33, has a

maximum volume of 2.5 L, a compression ratio of $r = 15$, and a cut-off ratio of $v_3/v_2 = 1.7$. The engine operates at 2800 rpm. The ambient air is at $p_0 = 0.9$ bars and $T_0 = 293$ K.

a. Find the relevant parameters of the cycle.
b. Find the power output of the engine.
c. Find the thermodynamic efficiency of the cycle and compare it with the Carnot efficiency in the same temperature range.

11.28 A four-stroke automobile engine operates at 3850 rpm according to the dual cycle, as shown in Fig. 11.20. The volume of the cylinder is 850 cm^3. The intake conditions are 0.9 bars and 353 K. The compression ratio is $r = 8$, the pressure ratio is $r_p = p_3/p_2 = 2$, and the cut-off ratio is $r_c = v_4/v_3 = 1.75$. The working fluid is an ideal diatomic gas of $M = 28.96$, $k = 1.4$.

a. Find the relevant parameters of the cycle.
b. Find the power output of the engine.
c. Find the thermodynamic efficiency of the cycle and compare it with the Carnot efficiency in the same temperature range.
d. Find the fuel consumption in km/L if the automobile runs at 70 km/h and uses a fuel with a heating value of 44000 kJ/kg.

11.29 Show that the efficiency of the dual cycle is given by Eq. (11.28).

11.30 An Ericsson cycle consists of the following steps:

Step A – An isothermal expansion from pressure p_1 and volume V_1 to pressure p_2.
Step B – A constant-pressure process to volume V_3.
Step C – An isothermal compression to the initial pressure p_1.
Step D – A constant-pressure process to return to the initial state.
Assume that the working fluid is an ideal diatomic gas with $M = 29$ and $k = 1.4$.
Given that $n = 2$ kmol, $p_1 = 5$ bars, $p_2 = 1$ bar, $V_1 = 10$ liters, and $V_3 = 30$ liters:

a. Draw the cycle on a p–v diagram.
b. In which step or steps is there positive heat transfer Q_H to the gas? What is the value of Q_H?
c. Draw the cycle on a T–s diagram.
d. What is the efficiency of the cycle?
e. Calculate ΔU for Step A and ΔU for Step B.
f. Calculate ΔH for Step A and ΔH for Step B.

11.31 Saturated Freon-12 at –20 °C enters the compressor of a certain cooling system at a rate of 150 kg/h and exits the compressor at 1.1 MPa and 80 °C. The temperature of the Freon at the condenser outlet is 35 °C.

a. Describe the system schematically.
b. Describe the process in a T–s and a p–v diagram.
c. Determine the isentropic efficiency of the compressor.
d. Determine the coefficient of performance and the cooling capacity.

11.32 A Freon-12 cooling system has a cooling capacity of 100 MJ/h. The evaporation temperature is –20 °C and the condensation temperature 50 °C: The refrigerant at the inlet to the compressor is saturated vapor and at the condenser outlet saturated liquid. The isentropic efficiency of the compressor is 0.8. The condenser is cooled by water entering at a temperature of 20 °C and leaving at 40 °C. Calculate:

a. The *COP* of the cycle.
b. The power of the compressor.
c. The supply rate of the cooling water to the condenser.
d. The rate of the entropy change in the condenser (Freon and cooling water).

11.33 A young engineer claims to have invented a method to improve the performance of a cooling device that operates on Freon-12. For this purpose the engineer adds to the device an ideal heat

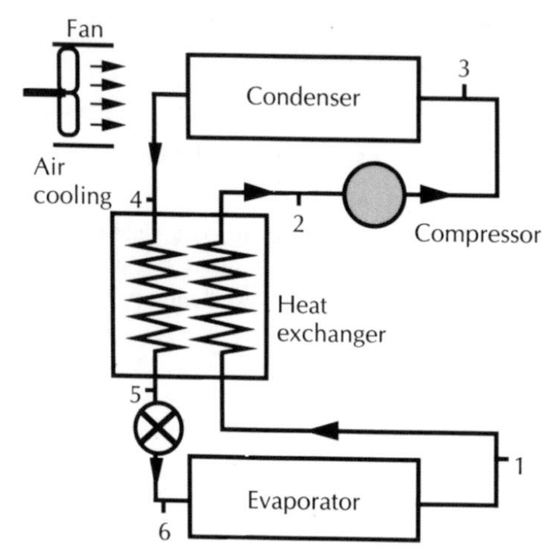

Figure 11.34

exchanger that brings into contact the fluids from the evaporator and the condenser as seen in Fig. 11.34. It is known that the refrigerant leaves the condenser as a saturated liquid at 1.2 MPa and comes out from the evaporator as saturated vapor at –10 °C. The isentropic efficiency of the compressor is 0.8.

a. If the device is rated at a cooling capacity of 20 kW determine whether the addition of the heat exchanger improves the performance of the cooling device.
b. If the condenser is cooled by air (ideal gas, $M = 29$, $k = 1.4$) at atmospheric pressure, calculate the air flowrate if its temperature rises by 2 °C when passing over the condenser.

11.34 An ammonia cooling system is designed for a cooling capacity of 20 kW. At the exit of the condenser the ammonia is saturated liquid at 1.2 MPa. Ammonia vapor leaves the evaporator at 0.2 MPa and a superheat of 5 °C. The compressor operates at 3000 rpm and has an isentropic efficiency of 0.9.

a. Describe the cycle on a *p–h* diagram.
b. Find the coefficient of performance of the cycle and compare it with that of a Carnot cycle.

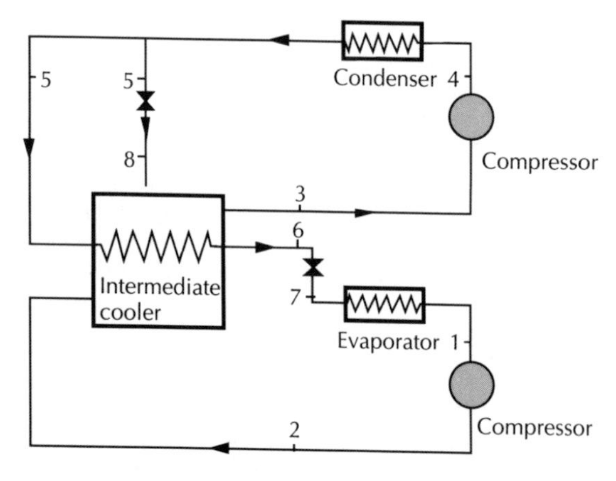

Figure 11.35

c. Calculate the gas flowrate through the compressor.
d. Find the cylinder volume of the compressor.

11.35 A Freon-12 cooling system designed to remove 100000 kJ/h contains an intermediate cooler that operates as a heat exchanger, Fig.11.35. The compression is completed in two steps. The isentropic efficiency of compression is 0.8.

Point 1 is saturated vapor at –20 °C, point 3 is saturated vapor at +10 °C, $T_6 = T_3$ and point 5 is saturated liquid at +40 °C.

a. Describe the cycle on a *p–h* diagram.
b. Arrange the properties of the states 1 through 7 in a table.
c. Calculate the cycle's coefficient of performance.
d. Calculate the total power of both compressors.

11.36 A cooling system of 6 kW capacity operates at the following conditions. The cooling material is Freon-12, the evaporation temperature –10 °C, and the condensation temperature 41 °C. The condenser is cooled by water entering at 28 °C, 240 kPa, and leaving at 33 °C, 105 kPa. The isentropic efficiency of the compressor is 0.75 and its mechanical efficiency is 0.88.

Describe the cycle on a *p–h* diagram, find the compressor power, the amount of cooling water, and the coefficient of performance for the following cases:

a. The state at the inlet to the compressor is that of a saturated vapor, and at the outlet of the condenser is that of a saturated liquid.
b. An ideal internal heat exchanger is placed between the outlet of the evaporator and the outlet of the condenser.

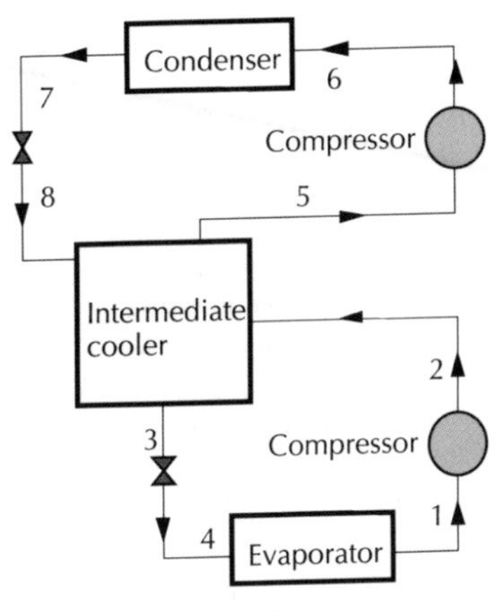

Figure 11.36

11.37 A Freon-12 double-stage deep cooling system has a direct contact intermediate cooler as shown in Fig.11.36. The evaporation temperature is –50 °C. The condenser temperature is 50 °C and the intermediate cooler temperature is 0 °C. The compressors have an isentropic efficiency of 0.85.

a. Find the ratio of the flowrates through the compressors.
b. Calculate the *COP* of the system.
c. Calculate the *COP* of a single-stage system operating under the same conditions.
d. Calculate the *COP* of an equivalent Carnot cycle.

11.38 An air-conditioning system, shown in Fig. 11.37 is required to cool 5000 kg/h of air from 24 °C to 7 °C. The system operates on Freon-12. The temperature of the evaporator is –2 °C and that of the condenser, 45 °C. Freon leaves the evaporator as a saturated vapor and the condenser as a saturated liquid. The condenser is cooled by water entering at 24 °C and leaving at 32 °C. The isentropic efficiency of the compressor is 0.85.

a. Describe the cycle on a *p–h* and on a *T–s* diagram.
b. Find the coefficient of performance (*COP*) of the cycle.
c. Find the power needed to operate the compressor.
d. Find the flowrate of the cooling fluid (water).
e. Find the coefficient of performance of a Carnot cycle, operating between the same temperatures.

11.39 A Freon-12 heat pump is set to maintain a temperature of 20 °C inside a building while producing 100 kW of heat. The isentropic efficiency of the compressor is 0.9, and the condenser operates at 35 °C. There are two ways to vaporize Freon-12 in the evaporator:

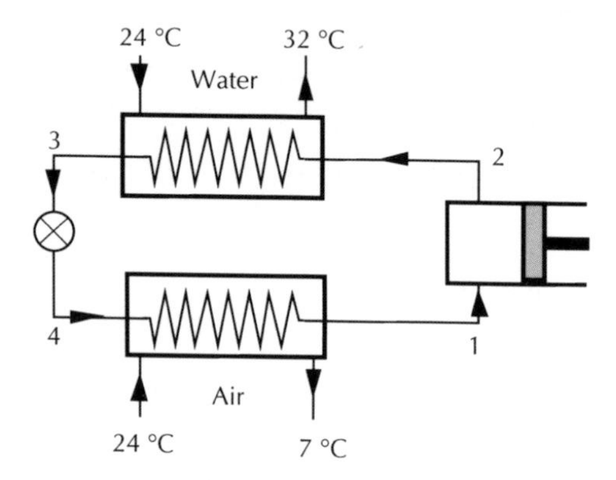

Figure 11.37

1. By passing the ambient air at 0 °C over the evaporator. The air leaves the evaporator at –8 °C and vaporization takes place at –10 °C.
2. By heating the ambient air by a solar collector to 15 °C, which then enters the evaporator, leaving it at 7 °C. Vaporization takes place at 5 °C.

a. Draw the two cycles on the same *p–h* diagram.
b. Complete a table with all the relevant parameters of the points of the two cycles.
c. Find the input power for each cycle.
d. Find the heat absorption in the evaporator for each cycle.
e. Find the ambient air inflow for the cycles.

11.40 A heat pump is used to keep a room at 24 °C while the temperature outside is 7 °C. The rate of heat loss from the wall is 15000 kJ/h. The "pump" uses ammonia as a working fluid. Assume that the ammonia enters the compressor dry saturated at the temperature of the evaporation and the isentropic efficiency of the compressor is 80%; the ammonia leaves the condenser as saturated liquid.

a. Describe the ammonia cycle in any convenient diagram assuming that in each heat exchanger the temperature difference is 3 °C.
b. Compute the mass of ammonia circulating.
c. Compute the power required for the heat pump.
d. Find the coefficient of performance of the cycle.
e. What would be the *COP* of a Carnot engine operating between room temperature and that outside?

11.41 Freon-12 is the working fluid of a refrigeration system that removes 100 kW at 0 °C while the environment is at 30 °C. The isentropic efficiency of the compressor is 0.8.

a. Find the *COP* of the refrigeration cycle with a single-stage compression.
b. Would you recommend using two-stage compression for this application? If not, explain why not. If so, suggest an intermediate pressure.

11.42 An ideal refrigeration cycle operates on Freon-12 between 1 MPa and 0.2 MPa. Determine:

a. The evaporator and condenser temperature.
b. The refrigeration effect per kilogram of Freon.
c. The work input per kilogram of Freon.
d. The coefficient of performance.
e. The *COP* of a Carnot refrigerator operating between the same temperatures.

11.43 Dry saturated steam at 20 °C is compressed reversibly by an adiabatic compressor to a pressure of 150 kPa. Subsequently it is cooled through a heat exchanger at constant pressure to a saturated liquid. It is then expanded through an adiabatic throttle valve to a pressure equal to the inlet pressure of the compressor, and heated at constant pressure back to its initial state. The diagram of the process is shown in Fig. 11.21. Calculate:

a. The coefficient of performance of the refrigeration cycle.
b. The power in kW required to remove 30000 kJ/h from the cold reservoir.

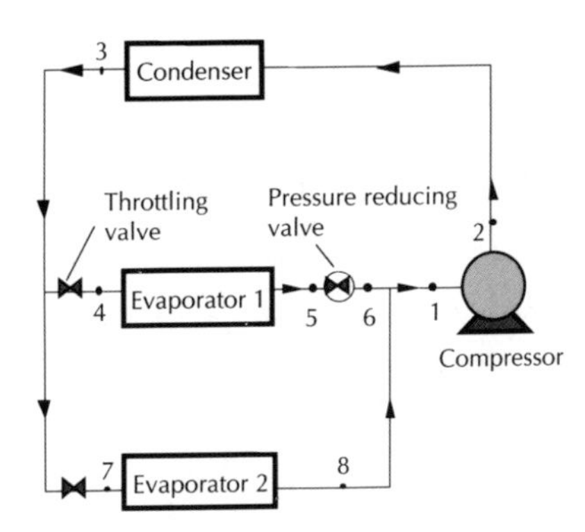

Figure 11.38

11.44 A Freon-12 refrigeration system has a single compressor connected to two evaporators, as shown in Fig. 11.38. The evaporation temperature in evaporator 1 is 5 °C and its cooling capacity is 10 kW. Evaporator 2 operates at –10 °C and has a cooling capacity of 25 kW. Freon leaves the condenser as a saturated liquid at 35 °C, while the state at the exit from each evaporator is that of saturated vapor. A pressure reducing valve between evaporator 1 and the compressor reduces the pressure isenthalpically to that of evaporator 2. The temperature at the discharge from the compressor is 60 °C.

a. Describe the process on a *p–h* diagram
b. Find the power requirement of the compressor.
c. Find the rate of heat removal in the condenser.
d. Find the *COP* of the process.

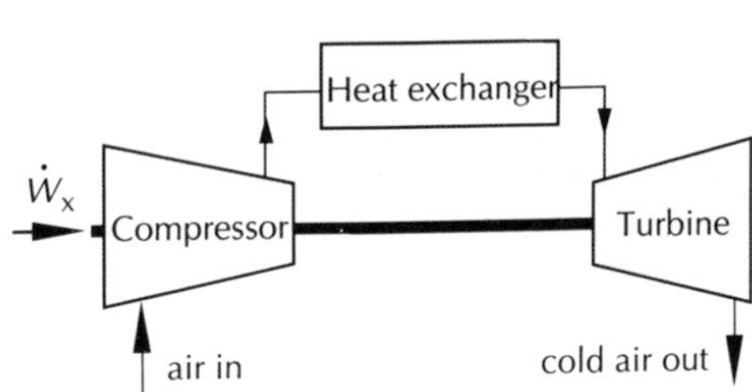

Figure 11.39

11.45 A refrigeration machine removes 100 kJ/min from a cold storage at –5 °C and discharges 125 kJ/min at 30 °C.

a. Determine the coefficient of performance of the machine.
b. Is the process reversible? Explain!

11.46 The operating fluid in a certain cooling system is air (ideal gas, $M = 29$, $k = 1.4$). The system consists of a compressor, heat exchanger and a turbine as shown schematically in Fig. 11.39. Atmospheric air at 100 kPa, 40 °C, enters the compressor and leaves at 900 kPa. It is then cooled at a constant pressure in the heat exchanger to 50 °C, using atmospheric air as coolant. The cooled high pressure air passes through a turbine that produces 100kW which augments the power input to the compressor. The adiabatic efficiencies of both the compressor and the turbine are 85%. The air that leaves the turbine is used to maintain a storage room at –18 °C.

a. Find the temperature at the exit of the turbine.
b. Determine the extra power to the compressor.
c. Determine the *COP* of the system.

11.47 An ammonia cooling system works according to the following steps:

1–2 Adiabatic compression with efficiency of 85%, $p_2/p_1 = p_4/p_2$.
2–3 Intercooling to 45 °C.

3–4 Adiabatic compression with efficiency of 85%.
4–5 Condensation at 45 °C.
5–6 Throttling.
6–1 Evaporation at –15 °C to saturated vapor. Heat removed 5.0 kW.

a. Draw the system schematically.
b. Show the cycle on a *p–h* diagram.
c. Find the *COP* and the power of the compressors.

11.48 A cooling system operates according to the following steps:

1–2 Reversible adiabatic compression of saturated vapor.
2–3 Cooling at a constant pressure corresponding to 40 °C.
3–4 Throttling.
4–1 Evaporation at 3 °C.
Determine the coefficient of performance of the cycle if the working fluid is

a. Freon-22 (R-22).
b. Water.

11.49 A Freon-22 refrigeration system is required to remove 25 kW from a cold storage room at –10 °C. Assume that the adiabatic efficiency of the compressor is 85% and that a 5 °C temperature difference is required in the heat exchangers.

Calculate the required compressor power for the range of outside temperatures between 15 °C and 45 °C. Plot the results as a function of the outside temperature.

11.50 An ideal, dry compression, refrigeration cycle using ammonia operates between 1 MPa and 0.2 MPa. Determine:

a. The evaporator and condenser temperatures.
b. The refrigeration effect per kilogram of ammonia.
c. The work input per kilogram of ammonia.
d. The coefficient of performance.
e. The coefficient of performance of a Carnot refrigeration cycle operating between the same temperatures.

11.51 In the freezing process of desalting sea water refrigerant 114 ($C_2Cl_2F_4$) was chosen as having desirable properties. The refrigeration cycle using $C_2Cl_2F_4$ operates between 340 K and 270 K. Determine:

a. The evaporator and condenser pressures in MPa.
b. The refrigeration effect in kJ/kg of $C_2Cl_2F_4$.
c. The work input in kJ/kg of $C_2Cl_2F_4$.
d. The coefficient of performance.
e. The coefficient of performance for a reversed Carnot refrigeration cycle operating between the same temperatures.

11.52 A compression refrigerating machine which employs ammonia as the refrigerant delivers saturated vapor at the temperature in the evaporator to a reversible adiabatic compressor. Liquid leaving the condenser is expanded through a throttle valve to the pressure in the evaporator. The temperature in the condenser depends on the temperature of the available cooling water.

a. For an evaporator temperature of –15 °C plot the coefficient of performance against temperature in the condenser for temperatures ranging from 5 °C to 50 °C.
b. For a condenser temperature of 15 °C plot the coefficient of performance against temperature in the evaporator for temperatures ranging from –40 °C to 0 °C.
c. For a condenser temperature of 15 °C plot the coefficient of performance if the work of compression is 25% in excess of the reversible work. Assume the compression process is adiabatic, though not reversible.

11.53 The irreversibility of a process was calculated in Example 11.9 as the difference between the decrease of exergy and the actual work. The irreversibility can also be calculated as the product of the environment temperature and the change of entropy of everything involved in the process, as given in Eq. 10.54).

Using Eq. (10.56) recalculate for Example 11.9 the rate of irreversibility in:

a. The high pressure turbine.
b. The low pressure turbine.
c. The preheaters.
d. The condenser.
e. The boiler.

CHAPTER TWELVE

Ideal gas mixtures and humid air

The laws of thermodynamics are applicable to all systems irrespective of their complexity or contents. In our development of thermodynamics so far, our treatment was limited to pure substances only, namely to systems whose composition does not change during the process and for which we have specific tables of properties.

In many engineering applications we deal with systems that contain mixtures of several pure substances. At times, a mixture can be considered a pure substance, provided its composition does not change during the process. Air is an example of a mixture treated as a pure substance. If, however, we had to consider a mixture of different proportions of the same components of air, its properties would be different, and it would be considered a different substance. Indeed, an infinite number of such "substances" could be conceived for mixtures of even two pure substances, if different proportions of them were taken. It would be an endless effort to try to list the properties of all possible mixtures. Thus, a method that relates the properties of a mixture to those of the individual pure substances, from which the mixture was made, is quite useful.

Various forms of mixtures are encountered in practical applications. Mixtures can appear as liquid or solid mixtures (in which case they are usually referred to as liquid or solid solutions), and they can also be in a gaseous form. In this chapter we treat only the simplest form of mixtures, namely that of mixtures of ideal gases in the absence of chemical reactions. In later chapters we shall extend the treatment to more complex forms of mixtures.

12.1 Basic definitions for gaseous mixtures

Consider a gaseous mixture at pressure p, temperature T, and volume V that contains c different components. Let us denote the molecular weight, the mass, and the number of moles of the i th component in the mixture by M_i, m_i, and n_i, respectively.

The total mass of the mixture is the sum of the masses of the individual components:

$$m = m_1 + m_2 + \ldots + m_i + \ldots + m_c = \sum_{i=1}^{c} m_i \tag{12.1}$$

Similarly, the number of moles of the mixture is equal to the sum of the number of moles of all the individual components:

$$n = n_1 + n_2 + \ldots + n_i + \ldots + n_c = \sum_{i=1}^{c} n_i \tag{12.2}$$

We use the following convention: an indexed quantity refers to the specific component, whereas a quantity without an index refers to the whole mixture.

The mole fraction of component i is defined by

$$y_i = \frac{n_i}{n} = \frac{n_i}{\sum n_i} \tag{12.3}$$

and the mass fraction, mf_i, by

$$mf_i = \frac{m_i}{m} = \frac{m_i}{\sum m_i} \tag{12.4}$$

We further define the molecular weight of the mixture as the average over all the components:

$$M = \frac{\sum n_i M_i}{\sum n_i} = \sum y_i M_i \tag{12.5}$$

We also define the gas constant of the mixture as

$$R = \frac{\overline{R}}{M} = \frac{\overline{R}}{\sum y_i M_i} \tag{12.6}$$

or

$$\frac{1}{R} = \sum \frac{y_i}{R_i} \tag{12.7}$$

EXAMPLE 12.1

Find the molecular weight of air, assuming it is composed of nitrogen, oxygen, argon, and water vapor with mole fractions 0.78, 0.21, 0.008, and 0.002, respectively.

SOLUTION

We use Eq. (12.5), noting that the molecular weights of N_2, O_2, Ar, and H_2O are 28.013, 32.000, 39.948, and 18.016, respectively:

$$\begin{aligned} M &= 0.78 \times 28.013 + 0.21 \times 32.0 + 0.008 \times 39.948 + 0.002 \times 18.016 \\ &= 28.926 \text{ kg/kmol} \end{aligned}$$

12.2 Equation of state for a mixture of ideal gases

It was mentioned, in the introduction to this chapter, that we would like to relate the properties of a mixture to those of the individual pure substance components. We shall introduce here two such methods: one is associated with Dalton and the other with Amagat.

12.2.1 Dalton's rule

Consider a mixture of c components occupying a volume V at pressure p and temperature T. Dalton's model expresses the properties of the mixture in terms of the properties of the individual components, each at the temperature and the volume of the mixture, Fig 12.1.

Dalton's rule (also called Dalton's law) states that the sum of the partial pressures of all the components is equal to the pressure of the whole mixture:

$$p = p_1 + p_2 + p_3 + \ldots + p_i + \ldots + p_c = \sum_{i=1}^{c} p_i \tag{12.8}$$

Dalton's rule is not a law in the thermodynamic sense, since it does not apply universally to all mixtures. It does, however, apply exactly to mixtures of ideal gases when the mixture itself is also an ideal gas. The proof is given below.

The partial pressure of each component, being an ideal gas, is given by

$$p_i = \frac{n_i \bar{R} T}{V} \tag{12.9}$$

The equation of state for the whole mixture is

$$p = \frac{n \bar{R} T}{V} \tag{12.10}$$

dividing Eq. (12.9) by Eq. (12.10) we obtain

$$\frac{p_i}{p} = \frac{n_i}{n} = y_i \tag{12.11}$$

It follows from Eq. (12.11) that

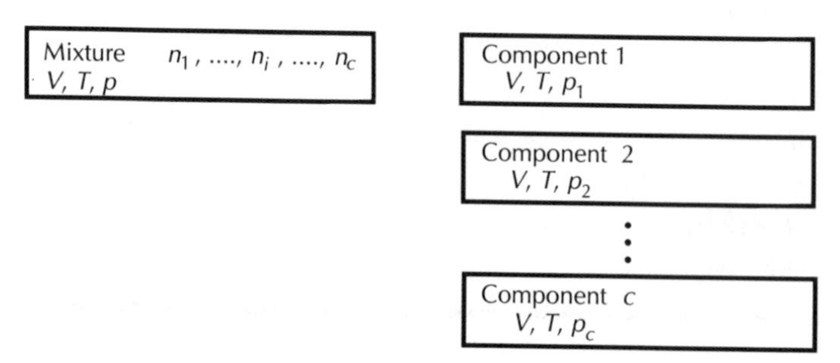

Figure 12.1 **Dalton model.**

$$\sum p_i = p\sum y_i = p \tag{12.12}$$

which proves Dalton's rule for mixtures of ideal gases.

Dalton's rule also applies relatively well to mixtures of real gases at low pressures. Attempts to apply Dalton's rule to gaseous mixtures at higher pressures or to liquid solutions usually result in large errors.

12.2.2 Amagat's rule

Another method for evaluating the properties of a mixture is to relate them to the properties of the individual components when each is maintained, by itself, at the pressure, p, and temperature, T, of the whole mixture, Fig. 12.2. The volume that each component occupies is V_i.

Amagat's rule (sometimes called Amagat's law) states that the sum of the individual volumes, V_i, of all the components, each at p and T, is equal to the volume of the whole mixture:

$$V = \sum_{i=1}^{c} V_i \tag{12.13}$$

As in the case of Dalton's rule, Amagat's rule is also not a thermodynamic law, since it does not apply universally to all systems. It does, however, apply exactly to mixtures of ideal gases when the mixture itself is also an ideal gas. The proof is given below.

$$\sum V_i = \sum \frac{n_i\bar{R}T}{p} = \frac{(\sum n_i)\bar{R}T}{p} = \frac{n\bar{R}T}{p} = V \tag{12.14}$$

Note also that

$$\frac{V_i}{V} = \frac{n_i}{n} = y_i \tag{12.15}$$

We see that for ideal gases, Dalton's rule and Amagat's rule are completely equivalent. For mixtures of real gases at high pressures the equivalence no longer holds. Under these conditions, it was found that Amagat's rule gives better results than Dalton's rule, albeit

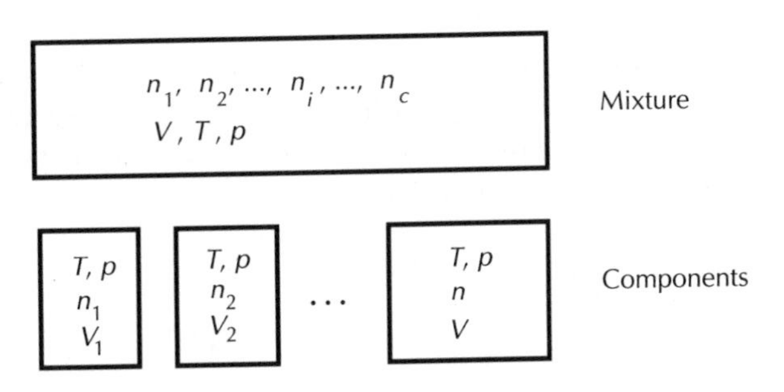

Figure 12.2 **Amagat's model.**

not exact. Dalton's rule, however, will be used in this chapter since it is more convenient for describing mixtures of ideal gases.

EXAMPLE 12.2

An analysis of exhaust gases from an automobile internal combustion engine yielded the following composition: 70% N_2, 15% CO_2, 11% O_2, and 4% CO (in volume percent).

a. Determine the mole fraction and the mass fraction of each component.
b. Determine the partial pressures of each component. Total pressure 100 kPa.
c. Determine the mass of 0.2 m^3 of the gas at 25 °C and 100 kPa.

SOLUTION

a. & b. Consider 1.0 kmol of the gas mixture. The properties of this gas and its components are provided in the table below.

The mass per kilomole is also the average molecular weight of the gases:

$$M = 30.84 \text{ kg/kmol},$$

and

$$R = \bar{R}/M = 8.3143/30.84 = 0.2696 \text{ kJ/kg K}$$

Substance	M_i kg/kmol	$y_i = V_i/V$	$p_i = y_i P$ kPa	$m_i = y_i M_i$ kg	$mf_i = m_i/m$
N_2	28	0.70	70.0	19.60	0.6355
CO_2	44	0.15	15.0	6.60	0.2140
O_2	32	0.11	11.0	3.52	0.1100
CO	28	0.04	4.0	1.12	0.0363
Mixture	30.84	1.00	100.0	30.84	1.0000

c. The mass is calculated from the equation of state:

$$m = \frac{pV}{RT} = \frac{100 \times 0.2}{0.2696 \times 298.15} = 0.249 \text{ kg}$$

12.3 Properties of mixtures of ideal gases

In order to calculate other properties of mixtures of ideal gases, we use the Gibbs–Dalton law. This law states that for mixtures that comply with Dalton's rule, the energy, the enthalpy, and the entropy of a *Dalton mixture* are equal to the sums of the energies, the enthalpies, and the entropies of the respective individual components:

$$U = \sum U_i = \sum m_i u_i = \sum n_i \bar{u}_i \qquad (12.16)$$

$$H = \sum H_i = \sum m_i h_i = \sum n_i \bar{h}_i \qquad (12.17)$$

$$S = \sum S_i = \sum m_i s_i = \sum n_i \bar{s}_i \tag{12.18}$$

The proof of the Gibbs–Dalton law will be given in Chapter 17.

We can also define specific properties for mixtures by dividing the extensive properties by the total mass, or total number of moles. Thus

$$u = U/m = \sum mf_i u_i \qquad \bar{u} = U/n = \sum y_i \bar{u}_i \tag{12.19}$$

$$h = H/m = \sum mf_i h_i \qquad \bar{h} = H/n = \sum y_i \bar{h}_i \tag{12.20}$$

$$s = S/m = \sum mf_i s_i \qquad \bar{s} = S/n = \sum y_i \bar{s}_i \tag{12.21}$$

The properties u, h, and s are derived properties for which only changes between states can be calculated. Absolute values are assigned to these properties by selecting reference states for each of the components. These reference states are selected arbitrarily, and can be either the same for all the components or different for each component. Property changes between states are given as

$$\Delta U = \sum m_i \Delta u_i = \sum n_i \Delta \bar{u}_i \tag{12.22}$$

$$\Delta H = \sum m_i \Delta h_i = \sum n_i \Delta \bar{h}_i \tag{12.23}$$

$$\Delta S = \sum m_i \Delta s_i = \sum n_i \Delta \bar{s}_i \tag{12.24}$$

The change in entropy of component i can be calculated with the help of Eqs (8.38)–(8.40), or similar expressions written in molar quantities. For example,

$$\Delta \bar{s}_i = \bar{c}_{pi} \ln\left(\frac{T_{2i}}{T_{1i}}\right) - \bar{R} \ln\left(\frac{p_{2i}}{p_{1i}}\right) \tag{12.25}$$

One should note that the pressure p_i in Eq. (12.25) is the partial pressure of component i rather than the total pressure of the mixture.

Similar relations hold for other extensive properties such as: available energy, available enthalpy, availability, etc.

We can also define specific heats for a mixture, making use of their definitions. Thus, the specific heat at constant volume for the mixture is

$$c_v = \left(\frac{\partial u}{\partial T}\right)_v = \left(\frac{\partial}{\partial T}\sum mf_i u_i\right)_v = \sum mf_i \left(\frac{\partial u_i}{\partial T}\right)_v = \sum mf_i c_{vi} \tag{12.26}$$

In molar quantities,

$$\bar{c}_v = \sum y_i \bar{c}_{vi} \tag{12.27}$$

Similarly, for the specific heat at constant pressure,

$$c_p = \sum mf_i c_{pi} \quad \text{and} \quad \bar{c}_p = \sum y_i \bar{c}_{pi} \tag{12.28}$$

When the composition of the mixture remains constant during a given process, it can be treated as a pure substance whose properties are computed from the equations given above. For example, air was treated in previous chapters as a pure substance, since its composition was assumed not to vary throughout all the processes.

The ratio of specific heats, k, of a mixture of ideal gases is

$$k = \frac{c_p}{c_v} = \frac{\sum mf_i\, c_{pi}}{\sum mf_i\, c_{vi}} \tag{12.29}$$

and in terms of molar quantities

$$k = \frac{\bar{c}_p}{\bar{c}_v} = \frac{\sum y_i \bar{c}_{pi}}{\sum y_i \bar{c}_{vi}} = 1 + \frac{\bar{R}}{\sum y_i \bar{c}_{vi}} \tag{12.30}$$

Equation (12.30) may be rewritten in terms of k_i as

$$\frac{1}{k-1} = \sum \frac{y_i}{k_i - 1} \tag{12.31}$$

EXAMPLE 12.3

One part of an insulated vessel contains 0.5 kg of oxygen (ideal gas, M = 32, k = 1.4) at 0.4 MPa and 80 °C. The second part of the vessel, whose volume is 0.1 m^3, contains 1 kg of CO_2 (assume ideal gas, M = 44, k = 1.3) at 0.8 MPa, Fig. 12.3. The membrane is ruptured and equilibrium is reached.

a. Find the final pressure and temperature.
b. Find the entropy change.
c. Is the process reversible? Explain.

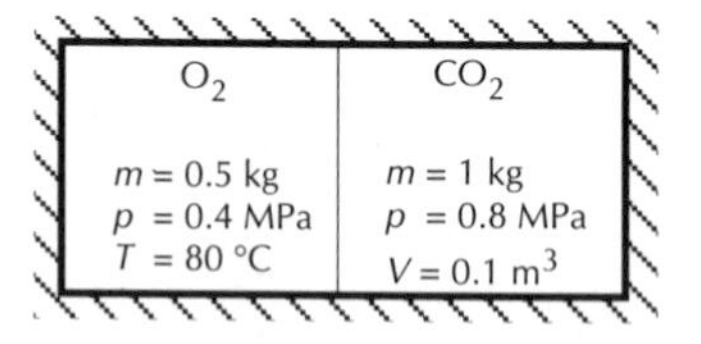

Figure 12.3

SOLUTION

Denote the initial state of oxygen by 1, of CO_2 by 2, and the final state of the mixture with no index. The initial conditions are shown in the table:

State	p kPa	T K	V m^3	m kg	c_v kJ/kg K
1	400	353.15	0.1147	0.5	0.6496
2	800	423.37	0.1000	1.0	0.6290

a. From the first law

$$\Delta U = Q - W = 0$$

$$m_1 c_{v1}(T - T_1) + m_2 c_{v2}(T - T_2) = 0$$

Thus

$$T = \frac{m_1 c_{v1} T_1 + m_2 c_{v2} T_2}{m_1 c_{v1} + m_1 c_{v2}} = \frac{0.5 \times 0.6496 \times 353.15 + 1 \times 0.6299 \times 423.37}{0.5 \times 0.6496 + 1 \times 0.6299} = 399.48 \text{ K}$$

and

$$p = \frac{(m_1/M_1 + m_2/M_2)\bar{R}T}{V_1 + V_2} = \frac{(0.5/32 + 1.0/44) \times 8.3143 \times 399.48}{0.11437 + 0.1000} = 594.2 \text{ kPa}$$

b. The change in entropy is calculated from Eq. (12.24), with Δs_i expressed in terms of volumes occupied by the components and temperatures, which are known. Hence,

$$\Delta S = m_1\left[c_{v1}\ln\frac{T}{T_1} + R\ln\frac{V}{V_1}\right] + m_2\left[c_{v2}\ln\frac{T}{T_2} + R\ln\frac{V}{V_2}\right]$$

$$= 0.5\left[0.6496\ln\frac{399.48}{353.15} + \frac{8.3143}{32}\ln\frac{0.2147}{0.1147}\right]$$

$$+1.0\left[0.6299\ln\frac{399.48}{423.37} + \frac{8.3143}{44}\ln\frac{0.2147}{0.1000}\right] = 0.2293 \text{ kJ/K}$$

c. The process is not reversible since the entropy in this adiabatic process has increased.

12.4 Gaseous mixtures involving a condensable component

It was shown in Chapter 4 that any pure substance has a characteristic saturation curve on a T–p diagram (see Fig. 4.4). At any given temperature, the equilibrium pressure of a pure substance, in the gaseous (vapor) phase, cannot exceed its saturation pressure. Any attempt to increase the pressure above the saturation pressure will result in condensation (liquefaction) of the vapor.

The same is true for a component in a gaseous mixture. That is, the partial pressure of a component cannot exceed the corresponding saturation pressure for the temperature of the mixture. An attempt to increase the partial pressure above saturation results in condensation of that component:

$$p_i^v \leq p_i^{sat}(T) \tag{12.32}$$

Condensation can also occur, obviously, by cooling the mixture, at constant pressure, when the saturation pressure is reached. When a gaseous mixture is in equilibrium (in contact) with the liquid of a given component, the partial pressure of that component in the mixture is equal to the saturation pressure at the temperature of the mixture and the equality holds in Eq. (12.32),

$$p_i^v = p_i^{sat}(T) \tag{12.33}$$

In this chapter, we are concerned with the properties of a gaseous mixture for which at least one of its components may partially condense out of the mixture. More specifically, we look into the properties of air with water vapor. In this case we consider all the components in the gaseous phase to be ideal gases. Water vapor at low pressures may also be considered an ideal gas. The liquid, of course, is not an ideal gas.

12.5 Moist air

A large number of engineering applications involve moist air. Thus the properties and possible treatments of moist air are discussed here extensively.

Air is composed of several components, such as nitrogen, oxygen, carbon dioxide, helium, etc., that under many everyday applications never condense. In addition, air includes water vapor that could condense when cooled, or could be added to the air by vaporization from water or steam. We consider all the non-condensable gases as dry air and the water vapor as moisture. The standard tables and diagrams for water and water vapor are also applicable to the moisture, provided the partial pressure is used instead of the pressure.

Consider the state of water vapor, as depicted in Fig. 12.4 on a *T–p* and a *T–s* diagram. Assume that the moisture in our system is at point 1, inside the superheated vapor range, at a partial pressure $p_1 = p^v = p_w$ and temperature T_1. The pressure at point 2, located on the saturation line at the same temperature, $T_2 = T_1$, is the corresponding saturation pressure, p^{sat}. The ratio of the pressure to the corresponding saturation pressure is called the *relative humidity*, ϕ, at state 1:

$$\phi = \frac{p^v}{p^{sat}} \tag{12.34}$$

The temperature at point 3, located on the saturation line at the same pressure, $p_3 = p^v$, is the corresponding saturation temperature, T^{sat}. It is also called the *dew point*, T_D, corresponding to state 1:

$$T_D = T^{sat}(p^v) \tag{12.35}$$

When moist air is cooled at a constant pressure, the partial pressure of the moisture, p_v does not change as long as the temperature remains above the saturation temperature. The process can be depicted on a *T–p* diagram as a vertical line coming down from point 1. The first drop of liquid appears when the saturation temperature, i.e. the dew point, is reached. If the cooling process continues, more and more vapor condenses. The water will have two phases: one in the gaseous phase, mixed with the dry air, and the other in a

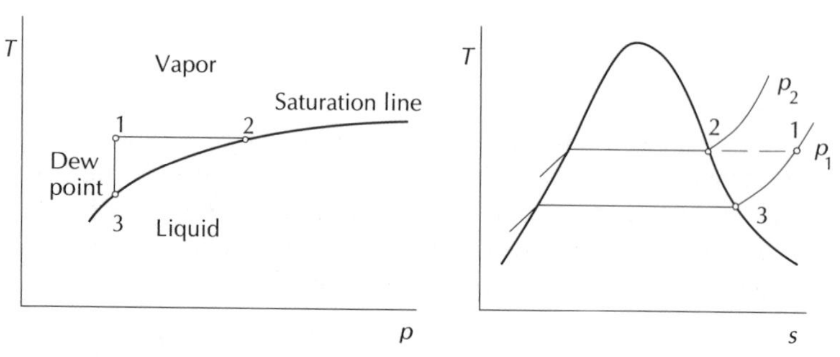

Figure 12.4 **T–p and T–s diagrams for moist air.**

liquid phase, separated from the air. Thus, the state of the vapor follows the saturation line on the T–p diagram.

We proceed now with several basic definitions relevant to moist air. Let the mass of the dry air in the mixture be denoted by m_a, and the mass of the moisture be denoted by m_w. The ratio of the mass of the moisture to that of the dry air is called the *humidity ratio* or the *specific humidity*, denoted by ω:

$$\omega = \frac{m_w}{m_a} \tag{12.36}$$

When dealing with moist air, it is common to relate the properties of the mixture to a unit mass of the dry air only, and not to a unit mass of the mixture. The reason is that the mass of dry air does not change when water condenses or evaporates into the air. So, for example, the specific enthalpy of moist air is the enthalpy of the mixture divided by the mass of the dry air.

The specific humidity may be related to the relative humidity as follows:

$$\omega = \frac{m_w}{m_a} = \frac{p^v M_w}{p_a M_a} = \frac{M_w}{M_a}\frac{p^v}{p - p^v} = 0.622\,\frac{\phi p^{sat}}{p - \phi p^{sat}} \tag{12.37}$$

The saturation specific humidity is found when $\phi = 1$,

$$\omega^{sat} = 0.622\,\frac{p^{sat}}{p - p^{sat}} \tag{12.38}$$

In general, ω is not linear with ϕ. However, for low temperatures (below about 35 °C), the saturation pressures are very small, compared to the atmospheric pressure, and may be neglected in the denominator. Under these conditions, the specific humidity is almost proportional to the relative humidity. Thus, for $p^{sat} \ll p$,

$$\omega \approx 0.622\,(p^{sat}/p)\phi \tag{12.39}$$

12.6 The first law for moist air

Moist air is considered an ideal mixture of dry air and water vapor. The first law, both for a closed system and for a control volume, applies to moist air in exactly the same way that it applies to any other system. Thus, for a closed system of moist air, the first law is

$$\Delta U = Q - W \tag{4.18}$$

and for a control volume

$$\left(\frac{dU}{dt}\right)_{cv} = \dot{Q} - \dot{W}_x + \sum_{i=1}^{k} h_i^0 \dot{m}_i \tag{6.29}$$

One has only to pay attention to the way the enthalpy and the energy are expressed for moist air. The enthalpy of moist air is evaluated by using the Gibbs–Dalton law for an ideal mixture, Eq. (12.17), of air and moisture. Thus,

$$H = m_a h_a + m_w h_w \tag{12.40}$$

The specific enthalpy of moist air is defined as the enthalpy of the mixture per unit mass of the dry air (rather than per unit mass of the mixture),

$$h = H/m_a = h_a + \omega h_w \tag{12.41}$$

We can express the specific enthalpy in terms of the temperature of the moist air. In the SI system of units, it is commonly accepted that 0 °C can be selected as a reference state for the dry air and for the liquid water. In the British system of units, 0 °F is usually selected. Other selections, of course, are possible according to the convenience of the user. Thus, the temperature is expressed in degrees Celsius (or, alternatively, in degrees Fahrenheit, in the British system of units):

$$h_a = c_{pa} T \tag{12.42}$$

and

$$h_w = h_{fg0} + c_{pw} T \tag{12.43}$$

where h_{fg0} is the change of enthalpy of vaporization at 0 °C. Substitution of Eqs (12.42) and (12.43) into Eq. (12.41) yields

$$h = c_{pa} T + \omega (h_{fg0} + c_{pw} T) \tag{12.44}$$

In addition to humid air streams, there may also be one or more liquid water streams entering or leaving the control volume. Typical examples are: spray-wetting of air, dehumidification by cooling with liquid condensation. The first law, written for the control volume in Fig. 12.5 with liquid streams and humid-air streams and neglecting kinetic and potential effects, becomes

$$\left(\frac{dU}{dt}\right)_{cv} = \dot{Q} - \dot{W}_x + \sum (\dot{m}_a h)_i + \sum (\dot{m}_L h_L)_i \tag{12.45}$$

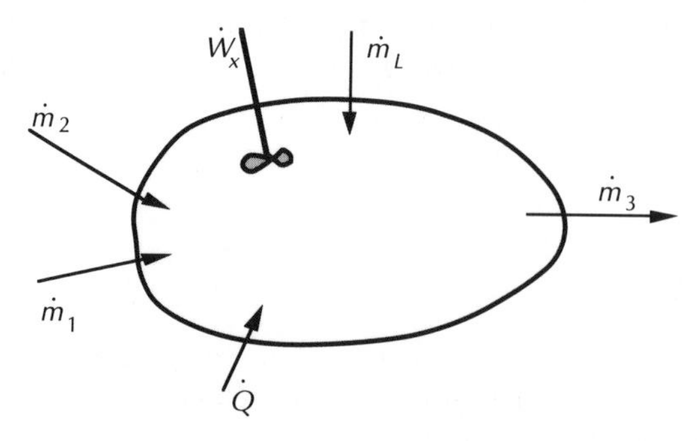

Figure 12.5 **Humid-air processes in a control volume.**

12.7 Adiabatic saturation

Several methods are available for the experimental evaluation of the specific humidity and the relative humidity of moist air. Some of these methods are indirect and rely on the response of various materials to humidity; others are more direct measurements. The indirect methods of determination of specific humidity, even though they may be simpler in application, require calibration with respect to direct measurement methods. The method of adiabatic saturation is a method of direct measurement of the specific humidity of moist air, which can be used to calibrate other methods.

When liquid water, at temperature T_w, is injected adiabatically into moist air, the moisture content of the air increases and, in general, the temperature of the moist air changes during the process. The process can continue up to the point when saturation is reached. The final temperature at saturation depends on the initial condition of the moist air and on the temperature of the injected water. In general, the temperature at saturation is not equal to the temperature of the injected water.

The term *adiabatic saturation* is used to describe a special case of saturating moist air where the final temperature at saturation and the temperature of the injected water are exactly equal. Indeed, for any given conditions of moist air (pressure, temperature, and humidity), there corresponds only one such saturation temperature. That temperature is called the *adiabatic saturation temperature*. The process of adiabatic saturation is shown schematically in Fig. 12.6.

The relation between the adiabatic saturation temperature and the initial condition of moist air can be found by applying the law of conservation of mass and the first law to moist air. The adiabatic saturation process is carried out at steady state. Conservation of mass is written for the dry air as

$$\dot{m}_{a2} = \dot{m}_{a1} = \dot{m}_a \tag{12.46}$$

and for the water

$$\dot{m}_a\omega_2 = \dot{m}_a\omega_1 + \dot{m}_L \tag{12.47}$$

The first law requires that

$$\dot{m}_a h_2 = \dot{m}_a h_1 + \dot{m}_L h_{f2} \tag{12.48}$$

Substituting $\dot{m}_L$ from Eq. (12.47) into Eq. (12.48) and dividing through by $\dot{m}_a$ yields

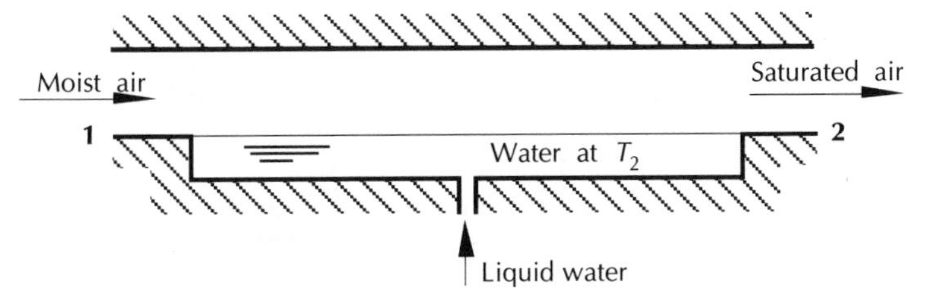

Figure 12.6 **Adiabatic saturation.**

$$h_2 = h_1 + (\omega_2 - \omega_1)h_{f2} \tag{12.49}$$

or

$$c_{pa}T_2 + \omega_2(h_{fgo} + c_{pw}T_2 - h_{f2}) = c_{pa}T_1 + \omega_1(h_{fgo} + c_{pw}T_1 - h_{f2}) \tag{12.50}$$

Equation (12.50) can be solved for the initial specific humidity, ω_1, in terms of T_2. Thus, by measuring T_2 one can calculate the initial specific humidity of the moist air. Hence

$$\omega_1 = \frac{c_{pa}(T_2 - T_1) + \omega_2(h_{fg0} + c_{pw}T_2 - h_{f2})}{(h_{fg0} + c_{pw}T_1 - h_{f2})} \tag{12.51}$$

where ω_2 is calculable from Eq. (12.38):

$$\omega_2 = \omega^{sat} = 0.622\frac{p^{sat}(T_2)}{p - p^{sat}(T_2)} \tag{12.52}$$

Alternatively, Eq. (12.50) may be solved for the adiabatic saturation temperature if the initial conditions of the moist air are fully known. The solution can be obtained by a trial and error method. A value for the temperature, T_2, is guessed. The corresponding value of h_{f2} is found from the steam tables and that of the saturation specific humidity is calculated from Eq. (12.52). If T_2 and the corresponding values of h_{f2} and ω_2 do not satisfy Eq. (12.50), a new guess for T_2 is required.

12.8 Wet bulb temperature

A much more practical method of measuring the specific humidity is by the use of two thermometers, a dry bulb and a wet bulb thermometer, Fig. 12.7.

The dry bulb thermometer measures the temperature of the air. The wet bulb is surrounded by a wick, soaked with water. Water evaporates from the wick into the air, thus causing the temperature to drop. The final temperature that is reached depends on the moisture in the air. The lower the humidity of the air, the lower the temperature of the wet bulb thermometer. The temperature of the wet bulb is also affected by the relative rates of heat and mass transfer between the air and the wick. The parameter controlling this ratio is the Lewis number, Le, which is the ratio between the thermal diffusivity, α, and the mass diffusivity, D:

$$\text{Le} = \alpha/D \tag{12.53}$$

For air, the Lewis number is very close to unity. In this case, the wet bulb temperature is

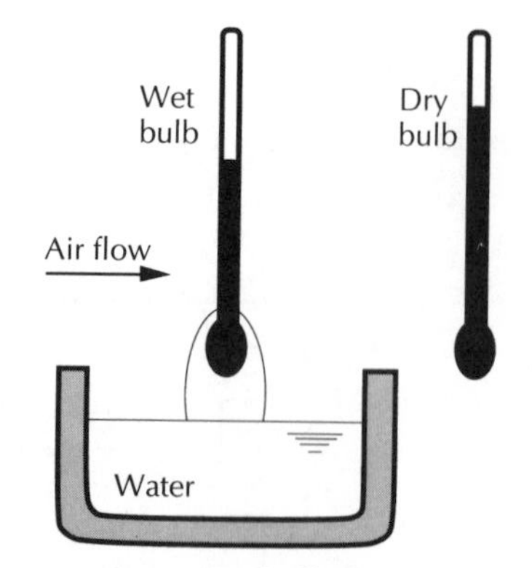

Figure 12.7 **Wet bulb thermometry.**

equal to the adiabatic saturation temperature. Thus, measuring simultaneously the dry bulb and wet bulb temperatures allows the calculation of the specific humidity of moist air, using Eq. (12.51).

12.9 The psychrometric chart

It is customary to present the properties of moist air in a diagram called the psychrometric chart. The chart is drawn for a given total pressure of moist air. The coordinates of the chart are the specific humidity and the enthalpy of moist air. It was found convenient to use an oblique grid for the coordinates of the h–ω diagram, Fig. 12.8.

The psychrometric chart also contains lines of constant dry bulb temperature, T, lines of constant wet bulb temperatures, T_{wb}, lines of constant relative humidity, ϕ, and lines of constant specific volume, v. The h, ω, and T lines are labeled along the edges of the chart, as shown in Fig. 12.9.

The dry bulb temperature lines on the psychrometric chart are straight lines. However, in contrast to the coordinates h and ω, which are straight and parallel lines, the constant temperature lines are not parallel. The slopes of these lines depend on the temperature and can be calculated from Eq. (12.44):

$$\left(\frac{\partial h}{\partial \omega}\right)_T = h_{fg0} + c_{pw}T = \text{const.} \tag{12.54}$$

We see from Eq. (12.54) that the slope $(\partial h/\partial \omega)_T$ is quite high, of the order of 2500 kJ/kg, and varies only slightly with temperature, at least over the range 0 °C to 60 °C that is of interest for moist air. For this reason, it was found that the data are better presented on an oblique coordinate system.

In some charts, the angle between the oblique coordinates is selected so that the temperature line of 0 °C would be vertical. Other temperature lines deviate slightly from the vertical. The deviation is greater for higher temperatures.

At any given temperature, the specific humidity of saturation can be calculated, using Eq. (12.38). The locus of all the points describing the saturation specific humidity is called the *saturation line*, and is shown on the psychrometric chart, Fig. 12.9.

Another set of lines on the chart are the *wet bulb temperature lines*. Each line is the locus of all the states on the chart that have the same adiabatic saturation temperature. For

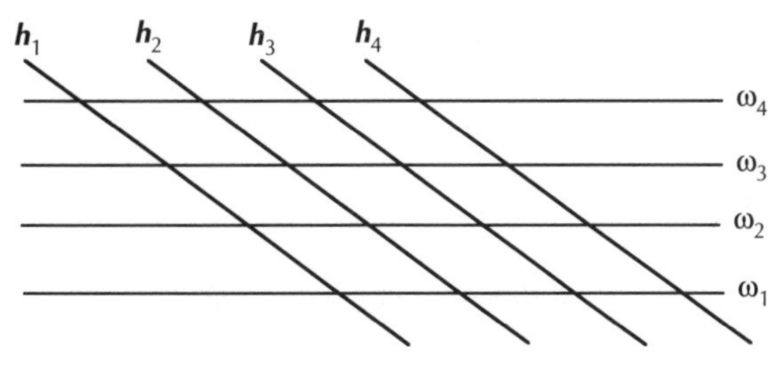

Figure 12.8 **The h–ω grid.**

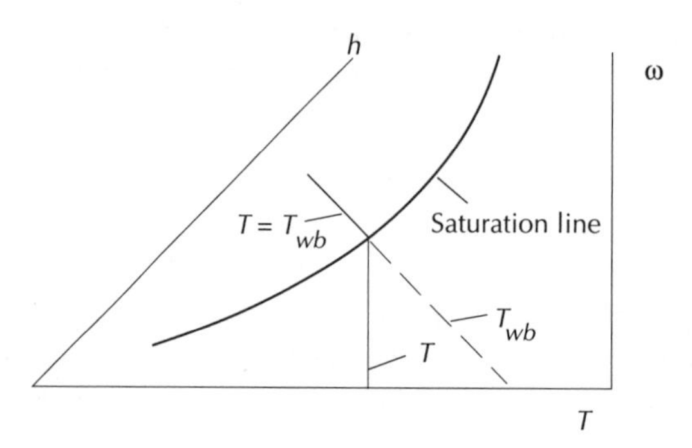

Figure 12.9 **Outline of the psychrometric chart.**

a given saturation temperature, the values of ω_2, h_{f2}, and h_2 are fixed. Thus, it follows from Eq. (12.49) that

$$h_1 = \omega_1 h_{f2} + (h_2 - \omega_2 h_{f2}) \tag{12.55}$$

The last term in the parentheses is constant. Therefore, h_1 is linear with ω_1. On the h–ω plot the wet bulb lines are straight lines, whose slope is h_{f2}.

Lines of constant relative humidity, shown on the psychrometric chart, are curved lines that can be calculated for any temperature and specific humidity.

When the water content of moist air exceeds the saturation value, the excess moisture condenses out of the air in a liquid form. As long as liquid water is in equilibrium with the moist air, the air is in a saturated state (the relative humidity is 1).

It is possible to extend the psychrometric chart to the two-phase region that includes both moist air and liquid water. In this two-phase region the air is saturated and, therefore, its temperature is the same as the wet bulb temperature. The enthalpy of the two-phase system per unit mass of dry air is

$$h = h_a + \omega^{sat} h_w + (\omega - \omega^{sat}) h_{f2} \tag{12.56}$$

A constant-temperature line coincides in this range with the wet bulb temperature line which is straight and has a slope of $(\partial h/\partial \omega)_T = h_{f2}$. Thus, a constant-temperature line consists of two straight lines with different slopes, one in the single-phase region and the other in the two-phase region. A typical constant-temperature line in both regions is shown in Fig. 12.9.

12.10 Processes in moist air

We now look at some standard processes in moist air and their representation on the psychrometric chart.

12.10.1 Heating

Consider a process in which moist air is heated steadily at a constant pressure. Heating the moist air does not change its moisture content. A heating process is, therefore, represented on the psychrometric chart by a straight horizontal line, as in Fig. 12.10.

The amount of heat involved in the heating process is calculated from the first law as the enthalpy change between state 1 and state 2:

$$Q_{12} = m_a(h_2 - h_1) \tag{12.57}$$

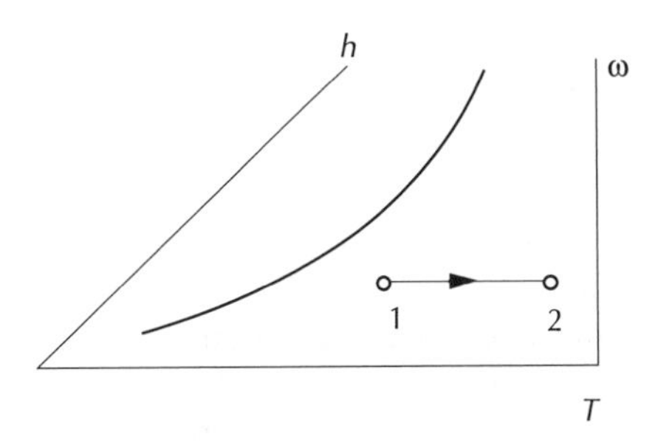

Figure 12.10 **Heating of moist air.**

The quantity Δh can be read off the psychrometric chart as the distance between the h-lines corresponding to states 1 and 2.

12.10.2 Cooling and dehumidification

Cooling of moist air is the reverse of heating. There is, however, a major difference between heating and cooling processes. During heating the moisture content of the gaseous phase does not change, whereas during cooling the moisture content of the gaseous phase remains the same only as long as saturation (point 2 in Fig. 12.11a) is not reached.

If the cooling process continues beyond saturation the air cannot retain all the moisture and two phases, in equilibrium with each other, are formed: a gaseous phase of saturated moist air, and a liquid phase of water at the same temperature. Point 3 in Fig. 12.11a corresponds to such a two-phase state. It represents a gaseous phase, at state 3_{sat}, and a liquid phase formed by the water condensed from the air in the amount of $(\omega_3 - \omega_{3sat})$. The heat interaction during the cooling process is calculated in the same way for heating. Thus, the heat interaction from state 1 to state 3 is

$$Q_{13} = m_a(h_3 - h_1) \tag{12.58}$$

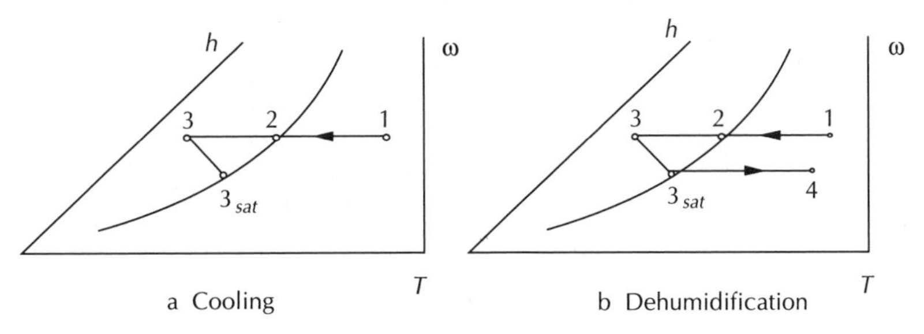

Figure 12.11 **Heating and cooling.**

where h_3 is read off the diagram at point 3. Since $h_3 < h_1$, the heat interaction during cooling is obviously negative.

The enthalpy of the final state 3 can also be calculated as the sum of the enthalpies of the two phases,

$$h_3 = h_3^{sat} + (\omega_3 - \omega_3^{sat})h_f(T_3)$$

where the enthalpy of the liquid, $h_f(T_3)$, is read from the steam table as that of the saturated liquid at T_3.

In many practical applications, only the moisture must be removed from the air without lowering its temperature. This *dehumidification* process consists of cooling the air below its dew point, removing the liquid that condenses, and reheating the air, as shown on the diagram in Fig. 12.11b.

Figure 12.12 shows schematically the principle of operation of a typical home dehumidifier. Such a dehumidifier is essentially a refrigeration system comprised of an evaporator, a compressor, a condenser, and a throttling valve, as described in section 11.9. The air is passed over the evaporator, its temperature is lowered, and moisture is condensed. In contrast to an ordinary air-conditioner, where the cool dehumidified air is returned to the room, in the dehumidifier it is passed over the condenser, where it is reheated before it is returned to the room.

The heat interaction in the cooling section may be found by writing the first law for a control volume which consists of the evaporator and liquid separator:

$$\dot{Q}_c + \dot{m}_a\left(h_1 - h_3^{sat}\right) - \dot{m}_L h_f = 0 \tag{12.59}$$

where

$$\dot{m}_L = \dot{m}_a(\omega_1 - \omega_3^{sat})$$

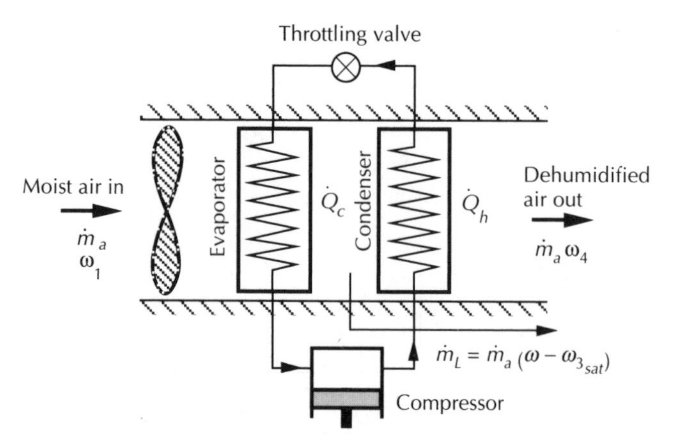

Figure 12.12 **Dehumidification of air.**

Hence,

$$\dot{Q}_c = \dot{m}_a\left[(h_3^{sat} - h_1) + (\omega_1 - \omega_3^{sat})h_f\right] \tag{12.60}$$

where the enthalpies of the vapor are read from the diagram, while h_f is taken from the steam tables. For the reheat section a first-law analysis on the condenser yields

$$\dot{Q}_h = \dot{m}_a(h_4 - h_3^{sat}) \tag{12.61}$$

12.10.3 Wetting moist air

Consider a steady state process where the moisture of the air is increased adiabatically by injecting water into it, Fig. 12.13.

Conservation of water and the first law require, respectively, that

$$m_L = m_a(\omega_2 - \omega_1) \tag{12.62}$$

and

$$m_a h_1 + m_L h_L = m_a h_2 \tag{12.63}$$

Substituting m_L from Eq. (12.62) into Eq. (12.63) and dividing through by m_a yields

$$h_1 + (\omega_2 - \omega_1)h_L = h_2 \tag{12.64}$$

or

$$\frac{h_2 - h_1}{\omega_2 - \omega_1} = h_L \tag{12.65}$$

which can be written in a differential form as

$$\frac{dh}{d\omega} = h_L \tag{12.66}$$

Equations (12.65) and (12.66) describe a straight line on the psychrometric chart with a slope of h_L.

If the enthalpy of the injected water is zero (water at 0 °C), then the trace of the process on the psychrometric chart coincides with a constant-enthalpy line. When the injected water (or steam) has a higher enthalpy, the slope increases. Yet for liquid water

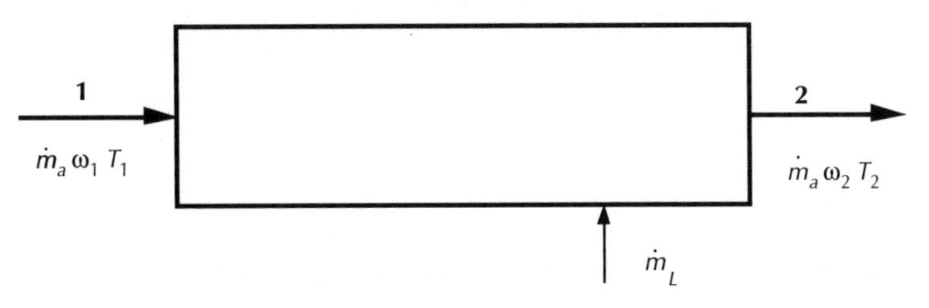

Figure 12.13 **Wetting moist air.**

at moderate temperatures, the slope is not much different from that of a constant-enthalpy line, resulting in a decrease of the temperature of the air.

The process of injecting liquid water into air forms the basis of desert coolers.

EXAMPLE 12.4

A desert cooler operates in an environment where the temperature is 40 °C and the relative humidity is 20%. A source of water at 45 °C is available.

a. Find the wet bulb temperature of the air.
b. Find the minimum temperature that can be reached by injecting the water into the air.
c. Find the amount of water that must be injected per unit mass of dry air, in order to reach the minimum temperature.

SOLUTION

a. The wet bulb temperature at state 1 is found from the psychrometric chart to be 22 °C.
b. Locate the initial state on the psychrometric chart, Fig. 12.14. Draw a line from the center of the auxiliary slope circle passing through the point marked with the enthalpy of water at 45 °C, h = 188.45 kJ/kg, as shown in Fig. 12.14. Draw a line parallel to it from state 1. All the points on that line represent states that may be reached from state 1 by injecting water into the air. The lowest temperature is reached at the intersection of the line with the saturation curve. The minimum temperature is, therefore, T_{min} = 22.3 °C.
c. The mass of the injected water is

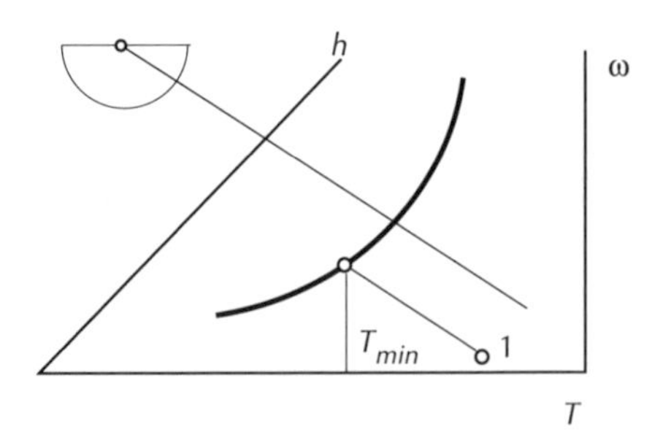

Figure 12.14

$$m_w / m_a = \omega_2 - \omega_1 = 0.0170 - 0.0093 = 0.0077 \text{ kg/kg dry air}$$

Humidification of air can be achieved easily just by adiabatically injecting water into the air. This process is not reversible. The reverse process, dehumidification of moist air, cannot, by itself, be affected adiabatically. An adiabatic dehumidification of air can, however, be achieved by using desiccants. Desiccants are materials that can, depending on their state, adiabatically absorb or desorb water from moist air. The desorption process is similar to the humidification of air, while the absorption process is similar to the dehumidification process.

12.10.4 Mixing of moist air streams

Another basic process is the adiabatic mixing of two or more streams of moist air. Consider two such streams entering an insulated mixing chamber, Fig. 12.15.

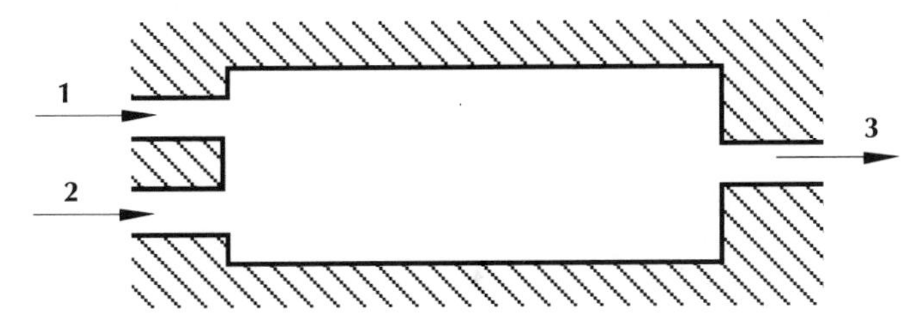

Figure 12.15 **Mixing streams of moist air.**

Stream 1 consists of a mass of m_{a1} of moist air at p, T_1, and ω_1, while stream 2 consists of a mass of m_{a2} at p, T_2 and ω_2. The state at the exit 3 can be calculated by applying the laws of conservation of mass for the dry air and for the water along with the first law, as follows,

$$m_{a3} = m_{a1} + m_{a2} \tag{12.67}$$

$$m_{a3}\omega_3 = m_{a1}\omega_1 + m_{a2}\omega_2 \tag{12.68}$$

$$m_{a3}h_3 = m_{a1}h_1 + m_{a2}h_2 \tag{12.69}$$

Dividing Eqs (12.68) and (12.69) by Eq. (12.67) yields

$$\omega_3 = \frac{m_{a1}\omega_1 + m_{a2}\omega_2}{m_{a1} + m_{a2}} \tag{12.70}$$

and

$$h_3 = \frac{m_{a1}h_1 + m_{a2}h_2}{m_{a1} + m_{a2}} \tag{12.71}$$

Equations (12.70) and (12.71) can be rearranged as follows:

$$\frac{\omega_3 - \omega_1}{\omega_2 - \omega_1} = \frac{h_3 - h_1}{h_2 - h_1} = \frac{m_{a2}}{m_{a1} + m_{a2}} \tag{12.72}$$

Equation (12.72) indicates that point 3 lies on the straight line connecting points 1 and 2 on the psychrometric chart. The exact location of point 3 on the line is determined by the flowrate ratios of streams 1 and 2, according to the fulcrum rule.

If the relative humidities of the two streams are high and their temperatures are quite different, there is a possibility that point 3 would lie in the two-phase region, even though none of the original streams were saturated. Indeed, one way in which rain is formed is when a mass of cold air mixes with a second mass of warm and humid air.

EXAMPLE 12.5

A mass of arctic air at 4 °C and $\phi = 0.85$ (point 1) mixes with twice its mass of warm air at 30 °C and $\phi = 0.9$ (point 2). Find the state of the air after mixing.

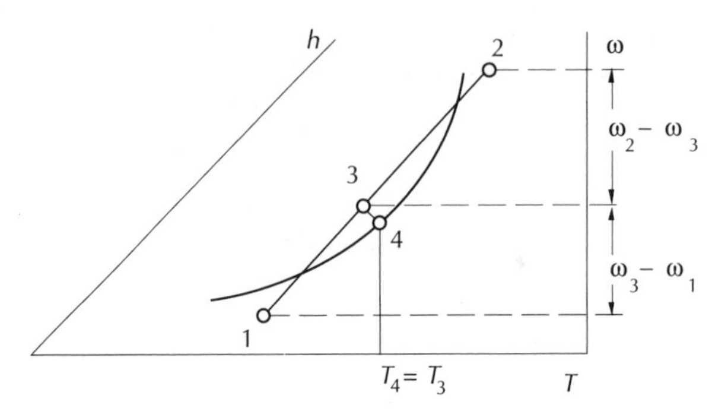

Figure 12.16

SOLUTION

We first locate the two points representing states 1 and 2 on the psychrometric chart, and connect them by a straight line. As seen in Fig. 12.16, that line crosses the saturation curve into the two-phase region.

The combined state of the two-phase system, point 3, comprised of saturated air and of liquid water in equilibrium with it, is at the point whose distance from point 1 is twice the distance from point 2, as per Eq. (12.72). The state of the saturated air, point 4, is located on the saturation line at the temperature of the mixture, i.e. at 22.3 °C, and a relative humidity of 100%, while the amount of water condensed out of the mixture, per kilogram of dry air at point 4, is

$$\Delta\omega = \omega_3 - \omega_4 = 0.0178 - 0.0172 = 0.0006 \text{ kg/kg air}$$

The following table summarizes the relevant properties given in terms of unit mass of dry air.

State	T	ϕ	ω
1	4	0.85	0.0042
2	30	0.90	0.0245
3	22.3	–	0.0178
4	22.3	1.00	0.0172

12.11 Cooling towers

Power plants and most process industries must reject large quantities of heat to the environment. In the absence of large bodies of water, such as the ocean, it is usually done by using cooling water in circulation. The water is cooled in a cooling tower by evaporating a small fraction of it into atmospheric air.

The operating principle of a cooling tower is as follows. The warm water is injected at the top of the tower and flows down counter-currently to atmospheric air that is introduced at the bottom of the tower, Fig. 12.17. The tower is filled with wood slats which impede the direct fall of the water streams and break them up repeatedly into drops. Part of the water evaporates into the oncoming air, and the temperature of the remaining water is lowered. The lowest possible temperature at the exit of the cooling tower is the wet bulb temperature of the air. In practical applications the water is cooled to a higher temperature. The difference between the wet bulb and the exit temperature of the water is called the *approach.*

An analysis of a cooling tower under steady state flow consists of a mass and an energy balance on the tower. Referring to the schematic of the cooling tower in Fig. 12.17 we note that the mass flow of the dry air does not change from inlet to outlet. A water balance for the tower yields

$$\Delta m_w = m_a(\omega_2 - \omega_1) \tag{12.73}$$

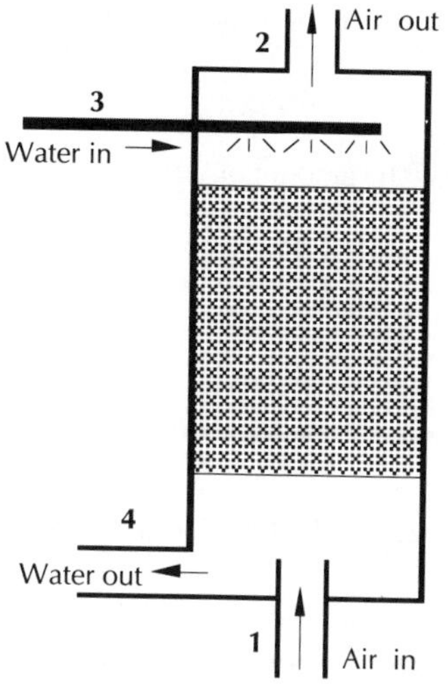

Figure 12.17 **Cooling tower.**

An overall energy balance on the tower results in

$$m_a(h_2 - h_1) + (m_w - \Delta m_w)h_4 - m_w h_3 = 0 \tag{12.74}$$

or, by substituting Eq. (12.73) and rearranging,

$$m_a\left[h_2 - h_1 - (\omega_2 - \omega_1)h_4\right] + m_w(h_4 - h_3) = 0 \tag{12.75}$$

The required mass of air can be calculated by solving Eq. (12.75) for m_a:

$$m_a = \frac{m_w c_{pL}(T_3 - T_4)}{(h_2 - h_1) - (\omega_2 - \omega_1)c_{pL}T_4} \tag{12.76}$$

EXAMPLE 12.6

Water at 42 °C enters a cooling tower at a rate of 20000 kg/h. It leaves the tower at 22 °C. Atmospheric air flows in the opposite direction to the water, at 24 °C/18 °C dry/wet bulb temperatures, and leaves at 32 °C and relative humidity 80%. Find:

a. The mass flowrate of the air through the tower.
b. The mass flowrate of the water leaving the tower.

SOLUTION

We label the streams as in Fig. 12.17. The data for the humid air are taken from the psychrometric chart and arranged in the following table:

State	T	T_{wb}	ϕ	h	ω
1	24.0	18.0	0.56	54.0	0.0105
2	32.0	29.0	0.80	94.8	0.0244

a. The air mass flowrate is found from Eq. (12.76):

$$\dot{m}_a = \frac{20000 \times (42.0 - 22.0) \times 4.186}{(94.8 - 54.0) - 4.186 \times (0.0244 - 0.0105) \times 22} = 42368.5 \text{ kg/h}$$

b. The amount of water added to the air is found from Eq. (12.73):

$$\Delta \dot{m}_w = \dot{m}_a(\omega_2 - \omega_1) = 42368.5 \times (0.0244 - 0.0105) = 588.9 \text{ kg/h}$$

Hence,

$$\dot{m}_4 = \dot{m}_3 - \Delta \dot{m}_w = 20000 - 588.9 = 19411 \text{ kg/h}$$

12.12 Exergy analysis

The equations for maximum work, maximum useful work, exergy, availability, and irreversibility that were developed in Chapter 10 are quite general and are, therefore, applicable also to systems where mixing takes place. One, however, must be careful to identify the correct equilibrium state relevant to the problem at hand.

In Example 10.6 we calculated the maximum useful work that can be obtained from a tank of compressed air relative to an environment of air at 101 kPa and 25 °C. We now solve a similar example, but with nitrogen in the tank instead of air.

EXAMPLE 12.7

A system consists of 0.032 m^3 of compressed nitrogen at 20 MPa and 25 °C inside a rigid tank, equipped with a control valve. The environment is air at 101 kPa and 25 °C. Find the maximum useful work that may be obtained from the system.

SOLUTION

This problem differs from Example 10.5 in that here the tank contains nitrogen instead of air. The nitrogen is allowed to mix with the air in the environment. Hence, in the final equilibrium state the nitrogen has a partial pressure equal to that of nitrogen in air, i.e. $p_{N2} = 0.79p_0$.

The maximum work is calculated by using Eq. (10.51), which was derived for a control volume with a single port that exhausts to the environment,

$$W^u_{rev} = -\Delta\Lambda_{cv} + b_0 \Delta m_{cv} \tag{10.51}$$

where b_0 is the exergy of the matter that leaves the control volume and attains equilibrium with the environment when it reaches its temperature and pressure. Here the relevant pressure is the partial pressure of nitrogen in the environment, p_0,

$$p_0 = p_{N_2} = 0.79 p_0 = 0.79 \times 101 = 79.8 \text{ kPa}$$

The equation for calculating the maximum useful work is exactly the same as in Example 10.5, but with the appropriate value for the equilibrium pressure,

$$W_{rev}^{u} = m[(u-u_0) - T_0(s-s_0) + p_0(v-v_0)]$$

$$= mRT_0\left[(0) + \ln\frac{p_0}{p} + \frac{p_0}{p} - 1\right] = pV\left[\ln\frac{p_0}{p} + \frac{p_0}{p} - 1\right]$$

$$= 20000 \times 0.032\left[\ln\frac{20}{0.0798} + \frac{0.0798}{20} - 1\right] = 2897.9 \text{ kJ}$$

Note that the work in this case is somewhat larger than what was calculated for air. The reason is that nitrogen at the pressure and temperature of the environmental air can still do some work if allowed to expand isothermally to the partial pressure of the nitrogen in the atmosphere. Of course such a process may require additional equipment such as semipermeable membranes. If, on the other hand, the nitrogen must be contained and not be allowed to mix with the air, then the maximum work would be the same as that for compressed air.

PROBLEMS

12.1 For an ideal mixture of ideal gases indicate whether the following statements are true, sometimes true, or false.

a. The sum of the partial pressures equals the pressure of the mixture.
b. The energy of the mixture equals the sum of the component energies.
c. The entropy of the mixture is greater than the sum of the entropies of the components.
d. While mixing two components at constant T, p, the energy is conserved.
e. While mixing two components at constant T, p, the entropy is conserved.

12.2 A mixture of 5 kg of N_2 (M = 28, k = 1.4), 1 kg of He (M = 4, k = 1.667), and 10 kg of CO_2 (M = 44, k = 1.3) at 1 bar and 77 °C is compressed to 3.2 bars in an adiabatic reversible process. Calculate the partial pressures of the components of the mixture after the compression.

12.3 A mixture of 1 kg of helium (M = 4, k = 1.667) and 2 kg of nitrogen (M = 28, k = 1.4) is at 0.2 MPa and 20 °C. Select 0.1 MPa and 0 °C as a reference state for each gas (at this state the enthalpy and the entropy are zero). Calculate:

a. The partial pressure of each component.
b. The volume of the mixture.
c. The energy, enthalpy, and entropy of the mixture.
d. The ratio of specific heats of the mixture.

12.4 A mixture of 1 kg of helium (M = 4, k = 1.66) and 2 kg of nitrogen (M = 28, k = 1.4) is compressed reversibly and adiabatically from 0.2 MPa and 20 °C to 1.0 MPa. Calculate:

a. The partial pressures of all the components before and after the compression.
b. The temperature after the compression.
c. The entropy change of the mixture due to compression.
d. The work of compression.

12.5 A cylinder–piston assembly contains a mixture of 2 kg of hydrogen and 2 kg of nitrogen at 180 kPa, 50 °C. Select the reference state of each gas at 100 kPa, 0 °C.

a. Determine the partial pressure of each component.
b. Determine the volume of the mixture.
c. Determine the energy, enthalpy, and entropy of the mixture.
d. Determine the ratio of specific heats of the mixture.

12.6 A mixture of 2.0 kg of helium and 5.0 kg of nitrogen at 0.1 MPa, 27 °C, is compressed adiabatically and isothermally to 0.7 MPa.

Assume ideal gases: for helium $M = 2$, $k = 5/3$, and for nitrogen $M = 28$, $k = 7/5$.

a. Determine the initial and final partial pressures.
b. Determine the final temperature.
c. Determine the changes in internal energy, enthalpy, and entropy of the mixture.
d. Determine the change of entropy of the helium and of the nitrogen.

12.7 n an adiabatic vessel 20 kg of oxygen at 20 °C and 100 kPa are separated by a partition from 1 kg of nitrogen at 500 °C and 20 MPa. The environment is at 20 °C. and 101 kPa. The partition is ruptured and the contents of the vessel mix.

Find the irreversibility of the mixing process.

12.8 A vessel contains a mixture of 5 kg of N_2, 1 kg of He, and 10 kg of CO_2 at 320 kPa, 77 °C.

a. Determine the volume of the vessel.
b. Determine the partial pressures of each component.
c. Determine the specific heat at constant pressure of the mixture.

12.9 An insulated rigid vessel is partitioned into three sections containing 7.0 g, 4.0 g, and 2.0 g of nitrogen, oxygen, and helium, respectively. The conditions in each section are 140 kPa, 60 °C. The partitions break and the gases mix. Determine:

a. The final pressure and temperature.
b. The energy, enthalpy, and entropy change in the process.

12.10 An insulated rigid vessel is partitioned into three sections containing 7.0 g of nitrogen at 140 kPa and 60 °C, 4.0 g of oxygen at 100 kPa and 100 °C, and 2.0 g of helium at 200 kPa and 90 °C. The partitions break and the gases mix. Determine:

a. The final pressure and temperature.
b. The energy, enthalpy, and entropy change in the process.

12.11 A rigid-wall container is divided into two compartments by a partition. One compartment contains l kmol of helium at 1 bar and 330 K, the other contains l kmol of hydrogen at 1 bar and 220 K. The partition is punctured, and the gases allowed to mix adiabatically.

a. What are the final pressure and the temperature of the mixture?
b. What is the change in entropy for the process?

Assume both gases are ideal and obey the Gibbs–Dalton law. Use the following data: for helium $k = 5/3$, for hydrogen $k = 7/5$.

12.12 Two partitions divide an adiabatic chamber into three compartments which contain 5 kmol of H_2, 3 kmol of N_2, and 2 kmol of O_2, respectively. The pressure and temperature in *each* compartment are $p = 1$ bar and $T = 20$ °C. The partitions are removed, and the gases mix. Assuming the gases are ideal find the entropy change of the mixing process.

12.13 Three kilograms of air at 100 kPa, 15 °C are mixed at constant pressure with 5 kg of nitrogen at 100 kPa, 120 °C. Assume that air consists of 79% N_2 and 21% O_2 by volume, and all the gases are ideal.

a. Find the final equilibrium temperature of the mixture.
b. Determine the change in entropy of the system.

12.14 A certain gas mixture at 20 °C and 0.12 MPa is composed of 30% CO_2, 50% O_2, and 20% N_2 by mass. The mixture passes through a heat exchanger in steady flow leaving at 45 °C and 0.1 MPa.

a. Find the heat interaction per kilogram of mixture.
b. Find the change of entropy per kilogram of mixture.

12.15 An insulated vessel is divided into three compartments of 50 L each. The end compartments contain argon (M = 40, k = 1.667) and helium (M = 4, k = 1.667) at the conditions shown in Fig. 12.18, while the center compartment is evacuated. The partitions are removed, the gases mix and reach equilibrium.

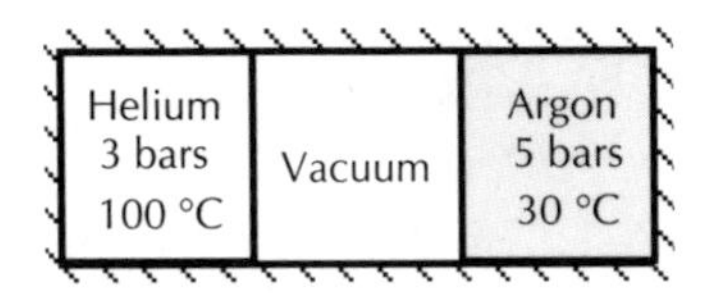

Figure 12.18

a. Find the temperature and the pressure at equilibrium.
b. Find the partial pressures of argon and helium at equilibrium.
c. Find the overall entropy change.

12.16 A rigid adiabatic vessel is divided by a floating adiabatic piston into two parts, Fig. 12.19. The lower part contains 3 gmol of oxygen (ideal gas, M = 32, k = 1.4) at 0.3 MPa, 227 °C, while the upper part contains 2 gmol of nitrogen (ideal gas, M = 28, k = 1.4) at 0.16 MPa, 27 °C.

The surroundings are at 102 kPa, 27 °C. The piston breaks and falls to the bottom of the vessel, the gases mix and attain equilibrium. Find:

a. The pressure and temperature of the mixture.
b. The entropy change of the process

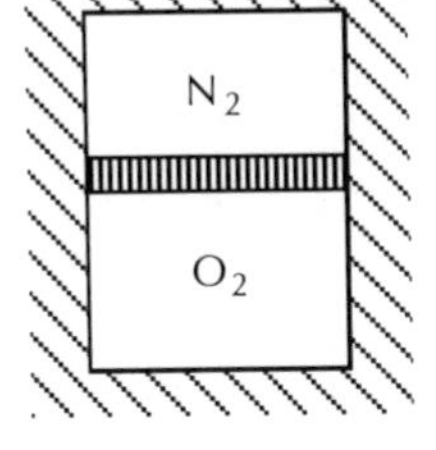

Figure 12.19

12.17 Two well-insulated vessels are interconnected by a pipe and a valve. One vessel, whose volume is 85 L, contains oxygen at 100 kPa, 38 °C, while the second, whose volume is 28 L, contains nitrogen at 630 kPa, 150 °C. The valve is opened and a flow starts. Two mixing modes are to be considered: one where the final state will be identical in both vessels; and a second where the valve is closed as soon as the pressures are equalized. In the latter case the final equilibrium states in each vessel will be different. Determine for each of the mixing modes:

a. The final pressure, temperature, and specific volume in each vessel.
b. The partial pressures of each component in each vessel.
c. The change of entropy.

12.18 Indicate whether the following statements are true, false, or sometimes true.

During an isothermal expansion of 1.0 kg of humid air the following properties do not change:

a. The relative humidity.
b. The specific humidity.
c. The specific enthalpy.
d. The dry bulb temperature.
e. The dew point.

Water is sprayed into air at a relative humidity of ϕ = 50% in an adiabatic constant-pressure process. For the gas phase:

f. The temperature decreases.
g. The enthalpy decreases.
h. The dew point does not change.
i. The specific humidity increases.
j. The relative humidity increases.

12.19 For humid air at 20 °C, 200 kPa, and a vapor mole fraction of y = 0.004, calculate:

a. The pressure of the dry air.
b. The relative humidity.
c. The specific humidity.
d. The dew point.

12.20 For an air pressure of 100 kPa, a temperature of 38 °C, and a relative humidity of 40% what is:

a. The dew point?
b. The wet bulb temperature?
c. The specific humidity?

12.21 The barometric pressure of the air on a hot and humid day is 762 mm Hg, the dry bulb temperature is 42 °C, and the relative humidity is 88%.

a. Find the partial pressure of the water vapor.
b. Determine the specific humidity.
c. Determine the dew point.

12.22 The humid air in Problem 12.21 is compressed adiabatically and reversibly to 600 kPa.

a. Recalculate parts a to c from Problem 12.21 for the new state.
b. Determine the work and heat interactions.

12.23 The conditions of a certain moist air are: 101 kPa, 38 °C, and 40% relative humidity. Determine the dew point, the wet bulb temperature, and the specific humidity.

12.24 Water at 30 °C enters a cooling tower at a rate of 36 m^3/min and exits at 20 °C. The air enters at 101 kPa, 21 °C dry bulb and 15 °C wet bulb temperatures, and leaves saturated at 28 °C.

a. Determine the volume of the entering air.
b. Determine the flowrate of the exiting water.

12.25 Air is compressed adiabatically at a rate of 3.0 kg/s from 100 kPa, 35 °C, 80% relative humidity to 300 kPa, 160 °C. Then the air passes through two cooling coils in which Freon (R12) evaporates at 100 kPa. In the first coil the compressed air is cooled till condensation just begins. The air is then cooled in the second coil to 5 °C.

a. Determine the temperature at the exit of the first coil.
b. Find the heat interaction in the first coil.
c. Find the heat interaction and the amount of condensation in the second coil.
d. Find the entropy change in the whole process.

12.26 Air at 0.17 MPa, 33 °C, and 80% relative humidity enters a cooling coil at a rate of 250 m^3/min and exits saturated at 0.15 MPa, 12 °C. The condensed water also exits at 0.15 MPa, 12 °C.

a. Determine the entering mass rates of dry air and of water.
b. Determine the exiting flowrate of the condensed liquid water.
c. Determine the required cooling capacity.

12.27 Saturated air at 0.1 MPa, 15 °C is heated to 40 °C and then used to dry dates. After the drying room the air is saturated.

a. Find the amount of air required to remove 1 kg of moisture from the dates.
b. Find the heat required per kilogram of moisture removed.

12.28 Air saturated with water vapor at 40 °C and 80 kPa is first compressed adiabatically and reversibly to 0.4 MPa, and then cooled at constant pressure back to 40 °C. Find:

a. The state of the humid air after compression.
b. The state of the humid air after cooling.
c. The work during compression and the heat interaction during cooling.

12.29 Using steam tables and appropriate equations find for air at 101.3 kPa, 25 °C, and 60% relative humidity:

a. The specific humidity.
b. The dew point.
c. The mass of 3 m^3 of humid air.
d. The enthalpy of 3 m^3 of humid air.

12.30 A chemical plant uses cooling water to remove heat from process equipment at a rate of 2×10^7 kJ/h. The water enters the equipment at 20 °C and leaves at 35 °C. In order to reuse the cooling water it is passed through a cooling tower through which atmospheric air at 18 °C and 50% humidity is fed at a rate of 300 m^3/s.

a. Determine the state of the air that leaves the cooling tower.
b. At what rate should the water be replenished?

12.31 A plant requires air at 30 °C and 90% humidity. This is done by mixing ambient air at 12 °C and 30% humidity with saturated steam at 160 °C and heating, if required. Find:

a. The amount of steam needed for an air supply of 200 kg/h.
b. The rate of heat to be supplied.

12.32 Air at 25 °C and 70% humidity is heated to 50 °C and then passed through a drying chamber used to dry peanuts. The air leaves the drying chamber saturated.

a. Find the amount of air needed to remove moisture from the peanuts at a rate of 6 kg/h.
b. Find the rate of heat to be supplied to the air before passing it through the drying chamber.

12.33 One kg of a mixture of air and water vapor at 20 °C, 100 kPa, and 75% relative humidity is held in a cylinder behind a frictionless piston. The mixture is compressed at constant temperature to 200 kPa.

a. What are the final relative and specific humidities?
b. Determine the mass of liquid water precipitated.
c. Find the work and heat for the process.

12.34 An air–water vapor mixture at 101 kPa and 13 °C, with a relative humidity of 80% enters at 200 m^3/min a heating chamber in which the temperature of the air is raised at constant pressure to 25 °C.

a. What is the final relative humidity of the air?
b. Determine the heat transfer from the heating coils to the mixture.
c. Find the change in entropy of the mixture.

12.35 Humid air at 10 °C, 40% relative humidity, and 150 kPa enters a heater at a rate of 100 m3/min and is heated at a constant pressure to 30 °C. Afterwards, the hot air enters an adiabatic mixing chamber, where it mixes with a stream of humid air at 20 °C, 100 kPa, 70% relative humidity, and a flowrate of 150 m^3/min. Find:

a. The relative humidity of the air leaving the heater.
b. The rate of heat transfer in the heater.
c. The relative humidity and the temperature at the outlet of the mixing chamber.

12.36 In order to maintain proper conditions in an assembly room for electronic components it is required to supply air at 20 °C and 20% relative humidity. Air, at a rate of 120 m^3/h, is taken from the environment at 100 kPa, 20 °C, dry bulb and 17 °C wet bulb, and is compressed adiabatically. The air is then cooled to 20 °C and the liquid water is separated from the air. Finally, the pressure of the air is decreased by a throttle valve, as shown in Fig. 12.20. The temperature at points 3, 4, 5 is 20 °C. The power of the compressor is 5 kW.

a. How much water is separated in the droplet separator?
b. How much heat is removed from the air by the cooling water?
c. What pressure is needed at point 2 in order for the required state to be obtained at point 6?

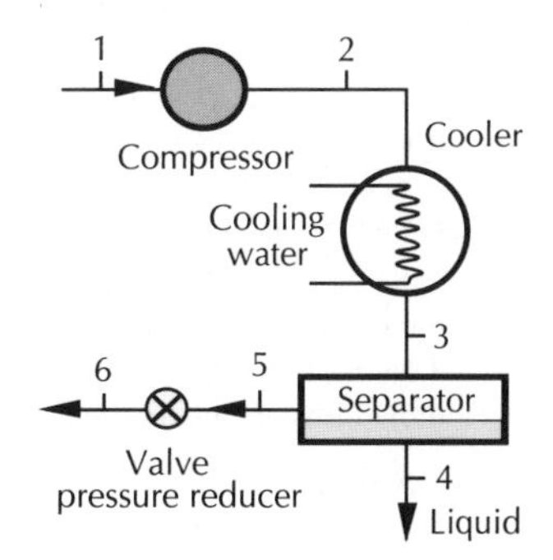

Figure 12.20

12.37 Air is compressed adiabatically and reversibly at a rate of 3 kg/s from a state of 1 bar, 35 °C, and a relative humidity of 0.8 to

3 bars. The compressed air is then cooled at a constant pressure of 3 bars by passing it over two cooling coils in which Freon-12 evaporates at 1 bar.

a. To what temperature can the air be cooled by the first cooling coil without water condensing from the air?
b. Calculate the heat interaction with the first cooling coil.
c. Calculate the heat interaction and the amount of water condensed over the second cooling coil, if the air temperature is lowered to 5 °C.
d. Calculate the overall entropy change.

12.38 Ambient air during winter at 1 bar, 5 °C, and 80% relative humidity (point 1) is being conditioned such that it enters a room at 1 bar, 30 °C, and 60% relative humidity (point 3). This is done by passing the humid air through the following stages:

1–2: Flow over a heating coil.
2–3: Water injection at 20 °C in an adiabatic process.

a. Draw the process on a psychrometric diagram.
b. Find the temperature at point 2.
c. Find the heat interaction of the process.
d, Find the amount of water used in the process.
e. Find the entropy change in process 1–2.

12.39 A rigid tank 30 L in volume is half filled with liquid water. The other half is filled with a mixture of air and water vapor. A valve at the bottom of the tank is opened and liquid water flows out of the tank until the last drop of liquid disappears. A constant-temperature bath maintains the temperature in the tank at 340 °C during the process, which is carried out slowly.

a. Find the final pressure in the tank if the initial pressure was 35 MPa.
b. Find the amount of liquid that was taken out of the tank.

12.40 Atmospheric air at 101 bars, 15 °C, and 55% relative humidity passes through the suction duct of a fan into a cooling tower at a rate of 100 m^3/min. The power input to the fan is 5 hp. The air leaves the tower saturated with water vapor at 32 °C. The temperature of the water entering the tower is 50 °C and 80 kg/min of cooled water leave the tower. Determine:

a. The rate at which the water is supplied to the tower.
b. The exit temperature of the cooled water.

12.41 Find the change in available work with respect to the atmosphere at T_0 = 21 °C, p_0 = 102 kPa, when 1 kmol of N_2 and 1 kmol of O_2 are mixed together at atmospheric temperature and pressure.

12.42 An insulated vessel containing 2 kg of oxygen (O_2) at 2.5 MPa, 300 °C, is connected via an insulated tube and a valve to a second vessel of 0.44 m^3 that contains 1.2 kg of nitrogen. The second vessel is maintained in good thermal contact with the environment. The valve is opened and oxygen flows from the first vessel to the second till the pressures are equalized and then the valve is closed again. The environment is air at 101 kPa and 28 °C.

Assume that oxygen and nitrogen are ideal gases: $M_{02} = 32$, $M_{N_2} = 28$, and $k = 1.4$.

a. Find the work and heat interactions of the vessels.
b. Find the maximum work between the two end states.
c. Find the heat interaction connected with the maximum work.
d. Find the irreversibility of the process.

12.43 A 0.15 m^3 adiabatic closed cylinder is divided by a heavy floating piston, whose weight is equivalent to a pressure difference of 0.65 MPa, into two equal parts, Fig. 12.21. The lower part contains oxygen (ideal gas, $M = 32$, $k = 1.4$) at 40 °C. The upper part contains nitrogen (ideal gas, $M = 28$, $k = 1.4$) at 0.30 MPa, 40 °C. After a while the piston disintegrates and the pieces fall to the bottom of the container. The environment is air at 101 kPa and 28 °C.

Assume that oxygen and nitrogen are ideal gases: M_{O_2} =32, M_{N_2} =28, and k = 1.4.

a. Find the final state inside the cylinder.
b. Find the irreversibility of the process.

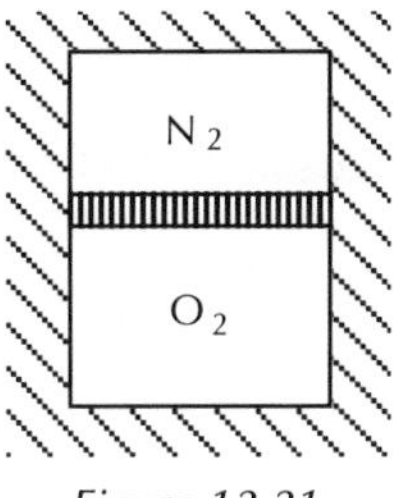

Figure 12.21

12.44 A rigid adiabatic vessel is divided by a floating adiabatic piston into two parts. The lower part contains 5 gmol of air at 0.3 MPa, 227 °C, while the upper part contains 3 gmol of nitrogen at 0.16 MPa, 27 °C, Fig. 12.22.

The surroundings are at 102 kPa, 27 °C. The piston breaks and falls to the bottom of the vessel, the gases mix and attain equilibrium. Find:

a. The pressure and temperature of the mixture.
b. The entropy change of the process.
c. The change in availability of everything involved in the process.

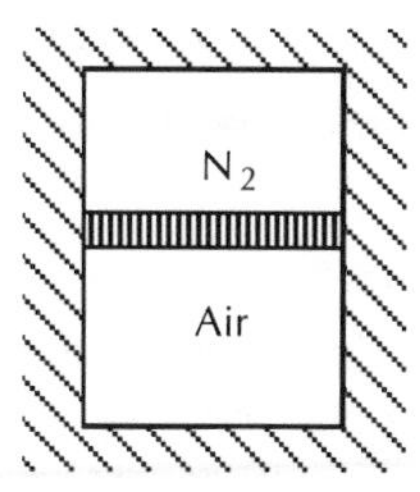

Figure 12.22

12.45 Two well-insulated vessels are interconnected by a pipe and a valve. One vessel, whose volume is 85 L, contains oxygen at 100 kPa, 38 °C, while the second, whose volume is 28 L, contains nitrogen at 630 kPa, 150 °C. The valve is opened and a flow starts. Two mixing modes are to be considered: one where the final state will be identical in both vessels; and a second where the valve is closed as soon as the pressures are equalized. In the latter case the final equilibrium states in each vessel will be different. For each of the mixing modes determine the irreversibility relative to an environment at 100 kPa, 27 °C.

12.46 The composition of the atmosphere in a deep coal mine is N_2 79%, O_2 20%, and CO_2 1%. The conditions in the mine are 120 kPa, 40 °C. A fork lift is operated by means of a 40 L cylinder of compressed nitrogen at 20.0 MPa, 40 °C. Assume all gases are ideal.

a. Determine the final equilibrium state of the nitrogen.
b. Find the maximum work that may be obtained from one cylinder of nitrogen.

12.47 The atmosphere in a coal mine is at 100 kPa and 35 °C. It may be assumed to consist of 21% oxygen and 79% nitrogen by volume. A 3 m^3 tank of oxygen at 1.5 MPa and 35 °C is available to provide work for operating machinery. What is the maximum work that can be delivered to the machinery:

a. Before discarding pure oxygen at atmospheric pressure?
b. If the restriction to atmospheric pressure in a is removed and the oxygen may be discarded into the surrounding atmosphere in any way you please?

12.48 Humid air at 100 kPa, 30 °C, and 90% relative humidity is compressed reversibly and adiabatically in a cylinder–piston assembly to 300 kPa.

a. Find the relative humidity after the compression.
b. Find the work and heat interactions.
c. Find the irreversibility relative to an environment at 100 kPa, 27 °C.

12.49 Humid air at 100 kPa, 30 °C and 90% relative humidity is compressed to 300 kPa in an internally reversible isothermal process in a cylinder–piston assembly while interacting with a reservoir at 10 °C.

a. Find the relative humidity after the compression.
b. Find the work and heat interactions.
c. Determine the irreversibility relative to an environment at 100 kPa, 27 °C.

CHAPTER THIRTEEN

Thermodynamic relations

We have already seen that thermodynamic properties are related to each other. The state principle (see Chapter 4) determines the number of independent properties of a system in a state of stable equilibrium. It also assures that any property can be expressed in terms of the independent properties.

In this chapter we explain in more detail different relations for thermodynamic properties and apply them to specific examples. These thermodynamic relations are also useful in preparing tables of thermodynamic properties that are hard to measure directly.

Certain properties, such as pressure, temperature, and the Joule–Thomson coefficient, are relatively easy to measure. Other properties, such as energy, entropy, etc., are much harder to determine experimentally, if their definitions are used as a basis for the measurements. For example, in order to determine the entropy change between two given states, as defined by Eqs (8.11) and (8.12), we must find a reversible process connecting the two end states and measure the temperatures and differential heat interactions during the process. This is quite a formidable task. The thermodynamic relations that we develop in this chapter allow us to determine entropy data on the basis of other measurements which are easier to obtain.

13.1 Some mathematical relations

In this chapter we frequently use four mathematical relations that exist between partial derivatives. A short review of these relations is given below.

Consider the following functional relationship:

$$z = z(x, y) \tag{13.1}$$

A differential change in z is given by

$$dz = \left(\frac{\partial z}{\partial x}\right)_y dx + \left(\frac{\partial z}{\partial y}\right)_x dy \tag{13.2}$$

The infinitesimal quantity dz is an exact differential, since the integral

$$\int_1^2 dz = z_2 - z_1 \tag{13.3}$$

depends only on the end states 1 and 2 and is independent of the path.

Now consider the following relationship:

$$dz = M(x,y)dx + N(x,y)dy \tag{13.4}$$

Comparing Eqs (13.4) and (13.2) we note that the infinitesimal quantity dz in Eq. (13.4) represents an exact differential only if the functions $M(x, y)$ and $N(x, y)$ are

$$M = \left(\frac{\partial z}{\partial x}\right)_y \text{ and } N = \left(\frac{\partial z}{\partial y}\right)_x \tag{13.5}$$

Furthermore, as a consequence of Eq. (13.5), the following relation holds:

$$\left(\frac{\partial N}{\partial x}\right)_y = \left(\frac{\partial M}{\partial y}\right)_x \tag{13.6}$$

Equation (13.6) may be shown to be true by substituting M and N from Eq. (13.5) and noting that for continuous functions the order of differentiation is immaterial.

Now let us consider the exact differential, given in Eq. (13.2), for the special case of z = const., i.e. $dz = 0$. This leads to

$$\left(\frac{\partial z}{\partial x}\right)_y dx = -\left(\frac{\partial z}{\partial y}\right)_x dy \tag{13.7}$$

Dividing through by dy and noting that z = const. we get

$$\left(\frac{\partial z}{\partial x}\right)_y \left(\frac{\partial x}{\partial y}\right)_z = -\left(\frac{\partial z}{\partial y}\right)_x \tag{13.8}$$

and finally

$$\left(\frac{\partial z}{\partial x}\right)_y \left(\frac{\partial x}{\partial y}\right)_z \left(\frac{\partial y}{\partial z}\right)_x = -1 \tag{13.9}$$

Another useful relationship can be derived as follows. Given the functions

$$z = z(x,y) \tag{13.1}$$

and

$$w = w(x,z) \tag{13.10}$$

the function w can be expressed as

$$w = w[x, z(x,y)] \tag{13.11}$$

and its exact differential as

$$dw = \left(\frac{\partial w}{\partial x}\right)_z dx + \left(\frac{\partial w}{\partial z}\right)_x dz \tag{13.12}$$

Differentiating Eq. (13.12) with respect to x, while y is constant, we get

$$\left(\frac{\partial w}{\partial x}\right)_y = \left(\frac{\partial w}{\partial x}\right)_z + \left(\frac{\partial w}{\partial z}\right)_x \left(\frac{\partial z}{\partial x}\right)_y \tag{13.13}$$

In this chapter we use extensively the four mathematical relationships given by Eqs (13.5), (13.6), (13.9), and (13.13).

13.2 Maxwell relations

The Maxwell relations relate the partial derivatives of properties to each other. In this section we consider only the relations between the properties p, v, T, and s.

For a simple system we have already seen that

$$du = Tds - pdv \tag{13.14}$$

and

$$dh = Tds + vdp \tag{13.15}$$

In parallel to the definition of specific enthalpy, $h = u + pv$, it is also useful to define new specific properties as follows:
Helmholtz free energy:

$$a = u - Ts \tag{13.16}$$

Gibbs free energy

$$g = h - Ts \tag{13.17}$$

The Helmholtz and the Gibbs free energies play an important role in the analysis of physical and chemical equilibria. They will be discussed in detail in Chapters 15–19. At this point we consider only the relationships between these and other properties.

Differentiation of Eqs (13.16) and (13.17) and substitution of Eqs (13.14) and (13.15), respectively, leads to

$$da = -sdT - pdv \tag{13.18}$$

and

$$dg = -sdT + vdp \tag{13.19}$$

Since u, h, a, and g are properties, their differentials are *exact differentials*. Thus, applying the relationships of Eq. (13.5) to Eqs (13.14), (13.15), (13.18), and (13.19) we obtain

$$T = \left(\frac{\partial u}{\partial s}\right)_v = \left(\frac{\partial h}{\partial s}\right)_p \tag{13.20}$$

$$p = -\left(\frac{\partial a}{\partial v}\right)_T = -\left(\frac{\partial u}{\partial v}\right)_s \tag{13.21}$$

$$v = \left(\frac{\partial h}{\partial p}\right)_s = \left(\frac{\partial g}{\partial p}\right)_T \tag{13.22}$$

$$s = -\left(\frac{\partial g}{\partial T}\right)_p = -\left(\frac{\partial a}{\partial T}\right)_v \tag{13.23}$$

Moreover, performing the operations of Eq. (13.6) on Eqs (13.14), (13.15), (13.18), and (13.19) we obtain, respectively,

$$\left(\frac{\partial T}{\partial v}\right)_s = -\left(\frac{\partial p}{\partial s}\right)_v \tag{13.24}$$

$$\left(\frac{\partial T}{\partial p}\right)_s = \left(\frac{\partial v}{\partial s}\right)_p \tag{13.25}$$

$$\left(\frac{\partial s}{\partial v}\right)_T = \left(\frac{\partial p}{\partial T}\right)_v \tag{13.26}$$

$$\left(\frac{\partial s}{\partial p}\right)_T = -\left(\frac{\partial v}{\partial T}\right)_p \tag{13.27}$$

The last four equations are known as the Maxwell relations for a simple system. Similar relations hold also for non-simple systems, but these are not discussed in this text.

EXAMPLE 13.1

Show that the Maxwell relations of Eqs (13.24) and (13.25) are equivalent.

SOLUTION

By applying Eq. (13.8) to the right hand side of Eq. (13.24) we obtain

$$\left(\frac{\partial T}{\partial v}\right)_s = +\left(\frac{\partial p}{\partial v}\right)_s \left(\frac{\partial v}{\partial s}\right)_p$$

Multiplying both sides by $(\partial v/\partial p)_s$ leads to

$$\left(\frac{\partial T}{\partial p}\right)_s = \left(\frac{\partial v}{\partial s}\right)_p$$

which is Eq. (13.25). Indeed, it can be shown in a similar way that all the Maxwell relations are equivalent and can be derived from each other.

EXAMPLE 13.2

Verify that the steam tables are consistent with the Maxwell relations. Check at two points:
a. 2.5 MPa and 300 °C (superheated vapor).
b. 25.0 MPa and 300 °C (compressed liquid).

SOLUTION

Since all the Maxwell relations are equivalent, to verify consistency we can use the most convenient form of the relations. Let us select Eq. (13.27) for that purpose, since for this relation the partial derivatives are evaluated at constant temperature and constant pressure, respectively. We approximate the partial derivatives by the appropriate finite differences, noting that a small error may be introduced owing to this procedure. Thus Eq. (13.27) is replaced by

$$\left(\frac{\Delta s}{\Delta p}\right)_T = -\left(\frac{\Delta v}{\Delta T}\right)_p$$

$(\Delta s/\Delta p)_T$ is computed from data at the same temperature,

$(\Delta v/\Delta T)_p$ is computed from data at the same pressure.

The relevant values taken from the steam tables at $T = 300$ °C are as follows:

T	p	s
300	2.0	6.7664
300	2.5	6.6438
300	3.0	6.5390

T	p	s
300	20	3.2071
300	25	3.1906
300	30	3.1741

p	T	v
2.5	250	0.08700
2.5	300	0.09890
2.5	350	0.10976

p	T	v
25	280	0.0012860
25	300	0.0013450
25	320	0.0014217

a. At 2.5 MPa, 300 °C (superheated vapor)

$$\left(\frac{\Delta s}{\Delta p}\right)_T = \frac{6.5390 - 6.7664}{3000 - 2000} = -0.0002274 \frac{\text{kJ}}{\text{kg K kPa}}$$

and

$$\left(\frac{\Delta v}{\Delta T}\right)_p = \frac{0.10976 - 0.08700}{350 - 250} = 0.0002276\,\text{m}^3/\text{kg K}$$

The units of the two values are equivalent (prove it!). The agreement is within 0.1%. The deviation is probably due to the fact that instead of the actual derivative we used a finite difference approximation.

b. At 25 MPa, 300 °C (compressed liquid)

$$\left(\frac{\Delta s}{\Delta p}\right)_T = \frac{3.1741 - 3.2071}{30000 - 20000} = -3.0 \times 10^{-6} \frac{\text{kJ}}{\text{kg K kPa}}$$

and

$$\left(\frac{\Delta v}{\Delta T}\right)_p = \frac{0.0014217 - 0.0012860}{320 - 280} = 3.39 \times 10^{-6} \text{ m}^3/\text{kg K}$$

Here the error, of about 13%, is somewhat larger, which is probably due to the sparsity of the data in the table of compressed liquid.

13.3 Clapeyron equation

The Maxwell relations are useful in calculating properties that are difficult to measure directly, from properties that are easier to determine experimentally. They also lead to several useful thermodynamic relationships between properties. The Clapeyron equation, which is derivable from the Maxwell relations, relates the saturation pressure and temperature to other thermodynamic properties.

Let us apply Eq. (13.25) to a pure substance in the vapor–liquid two-phase region. Under these conditions the pressure depends on the temperature only, and the change of volume, entropy, and enthalpy at constant temperature may be expressed as

$$dv = v_{fg}dx \qquad ds = s_{fg}dx \qquad dh = h_{fg}dx \tag{13.28}$$

where dx is the differential change in the quality of the vapor. Dividing ds by dv we obtain for this constant-temperature process,

$$\left(\frac{\partial s}{\partial v}\right)_T = \frac{s_{fg}}{v_{fg}} \tag{13.29}$$

Substituting the Maxwell relationship, Eq. (13.26),

$$\left(\frac{\partial s}{\partial v}\right)_T = \left(\frac{\partial p}{\partial T}\right)_v \tag{13.26}$$

into Eq. (13.29) we obtain

$$\left(\frac{\partial p}{\partial T}\right)_v = \frac{s_{fg}}{v_{fg}} \tag{13.30}$$

We note that in the two-phase region $p = p(T)$ only; hence,

$$\left(\frac{\partial p}{\partial T}\right)_v = \left(\frac{dp}{dT}\right)^{sat} \tag{13.31}$$

Moreover, $s_{fg} = h_{fg}/T$. Thus, Eq. (13.30) becomes

$$\left(\frac{dp}{dT}\right)^{sat} = \frac{h_{fg}}{Tv_{fg}} \tag{13.32}$$

Equation (13.32) is known as the *Clapeyron equation*. It may be generalized for any change from phase i to phase j (such as in melting, sublimation, transitions between solid phases, etc.) to yield the *general Clapeyron equation*

$$\left(\frac{dp}{dT}\right)^{sat} = \frac{h_{ij}}{Tv_{ij}} \tag{13.33}$$

where h_{ij} and v_{ij} are the respective changes of enthalpy and volume during phase transition.

The Clapeyron equation may be simplified for low pressure vaporization by assuming that the vapor behaves like an ideal gas and that the liquid volume is negligible. Under these assumptions Eq. (13.32) leads to

$$\left(\frac{dp}{dT}\right)^{sat} = \frac{h_{fg}}{T(RT/p)} = \frac{ph_{fg}}{RT^2} \tag{13.34}$$

or

$$\left(\frac{dp}{p}\right)^{sat} = \frac{h_{fg}}{R}\frac{dT}{T^2} \tag{13.35}$$

Equation (13.35) can be integrated directly, if h_{fg} is assumed to be constant (usually not a bad assumption at low pressures), to yield

$$p^{sat} = p_0^{sat}\exp\left[\frac{h_{fg}}{R}\left(\frac{1}{T_0}-\frac{1}{T}\right)\right] \tag{13.36}$$

Indeed, in many cases the saturation pressures of various substances are correlated by a similar equation

$$p^{sat} = A\exp(-B/T) \tag{13.37}$$

This equation gives good results for a small range of temperature variations. For a larger range of temperature variations it is only an approximation.

EXAMPLE 13.3

Calculate the saturation pressure of water at 50 °C using data from steam tables for 40 °C only. Compare the calculated saturation pressure at 50 °C with that in the steam tables.

SOLUTION

At 40 °C we read from the steam tables:

$p^{sat}(40\ ^\circ\mathrm{C}) = 7.384$ kPa

$h_{fg}(40\ ^\circ\mathrm{C}) = 2406.7$ kJ/kg

Thus using Eq. (13.36) we obtain

$$p^{sat}(50\ ^\circ\mathrm{C}) = p^{sat}(40\ ^\circ\mathrm{C})\exp\left[\frac{2406.7\times 18}{8.3143}\left(\frac{1}{313.15}-\frac{1}{323.15}\right)\right] = 12.357\ \mathrm{kPa}$$

as compared with 12.349 kPa from the steam tables.

EXAMPLE 13.4

A skater weighing 800 N uses skates whose sliding surface area is 0.4 cm² each. The following data are known for the triple point of water:

$$p = 0.611\,\text{kPa} \qquad T = 0.01\,^\circ\text{C}$$
$$v_s = 0.0010908\ \text{m}^3/\text{kg} \qquad h_s = -333.40\ \text{kJ/kg}$$
$$v_f = 0.0010002\ \text{m}^3/\text{kg} \qquad h_f = 0.0\ \text{kJ/kg}$$
$$v_g = 206.14\ \text{m}^3/\text{kg} \qquad h_g = 2501.40\ \text{kJ/kg}$$

Find the lowest temperature at which liquid water will form under the skate.

SOLUTION

Approximating the derivatives of Eq. (13.33) by finite differences and assuming that v_{sf} and h_{sf} do not vary with temperature we obtain, after rearrangement,

$$\Delta T = \frac{T v_{sf}}{h_{sf}} \Delta p$$

The maximum pressure under a skate is when the skater skates on one skate only. That pressure is the sum of the atmospheric pressure and the weight per unit area:

$$p = 0.1 + (800.0/0.4) \times 10^{4-6} = 20.1\,\text{MPa}$$

The temperature difference is, therefore,

$$\Delta T = \frac{273.16 \times (0.0010002 - 0.0010908)}{0 - (-333.40)} \left(20.1 \times 10^3 - 0.611\right) = -1.49\ ^\circ\text{C}$$

Thus: $T_{min} = 0.01 - 1.49 = -1.48\ ^\circ\text{C}$.

This is the lowest temperature for which ice melts under a skate.

13.4 Specific heats

The specific heat at constant volume was defined in Chapter 4 as

$$c_v = (\partial u/\partial T)_v \tag{4.24}$$

We have also shown that

$$du = Tds - pdv \tag{8.26}$$

Differentiating Eq. (8.26) with respect to T, at constant v, yields

$$\left(\frac{\partial u}{\partial T}\right)_v = T\left(\frac{\partial s}{\partial T}\right)_v - p\left(\frac{\partial v}{\partial T}\right)_v = T\left(\frac{\partial s}{\partial T}\right)_v \tag{13.38}$$

and combining Eqs (4.24) and (8.26) we obtain

$$c_v = T\left(\frac{\partial s}{\partial T}\right)_v \tag{13.39}$$

The corresponding expression for the specific heat at constant pressure is

$$c_p = T\left(\frac{\partial s}{\partial T}\right)_p \tag{13.40}$$

Equations (13.39) and (13.40) give a more uniform representation of the specific heats. Thus in general, for simple and non-simple systems, we could define the specific heats at constant α, β, ... as

$$c_{\alpha,\beta,\ldots} = T\left(\frac{\partial s}{\partial T}\right)_{\alpha,\beta,\ldots} \tag{13.41}$$

where α, β,... are the parameters (properties) that are held constant during differentiation.

Let us study now the variation of specific heats with pressure. Differentiation of Eq. (13.40) leads to

$$\begin{aligned}\left(\frac{\partial c_p}{\partial p}\right)_T &= T\left[\frac{\partial}{\partial p}\left(\frac{\partial s}{\partial T}\right)_p\right]_T = T\left[\frac{\partial}{\partial T}\left(\frac{\partial s}{\partial p}\right)_T\right]_p \\ &= -T\left[\frac{\partial}{\partial T}\left(\frac{\partial v}{\partial T}\right)_p\right]_p = -T\left[\frac{\partial^2 v}{\partial T^2}\right]_p\end{aligned} \tag{13.42}$$

Similarly it is found from Eq. (13.39) that

$$\begin{aligned}\left(\frac{\partial c_v}{\partial v}\right)_T &= T\left[\frac{\partial}{\partial v}\left(\frac{\partial s}{\partial T}\right)_v\right]_T = T\left[\frac{\partial}{\partial T}\left(\frac{\partial s}{\partial v}\right)_T\right]_v \\ &= T\left[\frac{\partial}{\partial T}\left(\frac{\partial p}{\partial T}\right)_v\right]_v = T\left[\frac{\partial^2 p}{\partial T^2}\right]_v\end{aligned} \tag{13.43}$$

The right hand sides of Eqs (13.42) and (13.43) are calculable solely on the basis of the equation of state, requiring no calorimetric data. Obviously, for an ideal gas, for which the equation of state is $pv = RT$, we obtain

$$T\left[\frac{\partial^2 p}{\partial T^2}\right]_v = -T\left[\frac{\partial^2 v}{\partial T^2}\right]_p = 0 \tag{13.44}$$

indicating that the specific heats of ideal gases do not change with pressure or volume, and, hence, are functions of temperature only.

Finally, it is interesting to evaluate the difference between the specific heat at constant pressure and the specific heat at constant volume for any substance. This difference is

$$c_p - c_v = T.\left[\left(\frac{\partial s}{\partial T}\right)_p - \left(\frac{\partial s}{\partial T}\right)_v\right] \tag{13.45}$$

Using Eq. (13.13) we obtain

$$c_p - c_v = T\left(\frac{\partial s}{\partial v}\right)_T\left(\frac{\partial v}{\partial T}\right)_p = T\left(\frac{\partial p}{\partial T}\right)_v\left(\frac{\partial v}{\partial T}\right)_p \tag{13.46}$$

where use was made of the Maxwell relation, Eq. (13.26). Here again the difference between the specific heats is calculable from the equation of state alone.

13.5 Energy and enthalpy variations at constant temperature

The Maxwell relations are now used to obtain two useful relations on the variation of energy and enthalpy at a constant temperature.

We begin by evaluating the derivative $(\partial u/\partial v)_T$ from Eq. (8.26):

$$\left(\frac{\partial u}{\partial v}\right)_T = T\left(\frac{\partial s}{\partial v}\right)_T - p \tag{13.47}$$

Applying the Maxwell relation Eq. (13.26) to the first term on the right hand side of Eq. (13.47) leads to

$$\left(\frac{\partial u}{\partial v}\right)_T = T\left(\frac{\partial p}{\partial T}\right)_v - p \tag{13.48}$$

which after some mathematical manipulations becomes

$$\left(\frac{\partial u}{\partial v}\right)_T = T^2\left[\frac{\partial(p/T)}{\partial T}\right]_v \tag{13.49}$$

An equivalent expression for enthalpy change with pressure at constant temperature is obtained from Eq. (8.29), leading to

$$\left(\frac{\partial h}{\partial p}\right)_T = -T^2\left[\frac{\partial(v/T)}{\partial T}\right]_p \tag{13.50}$$

Equations (13.49) and (13.50) express the isothermal changes in energy and enthalpy, respectively, in terms of primitive properties associated with the equation of state.

EXAMPLE 13.5

In Chapter 5 it was stated, without proof, that for a substance that obeys the equation of state of an ideal gas, $pv = RT$, the internal energy is a function of temperature only, i.e. $u = u(T)$. Prove that statement.

SOLUTION

Assume that $u = u(T,v)$. Substitution of $pv = RT$ into the right hand side of Eq. (13.49) leads to

$$\left(\frac{\partial u}{\partial v}\right)_T = T^2\left[\frac{\partial(p/T)}{\partial T}\right]_v = T^2\left[\frac{\partial(R/v)}{\partial T}\right]_v = 0$$

Hence the energy is not influenced by changes in volume and must be a function of temperature only, $u = u(T)$.

One can similarly show that if the enthalpy is assumed to be a function of temperature and pressure, $h = h(T,p)$, Eq. (13.50) yields for $pv = RT$

$$\left(\frac{\partial h}{\partial p}\right)_T = -T^2\left[\frac{\partial(v/T)}{\partial T}\right]_p = -T^2\left[\frac{\partial(R/p)}{\partial T}\right]_p = 0$$

Thus, for ideal gases, $h = h(T)$ only.

13.6 The Joule–Thomson coefficient

The Joule–Thomson coefficient relates the change of temperature to the change of pressure along a constant-enthalpy path:

$$c_{JT} = \left(\frac{\partial T}{\partial p}\right)_h \tag{6.42}$$

The Joule–Thomson coefficient is relatively easy to determine experimentally for a wide range of states. An experimental apparatus for measuring the Joule–Thomson coefficient is shown, schematically, in Fig. 13.1. It is, in principle, an adiabatic throttling device for which the inlet and outlet velocities are negligible.

Adiabatic throttling assures that the enthalpy does not change. Measuring the pressures and temperatures at the inlet (state 1) and outlet (state 2) allows the determination of the Joule–Thomson coefficient.

The Joule–Thomson coefficient can be related to other properties as

$$c_{JT} = \left(\frac{\partial T}{\partial p}\right)_h = -\left(\frac{\partial T}{\partial h}\right)_p\left(\frac{\partial h}{\partial p}\right)_T \tag{13.51}$$

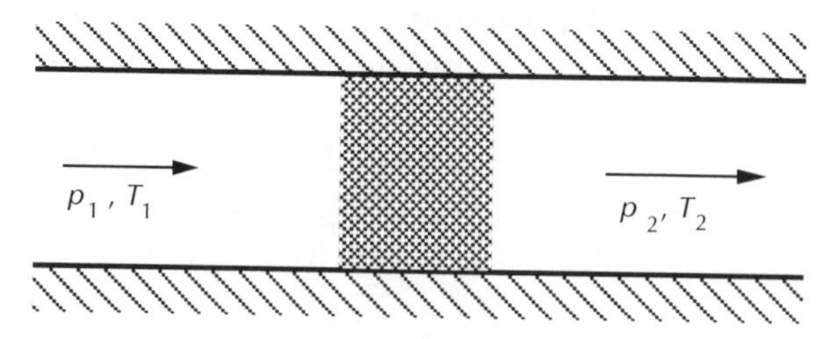

Figure 13.1 **Joule–Thomson apparatus.**

The first term on the right hand side of Eq. (13.51) is exactly the reciprocal of the specific heat at constant pressure, while the second term can be expressed in terms of properties calculable from the equation of state, by applying Eq. (13.50). Thus

$$c_{JT} = \frac{T^2}{c_p}\left[\frac{\partial(v/T)}{\partial T}\right]_p \tag{13.52}$$

It is easily seen from Eq. (13.52) that the Joule–Thomson coefficient is zero for an ideal gas. Indeed, the Joule–Thomson coefficient may be viewed as an indicator for the deviation of a real gas from ideality.

13.7 Volume change coefficients

The relative variation of volume with pressure and temperature is described by coefficients given below.

The volume expansion coefficient, β, is defined as the relative change of volume with temperature at constant pressure:

$$\beta = \frac{1}{v}\left(\frac{\partial v}{\partial T}\right)_p = \left(\frac{\partial \ln v}{\partial T}\right)_p \tag{13.53}$$

Isothermal compressibility, K_T, is defined as the relative change of volume with pressure at constant temperature:

$$K_T = -\frac{1}{v}\left(\frac{\partial v}{\partial p}\right)_T = -\left(\frac{\partial \ln v}{\partial p}\right)_T \tag{13.54}$$

Adiabatic compressibility, K_s, is defined as the relative change of volume with pressure at constant entropy:

$$K_s = -\frac{1}{v}\left(\frac{\partial v}{\partial p}\right)_s = -\left(\frac{\partial \ln v}{\partial p}\right)_s \tag{13.55}$$

The reciprocals of the compressibilities, K_T and K_s, are the isothermal bulk modulus of elasticity and the adiabatic bulk modulus of elasticity, respectively.

The isothermal modulus of elasticity, E_T, is defined as the relative change of pressure with volume at constant temperature:

$$E_T = \frac{1}{K_T} = -v\left(\frac{\partial p}{\partial v}\right)_T = -\left(\frac{\partial p}{\partial \ln v}\right)_T \tag{13.56}$$

and, similarly,

$$E_s = \frac{1}{K_s} = -v\left(\frac{\partial p}{\partial v}\right)_s = -\left(\frac{\partial p}{\partial \ln v}\right)_s \tag{13.57}$$

EXAMPLE 13.6

Express the difference between the specific heats in terms of the change coefficients.

SOLUTION

It was shown in Eq. (13.46) that $c_p - c_v = T(\partial p/\partial T)_v(\partial v/\partial T)_p$. Applying Eq. (13.8) to the term $(\partial p/\partial T)_v$, we obtain

$$c_p - c_v = -T\left(\frac{\partial p}{\partial v}\right)_T\left(\frac{\partial v}{\partial T}\right)_p^2 = -T\left(\frac{-1}{vK_T}\right)(Bv)^2 = \frac{vTB^2}{K_T}$$

EXAMPLE 13.7

Using the steam tables estimate for water at 30 MPa and 40 °C:

a. The volume expansion coefficient, B.
b. The isothermal compressibility, K_T.
c. The isothermal modulus of elasticity, E_T.

SOLUTION

We copy specific volume data from the compressed liquid table for states in the vicinity of 30 MPa and 40 °C and arrange them in the following table:

T	20 MPa	30 MPa	40 MPa
20 °C	0.0009928	0.0009886	0.0009846
40 °C	0.0009992	0.0009951	0.0009956
60 °C	0.0010084	0.0010042	0.0010057

a. The volume expansivity can be approximated by

$$\beta = \frac{1}{v}\left(\frac{\partial v}{\partial T}\right)_p = \frac{1}{v_i}\left[\frac{v_{i+1} - v_{i-1}}{T_{i+1} - T_{i-1}}\right]_p$$

$$= \frac{1}{0.0009992}\frac{0.0010042 - 0.0009886}{60 - 20} = 0.39 \times 10^{-3}\ 1/\text{K}$$

b. The isothermal compressibility is approximated by

$$K_T = -\frac{1}{v}\left(\frac{\partial v}{\partial p}\right)_T = -\frac{1}{v_i}\left[\frac{v_{i+1} - v_{i-1}}{p_{i+1} - p_{i-1}}\right]_T$$

$$= \frac{1}{0.0009951}\frac{0.0009992 - 0.0009956}{40 - 20} = 0.181 \times 10^{-3}\ 1/\text{MPa}$$

c. The isothermal modulus of elasticity is the reciprocal of the isothermal compressibility. Hence,

$$E_T = 1/K_T = 6634 \text{ MPa}$$

PROBLEMS

13.1 Verify that the steam tables are consistent with the Maxwell relations at the following points:

a. 5.0 MPa, 400 °C.
b. 20.0 MPa, 600 °C.
Choose the most convenient form of the Maxwell relations.

13.2 Prove that:

a. $\left(\frac{\partial u}{\partial v}\right)_T = T^2\left(\frac{\partial(p/T)}{\partial T}\right)_v$ b. $\left(\frac{\partial h}{\partial p}\right)_T = -T^2\left(\frac{\partial(v/T)}{\partial T}\right)_p$

13.3 Show that for a material that fulfills the van der Waals equation, $p = RT/(v-b) - a/v^2$, the following equations apply:

a. $\left(\frac{\partial c_v}{\partial v}\right)_T = 0$ b. $c_p - c_v = \frac{R}{1-\left(2a/RTv^3\right)(v-b)^2}$

c. $u = \frac{a}{v_0} - \frac{a}{v} + \int_{T_0}^{T} c_v\,dT + u_0$ d. $s = R\ln\frac{v-b}{v_0-b} + \int_{T_0}^{T}\left(\frac{c_v}{T}\right)dT + s_0$

13.4 The van der Waals equation of state is $(p + a/v^2)(v-b) = RT$. Derive the expressions for

a. $\left(\frac{\partial p}{\partial v}\right)_T$ b. $\left(\frac{\partial v}{\partial T}\right)_p$ c. $\left(\frac{\partial p}{\partial T}\right)_v$

13.5 a. Prove that

$$\left(\frac{\partial u}{\partial v}\right)_T = \frac{c_p - c_v}{\beta v} - p$$

b. Determine $(\partial u/\partial v)_T$ for saturated liquid water at 10 °C.

13.6 The properties of water at the triple point are as follows:

$T = 0.01\,°C$	$v_s = 0.0010908\ m^3/kg$	$h_s = -333.40$ kJ/kg
$p = 0.6113$ kPa	$v_f = 0.0010002\ m^3/kg$	$h_f = 0.04$ kJ/kg
	$v_g = 206.14\ m^3/kg$	$h_g = 2501.40$ kJ/kg

A man who weighs 90 kg skates on ice. The contact surface with the ice of each skate blade is 0.20 cm². Estimate the lowest temperature at which the ice will melt.

13.7 Determine the Joule–Thomson coefficient for water at the following points:

a. 400 °C, 5.0 MPa.
b. 600 °C, 20.0 MPa.

13.8 Find an expression for the Joule–Thomson coefficient for a gas that obeys the following equation of state: $p(v-b) = RT$.

13.9 In the following table some properties are given for sodium:

p kPa	T_{melt} °C	Δv_{melt} cm^3/kg
600.0	142.5	18.73
800.0	154.8	17.11
1000.0	166.7	15.56

Estimate the change in enthalpy during the melting of sodium at 155 °C.

13.10 From the pressure–enthalpy diagram for Freon-12:

a. Determine the latent heat of vaporization for Freon-12 at the triple point.
b. Determine the latent heat of sublimation for Freon-12 at the triple point.
c. Now use the diagram to determine the quantities needed to solve the Clapeyron equation and calculate h_{fg} for Freon-12 at –40 °C.

13.11 Using the ammonia tables estimate for saturated vapor and saturated liquid at 0 °C:

a. The volume expansion coefficient, B.
b. The isothermal compressiblity, K_T.
c. The isothermal modulus of elasticity, E_T.

13.12 Using Eq. (13.52) find an expression for the Joule–Thomson coefficient for a gas that obeys the van der Waals equation of state,

$$p = \frac{RT}{(v-b)} - \frac{a}{v^2}$$

13.13 Using Eq. (13.52) find an expression for the Joule–Thomson coefficient for a gas that obeys the Dieterici equation of state,

$$p(v-b)\exp\left(\frac{a}{RTv}\right) = RT$$

13.14 Using Eq. (13.46),

$$c_p - c_v = T\left(\frac{\partial p}{\partial T}\right)_v \left(\frac{\partial v}{\partial T}\right)_p$$

find the difference of specific heats for

a. An ideal gas.
b. A gas that obeys the van der Waals equation of state.
c. A gas that obeys the Dieterici equation of state.

13.15 A simple system satisfies the following equation of state:

$$pv = RT(1 + B/v)$$

a. Prove that the internal energy of this system is a function of temperature only.
b. Show that c_v does not depend on the specific volume.
c. Derive for the case c_v = const. a relationship between pressure and volume in a reversible adiabatic process.

13.16 The rate of change of the saturation pressure with temperature of helium at very low temperatures (below 1.4 K) may be approximated by

$$\frac{dp^{sat}}{dT} = 0.425T^7$$

a. Find an expression for the latent heat as a function of temperature and pressure.
b. Assuming that $\lim_{T\to 0} p^{sat} = 0$ find an expression for the latent heat as a function of temperature.
c. To what values do the specific volume and latent heat and the volume tend as the temperature approaches absolute zero?

13.17 The enthalpy of the melting of benzene (C_6H_6) at 1.01 bars and 5.5 °C is 558.9 kJ/kmol and its density is 894 kg/m^3. The density of the solid is 1014 kg/m^3.

Find the rate of change of melting temperature of benzene (C_6H_6) with pressure.

13.18 From the pressure–enthalpy diagram for carbon dioxide:

a. Determine the latent heat of vaporization for carbon dioxide at the triple point.
b. Determine the latent heat of sublimation for carbon dioxide at the triple point.
c. Now use the diagram to determine the quantities necessary to solve the Clapeyron equation and calculate h_{fg} for carbon dioxide at –40 °C.

13.19 The pressure on 100 g of water is increased reversibly and isothermally from 1 to 680 bars at 0 °C.

a. How much heat is transferred?
b. How much work is done?
c. Calculate the change in internal energy.

$\beta = -67\times10^{-6}$ 1/K $\qquad$ $K = 43\times10^{-12}$ cm^2/dyne.

13.20 The length x of an elastic rod in equilibrium depends upon the rod's temperature T and the tension force F. The energy and the entropy of the rod are given by

$$U = U_0 + C_x T \qquad S = S_0 + C_x \ln T - kx^2$$

Assume that: $k = 5.0$ N/mK , $C_x = 10$ J/K , and $U_0 = S_0 = 0$.

a. Find the equation of state of the rod, i.e. an equation of the type $f(x, F, T) = 0$.
b. Describe a Carnot cycle in the rod (including T–s and F–x diagrams) using the following properties: the hot reservoir temperature is 350 K, the minimum rod length at that temperature is 3.0 m; the work of the cycle is 70 J and its efficiency 5%.
c. Write the Maxwell relations for this system.

CHAPTER FOURTEEN

Equations of state and generalized charts

In Chapter 4 we have seen that for every real pure substance in a state of stable equilibrium there exists an equation of state, i.e. a relationship between volume, pressure, and temperature

$$f(v, p, T) = 0 \tag{4.5}$$

In general, the equation of state is based on experimental data and may be given in the form of tables of properties, e.g. steam tables. Many attempts have been made to express the equation of state in an algebraic form. However, these algebraic relationships are only an approximation that agrees well with the data for limited ranges of states. The equation of state for an ideal gas,

$$pv = RT \tag{5.5}$$

that was introduced in Chapter 5, is an example of a simple algebraic equation.

The range of applicability of the ideal gas equation is, indeed, quite limited. It is only accurate for states in which the volume of the system is considerably larger than the critical volume, i.e. for low pressures and/or high temperatures. A large number of equations of state have been proposed with the objective of improving the accuracy and range of applicability in describing the behavior of actual systems.

The present chapter examines several widely used equations of state for pure substances, and shows how one may obtain thermodynamic data from these equations.

The concept of reduced properties is introduced, leading to the rule of corresponding states. The generalized charts, which are based on this rule, are then presented. The chapter ends with the introduction of a new property, the fugacity.

14.1 Van der Waals equation

An early attempt to extend the validity of an algebraic equation of state to real substances was made in 1873 by van der Waals, who suggested an equation of state which was a variation on the ideal gas equation,

$$\left(p + \frac{a}{v^2}\right)(v - b) = RT \tag{14.1}$$

The volume in the ideal gas equation is replaced by $(v{-}b)$. The term b, which is characteristic of the substance, accounts for the volume that the molecules themselves occupy. The "free" volume, available for the motion of the molecules, is, therefore, $(v{-}b)$. The pressure, p, in the ideal gas equation is replaced here by $(p{+}a/v^2)$, to reflect the assertion that the actual pressure within the volume of the gas is somewhat higher than p which is measured at the surface. The measured pressure is lower due to the fact that surface molecules are attracted by other molecules from one side only. Table 14.1 lists the parameters a and b of the van der Waals equation for different substances.

Table 14.1 **Constants of the van der Waals equation of state.**

Substance	a m^6 kPa/kmol^2	b m^3/kmol
Carbon dioxide	365.4	0.04280
Ethane	557.1	0.06500
Freon-12	1076.1	0.09964
Helium	3.46	0.02371
Hydrogen	24.96	0.02668
Methane	232.4	0.04271
Nitrogen	136.8	0.03864
Oxygen	138.1	0.03184
Water	552.6	0.03042

The van der Waals equation approaches asymptotically the ideal gas equation as the specific volume increases. For small specific volumes it differs substantially from that of the ideal gas. Qualitatively the van der Waals equation provides a way to describe both gaseous and liquid phases. Quantitatively, however, the accuracy of the van der Waals equation is insufficient for most practical applications. Its importance lies in its use as a tool for analyzing trends in the variation of properties.

Figure 14.1 shows four typical isotherms of the van der Waals equation on a p–v diagram. For high temperatures, i.e. for $T_1 > T_c$, the isotherms tend to be hyperbolas, like those of ideal gases. For low temperatures ($T_2 < T_c$) the isotherms have both a minimum and a maximum. Points f and g represent two states at the same pressure along a given isotherm. If selected correctly, they can describe two phases, liquid and vapor, in mutual equilibrium.

The parameters of the critical point can be related to the constants a, b, and R of the

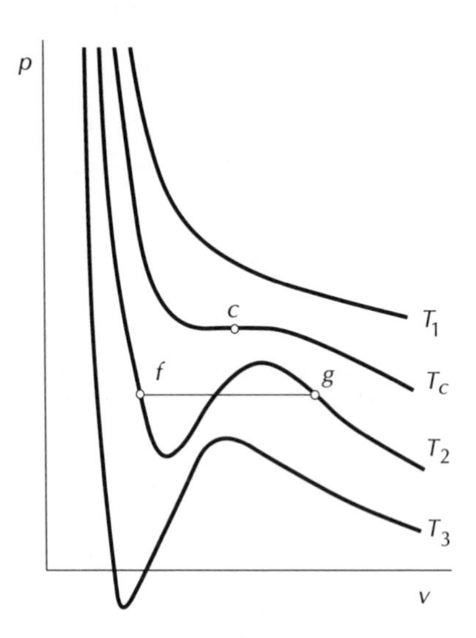

Figure 14.1 **Van der Waals isotherms.**

van der Waals equation by noting that the critical isotherm fulfills three conditions at the critical point: it passes through the critical point, its slope is zero, and it is a deflection point. Thus, at the critical point:

$$\left(\frac{\partial p}{\partial v}\right)_T = 0 \qquad \left(\frac{\partial^2 p}{\partial v^2}\right)_T = 0 \tag{14.2}$$

These two partial derivatives may be calculated from Eq. (14.1), leading to

$$\left(\frac{\partial p}{\partial v}\right)_T = -\frac{RT_c}{(v_c - b)^2} + \frac{2a}{v_c^3} = 0 \tag{14.3}$$

$$\left(\frac{\partial^2 p}{\partial v^2}\right)_T = \frac{2RT_c}{(v_c - b)^3} - \frac{6a}{v_c^4} = 0 \tag{14.4}$$

Solving Eqs (14.1), (14.3), and (14.4) for p_c, T_c, and v_c we obtain

$$v_c = 3b \tag{14.5}$$

$$p_c = \frac{a}{27b^2} \tag{14.6}$$

$$T_c = \frac{8a}{27bR} \tag{14.7}$$

An interesting feature of the van der Waals equation is that certain isotherms, e.g. T_3 in Fig. 14.1, exhibit regions of negative pressures, i.e. tension. These represent states of metastable equilibrium which under careful test conditions can actually be observed in real systems.

14.2 The Dieterici equation

The Dieterici equation*, proposed in 1899, is another equation of state with three parameters a, b , and R:

$$p e^{\frac{a}{RTv}} (v - b) = RT \tag{14.8}$$

which can be rearranged to read

$$p = \frac{RT}{v - b} e^{-\frac{a}{RTv}} \tag{14.9}$$

The isotherms of the Dieterici equation are similar to those of the van der Waals equation except that they have no points of negative pressures. In the vicinity of the critical point the Dieterici equation is a better approximation to real data than the van der Waals equation.

14.3 Empirical equations of state

Other equations of state offer better approximations to experimental data, because they are obtained by fitting empirical data to the equations.

Beattie–Bridgeman equation†

$$p = \frac{RT}{v}(1 - C)\left(1 + \frac{B}{v}\right) - \frac{A}{v^2} \tag{14.10}$$

where

$$A = A_0\left(1 - \frac{a}{v}\right) \qquad B = B_0\left(1 - \frac{b}{v}\right) \qquad C = \frac{c}{vT^3}$$

Thus five adjustable parameters, a, b, c, A_0, B_0, are available for fitting experimental data. The equation was applied to predict p–v–T data up to 200 atmospheres. It is very accurate as long as it is used within the range of the data from which the adjustable parameters were determined.

Redlich–Kwong equation (1949)‡

$$p = \frac{RT}{v - b} - \frac{a}{v(v + b)T^{0.5}} \tag{14.11}$$

where

* C.H. Dieterici, *Ann. Phys.Chem.*, **11**, 700 (1899).
† J.A. Beattie and O.C.Bridgeman, *Proc. Am. Acad. Arts Sci.*, **63**, 229 (1928)
‡ O. Redlich and J.N.S. Kwong, *Chem. Rev.*, **44**, 233 (1949).

$$a = \frac{0.4275R^2T_c^{2.5}}{p_c} \text{ and } b = \frac{0.0866RT_c}{p_c} \tag{14.12}$$

The Redlich–Kwong equation offers some improvement on the van der Waals equation but still has a limited range of validity.

Benedict–Webb–Rubin equation (1940)

$$p = \frac{RT}{v} + \frac{B_oRT - A_0 - C_0/T^2}{v^2} + \frac{bRT - a}{v^3} + \frac{a\alpha}{v^6} + \frac{c(1+\gamma/v^2)}{v^3T}\exp\left(-\frac{\gamma}{v^2}\right) \tag{14.13}$$

This equation has nine parameters, R, A_0, B_0, C_0, a, b, c, α, γ, that provide a better fit to a wider range of data.

14.4 Virial form of equation of state

The virial form is obtained by expanding the equation of state in series of v:

$$\frac{pv}{RT} = 1 + \frac{B}{v} + \frac{C}{v^2} + \frac{D}{v^3} + \ldots \tag{14.14a}$$

where B, C, D, etc., are called the second, third, and fourth virial coefficients, respectively, and are functions of temperature only.

An alternative virial form is obtained by expanding the equation of state in series of p:

$$\frac{pv}{RT} = 1 + B'p, + C'p^2, + D'p^3 \tag{14.14b}$$

The coefficients, B', C', D', etc., are also functions of temperature only.

14.5 Thermodynamic data from equations of state

Even though the equation of state includes data on volume, pressure, and temperature only, it can be used to determine other properties, e.g. internal energy, enthalpy, and entropy. However, determination of these properties for all ranges requires additional data, e.g. specific heat data as a function of temperature at a given pressure.

Consider the enthalpy as a function of temperature and pressure, $h = h(T, p)$. The differential of the enthalpy is then

$$dh = \left(\frac{\partial h}{\partial T}\right)_p dT + \left(\frac{\partial h}{\partial p}\right)_T dp \tag{14.15}$$

Substituting Eqs (4.40) and (13.50) into Eq. (14.15) yields

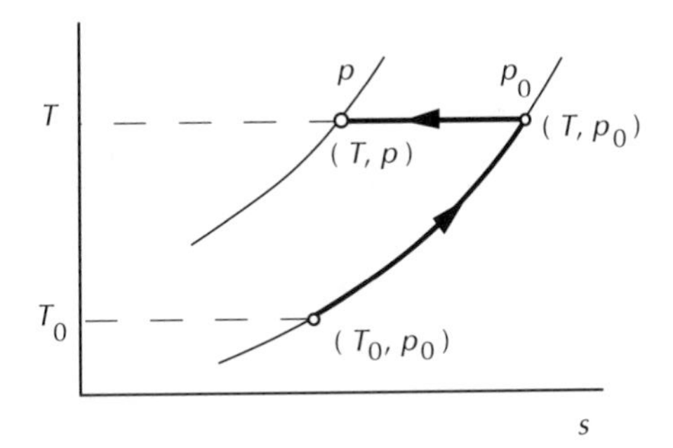

Figure 14.2 **Integration path for Eq. (14.18).**

$$dh = c_p dT - T^2\left[\frac{\partial(v/T)}{\partial T}\right]_p dp \tag{14.16}$$

Since enthalpy is a property its change between a reference state (T_0,p_0) and any other state (T, p) can be obtained by integration of Eq. (14.16), independent of the path connecting the end states.

Let us select an integration path consisting of two parts, as shown in Fig. 14.2. The first part is along a constant-pressure path where the integration proceeds from (T_0, p_0) to (T, p_0). The second part is at a constant temperature, T, from (T, p_0) to (T, p):

$$h - h_0 = \left[\int_{T_0}^{T} c_p dT\right]_{p0} + \left(\int_{p0}^{p} -T^2\left[\frac{\partial(v/T)}{\partial T}\right]_p dp\right)_T \tag{14.17}$$

At very low pressures (p_0~ 0), the specific heat may be determined as a function of temperature from spectroscopic measurements. Table 14.2 lists specific heats of various gases at low pressures. At these low pressures the gases may be considered ideal gases, where $v/T = R/p$ and c_p is independent of pressure. Hence,

$$h - h_0 = \left[\int_{T_0}^{T} c_{p_0}\, dT\right]_{p_0=0} + \left(\int_{p0}^{p} -T^2\left[\frac{\partial(v/T)}{\partial T}\right]_p dp\right)_T \tag{14.18}$$

Equation (14.18) allows the determination of enthalpy at any state on the basis of the equation of state and the specific heat at "zero" pressure.

Equivalent expressions can be obtained for the internal energy. Consider the internal energy to be a function of temperature and volume, $u(T,v)$. The differential of $u = u(T,v)$ is given by

$$du = \left(\frac{\partial u}{\partial T}\right)_v dT + \left(\frac{\partial u}{\partial v}\right)_T dv \tag{14.19}$$

Substituting Eqs (4.24) and (13.49) into Eq. (14.19) yields

Table 14.2 **Correlations of specific heats at low pressures for various gases ($\theta = T/100$ where T is in kelvin).**

Gas	M	Cp_0/R	Range	Error
N_2	28.013	$4.6979 - 61.676\theta^{-1.5} + 129.02\theta^{-2} - 98.673\theta^{-3}$	300–3500	0.43
O_2	31.999	$4.502123 + 0.0024180\theta^{1.5} - 21.477\theta^{-1.5} + 28.491\theta^{-2}$	300–3500	0.30
H_2	2.016	$6.7961 - 84.522\theta^{-0.75} + 140.12\theta^{-1} - 67.438\theta^{-1.5}$	300–3500	0.60
CO	28.01	$8.3164 - 0.084749\theta^{0.75} - 24.148\theta^{-0.5} + 21.260\theta^{-0.75}$	300–3500	0.42
OH	17.008	$9.8079 - 7.13830\theta^{0.25} + 2.08420\theta^{0.75} - 0.51309\theta$	300–3500	0.43
NO	30.01	$7.1302 - 0.205620\theta^{0.5} - 8.4930\theta^{-0.5} + 9.0073\theta^{-1.5}$	300–3500	0.34
H_2O	18.016	$17.2053 - 22.075\theta^{0.25} + 9.5290\theta^{0.5} - 0.44488\theta$	300–3500	0.43
CO_2	44.01	$-3.7357 + 0.52900\theta^{0.5} - 4.1034\theta + 0.024200\theta^{2}$	300–3500	0.19
NO_2	46.01	$46.045 + 216.10\theta^{-0.5} - 363.66\theta^{-0.75} + 232.55\theta^{-2}$	300–3500	0.26
CH_4	16.04	$-672.87 + 439.740\theta^{0.25} - 24.875\theta^{0.75} + 323.88\theta^{-0.5}$	300–2000	0.15
C_2H_4	28.054	$-95.395 + 123.15\theta^{0.5} - 35.6410\theta^{0.75} + 182.77\theta^{-3}$	300–2000	0.07
C_2H_6	30.07	$6.8950 + 17.260\theta - 0.640200\theta^{2} + 0.00728\theta^{3}$	300–1500	0.83
C_3H_8	44.097	$-4.042 + 30.46\theta - 1.571\theta^{2} + 0.03171\theta^{3}$	300–1500	0.40
C_4H_{10}	58.124	$3.954 + 12.0\theta - 1.1.833\theta^{2} + 0.034980\theta^{3}$	300–1500	0.54

$$du = c_v dT + T^2\left(\frac{\partial(p/T)}{\partial T}\right)_v dv \tag{14.20}$$

Here again the integration is independent of the path connecting the end states (T_0,v_0) and (T,v), since the internal energy is a property. Select a two-part integration path, as shown in Fig. 14.3. Thus

$$u - u_0 = \left[\int_{T_0}^{T} c_v dT\right]_{v0} + \left[\int_{v0}^{v} T^2\left[\frac{\partial(p/T)}{\partial T}\right]_v dv\right]_T \tag{14.21}$$

and finally

$$u - u_0 = \int_{T_0}^{T} c_{v0} dT + \left[\int_{v0}^{v} T^2\left[\frac{\partial(p/T)}{\partial T}\right]_v dv\right]_T \tag{14.22}$$

Since the enthalpy and the internal energy are related to each other by

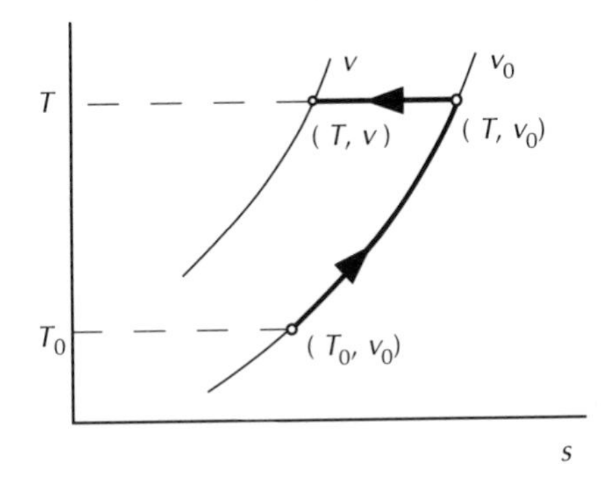

Figure 14.3 **Integration path for Eq. (14.22).**

$$h = u + pv \tag{4.37}$$

both properties can be evaluated either from Eqs (4.37) and (14.18) or from Eqs (4.37) and (14.22). The question as to which set of equations to use depends on the form of the equation of state. If the equation of state is explicit in volume, as in Eq. (14.14), then it is easier to perform the integration in Eq. (14.18). Equation (14.22) on the other hand is more convenient to integrate when the equation of state is explicit in pressure, e.g. the van der Waals equation.

Equations of state in conjunction with specific heat data can also be used to evaluate entropy. Entropy can be expressed in terms of temperature and volume. Thus the differential of entropy is given by

$$ds = \left(\frac{\partial s}{\partial T}\right)_v dT + \left(\frac{\partial s}{\partial v}\right)_T dv \tag{14.23}$$

Substituting the Maxwell relations, Eqs (13.26) and (13.39), into Eq. (14.23) yields

$$ds = \frac{c_v dT}{T} + \left(\frac{\partial p}{\partial T}\right)_v dv \tag{14.24}$$

which can be integrated between states (T_0,v_0) and (T,v) to yield

$$s - s_0 = \left[\int_{T0}^{T} c_v \frac{dT}{T}\right]_{v0} + \left[\int_{v0}^{v} \left(\frac{\partial p}{\partial T}\right)_v dv\right]_T \tag{14.25}$$

where $s_0 = s_0(T_0,v_0)$ is the entropy at the reference state. The integration of the first term is carried out along a constant-volume process and that of the second term along a constant-temperature line. This method is convenient when the pressure can be expressed explicitly in terms of volume.

An equivalent expression, which is more convenient when the volume is given explicitly in terms of pressure, can be obtained if the entropy is expressed as a function of temperature and pressure. The corresponding equations are

$$ds = \left(\frac{\partial s}{\partial T}\right)_p dT + \left(\frac{\partial s}{\partial p}\right)_T dp \tag{14.26}$$

$$ds = \frac{c_p dT}{T} - \left(\frac{\partial v}{\partial T}\right)_p dp \tag{14.27}$$

and

$$s - s_0 = \int_{T_0}^{T} \frac{c_p dT}{T} - \left[\int_{p_0}^{p} \left(\frac{\partial v}{\partial T}\right)_p dp\right]_T \tag{14.28}$$

where $s_0 = s_0(T_0, p_0)$ is the entropy at the reference state.

As mentioned above, good specific heat data are usually obtained from spectroscopic measurements at very low pressures ($p_0 \rightarrow 0$) and consequently high volumes. At these low pressures the integrand in Eq. (14.28) tends to infinity and may cause difficulties in the integration. One way to overcome the problem is by introducing a new parameter, D, equal to the difference between the actual volume and that of an ideal gas under the same conditions:

$$D = v - \frac{RT}{p} \tag{14.29}$$

Thus

$$\left(\frac{\partial v}{\partial T}\right)_p = \left(\frac{\partial D}{\partial T}\right)_p + \frac{R}{p} \tag{14.30}$$

and

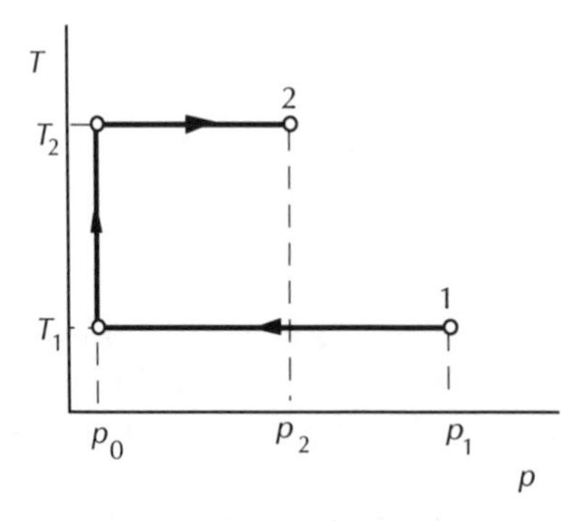

Figure 14.4 **Integration path for entropy change calculation.**

$$s - s_0 = \left[\int_{T_0}^{T} c_p \frac{dT}{T} \right]_{p_0} - \left[\int_{p_0}^{p} \left(\frac{\partial D}{\partial T} \right)_p dp \right]_T - R \ln \left(\frac{p}{p_0} \right) \tag{14.31}$$

The change of entropy between two states, (p_1, T_1) and (p_2, T_2), can be evaluated by integrating along a path as shown in Fig. 14.4:

$$s_2 - s_1 = R \ln \left(\frac{p_2}{p_1} \right) + \left[\int_{T_1}^{T_2} c_p \frac{dT}{T} \right]_{p_0} - \left[\int_{p_1}^{p_0} \left(\frac{\partial D}{\partial T} \right)_p dp \right]_{T_1} - \left[\int_{p_0}^{p_2} \left(\frac{\partial D}{\partial T} \right)_p dp \right]_{T_2} \tag{14.32}$$

Equation (14.32) is quite convenient to use, especially when a computer is available.

14.6 Rule of corresponding states

When data on the properties of various substances are compared, vast differences are found. For example, the specific volumes of hydrogen and water each at 100 kPa and 30 °C are 12.602 m^3/kg and 0.001004 m^3/kg, respectively, a ratio of over 12500:1.

Still, examination of p–v–T data for various substances indicates that there are great similarities between the properties when they are related to their respective critical values. Hence, we introduce the concept of a *reduced property* as the ratio of each property to its respective critical value. Thus

$$p_r = p / p_c \tag{14.33}$$

$$T_r = T / T_c \tag{14.34}$$

$$v_r = v / v_c \tag{14.35}$$

where p_c, T_c, and v_c are, respectively, the pressure, temperature, and specific volume at the critical point, and p_r, T_r, and v_r are the reduced pressure, reduced temperature, and reduced specific volume, respectively. Table 14.3 lists critical data for various substances.

The rule of corresponding states asserts:

All pure substances obey the same equations of state expressed in terms of reduced properties.

Mathematically, this means that

$$f(v_r, p_r, T_r) = 0 \tag{14.36}$$

is a universal function.

The rule of corresponding states is not a law in the thermodynamic sense, since it is only an approximation. It can be applied to substances of similar nature only, such as the families of hydrocarbons, or noble gases, but can exhibit deviations of 30%, or more, for dissimilar substances. Still, the reduced properties of all substances are of the same order of magnitude.

Table 14.3 **Critical data for various substances.**

Substance	Formula	Molecular weight	Temp. K	Pressure MPa	Volume m^3/kg
Ammonia	NH_3	17.03	405.5	11.28	0.0724
Argon	Ar	39.948	151	4.86	0.0749
Bromine	Br_2	159.808	584	10.34	0.1355
Carbon dioxide	CO_2	44.01	304.2	7.39	0.0943
Carbon monoxide	CO	28.011	133	3.50	0.0930
Chlorine	Cl_2	70.906	417	7.71	0.1242
Helium	He	4.003	5.3	0.23	0.0578
Hydrogen (normal)	H_2	2.016	33.3	1.30	0.0649
Krypton	Kr	83.80	209.4	5.50	0.0924
Neon	Ne	20.183	44.5	2.73	0.0417
Nitrogen	N_2	28.013	126.2	3.39	0.0899
Nitrous oxide	N_2O	44.013	309.7	7.27	0.0961
Oxygen	O_2	31.999	154.8	5.08	0.0780
Sulfur oxide	SO_2	64.063	430.7	7.88	0.1217
Water	H_2O	18.015	647.3	22.09	0.0568
Xenon	Xe	131.30	289.8	5.88	0.1186
Benzene	C_6H_6	78.115	562	4.92	0.2603
n-Butane	C_4H_{10}	58.124	425.2	3.80	0.2547
Carbon tetrachloride	CCl_4	153.82	556.4	4.56	0.2759
Chloroform	$CHCl_3$	119.38	536.6	5.47	0.2403
Dichlorodifluoromethane	CCl_2F_2	120.91	384.7	4.01	0.2179
Dichlorofluoromethane	$CHCl_2F$	102.92	451.7	5.17	0.1973
Ethane	C_2H_6	30.070	305.5	4.88	0.1480
Ethyl alcohol	C_2H_5OH	46.07	516	6.38	0.1673
Ethylene	C_2H_4	28.054	282.4	5.12	0.1242
n-Hexane	C_6H_{14}	86.178	507.9	3.03	0.3677
Methane	CH_4	16.043	191.1	4.64	0.0993
Methyl alcohol	CH_3OH	32.042	513.2	7.95	0.1180
Methyl chloride	CH_3Cl	50.488	416.3	6.68	0.1430
Propane	C_3H_8	44.097	370	4.26	0.1998
Propene	C_3H_6	42.081	365	4.62	0.1810
Trichlorofluoromethane	CCl_3F	137.37	471.2	4.38	0.2478

14.7 Generalized compressibility chart

In Chapter 5 we introduced the concept of the compressibility factor

$$Z = \frac{pv}{RT} \tag{5.9}$$

For ideal gases $Z = 1$, while for real gases the compressibility factor is a function of state. Thus, in general

$$Z = Z(p, T) \tag{14.37}$$

A chart of Z vs p with temperature as a parameter is called a compressibility chart. Such a chart can be prepared for any pure substance. However, if the compressibility chart is expressed in terms of reduced pressure, p_r, and reduced temperature, T_r, data for most pure substances can be reasonably well correlated by a single generalized chart, as indicated by the rule of corresponding states. A generalized compressibility chart was shown in Fig. 5.1. Since the chart constitutes a relationship between pressure, temperature, and specific volume, it is fully equivalent to an equation of state.

The compressibility chart may be used to determine the specific volume of a substance for which only sparse information exists. Indeed, the only data that are needed in order to evaluate the specific volume of a substance are the critical pressure and critical temperature. One should be aware, however, that the results may be off by as much as 30%.

EXAMPLE 14.1

Water at 30 MPa is heated isobarically from 400 °C to 500 °C, by a reservoir at 500 °C. For water: $M = 18.015$, $T_c = 647.3$ K, $p_c = 22.09$ MPa, $v_c = 0.003153 \text{m}^3/\text{kg}$. Find the specific volume of the water at both states, using:

a. The ideal gas assumption.
b. The generalized compressibility chart.
c. Steam tables.

SOLUTION

a. The volumes calculated from the ideal gas equation are

$$v_1 = \frac{RT_1}{p_1} = \frac{8.3143 \times 673.15}{18.015 \times 30000} = 0.01036 \text{ m}^3/\text{kg}$$

$$v_2 = \frac{RT_2}{p_2} = \frac{8.3143 \times 773.15}{18.015 \times 30000} = 0.01189 \text{ m}^3/\text{kg}$$

b. & c. Data and results are given, for comparison, in the following table:

State	p	T	T/T_c	p/p_c	Z	Specific volume m^3/kg		
	MPa	°C				a. RT/p	b. Chart	c. Tables
1	30.0	400	1.040	1.358	0.335	0.01036	0.003471	0.002790
2	30.0	500	1.194	1.358	0.715	0.01189	0.008501	0.008678

We note that while no approximation is perfect, the use of the compressibility chart yields results that are far better than the ideal gas relationship.

14.8 Generalized enthalpy chart

As demonstrated by Eqs (14.18) and (14.31), an equation of state can be used to generate data on enthalpy and entropy. In this sense the compressibility chart is equivalent to an equation of state, and as such can also be used to obtain enthalpy and entropy data.

Consider the expression for calculating enthalpy, Eq. (14.18),

$$h - h_0 = \int_{T_0}^{T} c_{p0}\, dT - \left[\int_{p0}^{p} T^2 \left[\frac{\partial (v/T)}{\partial T} \right]_p dp \right]_T \tag{14.18}$$

The second term on the right hand side of Eq. (14.18), which describes the variation of enthalpy along a constant-temperature line, can be determined from the compressibility chart as follows.

a. Substitute $v/T = ZR/p$ into the second term of Eq. (14.18) and perform the integration from a low pressure, p^*, where the gas may be considered ideal,

$$h(T,p) - h^*(T,p^*) = \left[\int_{p^*}^{p} \left(-T^2 \left[\frac{\partial (ZR/p)}{\partial T} \right]_p \right) dp \right]_T \tag{14.38}$$

b. Put Eq. (14.38) in dimensionless form by dividing by RT_c and rearrange it to obtain

$$\frac{h - h^*}{RT_c} = \left[\int_{p_r^*}^{p_r} \left(-T_r^2 \left(\frac{\partial Z}{\partial T_r} \right)_{p_r} \right) d \ln p_r \right]_T \tag{14.39}$$

Equation (14.39) expresses the difference between the enthalpy of a real substance and that of an ideal gas at the same temperature and pressure. Strictly speaking, Eq. (14.39) was developed for the deviation of enthalpy of the real substance at (p, T) from that of an ideal gas at (T, p^*). The enthalpy of an ideal gas is, of course, independent of pressure.

Figure 14.5 provides a plot of $(h^*-h)/(RT_c)$ as a function of p_r. It was constructed by integrating Eq. (14.39) using data from the generalized compressibility chart. The change of enthalpy between any two states can now be estimated by the following procedure, shown schematically in Fig. 14.6:

$$\begin{aligned} h(T_2,p_2) - h(T_1,p_1) &= \left[h(T_2,p_2) - h^*(T_2,p_2) \right] \\ &\quad - \left[h(T_1,p_1) - h^*(T_1,p_1) \right] + \left[h^*(T_2,p_2) - h^*(T_1,p_1) \right] \end{aligned} \tag{14.40}$$

The first two terms in the square brackets of Eq. (14.40) account for the deviation of the enthalpy of the real substance from that of the corresponding ideal gas. They are calculated by reading the appropriate terms off Fig. 14.5. The last term in Eq. (14.40), which stands for the enthalpy change of an ideal gas between the two states, is calculated from

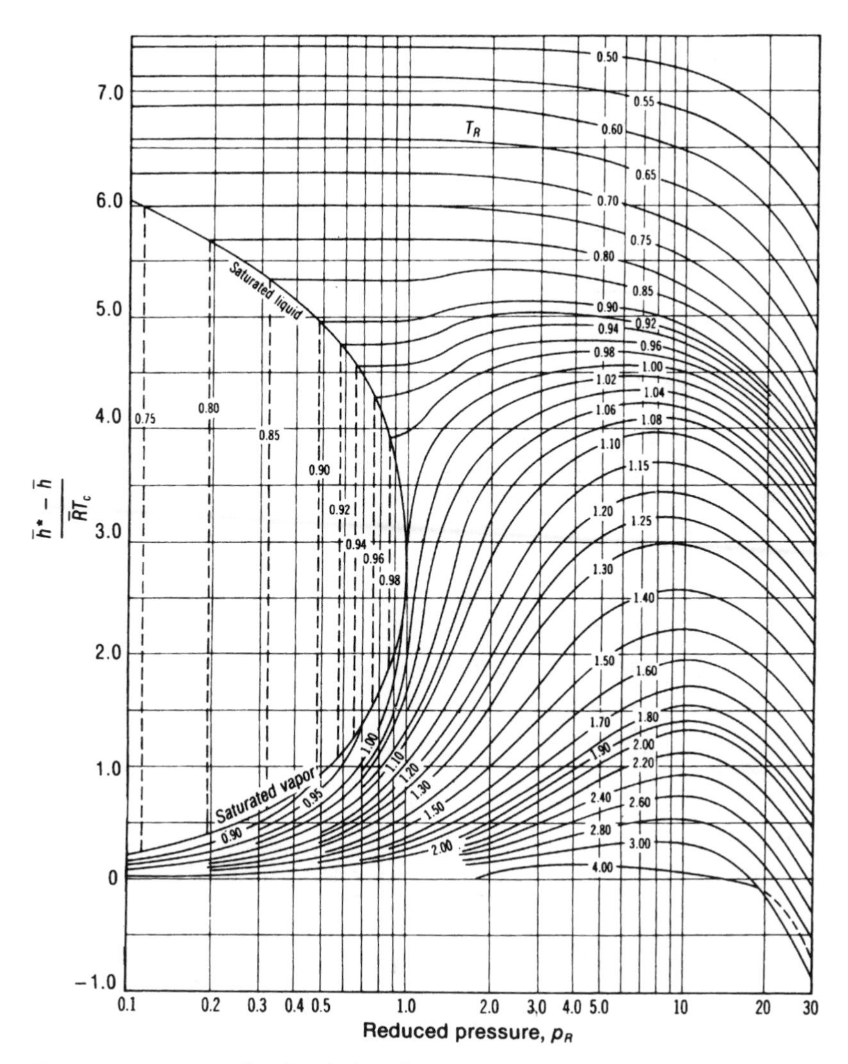

Figure 14.5 **Generalized enthalpy chart.**
(Source: G.J. Van Wylen and R.E. Sonntag, *Fundamentals of Classical Thermodynamics*, 3rd edn, Wiley, New York, 1986)

$$h^*(T_2, p_2) - h^*(T_1, p_1) = \int_{T_1}^{T_2} c_{p_0}\, dT \tag{14.41}$$

EXAMPLE 14.2

Water at 30.0 MPa is heated isobarically from 400 °C to 500 °C, by a reservoir at 500 °C. Select as a reference state saturated liquid water at 0 °C (same as in steam tables). Data for

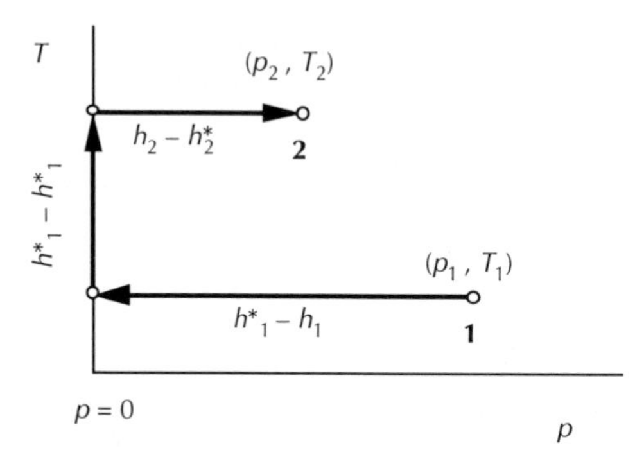

Figure 14.6 **Enthalpy calculation scheme.**

water: M = 18.016, T_c = 647.3 K, p_c = 22.09 MPa, v_c = 0.003153 m³/kg. The enthalpy of water vapor at 0 °C relative to the reference state is h_g(0 °C)= 2501.4 kJ/kg.

The specific heat of the vapor, at low pressures, is

$$\frac{c_{p_0}}{R} = 17.205 - 22.075\theta^{0.25} + 9.95270^{0.5} - 0.44488\theta$$

where $\theta = T/100$.

Find the specific enthalpy of the water at both states and the enthalpy difference, using:

a. The ideal gas assumption.
b. The generalized enthalpy chart.
c. Steam tables.

SOLUTION

a. The enthalpy of water relative to the reference state is calculated assuming the vapor to be an ideal gas:

$$h^* = h_{fg0} + \int_{T_0}^{T} c_p dT = h_{fg0} + 100R\int_{\theta_0}^{\theta} \frac{c_{p_0}}{R} d\theta$$

$$= 2501.4 + 100R[17.205(\theta - \theta_0) - 17.660(\theta^{1.25} - \theta_0^{1.25})$$

$$+ 6.6352(\theta^{1.5} - \theta_0^{1.5}) - 0.22244(\theta^2 - \theta_0^2)]$$

$$h_1^* = 3892.2 \text{ kJ/kg} \qquad h_2^* = 4102.2 \text{ kJ/kg}$$

b. For $p_r = p/p_c = 1.358$ we obtain from the enthalpy chart, Fig. 14.5:

State	T K	T/T_c	$(h^*-h)/RT_c$	$(h - h^*)$ kJ/kg	h kJ/kg
1	673.15	1.040	3.40	1015.4	2876.8
2	773.15	1.194	1.50	448.0	3654.2

c. From the steam tables h_1 = 2151.1 kJ/kg and h_2 = 3081.1 kJ/kg.

The results of the three methods are shown for comparison in the following table:

State	Specific enthalpy kJ/kg		
	Steam tables	Enthalpy chart	Ideal gas
1	2151.1	2876.8	3892.2
2	3081.1	3654.2	4102.2
$h_2 - h_1$	830.0	777.4	210.0

Note that enthalpy values obtained by using the generalized chart are not very accurate (relative to the values from the steam tables) but are substantially better than those of the ideal gas model. The enthalpy difference ($h_2 - h_1$), however, shows a much better approximation when the generalized charts are used.

14.9 Generalized entropy chart

A generalized entropy chart, which gives the difference between the entropy of a real substance and that of an ideal gas, can be derived from the generalized compressibility chart. The chart presents the deviation of entropy of a *generalized* substance from that of an ideal gas.

As the pressure approaches zero, $p \to 0$, every gas can be considered an ideal gas. At low pressures the ideal gas equations, which were developed in Chapter 5, are also applicable to real substances. Thus, for example, the entropy changes as $p \to 0$ may be calculated by

$$s_2^* - s_1^* = \int_{T_1}^{T_2} c_p \frac{dT}{T} - R \ln \frac{p_2}{p_1} \tag{14.42}$$

The only data required to evaluate the entropy of an ideal gas are the data on specific heat at low pressure as a function of temperature. These data are usually available, with good accuracy, from spectroscopic measurements.

Let us now compare the entropy of a real substance at (T, p) with the entropy of a corresponding ideal gas at the same temperature and pressure. By *corresponding* we mean the *coinciding* properties of the ideal gas with those of the real substance as the pressure approaches zero.

The change of entropy with pressure at constant temperature can be evaluated from the Maxwell relation, Eq. (13.27),

$$\left(\frac{\partial s}{\partial p}\right)_T = -\left(\frac{\partial v}{\partial T}\right)_p \tag{13.27}$$

in which the volume is replaced by $v = ZRT/p$. Hence,

$$ds = \left(\left[\frac{-\partial(ZRT/p)}{\partial T}\right]_p dp\right)_T \tag{14.43}$$

This equation can be rewritten as

$$-\frac{ds}{R}=\left[\left\{\left(T\frac{\partial Z}{\partial T}\right)_p+Z\right\}\frac{dp}{p}\right]_T \tag{14.44}$$

Equation (14.44) gives the change in entropy with pressure at a constant temperature for a real substance. For an ideal gas, where $Z = 1$, Eq. (14.44) simplifies to

$$-\frac{ds^*}{R}=\left[\frac{dp}{p}\right]_T \tag{14.45}$$

As $p\rightarrow 0$, real substances approach ideal gas behavior. To calculate the entropy deviation of a real substance from that of an ideal gas, we subtract Eq. (14.45) from Eq. (14.44) and integrate, along a constant-temperature line, from zero pressure to (T, p):

$$-\frac{s(T,p)-s^*(T,p)}{R}=\left[\int_0^p\left\{\left(T\frac{\partial Z}{\partial T}\right)_p+(Z-1)\right\}\frac{dp}{p}\right]_T \tag{14.46}$$

Equation (14.46) accounts for the deviation of the entropy of a real substance at (T, p) from that of an ideal gas at (T, p). It can also be rewritten in terms of reduced temperatures and pressures to yield

$$-\frac{s(T,p)-s^*(T,p)}{R}=\left[\int_0^p\left\{\left(T\frac{\partial Z}{\partial T}\right)_{p_r}+(Z-1)\right\}\frac{dp_r}{p_r}\right]_{T_r} \tag{14.47}$$

Equation (14.47) allows us to calculate the deviation of entropy of a real substance by using the generalized compressibility chart only. Figure 14.7 shows schematically a generalized entropy chart constructed on the basis of such calculations. A larger chart is given in Fig. A.4 in the Appendix.

Entropy change between any two states of a real substance can now be estimated even for substances for which the information is very sparse. Indeed, all that is needed are data on the critical temperature and critical pressure of the substance, as well as data on the specific heat at a pressure approaching zero. The calculation is performed according to the following scheme:

$$s_2-s_1=\left(s_1^*-s_1\right)-\left(s_2^*-s_2\right)+\left(s_2^*-s_1^*\right) \tag{14.48}$$

The first two terms in parentheses are found from the generalized entropy chart, while the last term is calculated from the appropriate equation for an ideal gas, Eq. (8.36).

The method of evaluation of the entropy change between two states is shown schematically in Fig. 14.8.

EXAMPLE 14.3

Water at 30.0 MPa is heated isobarically from 400 °C to 500 °C, by a reservoir at 500 °C. Select as a reference state saturated liquid water at 0 °C (same as in steam tables). Data for

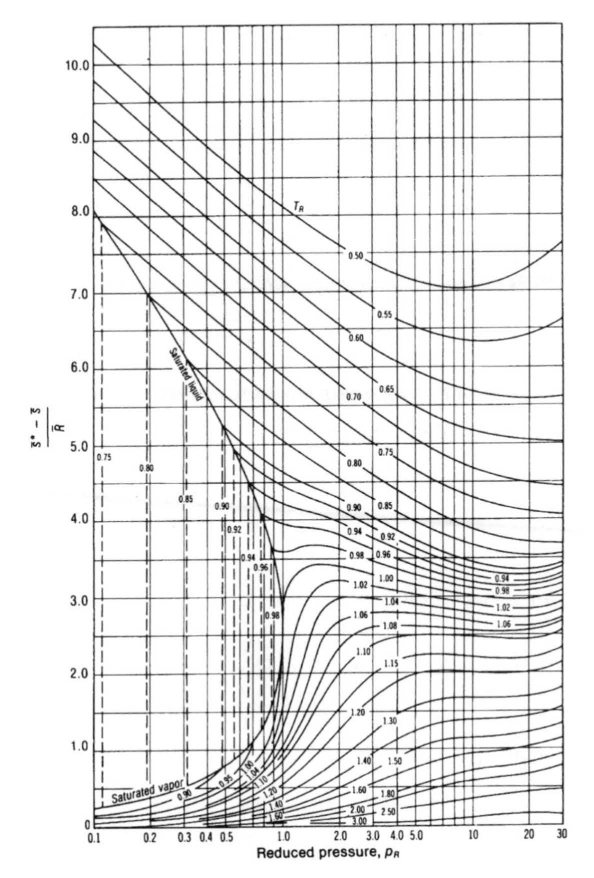

Figure 14.7 **Generalized entropy chart.**
(Source: G.J. Van Wylen and R.E. Sonntag, *Fundamentals of Classical Thermodynamics*, 3rd edn, Wiley, NewYork, 1986)

water: M = 18.016, T_c = 647.3 K, p_c = 22.09 MPa, v_c = 0,003153 m^3/kg. The entropy of water vapor at 0 °C relative to the reference state is s_g(0°C) = 9.1562 kJ/kg K.
The specific heat of the vapor, at low pressures, is

$$\frac{c_{p_0}}{R} = 17.205 - 22.075\theta^{0.25} + 9.95276\theta^{0.5} - 0.44488\theta$$

where $\theta = T/100$.

Find the specific entropy of the water at both states, using:

a. The ideal gas assumption.
b. The generalized enthalpy chart.
c. Steam tables.

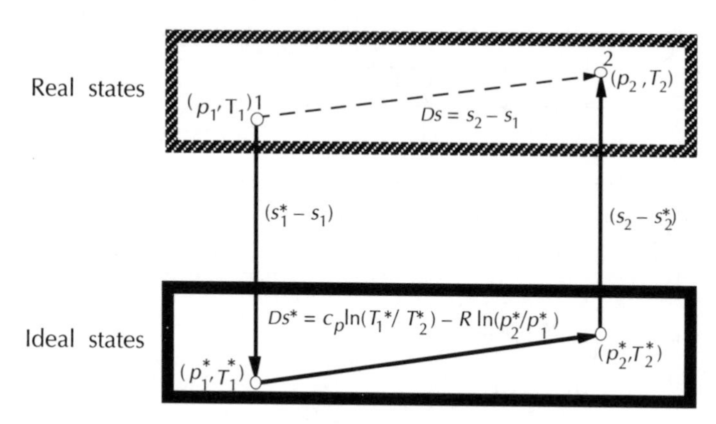

Figure 14.8 **Entropy calculation scheme.**

SOLUTION

a. Assuming the vapor is an ideal gas, its entropy relative to the reference state is

$$s^* = s_{g0}(0\ ^\circ\mathrm{C}) + \int_{T_0}^{T} \frac{c_p}{T} dT - R\ln\frac{p}{p_0} = s_{g0} + R\left[\int_{\theta_0}^{\theta} \frac{c_{p_0}}{R\theta} d\theta - \ln\frac{p}{p_0}\right]$$

$$= 9.1562 + R[17.2053(\ln\theta - \ln\theta_0) - 88.3009(\theta^{0.25} - \theta_0^{0.25})$$
$$+ 19.9055(\theta^{0.5} - \theta_0^{0.5}) - 0.44488(\theta - \theta_0) - (\ln p - \ln p_0)]$$

Thus: $s_1^* = 5.9128$ kJ/kg K and $s_2^* = 6.2036$ kJ/kg K.

b. For $p_r = p/p_c = 1.358$ we obtain from the entropy chart, Fig. 14.7:

State	T K	T/T_c	$(s^* - s)/R$	$(s - s^*)$ kJ/kg K	s kJ/kg K
1	673.15	1.040	2.75	−1.2691	4.6437
2	773.15	1.194	0.90	−0.4153	5.7883

c. From the steam tables: s_1 = 4.4728 kJ/kg K and s_2 = 5.7905 kJ/kg K.
The results of the three methods are shown for comparison in the following table:

State	Specific entropy kJ/kg K		
	Steam tables	Entropy chart	Ideal gas
1	4.4728	4.6437	5.9128
2	5.7905	5.7883	6.2036
$s_2 - s_1$	1.3177	1.1446	0.2906

Once again, the generalized chart gives a better approximation than the ideal gas model.

EXAMPLE 14.4

A pipe of 20 cm diameter carries butane at a rate of 100 kg/s from a refinery to the house of a customer. The butane enters the pipe at 175 °C and 7.5 MPa (state 1) and leaves it at 80 °C and 0.9 MPa (state 2). The environment is at 27 °C and 0.1 MPa. Use the generalized charts and find:

a. The entrance and exit velocities of the butane.
b. The heat interaction in the pipe.
c. The maximum power that can be obtained between the end states.
d. The rate of irreversibility of the process between the end states.

SOLUTION

The following data for butane are available: p_c = 3.8 MPa, T_c = 425 K, M = 58, c_{p0} = 2.09kJj/kg K. We arrange in a table the properties of butane at the end states:

State	p	T	p_r	T_r	Z	v	$\frac{h^*-h}{RT_c}$	$\frac{s^*-s}{R}$	h^*-h	s^*-s
	kPa	°C				$\frac{\text{m}^3}{\text{kmol}}$			$\frac{\text{kJ}}{\text{kmol}}$	$\frac{\text{kJ}}{\text{kmol K}}$
1	7.5	175	1.974	1.054	0.33	0.164	3.60	2.70	12720.9	22.4486
2	0.9	80	0.237	0.831	0.82	2.675	0.50	0.40	1776.8	3.3257

The specific volume in the table was found from $v = ZRT/p$.

a. The cross-sectional area of the pipe is

$$A = \pi r^2 = \pi \times 0.1^2 = 0.0314 \text{ m}^2$$

while the flowrate of butane in kmol/s is

$$\dot{n} = \frac{\dot{m}}{M} = \frac{100}{58} = 1.7241 \text{ kmol/s}$$

The entrance and exit velocities of the butane are, respectively,

$$\mathbf{v}_1 = \dot{n}\frac{v_1}{A} = 1.7241\frac{0.164}{0.0314} = 9.0 \text{ m/s}$$

$$\mathbf{v}_2 = \dot{n}\frac{v_2}{A} = 1.7241\frac{2.675}{0.0314} = 146.8 \text{ m/s}$$

b. The heat interaction is found from the first law for a control volume consisting of the pipe:

$$\dot{Q} = \dot{n}\left(h_2 - h_1 + \frac{\mathbf{v}_2^2 - \mathbf{v}_1^2}{2}\right)$$

where

$$h_2 - h_1 = h_2^* - h_1^* + \left(\frac{h_1^* - h_1}{RT_c} - \frac{h_2^* - h_2}{RT_c} \right) RT_c$$

$$= c_{p_0}(T_2 - T_1) + \left(\frac{h_1^* - h_1}{RT_c} - \frac{h_2^* - h_2}{RT_c} \right) RT_c$$

and

$$c_{p_0} = 1.75 \times 58 = 101.5 \text{ kJ/kmol}$$

Hence,

$$h_2 - h_1 = 101.5 \times (80 - 175) + (3.60 - 0.50) \times 8.3143 \times 425 = -1311.6 \text{kJ/kmol}$$

and

$$\dot{Q} = \dot{n} \left(h_2 - h_1 + \frac{\mathbf{v}_2^2 - \mathbf{v}_1^2}{2} \right)$$

$$= 1.7241 \times \left(-1311.6 + \frac{146.8^2 - 9.0^2}{2} \times \frac{58}{1000} \right) = 1.7241 \times (-695.79) = -1199.6 \text{ kW}$$

where the factor 58/1000 was used to convert the kinetic energy term from J/kg to kJ/kmol.

c. The maximum power that can be obtained between the end states is found from

$$\dot{W}_{x,max} = \sum \dot{n}_i b_i^0 = \dot{n} \left(h_2 - h_1 + \frac{\mathbf{v}_2^2 - \mathbf{v}_1^2}{2} - T_0(s_1 - s_2) \right)$$

where

$$s_2 - s_1 = c_{p_0} \ln \frac{T_2}{T_1} + R \left[-\ln \frac{p_2}{p_1} + \left(\frac{s_1^* - s_1}{R} - \frac{s_2^* - s_2}{R} \right) \right]$$

$$= 101.5 \ln \frac{353.15}{448.15} + 8.3143 \left(-\ln \frac{0.9}{7.5} + (2.70 - 0.40) \right) = 12.57 \text{ kJ/kmol K}$$

Hence,

$$\dot{W}_{x,max} = \dot{n} \left(h_2 - h_1 + \frac{\mathbf{v}_2^2 - \mathbf{v}_1^2}{2} - T_0(s_1 - s_2) \right)$$

$$= 1.7241 \times [-695.79 - 300.15 \times (-12.57)] = 5305.2 \text{ kW}$$

d. The rate of irreversibility of the process is

$$\dot{I} = \dot{W}_{x,max} - \dot{W}_x = \dot{W}_{x,max} = 5305.2 \text{ kW}$$

14.10 Fugacity

It is now appropriate to introduce a new property, the fugacity, that can also be represented by a generalized chart. The actual application of this property is postponed to later chapters, where the equilibrium of mixtures and chemical reactions is discussed. At this point the fugacity is defined, and it is shown how it can be evaluated by means of a generalized fugacity chart.

Consider the specific Gibbs free energy, which is defined as

$$g = h - Ts \tag{13.17}$$

The change of this property is

$$dg = dh - Tds - sdT = vdp - sdT \tag{14.49}$$

while the change at a constant temperature is

$$dg_T = vdp \tag{14.50}$$

or

$$dg_T = ZRTd \ln p \tag{14.51}$$

For an ideal gas, $Z = 1$, and therefore

$$dg_T^* = RTd\ln p \tag{14.52}$$

Fugacity is defined for any substance as a pseudo-pressure such that

$$dg_T = RTd \ln f \tag{14.53}$$

where, in general, $f = f(T, p)$.

Equation (14.53) defines only the differential of the fugacity. In order to complete the definition, a boundary condition is required. The latter is selected so that as the pressure approaches zero and the gas approaches ideal gas, the fugacity is equal to the pressure. The mathematical expression of this boundary condition is

$$\lim_{p \to 0} \left(\frac{f}{p} \right) = 1 \tag{14.54}$$

It follows from the above definition that the fugacity is equal to the pressure at very low pressures, while in general,

$$d \ln f = Zd \ln p \tag{14.55}$$

Subtracting $d\ln p$ from both sides of Eq. (14.55) yields

$$d \ln \left(\frac{f}{p} \right) = (Z - 1)d \ln p \tag{14.56}$$

or

$$d \ln \left(\frac{f}{p} \right) = (Z - 1)\, d \ln p = (Z - 1)\, d \ln p_r \tag{14.57}$$

Equation (14.57) can be integrated, along a constant-temperature line, from zero pressure to any pressure, p_r,

$$\ln\left(\frac{f}{p}\right) = \int_0^{p_r} \frac{(Z-1)}{p_r}\, dp_r \tag{14.58}$$

The integrand in Eq. (14.58) remains finite even at zero pressure. Equation (14.56) can be evaluated for any state (T, p) solely on the basis of data from the compressibility chart. Figure 14.9 shows a generalized fugacity chart.

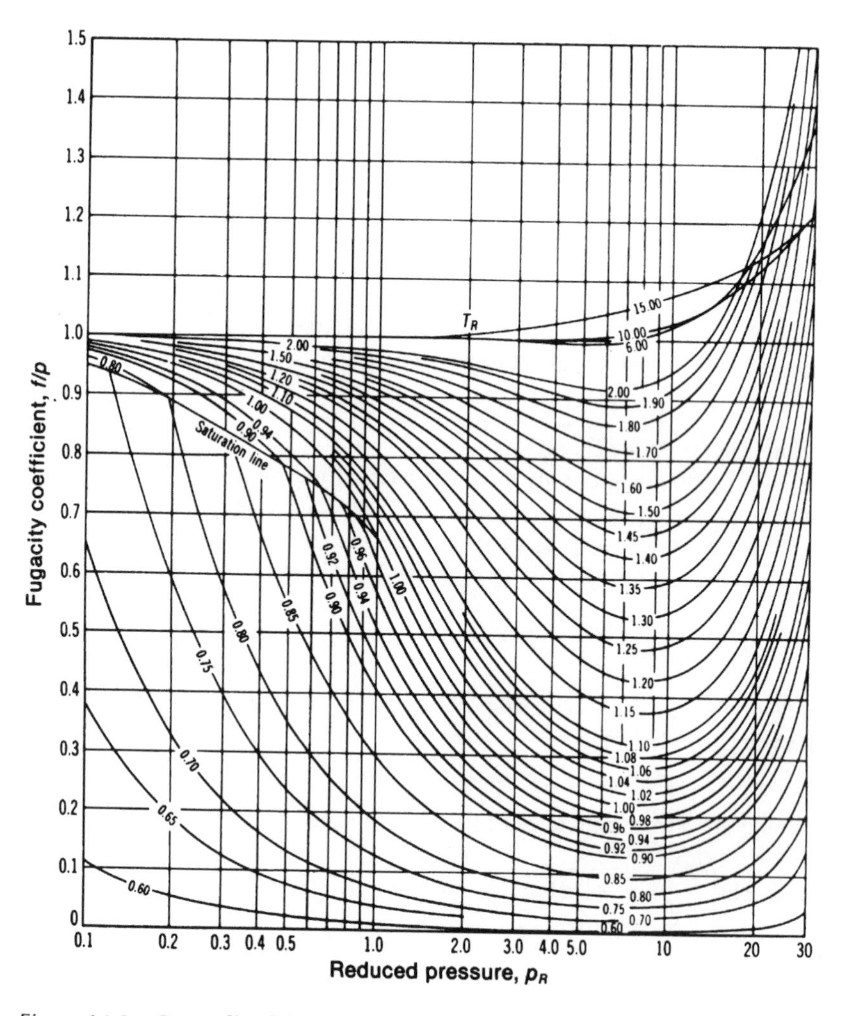

Figure 14.9 **Generalized fugacity chart.**
(Source: G.J. Van Wylen and R.E. Sonntag, *Fundamentals of Classical Thermodynamics*, 3rd edn, Wiley, NewYork, 1986)

EXAMPLE 14.5

Steam is compressed isothermally and reversibly at 400 °C from 5 MPa to 30 MPa. Find the work of compression per kilogram of steam, using:

a. The ideal gas assumption.
b. The generalized fugacity chart.
c. Steam tables.

SOLUTION

a. Assuming ideal gas, the work of compression is

$$W = -RT\ln\frac{p_2}{p_1} = -\frac{8.3143\times 673.15}{18.015}\ln\frac{30}{5} = -556.7 \text{ kJ/kg}$$

b. The work of a reversible isothermal process is

$$W = h_1 - h_2 - T(s_1 - s_2) = (\mu_1 - \mu_2)_T = -RT\ln\frac{f_2}{f_1} = -RT\left(\ln\frac{(f/p)_2}{(f/p)_1} + \ln\frac{p_2}{p_1}\right)$$

$$W = -RT\ln\frac{f_2}{f_1} = -\frac{8.3143\times 673.15}{18.015}\ln\frac{17.70}{4.85} = -402.2 \text{ kJ/kg}$$

State	p MPa	T °C	T/T_c	p/p_c	f/p	f
1	5.0	400	1.040	0.226	0.97	4.85
2	30.0	400	1.040	1.358	0.59	17.70

c. Using the steam tables, we find

State	p	h	s
1	5.0	3195.7	6.6459
2	30.0	2151.1	4.4728

and the work is

$$W = h_1 - h_2 - T(s_1 - s_2) = 1044.6 - 673.15\times 2.1731 = -418.2 \text{ kJ/kg}$$

We have shown again that the generalized charts are satisfactory for approximating properties in the absence of exact tables.

PROBLEMS

14.1 The following table is not complete. Fill in all the missing properties and their units by using the generalized charts. Select 0 °C, 100 kPa, as a reference state.

Compare the values for H_2O with values taken from the steam tables.

Property		H_2O	H_2O	H_2O	CH_4	CO_2
p	MPa	0.1	5	20	5	5
T	K	200	200	600	100	100
p_r						
T_r						
Z						
$(h^* - h)/RT_c$						
$(s^* - s)/R$						
h^*						
s^*						
f/p						
v						
h						
s						

14.2 A rigid container of volume $V = 0.24\ m^3$ contains propane at $p_1 = 10$ MPa and $T_1 = 400$ °C. The surroundings are at 27 °C and 0.1 MPa. Owing to damaged insulation the container cools down to a temperature of $T_2 = 60$ °C. Find:

a. The final pressure and quality of the propane.
b. The heat interaction with the surroundings.
c. The irreversibility of the process.

14.3 Ethane (C_2H_6) flows from a main pipeline at $T_0 = 40$ °C and $p_0 = 15$ MPa into an empty and well-insulated container of volume $V = 0.24\ m^3$. The flow stops when the pressures equalize. Calculate the final temperature of the ethane in the container:

a. Assuming ideal gas behavior.
b. Using the generalized chart.

14.4 Methane (CH_4) at $T_1 = 90$ °C and $p_1 = 20$ MPa is throttled through an adiabatic valve to a pressure of $p_2 = 3$ MPa. Calculate the final temperature.

14.5 The equation of state for hydrogen at high temperatures can be approximated by $p(v - b) = RT$, where $b = 0.0391\ m^3/kmol$.

Calculate the fugacity of hydrogen at $T = 1000$ °C and $p = 100$ MPa.

14.6 Estimate the melting temperature of ice at 300 MPa. Data for ice at 0.1 MPa: $T_{melt} = 0$ °C, $h_{sf} = 333.5$ kJ/kg, $s_{sf} = 1.2216$ kJ/kg K, $v_{sf} = -91 \times 10^{-6}\ m^3/kg$.

14.7 Find the first three virial coefficients in the volume expansion (Eq. 14.14) for a substance whose equation of state is given by the van der Waals equation.

14.8 One kg of CO_2 is compressed isothermally at 62 °C, in a cylinder–piston assembly, from 100 kPa to 12 MPa.

a. Determine the initial and final volumes.
b. Determine the heat and work interactions.

14.9 In a chemical plant benzene leaves a distillation column at a rate of 20 kg/s in a pipe 10 cm in diameter and enters a heat exchanger at 230 °C and 1.5 MPa (state 1). The benzene leaves the heat exchanger in a pipe 5 cm in diameter at 30 °C and 1.4 MPa (state 2). The environment is at 20 °C and 0.1 MPa. Use the generalized charts and:

a. Determine the entrance and exit velocities of the benzene.

b. Determine the heat interaction in the pipe.
c. Determine the maximum power that can be obtained between the end states.
d. Determine the rate of irreversibility of the process between the end states.

14.10 A van der Waals gas is a gas which obeys the following equation of state:

$$p = \frac{RT}{v-b} - \frac{a}{v^2}$$

where a and b are given constants.

a. Derive an expression for the internal energy of such a gas as a function of temperature and volume. Assume the specific heat at constant volume is constant.
b. One kg of such a gas is contained in an adiabatic chamber behind a partition, as shown in Fig. 14.10. The partition is broken, and the gas undergoes a free expansion till it comes to equilibrium in the total volume. (See sketch.) Find the final temperature in terms of T_1, V_1, V_2.

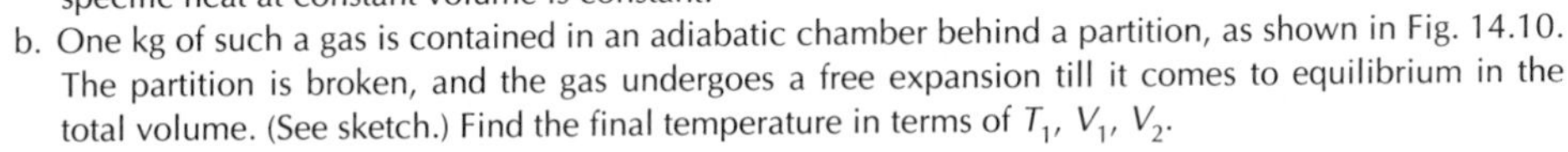

Figure 14.10

14.11 The pressure on 100 g of water is increased reversibly and isothermally at 0 °C from 1 bar to 680 bars.

a. What is the work interaction?
b. What is the heat transfer?
c. Calculate the change in internal energy using the following data: $\kappa_T = 4.8 \times 10^{-5}\ \text{bar}^{-1}$, $\beta = 3.2 \times 10^{-5}\ \text{K}^{-1}$, $c_p = 4.1\ \text{kJ/kg K}$, $\rho = 1025.5\ \text{kg/m}$.

14.12 It can be shown that steam may be assumed to behave as an ideal gas for pressures below 200 kPa. For higher pressures the deviation becomes larger.

Consider the steam tables, p and T data for saturated vapor at 1, 5, and 10 MPa and compare the specific volumes from the tables with values calculated by:

a. Using the ideal gas equation of state.
b. Using the law of corresponding states.

14.13 The critical constants for hydrogen sulfide, H_2S, are given as

M	T_c (K)	p_c (MPa)	v_c (m^3/kmol)	r_c
34.982	373.7	8.97	0.098	0.284

Calculate the volume of 1 kmol of hydrogen sulfide at 450 K and 20 MPa.

a. Assuming ideal gas behavior.
b. Using the rule of corresponding states.

14.14 The specific volume of CO_2 at 60 °C is given as a function of pressure in the following table:

p	bar	13.22	35.97	54.45	75.83	86.52
v	m^3/kg	2.000	0.667	0.400	0.250	0.200

a. Calculate the fugacity of CO_2 at 60 °C for the range of pressures 0 to 90 bar.
b. Plot a diagram of f/p vs p.

14.15 Assume that the density of liquid water is constant and water vapor follows the Bertolet equation of state

$$Z = 1 + \frac{9}{128}\frac{p_r}{T_r}\left(1 - \frac{6}{T_r^2}\right)$$

Data for water: $M = 18.02$ kg/kmol, $p_c = 22.02$ MPa, $T_c = 647.2$ K, $p_{sat}(120\ ^\circ\mathrm{C}) = 0.196$ MPa.
Estimate the fugacity of water at 120 °C for the following states:

a. Saturated vapor.
b. Saturated liquid.
c. Compressed liquid at 5.0 MPa.

14.16 Calculate the virial coefficient of gaseous butene (C_4H_8) at 242.2 K on the basis of the following data:

The vapor pressure at 242.2 K is 31.85 kPa.
The rate of change of saturation pressure with temperature is $dp/dT = 1.688$ kPa/K
The molar volume of the liquid is 0.086 m³/kmol
The evaporation enthalpy is given as a function of temperature by:
$h_{fg} = 1575.2 + 107.48\theta + 86.75\theta^2$, where $\theta = T/100$.

14.17 The composition of the atmosphere in a deep coal mine is N_2 79%, O_2 20%, and CO_2 1%. The conditions in the mine are 120 kPa, 40 °C . A forklift is operated by means of a 40 L cylinder of compressed nitrogen at 20.0 MPa, 40 °C.

Assume real gas behavior and use compressibility charts.

a. Determine the final equilibrium state of the nitrogen.
b. Find the maximum work that may be obtained from one cylinder of nitrogen.

14.18 CO_2 is compressed isothermally and reversibly from 0.1 MPa, 62 °C, to 11.1 MPa.

a. Estimate the change in specific volume.
b. Estimate the change in specific enthalpy.

14.19 A cylinder and piston assembly contain 1.2 kg of ethylene (C_2H_4) at 10MPa, 50 °C. The system is heated at a constant pressure till its volume doubles by a single reservoir at the lowest possible temperature. The environment is at 25 °C, 0.1 MPa.

Data for ethylene: $M = 28.05$ kg/kmol, $p_c = 5.12$ MPa, $T_c = 282.4$ K, $c_p = 5.74R$.

a. Find the temperature of the initial volume of the ethylene.
b. Find the final temperature of the ethylene.
c. Determine the heat and work interactions of the system.
d. Determine the irreversibility of the process.

14.20 The pressure of a certain gas (photon gas) is a function of its temperature only and is given by $p(T) = \frac{1}{3}U/V$ where U is the energy and V is the volume. A cylinder covered by a piston containing 1 kmol of this gas undergoes a Carnot cycle between the pressures p_1 and p_2.

a. Find expressions for the work of each process of the cycle.
b. Describe the process, schematically, on T–s and p–v diagrams.
c. Express the efficiency of the cycle as a function of the pressures.
d. Find the functional relationship between the pressure and the temperature.

14.21 The table of critical constants for carbon dioxide, CO_2, is

M	T_c (K)	p_c (MPa)	v_c (m³/kmol)
44.011	304.20	72.90	94

a. Assume ideal gas behavior and calculate the volume occupied by 1 kmol of carbon dioxide at 70 °C and 7.5 MPa.
b. Using the compressibility factor equation of state, calculate the volume of 1 kmol of carbon dioxide at 70 °C and 7.5 MPa.

14.22 The critical constants for hydrogen sulfide, H_2S, are given as

M	T_c (K)	p_c (MPa)	v_c (m^3/kmol)	Z_c
34.082	373.7	8.97	0.098	0.284

a. Assume ideal gas behavior and calculate the volume occupied by 1 kmol of hydrogen sulfide at 450 K and 20 MPa.
b. Using the rule of corresponding states calculate the volume of 1 kmol of hydrogen sulfide at 450 K and 20 MPa.

14.23 You are given the following relationship between enthalpy, entropy, and pressure for a pure substance:

$$H = Ap^{2/7}e^{2S/7R} + Bp + C$$

where A, B, and C are constants.
Find the equation of state for the substance (relationship between p, v and T).

14.24 For an ideal gas the expression for entropy may be stated as

$$s = c \ln T - R \ln p + s_0$$

where c, R, and s_0 are constants.
On the other hand, this equation may also be satisfied by gases that are not ideal.

a. State all that the equation implies regarding the specific heat at constant pressure. Prove that your answer is valid even if pv/RT is not unity.
b. Sketch on a T–v diagram lines of constant pressure for a gas which satisfies the expression for entropy. Are these lines curved or straight? In what way could this set of lines differ from that of an ideal gas?
c. Write the most general form of the equation of state, $f[p, v, T] = 0$, that will satisfy the expression for entropy. The perfect gas should be a special case of your general form. Show your general form on a $pv/RT - p$ chart.

14.25 The volume, pressure, and temperature at the critical point can be related to the constants a, b, and R of the Dieterici equation by noting that at the critical point the critical isotherm passes through that point, its slope is zero, and it is a deflection point. Express the constants a, b, and R in terms of the critical volume, pressure, and temperature.

14.26 Nitrogen is throttled adiabatically from 40 MPa, 40 °C, to 0.1 MPa. Note that at high pressures, nitrogen does not behave like an ideal gas. Estimate the temperature of nitrogen after it was throttled.

CHAPTER FIFTEEN

Multicomponent systems

In the previous chapters we have dealt with systems consisting essentially of pure substances. Property tables or equations were developed for these substances. In many practical situations, however, we encounter substances which are not pure or whose composition may change during the process. For example, in the process of making tea we dissolve sugar in hot water, thus changing the sugar concentration in the water. Obviously, the properties of sugared water depend on the sugar content of the solution. It is possible to have an infinite number of different compositions of the sugar–water mixture. Although the properties of any given composition can be measured and tabulated, it is impractical to do so for all the possible compositions.

In this chapter we show how the thermodynamic properties of a multicomponent system can be described in terms of the properties of the individual components. We also analyze processes that involve changes in the composition of the system.

15.1 Intensive state

In Chapter 4 we defined the intensive state of a pure substance. The same definition also applies to a system that consists of a substance that is not pure. We repeat here the definition of the intensive state:

The intensive state of a system is defined by the collection of all its intensive properties.

An intensive state is definable at any point in the system. It is obvious that a set of the independent intensive properties is sufficient to describe, uniquely, the intensive state.

If each point throughout the system has the same intensive state the system is called a homogeneous system. If, on the other hand, there are different intensive states at different points of the system then it is called a non-homogeneous or heterogeneous system.

15.2 Phase

A phase is a collection of all parts of the system that have the same intensive state.

Again the definition is the same as the one given in Chapter 4. It applies, however, to any system regardless of whether it consists of a pure substance or not. A system, whether in equilibrium or not, may have any number of phases, from one to infinity. The variations in properties between phases may be either discontinuous or continuous. When the variation of the intensive state between neighboring phases is discontinuous, we refer to the discontinuity as the phase boundary. For example, liquid water and ice may form two phases of H_2O with a discontinuous boundary, which may coexist even in equilibrium. Alternatively, the difference in the intensive state between adjacent phases may only be infinitesimal, i.e. the intensive state may vary continuously in a given region of the system. Consider for example air in a gravitational field. In that system there is a continuous change with height in the pressure, the density, and the concentration of nitrogen and oxygen. In this case the system may be considered as made up of an infinite number of phases, each phase being an infinitesimal horizontal slice of the system.

A phase may change its properties with time and still be considered to be the same phase, provided of course that the intensive state is uniform at any instant of time and the variations are continuous with time. Changes in the pressure, the temperature, the composition, and even the extent of the phase are allowed. This is similar to the definition of any system whose properties may change during a process and still be considered the same system. Consider for example a phase of liquid water. The pressure, the temperature, and even the quantity of liquid water may be changed during a process, yet it may be considered as the same phase whose properties have changed. Analogously, a person is considered the same person through the years, even though changes take place in that person's body as time goes on. The changes must, however, be traceable in time so as to maintain the identity of the person.

A phase that does not exchange matter with its environment is called a *closed phase*; one that does is called an *open phase*. An example of an open phase is the vapor in an evaporation process. The vapor constitutes an open phase because its quantity changes during evaporation. Another example is that of a mixture of salt and water where the concentration of the salt in the solution may be increased by dissolving more salt in it, or alternatively, decreased by evaporating some of the water. Of course, the solution can only be considered the same phase so long as all its intensive properties are uniform throughout.

15.3 Components of a phase

A *pure phase* is defined as a phase composed of a pure substance, usually a specific chemical compound. For example, a phase composed of pure H_2O is a pure phase. The properties of various chemical compounds are obtained from experimental data and are presented in tables, diagrams, or empirical equations. There are hundreds of thousands of different chemical compounds known to man and the task of documenting their properties is quite formidable.

A phase, composed of different chemical compounds, is called a *mixed* or *multicomponent phase*. Sometimes a mixed phase may be considered a pure phase, provided the proportions between its chemical compounds are the same for all possible changes taking place in the phase. For example, a phase made of air, which consists of fixed proportions of nitrogen, oxygen, and other gases, may be considered a pure phase if its composition remains the same for the process under consideration. Properties of a given mixture of chemical compounds may also be obtained experimentally and tabulated. Standard air is an example of such a mixture. Each combination of different compounds is actually a different substance. Therefore, the number of possible "mixed" pure substances is infinite. There is no hope of obtaining sufficient experimental data to document all possible multicomponent substances. Methods of describing the properties of a multicomponent phase, in relation to the properties of its individual chemical components, are the subject of the study of mixtures and solutions. A component of a phase can be any specific chemical compound or any combination thereof. For example, components of a phase could be N_2, CO_2, NaCl or even (80% N_2 + 20% O_2). In Chapter 12, while studying moist air, we considered dry air as one component of a fixed composition of nitrogen and oxygen, and water vapor as the other component. We could not consider the combination of air and water vapor as a single component because we were considering situations where variations in the relative amounts of the two components were important.

The number of moles of each component in the multicomponent phase is denoted by n_i and its mass by m_i. Obviously, there is a fixed relationship between the two,

$$m_i = M_i n_i \tag{15.1}$$

where M_i is the molecular weight of the component.

For example, consider a phase that is made up of 20 moles of O_2, 20 moles of N_2, and 60 moles of air (assume 80% N_2 + 20% O_2). We might consider it as having three components but in this case the proportions between the components are not unique. There is a large number of ways to describe the proportions between the three components for the same composition of the phase. A few of these ways are shown in the following table:

O_2	N_2	Air	Total
20	20	60	100
16	4	80	100
28	52	20	100

The three components are not considered, in this case, to be independent.

Note that we can describe the composition of the phase by only two components, say O_2 and N_2. In this case the description is unique (in our example the proportions are 32 and 68, respectively). Of course we could select another combination of two components such as O_2 and air or N_2 and air. In any of these cases the proportions will be unique. We say therefore that the phase has two independent components:

O_2	N_2	Air	Total
32	20		100
15		85	100
	−60	160	100

Note that if one of the selected components is a mixture of two, or more, pure substances then a negative number of moles may be found.
We define an independent component of a phase as

> *An independent component of a phase is one of a minimal set of pure substances, wherein all the possible compositions of the phase can be constructed by different combinations of the substances.*

The independent component of a phase can be determined only after one knows the range of compositions that the phase may have. Different applications may result in different selections of the number of independent components. Many texts do not distinguish clearly between the concept of a *component* and that of an *independent component.* Usually, this does not lead to confusion. In this book we shall often use the term component to denote an independent component. Let n be the total number of moles of all the components in the phase and let m be its total mass (extensive properties),

$$n = \sum_{i=1}^{c} n_i \qquad m = \sum_{i=1}^{c} m_i \tag{15.2}$$

and let the mole and mass fractions of component i (intensive properties) be defined, respectively, as

$$x_i = n_i / n \qquad \underline{m}_i = m_i / m \tag{15.3}$$

Obviously, it follows from Eqs (15.2) and (15.3) that

$$\sum_{i=1}^{c} x_i = 1 \qquad \sum_{i=1}^{c} \underline{m}_i = 1 \tag{15.4}$$

Let us now examine the question of the number of independent properties of a phase. Only equilibrium states are considered, since otherwise there could be any number of independent properties, depending on the deviation from equilibrium. The state principle, introduced in Chapter 4, leads to the conclusion that every closed simple system has exactly two independent properties. Furthermore, for simple compressible systems, it *guarantees* that V and U, the volume and the energy, are always independent. This conclusion is correct for any closed system. If, however, the quantities of each of the c (independent) components may be arbitrarily changed, then there are a total of $2 + c$ properties that may be independently changed. Thus an open phase with c components has $2 + c$ independent properties.

We can express any extensive property, Π (e.g. V, U, H, S, A, G, etc.), as a function of the independent properties of the system

$$\Pi = \Pi(V, U, n_1, n_2, ..., n_c) \tag{15.5a}$$

Other properties may also be selected instead of V and U, for example

$$\Pi = \Pi(p, T, n_1, n_2, ..., n_c) \tag{15.5b}$$

Since a phase is uniform in its intensive state it is possible to select a set of independent properties all of which can be intensive properties, except the one that describes the extent of the phase. It is convenient to select the temperature, pressure, and the mole fractions of the components as the independent intensive properties of the phase, and the total number of moles, n, as the extensive property necessary to describe the phase. Equation (15.2) may be written in terms of the mole fractions, x_i, as

$$\Pi = \Pi(p, T, x_1, x_2, ..., x_{c-1}, n) \tag{15.6}$$

Note that in Eq. (15.6) there are only $c-1$ independent mole fractions since $\sum x_i = 1$. The molar specific properties of the phase may be defined by

$$\bar{\pi} = \Pi / n \tag{15.7}$$

The specific property $\bar{\pi}$ is an intensive property and thus is a function of the independent intensive properties only:

$$\bar{\pi} = \bar{\pi}(p, T, x_1, x_2, \ldots, x_{c-1}) \tag{15.8}$$

The equivalent of Eq. (15.5) in terms of mass is

$$\Pi = \Pi(p, T, m_1, m_2, ..., m_c) \tag{15.9}$$

while the equivalent of Eq. (15.8) in terms of mass fractions, $\underline{m}_i$, is

$$\bar{\pi} = \bar{\pi}(p, T, \underline{m}_1, \underline{m}_2, \ldots, \underline{m}_{c-1}) \tag{15.10}$$

15.4 Partial properties

It is easy to define an intensive property for a pure phase as the relevant extensive property per unit mass, or per mole. Indeed, we have already used such properties as specific volume, specific energy, specific enthalpy, etc. There is no problem in defining similar properties for a multicomponent phase taken as a whole.

It is not, however, obvious how to assign properties to the individual components in a multicomponent phase. What is the volume, or the energy, of the sugar in a cup of tea? What is the volume, or the enthalpy, of the alcohol in a bottle of wine? In this section we define new properties, called *partial properties*, for the individual components in a multicomponent phase.

The *partial molal property* for component i in a multicomponent phase, corresponding to the extensive property Π, is denoted by $\bar{\pi}_i$ and defined as

$$\bar{\pi}_i = \left(\frac{\partial \Pi}{\partial n_i} \right)_{p,T,nj} \tag{15.11}$$

where the index n_j denotes the number of moles of each of the other components $j (j \neq i)$ that is kept constant during differentiation.

The interpretation of the partial property is as follows. If one adds a small (differential) quantity, dn_i, to a large phase, while keeping the pressure, temperature, and quantities of all the other components fixed, then the change in property Π, per mole of component i added, is the partial molal property of Π. For example, if the property Π is interpreted as the volume, $\Pi = V$, then the partial molal volume $\bar{v}_i$ means the change in the volume of the phase caused by adding to the phase 1 mole of component i while keeping the temperature, pressure, and quantities of all the other components in the phase constant.

The partial molal property does not indicate directly a property of the component within the phase, but only the change in the corresponding extensive property caused by a small addition of that component. Thus, a phase may be completely devoid of component i at a given state, yet its partial molal volume, $\bar{v}_i$, need not be zero. Indeed, $\bar{v}_i$ gives the change of the volume of the phase related to the addition of 1 mole of component i.

It can easily be seen that for a pure phase, i.e. for a phase consisting of one component only, the partial property is simply the corresponding specific property. For a pure phase the partial volume is exactly the same as the specific volume.

The partial property may also be defined in terms of mass. Thus

$$\pi_i = \left(\frac{\partial \Pi}{\partial m_i}\right)_{p,T,mj} \tag{15.12}$$

When the extensive property is differentiated with respect to the number of moles, the result is a partial molal property. Differentiation with respect to the mass results in a partial mass property. There is a definite relationship between these two quantities, namely the ratio of the latter to the former is exactly equal to the molecular weight of the component:

$$\bar{\pi}_i = M_i \pi_i \tag{15.13}$$

In most cases there is no need to use different notations for the two quantities. No confusion results if care is taken to maintain the equations dimensionally homogeneous. Therefore, in this book we shall not use different notations, unless required for clarity. Hence, from now on the bars denoting molal quantities will be omitted.

A common way to describe a multicomponent open phase is by giving its extensive properties as a function of temperature, pressure, and mole fractions of each component. Equation (15.5) is such an expression with regard to some general extensive property Π. Differentiating that equation with respect to all its variables we obtain an equation for the differential of the extensive property Π:

$$d\Pi = \left(\frac{\partial \Pi}{\partial T}\right)_{p,n} dT + \left(\frac{\partial \Pi}{\partial p}\right)_{T,n} dp + \sum_{i=1}^{c} \left(\frac{\partial \Pi}{\partial n_i}\right)_{p,T,nj} dn_i \tag{15.14}$$

The corresponding equation in terms of mass is

$$d\Pi = \left(\frac{\partial \Pi}{\partial T}\right)_{p,m} dT + \left(\frac{\partial \Pi}{\partial p}\right)_{T,m} dp + \sum_{i=1}^{c} \left(\frac{\partial \Pi}{\partial m_i}\right)_{p,T,mj} dm_i \tag{15.15}$$

Equations (15.14) and (15.15) may be rewritten, in terms of partial properties, as

$$d\Pi = \left(\frac{\partial \Pi}{\partial T}\right)_{p,n} dT + \left(\frac{\partial \Pi}{\partial p}\right)_{T,n} dp + \sum_{i=1}^{c} \bar{\pi}_i dn_i \tag{15.16}$$

and

$$d\Pi = \left(\frac{\partial \Pi}{\partial T}\right)_{p,m} dT + \left(\frac{\partial \Pi}{\partial p}\right)_{T,m} dp + \sum_{i=1}^{c} \pi_i dm_i \tag{15.17}$$

Examples for specific interpretations of Eq. (15.16) are

for volume: $\Pi = V$; $\pi_i = v_i$;

$$dV = \left(\frac{\partial V}{\partial T}\right)_{p,n} dT + \left(\frac{\partial V}{\partial p}\right)_{T,n} dp + \sum_{i=1}^{c} \bar{v}_i dn_i \tag{15.18}$$

for energy: $\Pi = U$; $\pi_i = u_i$;

$$dU = \left(\frac{\partial U}{\partial T}\right)_{p,n} dT + \left(\frac{\partial U}{\partial p}\right)_{T,n} dp + \sum_{i=1}^{c} \bar{u}_i dn_i \tag{15.19}$$

and for the Gibbs free energy: $\Pi = G$; $\pi_i = g_i$;

$$dG = \left(\frac{\partial G}{\partial T}\right)_{p,n} dT + \left(\frac{\partial G}{\partial p}\right)_{T,n} dp + \sum_{i=1}^{c} \bar{g}_i dn_i \tag{15.20}$$

Relationships between partial properties are similar to those between the corresponding specific properties. For example, the relationship between the partial enthalpy and the partial energy is

$$h_i = u_i + pv_i \tag{15.21}$$

as can be easily shown from the definitions of the individual terms:

$$h_i = \left(\frac{\partial H}{\partial n_i}\right)_{p,T,nj} = \left[\frac{\partial (U + pV)}{\partial n_i}\right]_{p,T,nj} = u_i + pv_i$$

Similarly

$$a_i = u_i - Ts_i \tag{15.22}$$

and

$$g_i = h_i - Ts_i \tag{15.23}$$

More insight into the role of partial properties can be gained by considering a phase at T, p and n_i ($i = 1, ..., c$). The intensive state of the phase is defined by T, p, and x_i, where $i = 1, ..., c{-}1$. Consider a process where the size of the phase changes while the intensive state remains fixed. Such a process may be carried out by adding to the phase matter with the same composition as that of the phase, at constant T and p. During this process all the intensive properties of the phase except its extent are fixed. A parameter that describes the extent of the phase is the total number of moles, n. If we start with an infinitesimal phase and add to it small quantities having the same intensive state, we can find the final property Π of the phase by integrating Eq. (15.14). In this case $dp = 0$, $dT = 0$, $dx_i = 0$, and the change in the amount of each component is $dn_i = x_i dn$.

$$\Pi = \int_0^n \sum_{i=1}^{c} \pi_i dn_i = \int_0^n \sum_{i=1}^{c} (\pi_i x_i)k \tag{15.24}$$

But, since the intensive state does not change, all the intensive properties are constant during this process, and so is the product $\pi_i x_i$. Integration of Eq. (15.24) is therefore quite simple and yields

$$\Pi = \sum_{i=1}^{c} (\pi_i x_i) n = \sum_{i=1}^{c} \pi_i n_i \tag{15.25}$$

Equation (15.25) gives the value of property Π in the final state of the phase. Since Π is a property, its value depends only on the state and does not depend on the process by which the state of the phase was reached. Any extensive property Π of a phase may be expressed over all the components as a sum of their partial properties weighted by the number of moles. Therefore, Eq. (15.25) is a general expression for Π. It also provides an interpretation of the concept of a partial property, as follows:

The contribution of a component of a phase to an extensive property is equal to the product of the corresponding partial property and the number of moles of the component.

The specific property $\bar{\pi} = \Pi / n$ for the phase is in general

$$\bar{\pi} = \Pi / n = \sum_{i=1}^{n} x_i \bar{\pi}_i \tag{15.26}$$

Some examples of Eqs (15.25)–(15.26) are

$$V = \sum_{i=1}^{n} n_i \bar{v}_i \qquad \bar{v} = V/n = \sum_{i=1}^{n} x_i \bar{v}_i \tag{15.27a}$$

$$H = \sum_{i=1}^{n} n_i \bar{h}_i \qquad \bar{h} = H/n = \sum_{i=1}^{n} x_i \bar{h}_i \tag{15.27b}$$

$$S = \sum_{i=1}^{n} n_i \bar{s}_i \qquad \bar{s} = S/n = \sum_{i=1}^{n} x_i \bar{s}_i \tag{15.27c}$$

$$G = \sum_{i=1}^{n} n_i \bar{g}_i \qquad \bar{g} = G/n = \sum_{i=1}^{n} x_i \bar{g}_i \tag{15.27d}$$

etc.

EXAMPLE 15.1

The following table lists the partial volumes of water (H_2O), v_1, and ethanol (C_2H_5OH), v_2, as a function of mole fraction of ethanol, x_2, in a binary phase of ethanol and water at 20 °C and 1.0 bar.

x_2	0.1	0.2	0.4	0.6
$v_1(\text{cm}^3/\text{kmol})$	18110	17670	17010	16210
$v_2(\text{cm}^3/\text{kmol})$	53100	55400	57100	57870

Find the volume of a phase comprised of 50 g of water and 50 g of ethanol.

SOLUTION

The molecular weight of water is $M_1 = 18$, and that of ethanol is $M_2 = 46$. The mole fraction of ethanol in a 50 g H_2O–50 g C_2H_5OH solution is

$$x_2 = \frac{n_2}{n_1 + n_2} = \frac{m_2/M_2}{m_1/M_1 + m_2/M_2} = \frac{50/46}{50/18 + 50/46} = 0.2812$$

Interpolation from the table yields

$v_1 = 17402$ cm³/kmol

$v_2 = 56090$ cm³/kmol

The volume of the phase is found from Eq. (15.25):

$$V = v_1 n_1 + v_2 n_2 = \left(\frac{50}{18} \times 17402 + \frac{50}{46} \times 56090\right) \times 10^{-3} = 109.3 \text{ cm}^3$$

15.5 Gibbs equation

In this section we extend the energy equations for closed systems to phases where the composition may change. For a closed system in equilibrium, the energy-related functions can be expressed in terms of the relevant independent properties as

$$U = U(S,V) \qquad dU = TdS - pdV \tag{15.28a}$$

$$H = H(S,p) \qquad dH = TdS + Vdp \tag{15.28b}$$

$$A = A(T,V) \qquad dA = -SdT - pdV \tag{15.28c}$$

$$G = G(T,V) \qquad dG = -SdT + Vdp \tag{15.28d}$$

In a multicomponent phase there are $c + 2$ independent properties, and therefore the energy-related functions are

$$U = U(S,V,n_1,n_2,\ldots,n_c) \tag{15.29}$$

$$H = H(S, p, n_1, n_2, \ldots, n_c) \tag{15.30}$$

$$A = A(T, V, n_1, n_2, \ldots, n_c) \tag{15.31}$$

$$G = G(T, p, n_1, n_2, \ldots, n_c) \tag{15.32}$$

Equations (15.29)–(15.32) apply to all systems, whether of fixed or variable composition, and are different representations of the energy-related functions. They can be related to each other by

$$\begin{aligned} H &= U + pV \\ A &= U - TS \\ G &= H - TS \end{aligned} \tag{15.33}$$

Consider now changes in the energy-related functions, which can be calculated by differentiating Eqs (15.29)–(15.32):

$$dU = \left(\frac{\partial U}{\partial S}\right)_{V,n} dS + \left(\frac{\partial U}{\partial V}\right)_{S,n} dV + \sum_{i=1}^{c} \left(\frac{\partial U}{\partial n_i}\right)_{S,V,n_j} dn_i \tag{15.34}$$

$$dH = \left(\frac{\partial H}{\partial S}\right)_{p,n} dS + \left(\frac{\partial H}{\partial p}\right)_{S,n} dp + \sum_{i=1}^{c} \left(\frac{\partial H}{\partial n_i}\right)_{p,S,n_j} dn_i \tag{15.35}$$

$$dA = \left(\frac{\partial A}{\partial T}\right)_{V,n} dT + \left(\frac{\partial A}{\partial V}\right)_{T,n} dV + \sum_{i=1}^{c} \left(\frac{\partial A}{\partial n_i}\right)_{V,T,n_j} dn_i \tag{15.36}$$

$$dG = \left(\frac{\partial G}{\partial T}\right)_{p,n} dT + \left(\frac{\partial G}{\partial p}\right)_{T,n} dp + \sum_{i=1}^{c} \left(\frac{\partial G}{\partial n_i}\right)_{p,T,n_j} dn_i \tag{15.37}$$

These equations express the changes in the energy-related functions of an open phase in terms of the changes of its independent properties. The partial derivatives in these equations are thermodynamic properties. We now express these derivatives in terms of more familiar properties.

The partial derivatives in Eqs (15.34)–(15.37) can be expressed in terms of other properties by using the appropriate Maxwell relations. At this point it should be stressed that the Maxwell relations, which were developed in Chapter 13 for a closed system of a pure substance, are also applicable to a multicomponent open system, provided the derivatives are calculated while the composition of the system is fixed. This fact is emphasized by adding the subscript n to the list of parameters that are kept constant. Thus, Eqs (13.20)–(13.23) are modified to

$$T = \left(\frac{\partial U}{\partial S}\right)_{V,n} = \left(\frac{\partial H}{\partial S}\right)_{p,n} = \left(\frac{\partial u}{\partial s}\right)_{v,n} = \left(\frac{\partial h}{\partial s}\right)_{p,n} \tag{15.38}$$

$$p = -\left(\frac{\partial U}{\partial V}\right)_{S,n} = -\left(\frac{\partial A}{\partial V}\right)_{T,n} = -\left(\frac{\partial u}{\partial v}\right)_{s,n} = -\left(\frac{\partial a}{\partial v}\right)_{T,n} \tag{15.39}$$

$$V = \left(\frac{\partial G}{\partial p}\right)_{T,n} = \left(\frac{\partial H}{\partial p}\right)_{S,n} \qquad v = \left(\frac{\partial g}{\partial p}\right)_{T,n} = \left(\frac{\partial h}{\partial p}\right)_{s,n} \tag{15.40}$$

$$S = -\left(\frac{\partial G}{\partial T}\right)_{p,n} = -\left(\frac{\partial A}{\partial T}\right)_{V,n} \qquad s = -\left(\frac{\partial g}{\partial T}\right)_{p,n} = -\left(\frac{\partial a}{\partial T}\right)_{v,n} \tag{15.41}$$

Equations (15.38)–(15.41) may now be used to replace the partial derivatives in Eqs (15.34)–(15.37) to yield

$$dU = TdS - pdV + \sum_{i=1}^{c}\left(\frac{\partial U}{\partial n_i}\right)_{S,V,n_j} dn \tag{15.42}$$

$$dH = TdS + Vdp + \sum_{i=1}^{c}\left(\frac{\partial H}{\partial n_i}\right)_{S,p,n_j} dn_i \tag{15.43}$$

$$dA = -SdT - pdV + \sum_{i=1}^{c}\left(\frac{\partial A}{\partial n_i}\right)_{T,V,n_j} dn_i \tag{15.44}$$

$$dG = -SdT + Vdp + \sum_{i=1}^{c}\left(\frac{\partial G}{\partial n_i}\right)_{T,p,n_j} dn_i \tag{15.45}$$

The summations in Eqs (15.42)–(15.45) are equal to each other, as can be seen by taking the derivatives of Eqs (15.33). Furthermore, since the numbers of moles are independent properties and may be changed arbitrarily, each partial derivative within a given summation must be equal to the respective partial derivative of any other summation, and is an intensive thermodynamic property of the phase. This property is called the *chemical potential* of component *i* and is denoted by μ_i:

$$\left(\frac{\partial U}{\partial n_i}\right)_{S,V,nj} = \left(\frac{\partial H}{\partial n_i}\right)_{S,p,nj} = \left(\frac{\partial A}{\partial n_i}\right)_{T,V,nj} = \left(\frac{\partial G}{\partial n_i}\right)_{T,p,nj} = \mu_i \tag{15.46}$$

The chemical potential accounts for the effects of change in the amount of chemical component *i* on the energy functions. The concept of chemical potential was first introduced by J. W. Gibbs. Applications of the chemical potential and further elaborations on its physical meaning are given in the following chapters.

It is possible now to express the changes in the energy-related functions in terms of the thermodynamic functions and the chemical potential:

$$dU = Tds - pdV + \sum \mu_i dn_i \tag{15.47}$$

$$dH = Tds + Vdp + \sum \mu_i dn_i \tag{15.48}$$

$$dA = -SdT - pdV + \sum \mu_i dn_i \tag{15.49}$$

$$dG = -SdT + Vdp + \sum \mu_i dn_i \tag{15.50}$$

By comparing Eq. (15.20) with Eq. (15.50) we find that

$$\mu_i = g_i \tag{15.51}$$

Expressed in words, the chemical potential of component i is equal to the partial Gibbs free energy. The two terms may be used interchangeably. Even though there is no real difference between the two, we shall use the notation g_i when we want to emphasize the partial property aspect, and the notation μ_i when the chemical potential is emphasized.

Equations (15.47)–(15.50) are alternative forms of what is known as the *Gibbs equation.*

Dividing through both sides of Eqs (15.47)–(15.50) by the total number of moles, n, yields the Gibbs equation expressed in terms of intensive properties:

$$du = Tds - pdv + \sum \mu_i dx_i \tag{15.52}$$

$$dh = Tds + vdp + \sum \mu_i dx_i \tag{15.53}$$

$$da = -sdT - pdv + \sum \mu_i dx_i \tag{15.54}$$

$$dg = -sdT + vdp + \sum \mu_i dx_i \tag{15.55}$$

Equations (15.47), (15.50), and (15.52)–(15.55) are general expressions of the changes in the energy-related functions in terms of the independent properties. For cases where the components of the system remain fixed the summation terms vanish and the equations revert back to those for the closed system.

15.6 The Gibbs–Duhem equation

We now consider the variation of property Π under arbitrary variations of the independent properties, such as the pressure, p, temperature, T, and the number of moles, n_i, of each component. Mathematically, it is obtained by differentiating Eq. (15.25) by parts,

$$d\Pi = \sum_{i=1}^{c} \pi_i dn_i + \sum_{i=1}^{c} n_i d\pi_i \tag{15.56}$$

Comparison with Eq. (15.16) yields

$$\sum_{i=1}^{c} \pi_i dn_i + \sum_{i=1}^{c} n_i d\pi_i = \left(\frac{\partial \Pi}{\partial T}\right)_{p,n} dT + \left(\frac{\partial \Pi}{\partial p}\right)_{T,n} dp + \sum_{i=1}^{c} \pi_i dn_i \tag{15.57}$$

leading to

$$\sum_{i=1}^{c} n_i d\pi_i = \left(\frac{\partial \Pi}{\partial T}\right)_{p,n} dT + \left(\frac{\partial \Pi}{\partial p}\right)_{T,n} dp \tag{15.58}$$

An equivalent form is obtained by dividing each term by the total number of moles, n :

$$\sum_{i=1}^{c} x_i d\pi_i = \left(\frac{\partial \pi}{\partial T}\right)_{p,n} dT + \left(\frac{\partial \pi}{\partial p}\right)_{T,n} dp \tag{15.59}$$

where $\pi = \Pi / n$ is the average specific property associated with Π.

Equations (15.58) and (15.59) give the *general form* of the *Gibbs–Duhem equation*, which relates changes in the partial properties to changes in the other independent properties.

A common application of the Gibbs–Duhem equation is for calculating changes in the partial properties of phases at a constant pressure and temperature. Under these conditions Eqs (15.58) and (15.59) simplify to

$$\left(\sum_{i=1}^{c} n_i d\pi_i\right)_{p,T} = 0 \tag{15.60}$$

and

$$\left(\sum_{i=1}^{c} x_i d\pi_i\right)_{p,T} = 0 \tag{15.61}$$

A special case of Eq. (15.58), written for the Gibbs free energy, $\Pi = G$, is

$$\sum_{i=1}^{c} n_i dg_i = \left(\frac{\partial G}{\partial T}\right)_{p,n} dT + \left(\frac{\partial G}{\partial p}\right)_{T,n} dp \tag{15.62}$$

which, by using Eqs (15.40) and (15.41), becomes

$$\sum_{i=1}^{c} n_i dg_i = -SdT + Vdp \tag{15.63}$$

The equivalent forms in terms of specific properties are

$$\sum_{i=1}^{c} x_i dg_i = \left(\frac{\partial g}{\partial T}\right)_{p,T} dT + \left(\frac{\partial g}{\partial p}\right)_{T,n} dp \tag{15.64}$$

and

$$\sum_{i=1}^{c} x_i dg_i = -sdT + vdp \tag{15.65}$$

Equations (15.63) and (15.65) are two equivalent forms of the *Gibbs–Duhem equation.*

EXAMPLE 15.2

The partial enthalpy of component A in a binary mixture is given by

$$h_A = h_A^0(p,T) - 2bx^2$$

where b is a constant and x is the mole fraction of component B.

a. What is the physical meaning of $h_A^0(p,T)$?
b. Derive an expression for the partial enthalpy of B in the binary mixture.
c. Derive an expression for the specific enthalpy of the binary mixture.
d. Plot schematically the specific enthalpy and the two partial enthalpies vs $x = x_B$.
e. Derive an expression for the heat interaction, Q, that results by adding 1 mole of pure component A, at constant p and T, to a large phase of the binary mixture.
f. Repeat part e for an initial phase of only 1 mole.
g. Find the heat interaction when 1 mole of the mixture at $x_A = 0.1$ is added to 1 mole of the mixture of $x_A = 0.9$.

SOLUTION

a. The term $h_A^0(p,T)$ is the specific enthalpy of pure A. It can be obtained by setting $x = x_B = 0$ in the equation for the partial enthalpy of A.
b. An equation for the partial enthalpy of B can be obtained by rewriting Eq. (15.61) for a binary mixture in terms of enthalpies:

$$(1-x)dh_A + xdh_B = 0$$

at constant p and T. Hence

$$dh_B = -\frac{1-x}{x}dh_A = -\frac{1-x}{x}(-4bx\,dx) = 4b(1-x)\,dx$$

which upon integration with the boundary condition $h_B = h_B^0$ at $x = 1$ yields

$$h_B = h_B^0 - 2b(1-x)^2$$

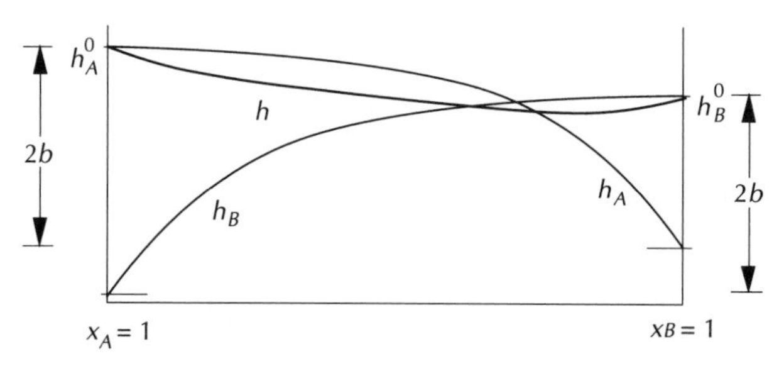

Figure 15.1

c. The specific enthalpy of the solution is calculated by Eq. (15.27):

$$h = x_A h_A + x_B h_B = x_A h_A^0 + x_B h_B^0 - 2b\left(x_A x_B^2 + x_B x_A^2\right)$$
$$= x_A h_A^0 + x_B h_B^0 - 2bx_A x_B$$

d. The three curves are plotted schematically in Fig. 15.1 (p. 337).

e. For a large phase it may be assumed that the addition of 1 mole does not change the mole fractions of the components, and since p and T are constant, $h_i = h_i(T, p, x_i)$ does not change either. For an isobaric process the heat interaction is equal to the change in enthalpy

$$Q = H_2 - H_1 = \left[n_A h_A + n_B h_B\right]_2 - \left[\left(n_A h_A + n_B h_B\right)_1 + h_A^0\right]$$

where n_{A1} and n_{B1} are the respective initial number of moles of A and B in the phase, and n_{A2} and n_{B2} are the respective final number of moles of A and B in the phase. Addition of 1 mole of A results in

$$n_{A2} = n_{A1} + 1 \qquad n_{B2} = n_{B1}$$
$$h_{A2} = h_{A1} \qquad h_{B2} = h_{B1}$$

and

$$Q = h_A - h_A^0 = -2bx_B^2 = -2bx_1^2$$

f. In this case the initial number of moles in the phase is $n_1 = 1$. Denoting the initial mole fraction of B by x_1 we have

$$n_{A1} = (1 - x_1) \,.\, n_1 = 1 - x_1$$
$$n_{B1} = x_1 n_1 = x_1$$

$$x_{A1} = \frac{n_{A1}}{n_1} = 1 - x_1 \qquad x_{B1} = \frac{n_{B1}}{n_1} = x_1$$

$$h_{A1} = h_A^0 - 2b\, x_1^2 \qquad h_{B1} = h_B^0 - 2b\,(1 - x_1)^2$$

At the final state

$$n_2 = 2\, n_{A2} = 1 + n_{A1} = 2 - x_1 \quad \text{and} \quad n_{B2} = n_{B1} = x_1$$

$$x_{A2} = \frac{n_{A2}}{n_2} = \frac{2 - x_1}{2} = 1 - \frac{x_1}{2} \qquad x_{B2} = \frac{n_{B2}}{n_2} = \frac{x_1}{2}$$

$$h_{A2} = h_A^0 - 2b\left(\frac{x_1}{2}\right)^2 \qquad h_{B2} = h_B^0 - 2b\left(1 - \frac{x_1}{2}\right)^2$$

The heat interaction in this case is

$$Q = H_2 - H_1 = \left[n_{A2}\, h_{A2} + n_{B2} h_{B2}\right] - \left[n_{A1}\, h_{A1} + n_{B1} h_{B1} + h_A^0\right]$$
$$= n_2\left[x_{A2}\, h_{A2} + x_{B2} h_{B2}\right] - \left[x_{A1}\, h_{A1} + x_{B1} h_{B1} + h_A^0\right]$$

$$Q = 2\left[\left(1-\frac{x_1}{2}\right)\left(h_A^0 - 2b\left(\frac{x_1}{2}\right)^2\right) + \left(\frac{x_1}{2}\right)\left(h_B^0 - 2b\left(1-\frac{x_1}{2}\right)^2\right)\right]$$

$$-\left[(1-x_1)\left(h_A^0 - 2bx_1^2\right) + x_1\left(h_B^0 - 2b(1-x_1)^2\right) + h_A^0\right] = -bx_1^2$$

g. Let the initial mole fraction in the first and second phases, respectively, be denoted by $x_{A1} = 1 - x_{B1} = 0.1$ and $x_{A2} = 1 - x_{B2} = 0.9$:

$$h_{A1} = h_A^0 - 2b\times 0.1^2 \qquad h_{B1} = h_B^0 - 2b\times 0.9^2$$

$$h_{A2} = h_A^0 - 2b\times 0.9^2 \qquad h_{B2} = h_B^0 - 2b\times 0.1^2$$

At the final state $n = 2$.

Finally, we have 2 moles with mole fraction, x_A, calculated by

$$x_A = \frac{x_{A1} + x_{A2}}{2} = \frac{0.1+0.9}{2} = 0.5 = x_B$$

$$h_A = h_A^0 - 2b\times 0.5^2 \qquad h_B = h_B^0 - 2b\times 0.5^2$$

The heat interaction in this case is

$$Q = H_f - H_i = n\left[x_A h_A + x_B h_B\right] - \left[\left(x_{A1} h_{A1} + x_{B1} h_{B1}\right) + \left(x_{A2} h_{A2} + x_{B2} h_{B2}\right)\right]$$

$$= 2\left[0.5\left(h_A^0 - 2b\times 0.5^2\right) + 0.5\left(h_A^0 - 2b\times 0.5^2\right)\right]$$

$$- \left[0.9\left(h_A^0 - 2b\times 0.9^2\right) + 0.1\left(h_B^0 - 2b\times 0.1^2\right)\right] = -0.64b$$

15.7 Fugacity of a component in a solution

We have already seen that the fugacity of a pure substance is a pseudo-pressure which must be equal in all phases in equilibrium. When there is a difference in the fugacity between two phases, matter will be transferred from the phase of the higher fugacity to that of the lower fugacity. This process will continue until the fugacities become equal or until the phase of the higher fugacity is depleted.

We now introduce the concept of fugacity of a component in a multicomponent phase so that the transfer of the component between the phases is described in terms of that property, similarly to that in a pure phase.

The fugacity of component i in a mixture is defined, to within a constant, by

$$\left(dg_i\right)_T = \left(d\mu_i\right)_T = RT\, d\ln f_i \qquad (15.66)$$

The chemical potential of the component is in general a function of the intensive properties of the phase

$$g_i = \mu_i = \mu_i(p, T, x_1, x_2, \ldots, x_{c-1}) \tag{15.67}$$

Therefore, the fugacity of component i is also a function of the same independent intensive properties

$$f_i = f_i(p, T, x_1, x_2, \ldots, x_{c-1}) \tag{15.68}$$

Equation (15.66), integrated at constant T, yields

$$g_i = \mu_i = RT \ln f_i + F(T) \tag{15.69}$$

The above relation holds for any proportions of the components. Hence, it also applies for the special case where the mole fraction of component i is one, $x_i = 1$, i.e. for pure component i. In the case of a pure component

$$g_i^0 = \mu_i^0 = RT \ln f_i^0 + F(T) \tag{15.70}$$

Elimination of $F(T)$ between the last two equations leads to

$$g_i = \mu_i = \mu_i^0 + RT \ln(f_i / f_i^0) \tag{15.71}$$

or, equivalently,

$$f_i = f_i^0 \exp\left(\frac{\mu_i - \mu_i^0}{RT}\right) \tag{15.72}$$

Equation (15.72) defines the fugacity of a component in a mixture at a given pressure, temperature, and composition in terms of the fugacity, f_i^o, of the pure component at the same pressure and temperature.

15.8 Standard state and activity

We have seen that the fugacity of a component in a phase is in general a function of the pressure, the temperature, and the composition:

$$f_i = f_i(p, T, x_1, x_2, \ldots, x_{c-1}) \tag{15.73}$$

In order to describe the dependency of the fugacity of a given component on the composition of the phase it is customary to select a *standard state* for that component. The selection of the standard state may be somewhat arbitrary but it must be well defined. Usually, the standard state for a component in a phase is selected to be at the same conditions as the phase but containing only the pure component:

$$f_i^{std} = f_i(p, T, x_i = 1) \tag{15.74}$$

In this case the standard state was selected to be the same as that defined by Eq. (15.70). In other cases it may be more convenient to select the standard states differently.

We now define a new intensive property, the *activity*, which is used extensively in the study of thermodynamics of solutions. The activity of a component i in a mixture is defined as the ratio of its fugacity to the fugacity of the pure component at the corresponding standard state. Like the fugacity, the activity of a component is, in general, a function of all the intensive properties of the phase

$$a_i = \frac{f_i}{f_i^{std}} = a_i(p, T, x_1, x_2, \ldots, x_{c-1}) \tag{15.75}$$

An alternative standard state of component i is that of an ideal gas state at p and T. We denote all the properties of that state by an asterisk. Thus, the fugacity of component i at the ideal-gas standard state and the activity relative to that state are, respectively:

$$f_i^* = p \text{ and } a_{i*} = \frac{f_i}{p} \tag{15.76}$$

15.9 Fugacity relations

The fugacity plays an important role in thermodynamics. Therefore, it is worth while to investigate the relationships between the fugacity and the various partial properties of the phase.

In Chapter 13 we developed the Maxwell relations as a tool for interrelating partial derivatives of properties. In the beginning of this chapter these relations were extended to a multicomponent phase. Now they are used to relate the fugacity and its derivatives to other properties.

The volume of a phase can be expressed as the partial derivative of the Gibbs free energy with respect to the pressure, Eq. (15.40),

$$V = \left(\frac{\partial G}{\partial p}\right)_{T,n} \tag{15.40}$$

Differentiation, at constant p, T, n_j, yields

$$\left(\frac{\partial V}{\partial n_i}\right)_{p,T,nj} = \left[\frac{\partial}{\partial n_i}\left(\frac{\partial G}{\partial p}\right)_{T,n}\right]_{p,T,nj} \tag{15.77}$$

The left hand side of Eq. (15.77) is the partial volume. By changing the order of differentiation on the right hand side we obtain

$$v_i = \left(\frac{\partial g_i}{\partial p}\right)_{T,n} = \left(\frac{\partial \mu_i}{\partial p}\right)_{T,n} \tag{15.78}$$

Starting with Eq. (15.41) and following similar steps as above, we obtain an equivalent expression for the partial entropy, s_i:

$$s_i = -\left(\frac{\partial g_i}{\partial T}\right)_{p,n} = -\left(\frac{\partial \mu_i}{\partial T}\right)_{p,n} \tag{15.79}$$

Differentiating $\partial(g_i/T)/\partial T$ by parts and using Eq. (15.79) we obtain

$$\left[\frac{\partial(g_i/T)}{\partial T}\right]_{p,n_j} = -\frac{g_i}{T^2} + \frac{1}{T}\left(\frac{\partial g_i}{\partial T}\right)_{p,n_j} = \frac{-g_i - Ts_i}{T^2} \tag{15.80}$$

Equation (15.80) combined with Eq. (15.23) yields an expression for the partial enthalpy:

$$\frac{h_i}{T^2} = -\left[\frac{\partial(g_i/T)}{\partial T}\right]_{p,n_j} \tag{15.81}$$

Equations (15.78), (15.79), and (15.80) may be used together with Eq (15.69) to derive important relationships between the fugacity of a component in a phase and the partial properties v_i, s_i, and h_i for the same phase. Thus, expressing g_i in terms of the fugacity, Eq. (15.69), leads to the following relationships:

For the partial volume

$$v_i = RT\left(\frac{\partial \ln f_i}{\partial p}\right)_{T,n} \tag{15.82}$$

and

$$v_i - v_i^0 = RT\left(\frac{\partial \ln f_i/f_i^0}{\partial p}\right)_{T,n} = RT\left(\frac{\partial \ln a_i}{\partial p}\right)_{T,n} \tag{15.83}$$

For the partial entropy

$$\frac{s_i - s_i^0}{R} = -\left[\frac{\partial(T\ln f_i/f_i^0)}{\partial T}\right]_{p,n} = -\left[\frac{\partial(T\ln a_i)}{\partial T}\right]_{p,n} \tag{15.84}$$

For the partial enthalpy

$$\frac{h_i - h_i^0}{RT^2} = -\left[\frac{\partial \ln(f_i/f_i^0)}{\partial T}\right]_{p,n} = -\left[\frac{\partial \ln(a_i)}{\partial T}\right]_{p,n} \tag{15.85}$$

These last four equations are used extensively when dealing with solutions and with chemical reactions.

15.10 Partial and specific properties for a binary phase

A *binary phase* is a phase that is composed of two components, say component A and component B.

Consider a binary phase of components A and B, for which specific volume data are given as a function of the independent properties:

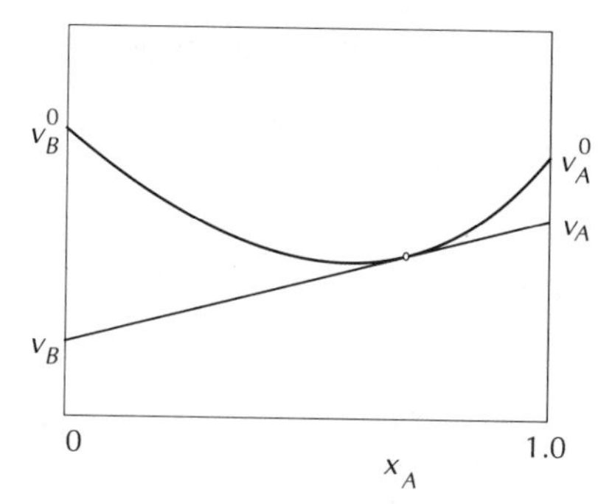

Figure 15.2 **Specific volume of a binary phase.**

$$v = v(p, T, x_A) \tag{15.86}$$

Figure 15.2 shows a typical plot of such data for fixed pressure and temperature. At the limits of $x_A = 0$ and $x_A = 1$ the specific volumes are those of pure B, denoted by v_B^0, and of pure A, denoted by v_A^0, respectively. The partial volume of A may be calculated as a function of x_A (at constant p and T) as follows:

$$v_A = \left(\frac{\partial V}{\partial n_A}\right)_{p,T,n_B} = \left[\frac{\partial((n_A + n_B)v)}{\partial n_A}\right]_{p,T,n_B} \tag{15.87}$$

which after differentiation becomes

$$v_A = v + n\left(\frac{\partial v}{\partial n_A}\right)_{p,T,n_B} \tag{15.88}$$

Now, at constant $n_B, dn = dn_A + dn_B = dn_A$ and

$$dn_A = d(nx_A) = ndx_A + x_A dn = ndx_A + x_A dn_A$$

Hence

$$dn_A = \frac{n}{1 - x_A} dx_A \tag{15.89}$$

Substituting dn_A from Eq. (15.89) into Eq. (15.88) we obtain

$$v_A = v + (1 - x_A)\left(\frac{\partial v}{\partial x_A}\right)_{p,T} \tag{15.90}$$

Equation (15.90) is used to evaluate the partial volume of a component in a binary phase when experimental data on specific volume are known. It is representative of a family of equations for each of the specific properties of a binary phase such as:

the specific energy,

$$u_A = u + (1 - x_A)\left(\frac{\partial u}{\partial x_A}\right)_{p,T} \tag{15.91}$$

the specific enthalpy,

$$h_A = h + (1 - x_A)\left(\frac{\partial h}{\partial x_A}\right)_{p,T} \tag{15.92}$$

the specific entropy,

$$s_A = s + (1 - x_A)\left(\frac{\partial s}{\partial x_A}\right)_{p,T} \tag{15.93}$$

the specific Gibbs free energy,

$$g_A = g + (1 - x_A)\left(\frac{\partial g}{\partial x_A}\right)_{p,T} \tag{15.94}$$

and the specific Helmholtz free energy,

$$a_A = a + (1 - x_A)\left(\frac{\partial a}{\partial x_A}\right)_{p,T} \tag{15.95}$$

15.11 Mixing

Intuitively one might think that mixing a quart of water with a quart of alcohol would result in two quarts of mixture. As it turns out, to the chagrin of the jolly drinker, the actual volume of the mixture is slightly less than the expected sum of volumes of the ingredients. This section deals with the characterization of the mixing process in terms of properties of the pure constituents.

A mixing process is one where a multicomponent phase at pressure p, temperature T, and mole fractions x_i is produced from the corresponding pure substances each at the same p and T. The change in an extensive property that results from the mixing process is called the "property" of mixing. Thus, the change in volume upon mixing, i.e. the volume of mixing, is

$$\Delta v_{mix} = v - \sum_{i=1}^{c} x_i v_i^0 \tag{15.96}$$

where v is the specific volume of the mixture, $v = V/n$, and v_i^0 is the specific volume of the pure substance at the same p and T. After rearrangement Eq. (15.96) yields

$$\Delta v_{mix} = \sum_{i=1}^{c} x_i(v_i - v_i^0) \tag{15.97}$$

The enthalpy of mixing is given by

$$\Delta h_{mix} = h - \sum_{i=1}^{c} x_i h_i^0 \tag{15.98}$$

and again after rearrangement,

$$\Delta h_{mix} = \sum_{i=1}^{c} x_i(h_i - h_i^0) \tag{15.99}$$

Similarly, the entropy of mixing is

$$\Delta s_{mix} = \sum_{i=1}^{c} x_i(s_i - s_i^0) \tag{15.100}$$

And, in general, the change of property π in mixing is

$$\Delta \pi_{mix} = \pi(p, T, x_1, \ldots, x_{c-1}) - \sum_{i=1}^{c} x_i \pi_i^0 \tag{15.101}$$

and after rearrangement,

$$\Delta \pi_{mix} = \sum_{i=1}^{c} x_i(\pi_i - \pi_i^0) \tag{15.102}$$

PROBLEMS

15.1 For each of the following open systems determine the set of independent components, and the number of independent intensive properties (check the phase rule).

Assume air to consist of 21% oxygen and 79% nitrogen.

a. Air in gaseous phase only.
b. Air that may be cooled till part of it liquefies.
c. Liquid water in equilibrium with moist air.
d. Ice, liquid water, and water vapor in equilibrium.
e. Ice, liquid water, and moist air in equilibrium.
f. Solid carbon and a gaseous mixture of CO and CO_2. Assume no chemical reaction.
g. Solid carbon and a gaseous mixture of CO and CO_2. A chemical reaction according to C + CO_2 = 2CO is possible.
h. A liquid solution of KCl and NaCl in water in equilibrium with crystals of the two salts and vapor.
i. A liquid solution of KCl and NaCl in water in equilibrium with crystals of the two salts, ice, and vapor.

15.2 An empirical expression for the volume of salt water at 1 bar and 25 °C is given as

$$v = 0.018 - 0.0016x + 0.0025x^2 - 0.0012x^3$$

where x–mole fraction of salt in solution

v–specific volume per mole solution

a. Find the volume of 1 mole of salt water for the following values of x:
   0.0 0.01 0.03 0.1 0.3
b. Find the partial volume of water for the same values of x.
c. Find the partial volume of salt for the same values of x.
d. Find the weight percentage of the salt for the same values of x.

15.3 The density of a BrF_5 solution in BrF_3 at standard conditions is given by the following equation: $\rho = 2803.0 - 388.4x + 64.1x^2 - 18.3x^3$, where x is the mole fraction of BrF_5 in the solution, and ρ is given in kg/m³.

Find the partial volumes of BrF_3 and of BrF_5 in solutions of 20%, 40%, and 60% BrF_5.

15.4 The following table lists the partial volumes of water (H_2O), v_1, and ethanol (C_2H_5OH), v_2, as a function of mole fraction of ethanol, x_2, in a binary phase of ethanol and water at 20 °C and 1.0 bar:

x_2	0.1	0.2	0.4	0.6
$v_1\left(\text{cm}^3/\text{kmol}\right)$	18110	17670	17010	16210
$v_2\left(\text{cm}^3/\text{kmol}\right)$	53100	55400	57100	57870

a. Find the volume of a phase comprised of 30 g of water and 70 g of ethanol.
b. Plot the specific volume of the mixture as a function of the mole fraction of the water.

15.5 The fugacity of component A in a binary phase of A and B is given by:

$$f_A = K_A x_A (2 - x_A)$$

where x_A is the mole fraction of component A and K_A is a constant.

What does K_A represent?

Find the fugacity of component B as a function of x_B.

15.6 The specific enthalpy of a certain liquid binary phase of A and B is given by

$$h = K_A x + K_B (1 - x) + bx(1 - x^2)$$

where x is the mole fraction of component A.

Assume that the properties of the pure components A and B are known as functions of the pressure and temperature.

a. Can you assign a physical meaning to K_A and K_B?
b. Find the partial enthalpies of each component in the phase.
c. Determine the heat interaction when 2.0 kmol of pure component A is mixed at constant pressure and temperature with 4.0 kmol of a phase where the mole fraction of component A is x.

15.7 a. Calculate and plot the chemical potential of water at 200 °C as a function of pressure (from 0.01 MPa to 20 MPa).
b. Calculate and plot the fugacity of water at 200 °C as a function of pressure (from 0.01 MPa to 20 MPa).

15.8 The specific volume of an H_2SO_4 solution in water at 25 °C and 1.0 bar for molality values of $m < 6$ is given in the following empirical equation:

$$v = 1001.8 + 35.350m + 0.863m^2$$

where v is given in cm³/kg.

a. Find a similar equation where the variable is the mole fraction of H_2SO_4.
b. Find an expression for the partial volumes of water and acid for molality values of $m < 6$.

15.9 The enthalpy of a certain liquid phase of a binary solution is given by

$$h = K_A x_A + K_B x_B + b x_A x_B (1 + x_A)$$

Assume that the properties of the pure components are known as functions of pressure and temperature.

a. What is the meaning of the constants K_A, K_B?
b. Find the partial enthalpy of each component.
c. Determine the heat interaction required to maintan the pressure and temperature constant when 2 kmol of component A are mixed with 4 kmol of component B.

CHAPTER SIXTEEN

Equilibrium

The concept of equilibrium is fundamental to thermodynamics. In Chapter 2 the concept was defined and discussed in general terms. Here we look for a criterion that mathematically relates the equilibrium state to the appropriate properties of the system. To do so we invoke the second law of thermodynamics which is related to the concept of equilibrium.

16.1 Maximum entropy criterion

The second law of thermodynamics assures that for any given state of a system there is a corresponding state of stable equilibrium, which the system can reach without interaction with its environment. A process that brings the system from a given state to the corresponding stable state must be irreversible. The reverse process, if it exists, would contradict the very definition of equilibrium.

In Chapter 8 we saw that a real process could take place in an isolated system only if the entropy does not decrease in the process. The energy of the isolated system is always fixed and does not change in any process. Expressed mathematically this reads

$$(dS)_E \geq 0 \tag{16.1}$$

for a real process.

When an isolated system is in a state of equilibrium its entropy has the highest possible value of all the neighboring states. If a process that caused a change to another state existed, it would reduce the entropy of the system and, therefore, could not be possible.

No real spontaneous process can take place in an isolated system in a state of equilibrium. Nevertheless, we can *calculate* the change of entropy between the equilibrium state and any other state at the same energy. A criterion that provides a test of whether a state is in equilibrium can be stated as

A state is an equilibrium state if, and only if, for any change to a neighboring state of equal energy the entropy does not increase.

$$(\delta S)_E \leq 0 \tag{16.2}$$

for any variation from equilibrium. The notation δ indicates a small (calculated) change, starting from a state of equilibrium, while d is reserved for the differential of a real process.

Equation (16.2) can serve to identify the equilibrium state. It should be noted that, for the purpose of identification, equilibrium states of equal energy are equivalent to states of an isolated system.

EXAMPLE 16.1

An isolated box, shown in Fig. 16.1, contains 10 kg of air (assume ideal gas, $M = 29$, $k = 1.4$). Half the air is at 200 °C (state A) and the other half is at 20 °C (state B). The air is allowed to reach equilibrium.

a. What is the equilibrium state of the system?
b. Show that the entropy at equilibrium is higher than the entropy at the initial state.
c. Plot the change of entropy as a function of temperature difference between the two halves of the air in the box, and show that ΔS is negative for any state relative to equilibrium.

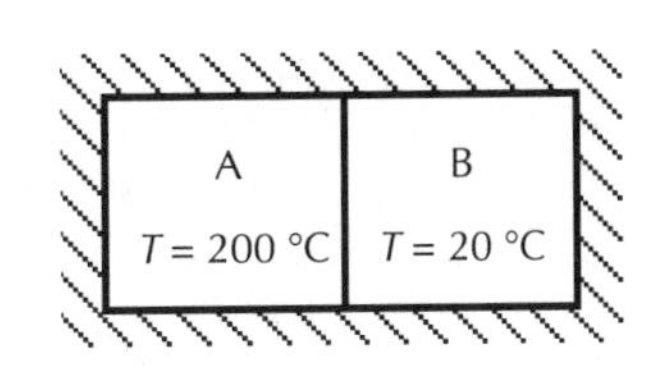

Figure 16.1

SOLUTION

a. The equilibrium state is the one for which the properties are uniform while the total energy is unchanged.
b. The equilibrium temperature can be calculated from the fact that the energy of the system does not change, $\Delta E = 0$, assuming that

$$\Delta E = \sum_{i=1}^{C} m_i c_v \Delta T_i$$

leads to

$$T = \frac{T_A + T_B}{2} = \frac{200 + 20}{2} = 110\ ^\circ\mathrm{C}$$

The change of entropy is

$$\Delta S = \tfrac{1}{2} m c_v \left[\ln\left(\frac{T}{T_A}\right) + \ln\left(\frac{T}{T_B}\right) \right] = \frac{mR}{2(k-1)} \ln\left(\frac{T^2}{T_A T_B}\right)$$

$$= \frac{10 \times 8.3143}{2 \times (1.4 - 1) \times 29} \ln\left(\frac{383.15^2}{293.15 \times 473.15}\right) = 0.2034\ \ \mathrm{kJ/K} > 0$$

which is in agreement with Eq. (16.1).

c. A possible change from the state of equilibrium is a change that brings part A to a temperature $T_A \neq T$ and part B to a corresponding temperature T_B, which is calculable from the first law as

$$T_B = 2T - T_A$$

We can also calculate δS for such a change:

$$\delta S = \tfrac{1}{2} mc_v \left[\ln\left(\frac{T_A}{T}\right) + \ln\left(\frac{T_B}{T}\right) \right] = \frac{mR}{2(k-1)} \ln\left(\frac{T_A T_B}{T^2}\right)$$

Figure 16.2 shows that in this example, the highest entropy is associated with the equilibrium state where the temperature is uniform. A variation from the state of equilibrium, characterized by two regions of different temperatures at the same energy, results in $(\delta S)_E \leq 0$.

T_A	T_B	δS	T_A	T_B	δS
110	110	0.000000	140	80	−0.022038
111	109	−0.000024	150	70	−0.039273
112	108	−0.000098	160	60	−0.061555
113	107	−0.000220	170	50	−0.088978
115	105	−0.000610	180	40	−0.121660
120	100	−0.002442	190	30	−0.159744
130	90	−0.009778	200	20	−0.203400

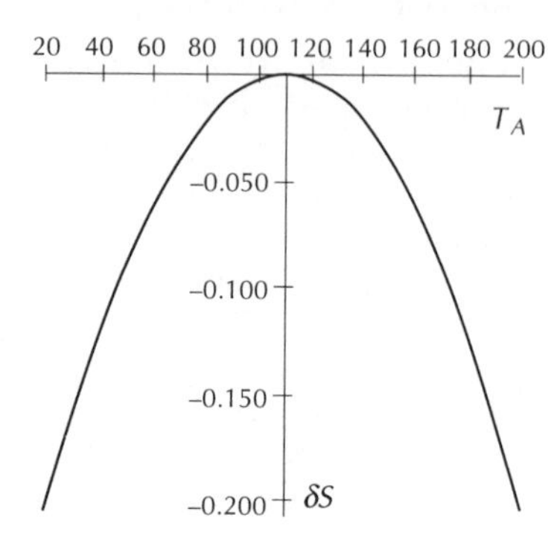

Figure 16.2

The criterion for equilibrium, given in Eq. (16.2), is a very general criterion, but it is not always convenient for applications. For a wide range of applications, alternative, though equivalent, criteria are much more useful. Two of these are presented below.

16.2 Minimum energy criterion

A well-known criterion for equilibrium, used extensively in mechanics, is the principle of minimum energy. An exact statement of the criterion is

$$(\delta E)_S \geq 0 \tag{16.3}$$

(for any variation from equilibrium). Again, the notation δ indicates a small (calculated) change from the state of equilibrium to a neighboring state.

It can be shown that the criterion of minimum energy, Eq. (16.3), is equivalent to the criterion of maximum entropy, Eq. (16.2)*.

* To be exact, the criterion of maximum entropy (Eq. 16.2) applies to all systems regardless of their state. The criterion of minimum energy (Eq. 16.3) applies only to normal states and does not apply to special states. Special states represent an extension of the state definition given in Chapter 2. They are associated with systems that can be defined without reference to a boundary. For such systems negative absolute temperatures are meaningful.

Special states are not discussed in this text. For normal states the two criteria are completely equivalent.

16.3 Minimum Gibbs free energy

It was shown in Chapter 10 that if the availability of a system is positive the system can produce useful work while interacting with the environment. The availability is positive if, and only if, the system and the environment are not in mutual equilibrium. The maximum useful work that a system can produce in conjunction with the environment is expressed in terms of the difference in the property called available work.

Useful work can be produced even if the system is uniform at the temperature and pressure of the environment, $T = T_0$, $p = p_0$. For example, an electric storage battery can produce useful work even though its temperature and pressure are equal to the temperature and pressure of the environment. It is sufficient that the battery is not in a state of stable equilibrium. When the stable equilibrium state is reached, i.e. the voltage is zero, no more work can be produced. At this state the available work has its lowest possible value. Any other state would have a higher value of available work with respect to an environment at T and p.

The available work with respect to an environment at the same temperature and pressure can be found by substituting $T_0 = T$ and $p_0 = p$ into Eq. (10.18), resulting in

$$\Lambda = U + pV - TS = H - TS = G \tag{16.4}$$

It follows that if we compare the Gibbs free energy, G, of the equilibrium state to that of any neighboring state having the same temperature and pressure the value at equilibrium is the lowest. Thus an alternative criterion for equilibrium can be formed in terms of the Gibbs free energy. Expressed mathematically

$$(\delta G)_{p,T} \geq 0 \tag{16.5}$$

(for any variation from equilibrium).

The criterion for equilibrium is employed in the following manner. In order to show that a given state is in equilibrium we compare its Gibbs free energy to that of the neighboring states. This comparison can be done by considering small possible variations from the original state and calculating the change in the Gibbs free energy associated with the variation. If we find even a single neighboring state that violates this criterion, i.e. a state that has a lower Gibbs free energy, we must conclude that the original given state is not an equilibrium state. Only if no such neighboring state can be found is the original state a state of equilibrium.

16.4 The chemical potential

In nature, systems in equilibrium may be comprised of one or more phases. At times, new phases may be created while existing phases disappear. For example, when water vapor is compressed, a liquid phase may be created. When a saline solution is cooled, salt may precipitate out of the solution to form a solid phase. When a vessel containing a salt solution and solid salt is heated up, the salt phase may disappear by dissolving into the solution.

One may ask what causes a component to leave one phase and move into another? The tendency of a component to leave a phase is called the *escaping tendency of the component*. A component tends to escape from regions of high escaping tendency to regions of low escaping tendency. When two phases are in equilibrium, the escaping tendency in one phase is equal to that of the other and so there is no net tendency to transfer matter between the phases. We shall show that the escaping tendency is actually the same as the partial Gibbs free energy or the chemical potential of the component.

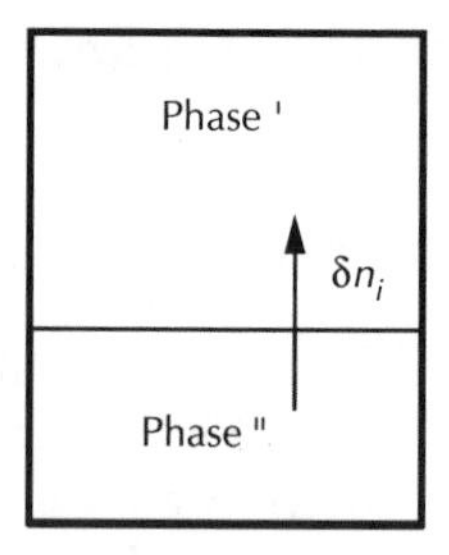

Figure 16.3

Consider a system that consists of several phases, Fig. 16.3. In stable equilibrium the temperature must be uniform throughout the system. Example 16.1 demonstrates this fact. The pressure, on the other hand, may or may not be uniform. We can find many examples of systems in equilibrium where the pressure is not uniform. A column of water in a gravitational field can be in equilibrium while its pressure varies with height. The pressures in a liquid and in a vapor, separated by a curved surface in a capillary tube, are different even in equilibrium. Indeed, only when the interface between the two phases is not curved and no external force fields exist, are the pressures of the two phases equal. We see that the pressure by itself cannot be used to identify the equilibrium state. The property that controls the transfer of matter between phases can be deduced from the minimum Gibbs free energy criterion.

Returning to the system in Fig. 16.3, let us consider a small variation from the state of equilibrium that involves the transfer of a small amount of component i from one phase, say phase ($'$), to phase ($''$), while the temperature, the pressure and the amounts of the other components remain unchanged. In this case $\delta n'_i < 0$. Alternatively, we could transfer a small amount of component i from phase ($''$) to phase ($'$), $\delta n'_i > 0$. There is no change in the total amount of component i in the system for both variations. Thus

$$\delta n_i = \delta n'_i + \delta n''_i = 0 \tag{16.6}$$

or

$$\delta n'_i = -\delta n''_i \tag{16.7}$$

We can now calculate the change of Gibbs free energy that results from the transfer, by applying Eq. (15.50) to each phase:

$$(\delta G)_{pT} = g'_i \delta n'_i + g''_i \delta n''_i = (g'_i - g''_i)\delta n'_i \tag{16.8}$$

The criterion of minimum Gibbs free energy, Eq. (16.5), together with Eq. (16.7) requires that the following expression is always true for any variation from a state of equilibrium:

$$(\delta G)_{pT} = (g'_i - g''_i)\delta n'_i \geq 0 \tag{16.9}$$

This expression must hold for both positive and negative values of $\delta n'_i$. The expression $(g'_i - g''_i)$ could be neither positive nor negative. If it were positive we could violate Eq. (16.9) by selecting a negative $\delta n'_i$. If, on the other hand, it were negative, then we could violate Eq. (16.9) by selecting a positive $\delta n'_i$. We must conclude, therefore, that $(g'_i - g''_i) = 0$ for the two phases to be in equilibrium. Hence,

$$g'_i - g''_i \tag{16.10}$$

We see that the property that controls the transfer of a component from one phase to another is the partial Gibbs free energy. A component tends to escape from regions of higher into regions of lower Gibbs free energy, which is why the partial Gibbs free energy is also the *escaping tendency* or the *chemical potential.* We shall denote the chemical potential of component *i* by μ_i. From the discussion above it follows that

$$\mu_i = g_i \tag{16.11}$$

Even though there is no real difference between these two quantities, we shall use both notations. The chemical potential, μ_i, will be used when we want to emphasize equilibrium aspects, and the partial Gibbs free energy when we want to emphasize partial property aspects.

16.5 Gibbs phase rule

The Gibbs phase rule relates the number of independent intensive phase properties (also called *degrees of freedom*) to the number of phases coexisting in equilibrium.

The number of degrees of freedom in a heterogeneous simple system is given by

$$F = 2 + c - r \tag{16.12}$$

where F is the number of degrees of freedom;
c is the number of components of the system;
r is the number of phases in equilibrium.

The number of independent intensive properties of each phase was shown before to be $c + 1$ (for example, p, T, and c -1 mole fractions). In the absence of limiting conditions, the number of independent properties of r phases could therefore be $r\ (c + 1)$. On the other hand, there are some relationships between properties that must hold for phases in equilibrium. The temperature, the pressure, and the chemical potential of each component must be equal for any two phases. Thus all together there are $(r-1)(c+2)$ conditions that the intensive properties must satisfy. The number of independent properties is then

$$F = r(c+1) - (r-1)(c+2) = 2 + c - r$$

The Gibbs rule holds true only for systems where the pressures of all phases in equilibrium are equal. Thus it always holds for simple systems.

The Gibbs phase rule, applied to a system of a pure substance ($c = 1$), simplifies to

$$F = 3 - r \tag{16.13}$$

For a pure substance there can be no more than three phases in equilibrium (in which case there are no degrees of freedom). The number of degrees of freedom that correspond to the number of phases for equilibrium in a system of a pure substance are shown in the following table:

r	1	2	3
F	2	1	0

Thus, when a simple system of a pure substance is in equilibrium in one phase, two intensive properties are independent. For example, we could arbitrarily assign the system values for both the pressure and the temperature.

When there are two phases in equilibrium, only one intensive property is independent. Once we select (arbitrarily) the pressure, the temperature is fixed and is no longer independent, and vice versa.

When three phases are in equilibrium, there are zero degrees of freedom. Thus the temperature and the pressure are fixed. The triple point of water is an example of such a state. At the triple point, the pressure and temperature each have a unique value.

16.6 Phase equilibrium of a pure substance

In this section, we discuss systems of pure substances that may be in equilibrium in one or more phases.

Consider the system, shown in Fig. 16.4, which comprises liquid water in thermodynamic equilibrium with its vapor. Let us focus our attention on points A and B in the liquid and vapor phases, respectively. The temperature is, obviously, equal in both phases, and so is the chemical potential. Mechanical equilibrium requires that the pressures are also equal, $p_A = p_B$. When the pressure is equal in both phases it is called the saturation pressure, p^{sat}. Hence,

$$p_A = p_B = p^{sat} \tag{16.14}$$

Now consider the capillary tube immersed in the liquid, as shown in Fig. 16.4. The interface is curved owing to surface tension and the water level is at height z above the level of A. Here also the liquid (point C) is in equilibrium with the vapor (point D). The pressure at C is lower than that at A owing to the column of liquid:

$$p_C = p_A - \rho^L gz = p^{sat} - \rho^L gz = p^L \tag{16.15}$$

Similarly, the pressure of the vapor at D is

$$p_D = p_B - \rho^V gz = p^{sat} - \rho^V gz = p^V \tag{16.16}$$

The pressure difference between the vapor and the liquid in the capillary tube, $(p^V - p^L)$, is

$$p^V - p^L = (\rho^L - \rho^V)gz \tag{16.17}$$

Since $\rho^L >> \rho^V$ there is a pressure difference between the

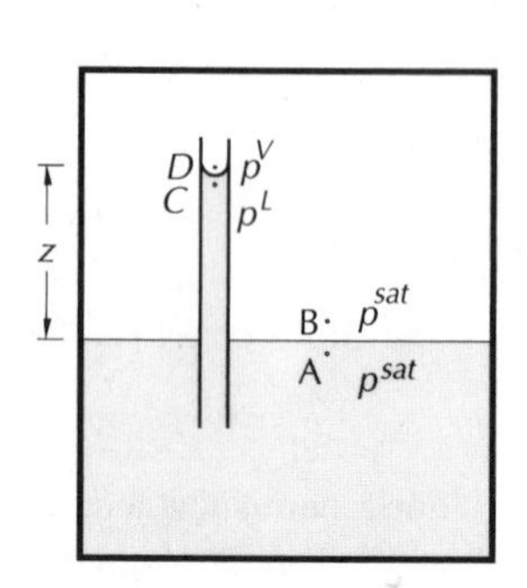

Figure 16.4

vapor and the liquid. Yet the two phases are in equilibrium.

The use of the van der Waals equation of state can help to illustrate qualitatively the various aspects of equilibrium. The van der Waals equation is

$$\left(p+\frac{a}{v^2}\right)(v-b) = RT \tag{14.1}$$

Figure 16.5 depicts schematically a typical isotherm of the van der Waals equation, at a subcritical temperature. At critical and supercritical temperatures, p and T fix uniquely the state of the system. On the other hand, for a given selection of p and T at a subcritical temperature, either one or two or even three different states correspond to different specific volumes. Let us now examine the relative stability of these states, using the chemical potential as a criterion for that purpose.

In general, the change of the chemical potential for a pure substance is given by

$$d\mu = dg = -sdT + vdp$$

while the change along an isotherm, where T = const., is

$$d\mu_T = vdp \tag{16.18}$$

We can integrate vdp along a subcritical isotherm, starting from branch L, to yield the variation of the chemical potential along the isotherm. The results are plotted schematically on a p–μ diagram, shown in Fig. 16.6.

We note that there are three branches of the isotherm in the p–μ diagram. One branch corresponds to the liquid phase (denoted L), one branch to the vapor phase (V), and a third branch that connects the two.

We see that three different states can have the same values of pressure and temperature; however, their respective chemical potentials are different. Phases corresponding to states of different chemical potentials cannot coexist in equilibrium. The phase at a lower chemical potential is more stable than the one at a higher chemical potential. If we fix the pressure and temperature of the system, the equilibrium state will be that of the lowest chemical potential. Usually this will result in a single phase.

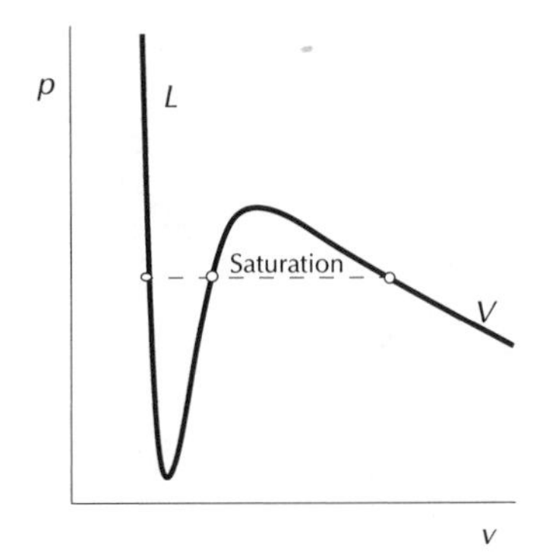

Figure 16.5

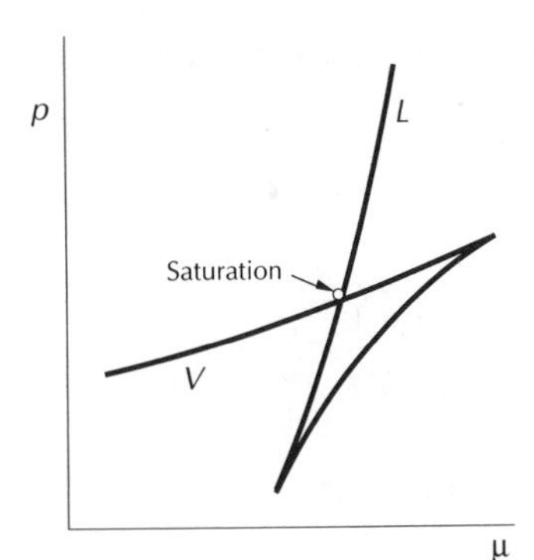

Figure 16.6

On the other hand, two phases at different pressures can coexist in equilibrium, provided their respective temperatures and chemical potentials are equal. For example, the two phases at the curved interface of a capillary tube can be in equilibrium even though, because of surface tension, the pressures across the interface are not equal. Similarly, the pressure inside a spherical bubble of vapor in equilibrium with a large liquid phase is different from the pressure in the liquid. This fact is demonstrated in the following section.

16.7 Equilibrium between vapor bubble and liquid phase

Consider a spherical vapor bubble of diameter D surrounded by a large liquid phase in equilibrium with it. The pressure inside the vapor bubble, p_B, can be found as follows. Consider the bubble in Fig. 16.7 cut by the A–A plane. The free body thus formed is a hemisphere. The net force on the plane A–A must be zero. Hence, the surface tension force

$$F_s = \pi D\sigma \tag{16.19}$$

must be balanced by the pressure force

$$F_p = \frac{\pi D^2}{4}\left(p^V - p^L\right) \tag{16.20}$$

leading to

$$\pi D\sigma = \frac{\pi D^2}{4}\left(p^V - p^L\right) \tag{16.21}$$

Thus, mechanical equilibrium requires that

$$p^V - p^L = \frac{4\sigma}{D} \tag{16.22}$$

On the other hand the vapor phase is in equilibrium with the liquid phase, and therefore the chemical potentials of the two phases must be equal. At saturation, where the interface is flat, there is no pressure difference between the phases, and the two phases have

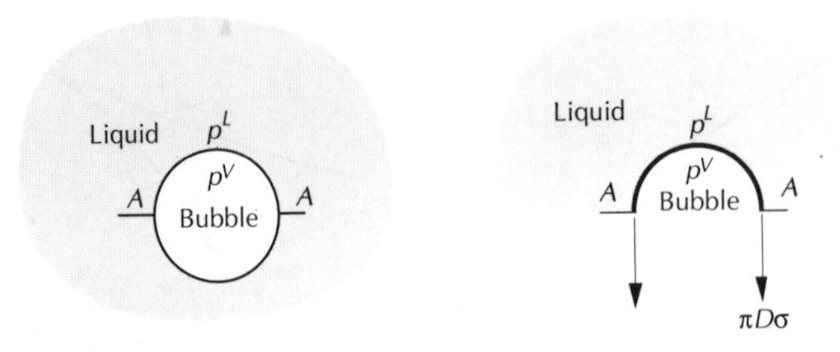

Figure 16.7

the same chemical potential,

$$\mu_{sat}^{L} = \mu_{sat}^{V} = \mu_{sat} \tag{16.23}$$

The chemical potential must also be equal for states where the interface is curved, and the pressure of the two phases is different, thus

$$\mu^{L} - \mu_{sat} = \mu^{V} - \mu_{sat}$$

$$\int_{p_{sat}}^{p^L} v^L\, dp^L = \int_{p_{sat}}^{p^V} v^V\, dp^V \tag{16.24}$$

In order to perform the integration it is necessary to know how the specific volume varies with pressure. For a wide range of states it is possible to assume that the volume of the liquid is constant while the vapor can be considered an ideal gas. Under these assumptions integration of Eq. (16.24) yields

$$v^L\left(p^L - p_{sat}\right) = \int_{p_{sat}}^{p^V} \frac{RT}{p^V}\, dp^V = RT \ln \frac{p^V}{p_{sat}} \tag{16.25}$$

Hence,

$$p^V = p_{sat} \exp\left[\frac{v^L\left(p^L - p_{sat}\right)}{RT}\right] \tag{16.26}$$

and

$$p^L = p_{sat} + \frac{RT}{v^L} \ln \frac{p^V}{p_{sat}} \tag{16.27}$$

A similar situation exists for a droplet of liquid inside a large vapor phase. Indeed, the whole discussion could be repeated remembering only that the liquid is inside the droplet and the vapor is outside. Equations (16.26)–(16.27) apply also for this case.

EXAMPLE 16.2

A water droplet is suspended in a large vapor phase at 150 kPa and 110 °C.

a. Find the equilibrium pressure inside the droplet.
b. Calculate the diameter of the droplet if the surface tension of water is given as a function of temperature by

$$\sigma = \left(75.64 - 13.91\theta - 3.0\theta^2\right) \times 10^{-3}\ \text{N/m}$$

where $\theta = T/100$ and T is the temperature in °C.

SOLUTION

The pressure in the vapor phase (p = 150 kPa) is higher than the saturation pressure at 110 °C, which is p_{sat} = 143.3 kPa. Thus, the vapor is in a metastable state. It can be in equilibrium with the liquid at a higher pressure.

a. The equilibrium pressure inside the liquid droplet is calculated from Eq. (16.27):

$$p^L = p_{sat} + \frac{RT}{v^L}\ln\frac{p^V}{p_{sat}} = 143.3 + \frac{8.3143\times383.15}{18.02\times0.001052}\ln\frac{150}{143.3} = 7822\ \text{kPa}$$

b. The equilibrium diameter of a water droplet in a large vapor phase at 150 kPa is found from Eq. (16.22):

$$D = \frac{4\sigma}{p^L - p^V} = \frac{4\times10^{-3}}{p^L - p^V}\left[75.64 - 13.91\left(\frac{T}{100}\right) - 3.0\left(\frac{T}{100}\right)^2\right]$$

Hence,

$$D = \frac{4\times10^{-3}}{7822-150}\left[75.64 - 13.91\left(\frac{110}{100}\right) - 3\left(\frac{110}{100}\right)^2\right] = 0.0000296\,\text{m} = 0.0296\,\text{mm}$$

16.8 Equilibrium of multicomponent phases

The conditions for equilibrium of multicomponent phases are similar to those of pure substances. The temperature must be uniform in equilibrium regardless of the number of phases and components. In addition, the chemical potential of each component must be equal in all the phases where it is a real component. Consequently, the fugacity of each component must be uniform throughout the system.

Equilibrium in multicomponent phases is treated in Chapters 17 and 18.

PROBLEMS

16.1 A salt solution in water at 100 bar, 40 °C, and a mole fraction of water of $x = 0.9$ is at equilibrium with pure water through a membrane semipermeable to water, Fig. 16.8. Given below is an empirical equation for the Gibbs free energy per mole solution at 100 bar and 40 °C, as a function of the water mole fraction:

$$g = Ax + B(1-x) - Cx(1-x)$$

where A = 3000 kJ/kmol, B = 4000 kJ/kmol, C = 3600 kJ/kmol.

Assume the specific volume of pure water is constant, $v_w = 0.001\ \text{m}^3/\text{kg}$.

a. What is the condition for the existence of such an equilibrium?
b. What is the pressure of pure water which is in equilibrium with this solution?

Hint: What is the meaning of A?

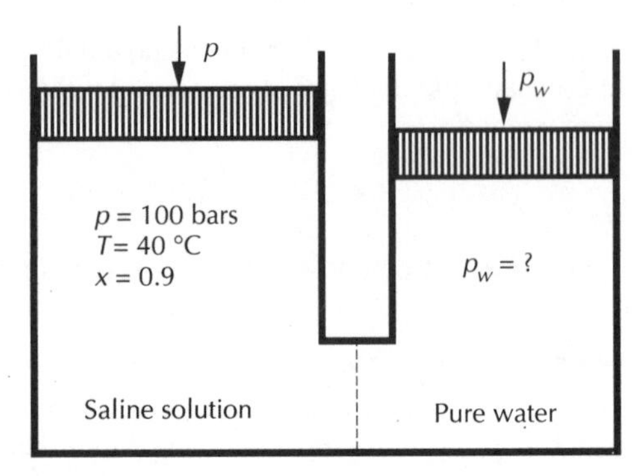

Figure 16.8

16.2 At high enough pressures carbon has two phases in equilibrium – diamond and graphite. The following data are given for the pure phases at 1 bar and 25 °C:

	v(m^3/kg)	g (kJ/kg)	β (bar^{-1})
Graphite	0.446×10^{-3}	0.0	0.310×10^{-6}
Diamond	0.284×10^{-3}	238.6	0.158×10^{-6}

where $\beta = -(\partial \ln v/\partial p)_T$. Assuming β does not change with pressure, find the pressure at which the two phases coexist in equilibrium at 25 °C.

16.3 Find the diameter of the smallest steam bubble which will grow in liquid water at 1 bar and 120 °C. The surface tension of water is given by the following equation:

$$\sigma = (75.64 - 13.91\theta - 3.0\theta^2)\times10^{-3}\ \text{N/m}$$

where $\theta = T$(°C)/100.

16.4 A gas main carries helium at a pressure of 10 kPa and a temperature of 20 °C. It is connected through a membrane which is permeable only to helium to a constant-volume chamber which contains 1 kmol of helium, 2 kmol of hydrogen, and 3 kmol of nitrogen. The initial pressure in the chamber is 10 kPa. The chamber is maintained at a temperature of 20 °C by a bath which surrounds it. Assume that monatomic and diatomic gases have molal specific heats at constant pressures of $5R/2$ and $7R/2$, respectively. Find:

a. The final pressure in the chamber when flow through the membrane ceases.
b. The heat interaction with the bath between the initial and final states.

16.5 A main carrying liquid water at 10 MPa pressure and at a temperature of 100 °C is connected through a membrane, permeable only to water vapor but not liquid water, to a constant-volume chamber which initially contains 1 kg of water vapor at 101 kPa. The chamber is maintained at a temperature of 100 °C by a bath which surrounds it. The chamber walls resist condensation (non-wetting). Find:

a. The final pressure in the chamber when flow through the membrane ceases.
b. The heat interaction with the bath between the initial and final states.

16.6 A rigid vessel contains 1 kg of supersaturated water vapor at 16 kPa and 40 °C (assume water vapor at pressures lower than 1 bar to behave like an ideal gas).

a. Find s, u, h, and v for the water vapor.
b. Find the equilibrium state of the water in the vessel, if the temperature is kept constant by the use of a suitable reservoir.
c. Find the heat interaction of the reservoir in the process of reaching equilibrium.
d. Find the equilibrium state that the water in the vessel will reach in an adiabatic process.
e. Compute the irreversibility of processes b and d with respect to the reservoir.

16.7 Supersaturated water vapor at 16 kPa and 40 °C flows through an adiabatic pipe without friction at a speed of 500 m/s. At a certain place there is a condensation shock wave which causes the water to reach a steady two-phase equilibrium state. Find the state of the water immediately following the condensation wave.

16.8 An equation for the surface tension of water is: $\sigma = 0.118(1-T_r)^{0.9}$.

a. Compare the surface tension calculated by this equation and the equation given in Example 16.2. Plot the results up to the critical point.
b. Evaluate $d\sigma/dT$ at 100 °C.

CHAPTER SEVENTEEN

Ideal solutions

The properties of a multicomponent phase depend, in general, on pressure, temperature, and mole fractions of all the components. For example, the fugacity of component i is

$$f_i = f_i(p, T, x_1, x_2, ..., x_{c-1}) \tag{17.1}$$

The fugacity of a pure component i at the pressure and temperature of the multicomponent phase is denoted by f_i^0. It is a function of p and T only,

$$f_i^0 = f_i^0(p, T) = f_i(p, T, x_i = 1) \tag{17.2}$$

An ideal solution is defined as a special case of a multicomponent phase for which the fugacity of each component is proportional to its mole fraction. Thus for an ideal solution

$$f_i = x_i f_i^0 \tag{17.3}$$

Ideal solutions are idealizations of real solutions, and in general they do not provide an accurate description of a real solution. Ideal solutions, however, simplify considerably the thermodynamic and mathematical treatment of real solutions, and in many cases they give fairly accurate results. The ideal solution almost always serves as a first step in the analysis of a real problem.

We now investigate some of the characteristics of ideal solutions. More specifically we determine what changes may take place when an ideal solution is formed from its components while the pressure and the temperature are kept constant.

17.1 Mixing volume

Consider an ideal solution at pressure p, temperature T, having a composition n_1, n_2, ..., n_c. Let us evaluate the change of volume that took place when this solution was formed by mixing its pure components, each at the same pressure and temperature.

The final volume of the solution, V_2, is given, by definition, by the weighted sum of the partial molar volumes of its components:

$$V_2 = \sum_{i=1}^{c} n_i v_i \tag{17.4}$$

The initial volume, V_1, is given as the sum of the individual volumes of the components:

$$V_1 = \sum_{i=1}^{c} n_i v_i^0 \tag{17.5}$$

The change in volume upon mixing is therefore

$$\Delta V_{mix} = V_2 - V_1 = \sum_{i=1}^{c} n_i (v_i - v_i^0) \tag{17.6}$$

The difference $(v_i - v_i^0)$ can be calculated in terms of the fugacity using Eqs (15.78) and (15.82), noting that $\mu_i = g_i$ and that constant n_i also implies constant x,

$$v_i = \left(\frac{\partial \mu_i}{\partial p}\right)_{T,x} = RT\left(\frac{\partial \ln f_i}{\partial p}\right)_{T,x} \tag{17.7}$$

and similarly,

$$v_i^0 = \left(\frac{\partial \mu_i^0}{\partial p}\right)_{T} = RT\left(\frac{\partial \ln f_i^0}{\partial p}\right)_{T}$$

leading to

$$v_i - v_i^0 = RT\left[\frac{\partial \ln(f_i/f_i^0)}{\partial p}\right]_{Tx} \tag{17.8}$$

For an ideal solution, f_i may be taken from Eq. (17.3) to yield

$$v_i - v_i^0 = RT\left(\frac{\partial \ln x_i}{\partial p}\right)_{T,x} = 0 \tag{17.9}$$

Substitution of Eq. (17.9) into Eq. (17.6) results in

$$\Delta V_{mix} = 0 \tag{17.10}$$

Hence, there is no change in the volume upon the mixing of components to form an ideal solution. Some authors use this fact and define an ideal solution as one for which the mixing volume is zero.

Since the mixing volume of an ideal solution is zero its specific volume may be calculated from the specific volumes of the pure components by

$$v_1 = \sum_{i=1}^{c} x_i v_i^0 \tag{17.11}$$

17.2 Enthalpy of mixing

We now evaluate the mixing enthalpy, namely the change of enthalpy that takes place when a solution is formed by mixing its pure components, each at the same pressure and temperature, p and T.

The final enthalpy, H_2, is given by the weighted sum of the partial enthalpies, while the initial enthalpy, H_1, is given as the sum of the individual enthalpies of the pure components. The change in enthalpy is then

$$\Delta H_{mix} = H_2 - H_1 = \sum_{i=1}^{c} n_i (h_i - h_i^0) \tag{17.12}$$

The difference $(h_i - h_i^0)$ can be calculated in terms of the fugacity using Eqs (15.85) and noting that $\mu_i = g_i$ and that constant n_i also implies constant x_i,

$$\frac{(h_i - h_i^0)}{RT^2} = -\left[\frac{\partial \ln(f_i/f_i^0)}{\partial T}\right]_{p,n} = -\left[\frac{\partial \ln a_i}{\partial T}\right]_{p,n} \tag{17.13}$$

For ideal solutions

$$a_i = x_i \tag{17.14}$$

Hence,

$$\frac{(h_i - h_i^0)}{RT^2} = -\left[\frac{\partial \ln x_i}{\partial T}\right]_{p,x} = 0 \tag{17.15}$$

leading to the conclusion that for an ideal solution

$$\Delta H_{mix} = 0 \tag{17.16}$$

Since there is no change in the enthalpy upon mixing the components of an ideal solution the enthalpy of the mixture can, therefore, be calculated from the enthalpies of the pure components:

$$h_1 = \sum_{i=1}^{c} x_i h_i^0 \tag{17.17}$$

17.3 Entropy of mixing

We now evaluate the mixing entropy, i.e. the change of entropy that occurs when a solution is formed by mixing its pure components, each at the same pressure and temperature, p and T. The entropy change upon mixing is

$$\Delta S_{mix} = S_2 - S_1 = \sum_{i=1}^{c} n_i \left(s_i - s_i^0\right) \tag{17.18}$$

The difference $(s_i - s_i^0)$ can be calculated in terms of the fugacity using Eq. (15.84):

$$s_i - s_i^0 = -\left(\frac{\partial[RT \ln(f_i / f_i^0)]}{\partial T}\right)_{p,x} = -\left(\frac{\partial(RT \ln x_i)}{\partial T}\right)_{p,x} = -R \ln x_i \tag{17.19}$$

Hence,

$$\Delta S_{mix} = -R\sum_{i=1}^{c} n_i \ln x_i = nR\sum_{i=1}^{c}(-x_i \ln x_i) \tag{17.20}$$

Unlike the volume and the enthalpy, the entropy does change when components are mixed to form an ideal solution. It can be easily shown that the entropy of mixing is always positive. Indeed, each term in the sum of Eq. (17.20) is positive, $-x_i \ln x_i > 0$, since each mole fraction, x_i, is less than unity. Therefore

$$\Delta S_{mix} > 0 \tag{17.21}$$

Other properties of mixing for ideal solutions can be easily obtained from the above relationships. Thus,

$$\Delta U_{mix} = 0 \tag{17.22}$$

$$\Delta A_{mix} = RT\sum_{i=1}^{c} n_i \ln x_i = nRT\sum_{i=1}^{c} x_i \ln x_i \tag{17.23}$$

and

$$\Delta G_{mix} = RT\sum_{i=1}^{c} n_i \ln x_i = nRT\sum_{i=1}^{c} x_i \ln x_i \tag{17.24}$$

17.4 Binary mixtures

Mixtures can, in general, have any number of components. The simplest, and the least complicated to handle analytically, is a binary mixture, i.e. a mixture that consists of two components only.

For a binary mixture the number of components is $c = 2$. Hence, the Gibbs rule, applied to this case, reads

$$F = 2 + c - r = 4 - r \tag{17.25}$$

A single-phase binary mixture in a state of equilibrium has three degrees of freedom; that is, three intensive properties may be arbitrarily changed. These could be, for example, pressure, temperature, and the mole fraction of one of the components (p, T, x).

When two phases coexist in equilibrium there are two degrees of freedom. These can be either p and T or p and x or T and x. Consider a binary mixture of A and B in two phases, liquid and vapor, each being an ideal solution. The concentration of component A in the liquid phase is denoted by x while that in the vapor phase is denoted by y. Figure 17.1 shows two phases of a binary system and lists some of the relevant properties of each phase. Even in equilibrium, the values of x and y need not be equal; neither do the other properties, such as partial volumes, partial enthalpies, etc. There are, however, definite relationships between the properties of the two phases. We now investigate these relationships.

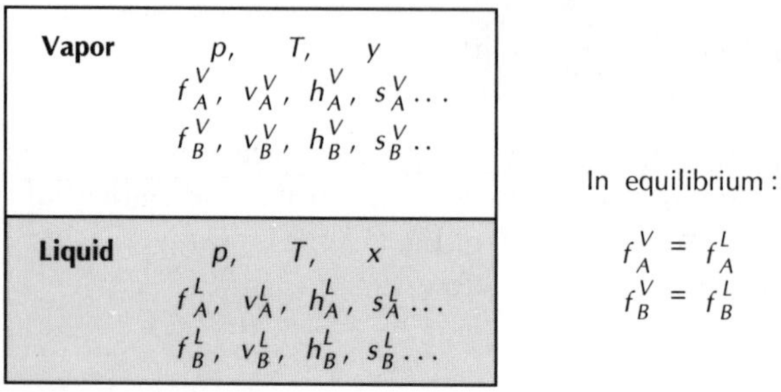

Vapor
p, T, y
f_A^V, v_A^V, h_A^V, s_A^V...
f_B^V, v_B^V, h_B^V, s_B^V..
Liquid
p, T, x
f_A^L, v_A^L, h_A^L, s_A^L...
f_B^L, v_B^L, h_B^L, s_B^L...
In equilibrium:
$f_A^V = f_A^L$
$f_B^V = f_B^L$

Figure 17.1

We have already seen in Chapter 16 that for a system in equilibrium the fugacities of each component are the same in all phases. This fact is used in relating other properties between phases.

The fugacity of component A in the liquid phase of an ideal solution is given by Eq. (17.3):

$$f_A^L = xf_A^0 \tag{17.26}$$

A similar expression may be written for component B:

$$f_B^L = (1-x)f_B^0 \tag{17.27}$$

Figure 17.2 depicts schematically the fugacity-concentration relationship for an ideal binary solution. The vapor phase may be assumed to be an ideal gas mixture. This assumption holds well for gases at low pressures. Hence, for components A and B in the vapor phase we have

$$f_A^V = p_A = yp \text{ and } f_B^V = p_B = (1-y)p \tag{17.28}$$

In equilibrium the fugacity of a component in the binary vapor phase is equal to that in the liquid phase:

T = const.
f_A
$f_A^0 = p_A^{sat}$
$f_B^0 = p_B^{sat}$
f_B
0
1.0
x

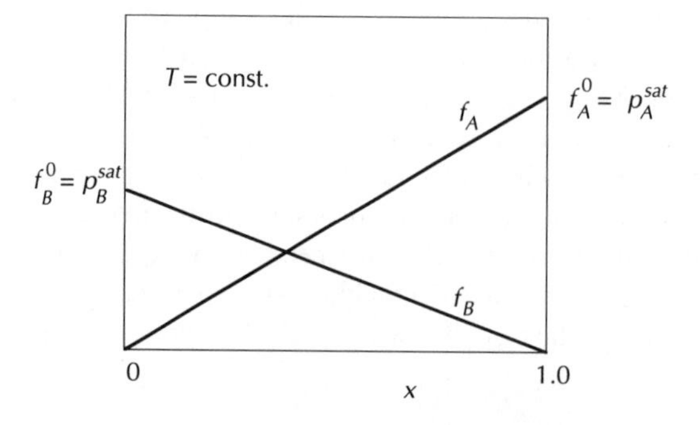

Figure 17.2 **An $f-x$ plot for an ideal binary solution.**

$$f_A^L = f_A^V \text{ and } f_B^L = f_B^V \tag{17.29}$$

Hence, from Eqs (17.26)–(17.29) we obtain

$$xf_A^0 = yp \text{ and } (1-x)f_B^0 = (1-y)p \tag{17.30}$$

The fugacity of a pure component, f_A^0, in the liquid phase is also equal to that of pure vapor in equilibrium with the liquid. Assuming the vapor to be an ideal gas, its fugacity is equal to its pressure. Thus the fugacity of the pure liquid component is equal to its vapor pressure, and the latter is approximately equal to the saturation pressure of the pure component at the temperature of the mixture. Hence,

$$f_A^0 = p_A^{sat} \quad \text{and } f_B^0 = p_B^{sat} \tag{17.31}$$

Combining Eq. (17.31) with Eq. (17.30) leads to an expression that relates the concentration of a component in a liquid mixture to that in the vapor phase in equilibrium with the liquid,

$$y = x\frac{p_A^{sat}}{p} \text{ and } (1-y) = (1-x)\frac{p_B^{sat}}{p} \tag{17.32}$$

From these equations the total pressure, p, in equilibrium with the solution (i.e. the saturation pressure of that solution) is extracted:

$$p = xp_A^{sat} + (1-x)p_B^{sat} = p_B^{sat} + x\left(p_A^{sat} - p_B^{sat}\right) \tag{17.33}$$

The mole fraction of a component in the vapor phase may be related to the mole fraction of that component in the liquid phase by substituting Eq. (17.33) into Eq. (17.32), and dividing the numerator and the denominator by p_A^{sat}. Thus

$$y = \frac{x}{x+(1-x)\alpha} = \frac{x}{\alpha+(1-\alpha)x} \tag{17.34}$$

where $\alpha = p_B^{sat} / p_A^{sat}$ is called the volatility ratio. Equation (17.34) may be solved for x when y is known,

$$x = \frac{\alpha y}{1+(\alpha-1)y} \tag{17.35}$$

The relationship between the concentrations of liquid and vapor is shown in Fig. 17.3. It can be seen from Eq. (17.33) that the saturation pressure of the solution plotted against the concentration of component A in the liquid phase, is a straight line. This line is called the liquid line. For a given liquid composition there is a corresponding composition of the vapor, given by Eq. (17.34). Hence, point b represents the composition of the vapor in equilibrium with the liquid; that is, the fugacity of the vapor at point b is equal to the fugacity of the liquid at point a, and the two phases are in mutual equilibrium. For each point on the liquid line a corresponding vapor point may be found. The line connecting all the vapor points is called the vapor line.

The region above the liquid line represents compressed liquid states, characterized by higher pressures, in analogy to that of a single-component compressed liquid. The region below the vapor line corresponds to superheated vapor of the binary mixture.

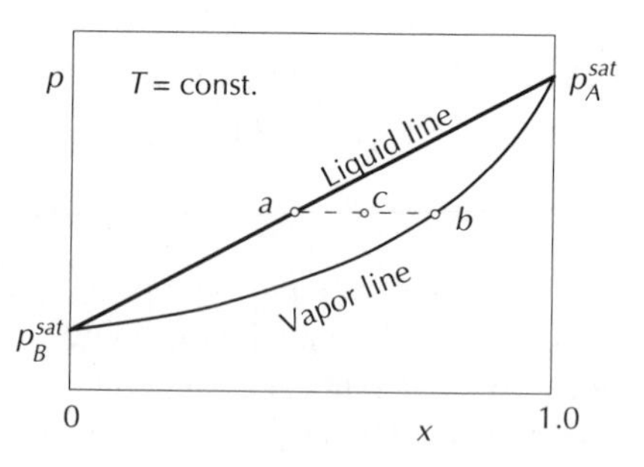

Figure 17.3

The region between the two lines represents the two-phase region. Point *c* in that region is a virtual point, representing a weighted average of the two distinct phases at *a* and *b*, respectively. The intensive properties of the two phases are fixed by the pressure and temperature alone, and the number of moles in each phase are related to each other by the inverse fulcrum rule $n^V / n^L = ac / cb$.

Consider now a liquid binary mixture of A and B maintained at constant temperature, *T*, inside a piston–cylinder assembly, as shown in Fig. 17.4.

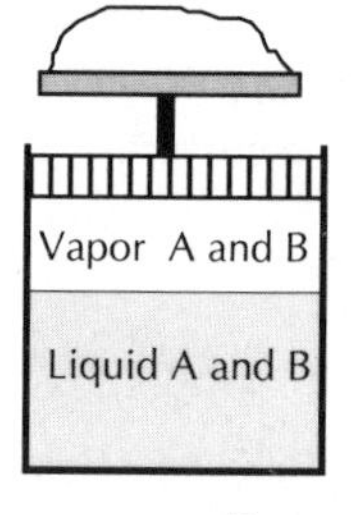

Figure 17.4

We now follow an isothermal process in which the pressure is gradually reduced from a high value, point 1, to a low value, point 5, as shown in Fig. 17.5 by the vertical line connecting points 1 and 5. Initially, at point 1, there is only one phase of a compressed liquid. There are three degrees of freedom, and thus the pressure may be changed although the temperature and concentration remain fixed. When the pressure reaches the liquid line, a second phase, that of vapor, begins to form. As the pressure is further reduced the vapor phase grows at the expense of the liquid phase. In this region there are only two degrees of freedom. Therefore, the temperature and pressure fix the intensive state of each phase.

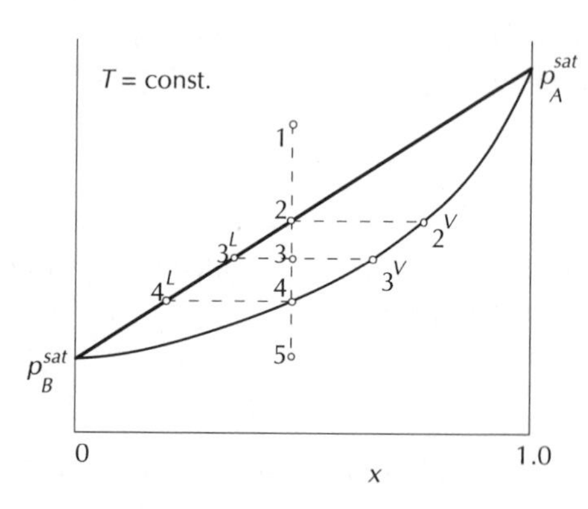

Figure 17.5

The amounts of matter in each phase are such that the weighted average concentration of the two phases is exactly equal to the initial concentration. At point 3, for instance, the composition of the liquid is given by point 3^L and that of the vapor by point 3^V. The lowest pressure, corresponding to the given initial conditions, for which two phases can still coexist, is at point 4, where a minute amount of liquid at 4^L is in equilibrium with the vapor at 4. We note that the pressure varies from p_2 to p_4 during the phase transition from liquid to vapor. This is in contrast to the phase transition in a pure substance that takes place at a constant pressure. Pressure reduction beyond point 4 brings the binary mixture into the superheated vapor single-phase region.

When three phases coexist in equilibrium there is only one degree of freedom, and when four phases coexist there is no degree of freedom; that is, no intensive property can be varied arbitrarily.

EXAMPLE 17.1

An ideal liquid solution at 30 °C consists of 2 kmol of component A ($p_A^{sat} = 40$ kPa) and 6 kmol of component B ($p_B^{sat} = 50$ kPa). Find:

a. The saturation pressure of the solution at 30 °C.
b. The composition of the vapor phase which is in equilibrium with the liquid.
c. The composition of the last drop of liquid that evaporates during an isothermal expansion (reduction in pressure) in a piston–cylinder assembly.
d. The composition of the last drop of liquid that evaporates, if the vapor is continuously removed.

SOLUTION

Let

$$p_A = p_A^{sat} = 40 \text{ kPa} \qquad p_B = p_B^{sat} = 50 \text{ kPa} \qquad \alpha = \frac{p_B}{p_A} = \frac{50}{40} = 1.25$$

and let

$$x = x_A = \frac{n_A}{n_A + n_B} = \frac{2}{2+6} = 0.25 \qquad 1 - x = x_B = 0.75$$

a. The pressure of an ideal solution is given by Eq. (17.33):

$$p = xp_A + (1-x)p_B = 0.25 \times 40 + 0.75 \times 50 = 47.5 \text{ kPa}$$

b. The composition of the gaseous phase, in equilibrium with the liquid, is found from Eq. (17.32):

$$y = x\frac{p_A}{p} = 0.25\frac{40}{47.5} = 0.2105 \quad \text{and} \quad 1 - y = 0.7895$$

c. When the liquid in a closed vessel evaporates completely, the total content as well as the amount of each component do not change. Hence, the final composition of the vapor is equal to the initial composition of the liquid, i.e.

$$y_A = y = 0.25 \text{ and } y_B = (1-y) = 0.75$$

The last drop of liquid is in equilibrium with the vapor at the final composition. The composition of the last drop of liquid is found from Eq. (17.35):

$$x_A = x = \frac{\alpha y}{1 + (\alpha - 1)y} = \frac{1.25 \times 0.25}{1 + 0.25 \times 0.25} = 0.2941 \text{ and } x_B = 1 - x = 0.7059$$

d. At any composition the vapor is richer in component B than the liquid. Therefore, if the vapor is removed as soon as it is created then the liquid becomes richer in component A. As the vaporization continues, the concentration of A in the liquid increases until it reaches the state of pure A when the last drop evaporates.

17.5 Ideal gas mixtures

Ideal gas mixtures discussed in Chapter 12 constitute a special case of ideal solutions, and, therefore, all the mixing relationships derived above hold for ideal gas mixtures. Hence, Amagat's rule, Eq. (12.13), which states that the volume of the mixture at p and T is equal to the sum of the volumes of the components, each at p and T, is equivalent to the statement that the mixing volume in an ideal gas mixture is zero.

Similarly, the mixing energy and the mixing enthalpy are also zero. The mixing entropy of an ideal gas mixture is given by Eq. (17.20).

The partial pressure mentioned in Chapter 12 is, of course, not a partial property. The choice of the term is historical and rather inappropriate.

17.6 Phase equilibria in multicomponent mixtures

Understanding phase equilibria in multicomponent systems is important in such diverse areas as distillation, absorption, and extraction. Phenomena such as elevation of the boiling point of a salt–water mixture, osmosis, limits of solubility, etc., are governed by the laws of phase equilibria. In this section we derive a general relationship for phase equilibria in ideal solutions and apply it to special cases of engineering importance.

Consider two phases in mutual equilibrium, each containing at least one common component denoted by the subscript i. Two such phases are shown in Fig. 17.6. For these phases to be in equilibrium several conditions must be met. Firstly, the temperature, T, has to be equal in both phases:

$$T' = T \tag{17.36}$$

Moreover, the chemical potential, or, equivalently, the fugacity of *each* component, must be equal in both phases:

$$\mu'_i = \mu_i \text{ or } f'_i = f_i \tag{17.37}$$

When each of the phases is an ideal solution

$$f'_i = f'_i\,(T, p', x'_i) \tag{17.38}$$

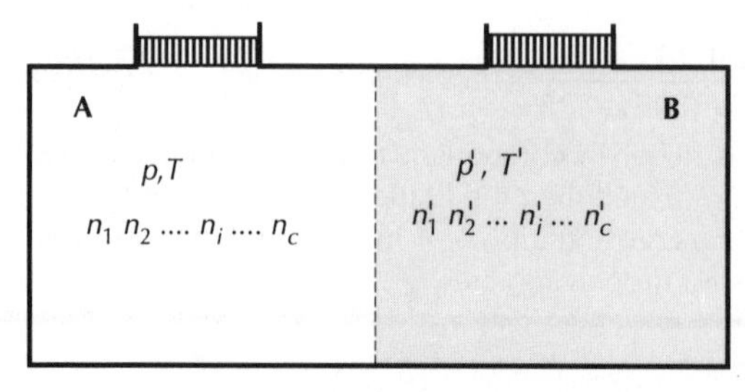

Figure 17.6 **Two phases in equilibrium.**

and

$$f_i = f_i(T, p, x_i) \tag{17.39}$$

In equilibrium there is no need for the pressures of the two phases to be equal. If the interface is planar and cannot withstand any forces, the pressures must be equal. When, on the other hand, the interface is curved or rigid, then equilibrium may exist even if the pressures of the two phases are not equal. For example, in a capillary tube, the pressure in the liquid may differ from that in the gaseous phase, yet the liquid can be in equilibrium with the vapor.

We now consider two phases in equilibrium where some of the independent properties are varied. These variations can be arbitrary provided the two phases are maintained in mutual equilibrium. The latter requirement imposes certain limitations on these changes. For example, the change of temperature must be equal in both phases at all times. Moreover, since mutual equilibrium is maintained during these changes, Eq. (17.37) implies that

$$d \ln f'_i = d \ln f_i \tag{17.40}$$

The total differentials of Eq. (17.40) may be expressed in terms of the respective independent properties given by Eqs (17.38) and (17.39),

$$\begin{aligned} &\left(\frac{\partial \ln f'_i}{\partial T}\right)_{p',x'} dT + \left(\frac{\partial \ln f'_i}{\partial p'}\right)_{T,x'} dp' + \left(\frac{\partial \ln f'_i}{\partial x'_i}\right)_{p',T} dx'_i \\ &\quad = \left(\frac{\partial \ln f_i}{\partial T}\right)_{p,x} dT + \left(\frac{\partial \ln f_i}{\partial p}\right)_{T,x} dp + \left(\frac{\partial \ln f_i}{\partial x_i}\right)_{p,T} dx_i \end{aligned} \tag{17.41}$$

Using Eq. (17.3) and rearranging we obtain

$$\left[\left(\frac{\partial \ln f'_i}{\partial T}\right)_{p',x} - \left(\frac{\partial \ln f_i}{\partial T}\right)_{p,x}\right] dT + \left(\frac{\partial \ln f'_i}{\partial p'}\right)_{T,x'} dp' - \left(\frac{\partial \ln f_i}{\partial p}\right)_{T,x} dp + \frac{dx'_i}{x'_i} - \frac{dx_i}{x_i} = 0 \tag{17.42}$$

The partial derivatives in Eq. (17.42) can be expressed in terms of partial properties using the appropriate expressions developed in Chapter 15. From Eq. (15.82) we obtain

$$\left(\frac{\partial \ln f'_i}{\partial p'}\right)_{T,x'} = \frac{v'_i}{RT} \quad \text{and} \quad \left(\frac{\partial \ln f_i}{\partial p}\right)_{T,x} = \frac{v_i}{RT} \tag{17.43}$$

From the expression for enthalpy, Eq. (15.85) we have

$$\left[\frac{\partial \ln(f'_i / p)}{\partial T}\right]_{p',n} = -\frac{h'_i - h^*_i}{RT^2} \tag{17.44}$$

and

$$\left[\frac{\partial \ln(f_i / p)}{\partial T}\right]_{p,n} = -\frac{h_i - h_i^*}{RT^2} \tag{17.45}$$

Subtracting Eq. (17.44) from Eq. (17.45) we obtain

$$\left(\frac{\partial \ln f_i}{\partial T}\right)_{p,n} - \left(\frac{\partial \ln f_i'}{\partial T}\right)_{p',n} = \frac{h_i' - h_i}{RT^2} \tag{17.46}$$

and substitution of Eqs (17.43) and (17.46) into Eq. (17.42) leads to

$$\frac{v_i' dp' - v_i dp}{RT} - \frac{h_i' - h_i'}{RT^2} dT + \left(\frac{dx_i'}{x_i'} - \frac{dx_i}{x_i}\right) = 0 \tag{17.47}$$

Equation (17.47) is a general expression that relates the variation of the independent properties of two phases of ideal solutions, in mutual equilibrium. We now use this expression to derive relationships for several physical phenomena in multicomponent phase equilibria (see Table 17.1).

17.7 Equilibrium between a pure and a multicomponent phase

We now consider an important special case of phase equilibria whereby the primed phase in Eq. (17.47) is a pure phase of substance i, as shown in Fig. 17.7.

We denote the properties of the pure phase of component i, in equilibrium with the mixture, by the index iE, the properties of the whole multicomponent phase by no index, and the partial properties of a component of the multicomponent phase, as usual, by the index i. Thus, v_{iE} is the specific volume in the pure phase, $v = V/n$ is the specific volume of the multicomponent phase, and v_i is the partial volume of component i in that phase, $v_i = (\partial V / \partial n_i)_{p,T,n_j}$. The pressure of the pure phase is denoted by p_{iE} and that of the multi component phase is denoted by p. There is no meaning in this notation to p_i, since there is no such partial property.

It is obvious, from discussions in Chapter 16, that the temperatures of the two phases in mutual equilibrium must be equal. It was also shown that the chemical potentials of

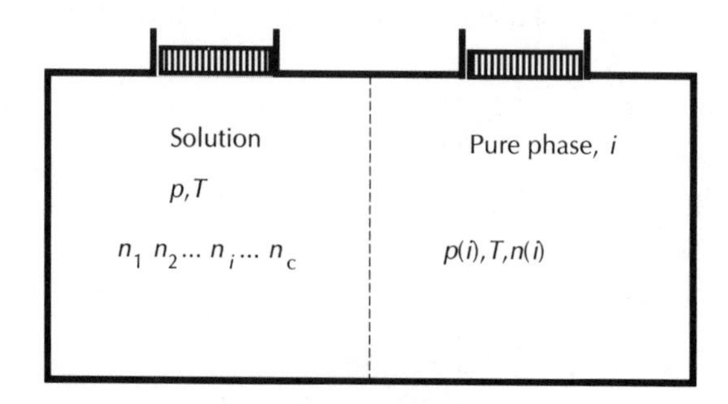

Figure 17.7 **Equilibrium between a pure phase and a solution.**

this component must be the same in both phases. The pressure, on the other hand, need not be equal in both phases.

We now rewrite Eq. (17.47) for this case, by letting the primed phase be the pure component, denoted by iE:

$$\frac{v_i dp - v_{iE} dp_{iE}}{RT} - \frac{h_i - h_{iE}}{RT^2} dT + \frac{dx_i}{x_i} = 0 \tag{17.48}$$

Equation (17.48) relates the properties of a component in a mixture to those of a pure phase of the same component in equilibrium with the mixture. Several applications of this equation are presented in the following sections.

EXAMPLE 17.2

A binary solution, of components A and B, at $p_0 = 10$ MPa, $T = 30$ °C, and mole fraction of component A, $x_A = 0.98$, is in equilibrium with a phase of pure A, through a membrane permeable to A only. The Gibbs free energy for this solution is given by

$$g = C_A x + C_B(1-x) + RT[x \ln x + (1-x)\ln(1-x)]$$

where $C_A = 3000$ kJ/kmol
$C_B = 3000$ kJ/kmol
$R = 8.3143$ kJ/kmol K

and x is the mole fraction of component A. Assume the specific volume of pure A is constant at $v_A = 0.020$ m³/kmol.

a. List the conditions for equilibrium in this case.
b. Interpret the meaning of the constants C_A and C_B.
c. Is this solution ideal?
d. Find the pressure of a phase of pure A which is in equilibrium with the solution.

SOLUTION

a. The conditions for equilibrium are:
   (i) The temperatures of the two phases must be equal.
   (ii) The chemical potential of component A must be equal in both phases, $g_A = g_{AE}$.
b. The meaning of C_A and C_B can be easily understood by looking at the extreme states:
   At $x = 1$, $g = C_A = g_A^0$; thus C_A is the chemical potential of the pure A.

   At $x = 0$, $g = C_B = g_B^0$; thus C_B is the chemical potential of the pure B.
c. The chemical potential of component A in the solution is calculated from the given expression of the specific Gibbs free energy, Eq. (15.88):

$$g_A = g + (1-x)\left(\frac{\partial g}{\partial x}\right)_{p,T} = C_A x + C_B(1-x) + RT[x\ln x + (1-x)\ln(1-x)]$$
$$+ (1-x)\big(C_A - C_B + RT[\ln x - \ln(1-x)]\big)$$

which simplifies to

$$g_A = C_A + RT\ln x = g_A^0 + RT\ln x$$

and similarly

$$g_B = C_B + RT\ln(1-x) = g_B^0 + RT\ln(1-x)$$

The fugacity of each component is given in Eq.(15.68) by

$$f_A = f_A{}^0 \exp\left(\frac{\mu_A - \mu_A^0}{RT}\right) = f_A{}^0 \exp\left(\frac{g_A - g_A^0}{RT}\right) = x f_A{}^0$$

and

$$f_B = f_B^0 \exp\left(\frac{\mu_B - \mu_B^0}{RT}\right) = f_B^0 \exp\left(\frac{g_B - g_B^0}{RT}\right) = (1-x) f_B^0$$

which is consistent with the definition of an ideal solution, Eq. (17.3).

d. Consider a solution of A and B in equilibrium with a pure phase of A. The solution is maintained at a fixed pressure p_0 = 10 MPa, and temperature 30 °C, while the amount of B is slowly being changed. Initially, when the solution contains no component B, its pressure must be the equilibrium pressure of pure A. Then component B is slowly added to the solution until the mole fraction of A drops to 0.98. The chemical potential of A changes with x according to

$$g_A(p_0, T, x) = g_A^0(p_0, T) + RT\ln x$$

For equilibrium to exist, the chemical potential of pure A must be equal to that of component A in the solution. The pressure of the pure phase changes with the composition of the solution. The chemical potential of the pure phase of A at 30 °C is given as a function of its pressure by

$$g_A(p, T) = g_A^0(p_0, T) + \int_{p_0}^{p} v_A dp = g_A^0(p_0, T) + v_A(p - p_0)$$

Hence

$$RT\ln x = v_A(p - p_0)$$

The pressure of the phase of pure A is therefore

$$p = p_0 + \frac{RT}{v_A}\ln x = 10.0 + \frac{8.3143 \times 303.15}{0.02 \times 1000}\ln 0.98 = 10.0 - 2.55 = 7.45\ \text{MPa}$$

17.8 Effect of solute concentration on boiling point

It is well known that a salt–water solution boils at a higher temperature than pure water. This phenomenon, illustrated in Fig. 17.8, is easily explained by Eq. (17.48). Here the pressures of both phases are unchanged, $dp = dp_{iE} = 0$. Let us denote the solvent by the index 1 and the solute by 2. Now Eq. (17.48), written for the solvent, $i = 1$, becomes

$$\frac{dT}{dx_1} = \frac{RT^2}{(h_1 - h_{1E})x_1} \tag{17.49}$$

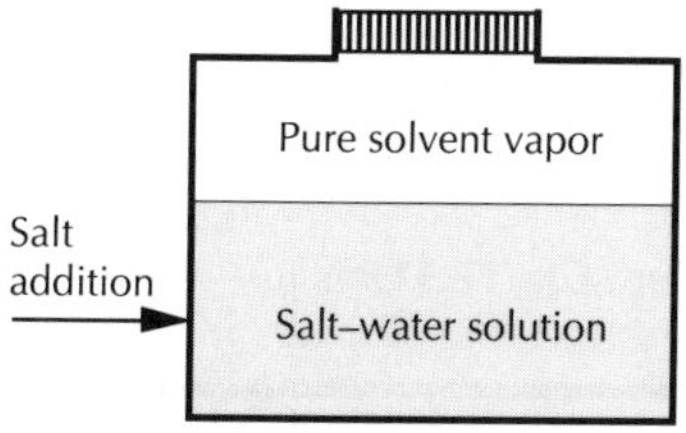

Pure solvent vapor

Salt addition

Salt–water solution

Figure 17.8 **Effect of solute on boiling point.**

where h_1 is the partial enthalpy of liquid water, which is approximately equal to its saturation liquid enthalpy, while h_{1E} is the specific enthalpy of pure water vapor; hence, $h_1 - h_{1E} \approx -h_{fg}$. Noting that $x_1 = 1 - x_2$, $dx_1 = -dx_2$, Eq. (17.49) is rewritten as

$$\frac{dT}{dx_2} = \frac{RT^2}{h_{fg}x_1} = \frac{RT^2}{h_{fg}(1-x_2)} \tag{17.50}$$

or

$$\frac{dT}{T^2} = \frac{Rdx_2}{h_{fg}x_1} = \frac{Rdx_2}{h_{fg}(1-x_2)} \tag{17.50}$$

Integration between the state of pure water ($x_2 = 0$) and a final solute concentration x_2 yields the boiling point elevation of water due to salt:

$$\frac{1}{T_b} - \frac{1}{T_b^0} = \frac{R}{h_{fg}} \ln(1-x_2)$$

or

$$T_b - T_b^0 = -\frac{RT_bT_b^0}{h_{fg}} \ln(1-x_2) \approx \frac{RT^2}{h_{fg}} x_2 \tag{17.51}$$

EXAMPLE 17.3

What is the boiling point elevation of a 10% by weight salt-in-water solution at atmospheric pressure of $p = 101.35$ kPa?

SOLUTION

A 100 g amount of a 10% solution contains 10 g of NaCl ($M_2 = 58.5$) and 90 g of water ($M_1 = 18.0$). Hence

$$x_2 = \frac{m_2/M_2}{m_2/M_2 + m_1/M_1} = \frac{10/58.5}{10/58.5 + 90/18} = 0.03306$$

From the steam tables we have for $p = 101.35$ kPa:
$h_{fg} = 2257.0$ kJ/kg and $T_b = 100$ °C = 373.15 K

Hence, Eq. (17.80) yields

$$T_b - T_b^0 = \frac{RT^2 x_2}{h_{fg}} = \frac{8.3143 \times 373.15^2 \times 0.03306}{18 \times 2257.0} = 0.942\ ^\circ\mathrm{C}$$

The effect of the solute on boiling point elevation, Eq. (17.51), is just one example of the application of Eq. (17.48).

17.9 Effect of pressure on solubility

Consider a pure solid in equilibrium with a solid–liquid solution, Fig. 17.9. In this case both phases are at the same pressure and temperature, i.e. $p = p_{1E}$ and $dT = 0$; therefore, Eq. (17.48) simplifies to

$$\frac{v_1 - v_{1E}}{RT} dp + \frac{dx_1}{x_1} = 0 \qquad (17.52)$$

or

$$\left(\frac{\partial \ln x_1}{\partial p}\right)_T = -\frac{v_1 - v_{1E}}{RT} \qquad (17.53)$$

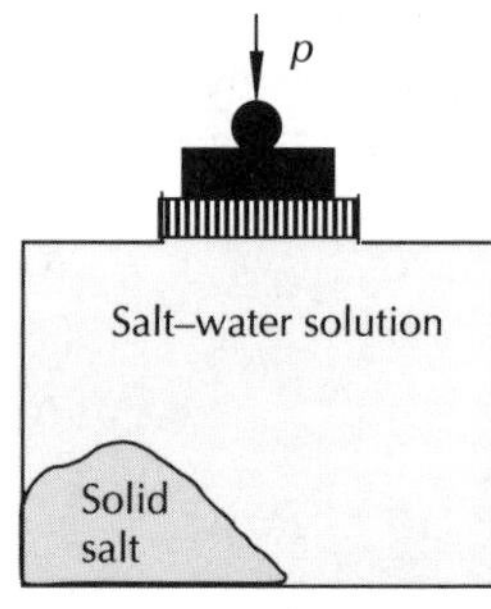

Figure 17.9 **Effect of pressure on salt solubility.**

17.10 Effect of temperature on solubility

Consider a pure solid in equilibrium with a solid–liquid solution, shown in Fig. 17.10. We look for the change of solubility with temperature while the pressure remains constant. In this case there is no pressure change in both phases, $dp = 0$, and Eq. (17.48) simplifies to

$$\left(\frac{\partial \ln x_i}{\partial T}\right)_p = \frac{h_i - h_{iE}}{RT^2} \qquad (17.54)$$

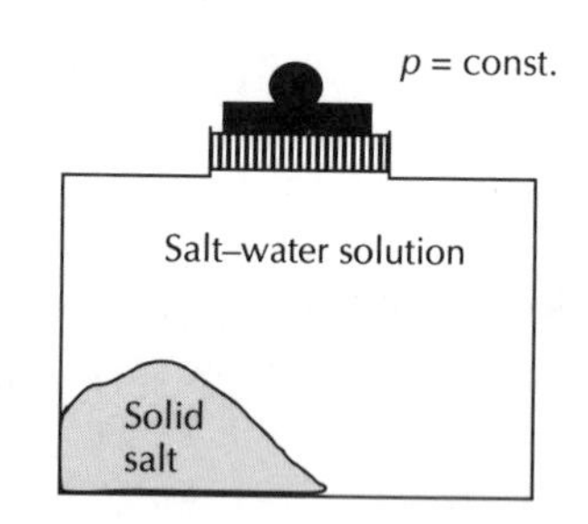

Figure 17.10 **Effect of temperature on salt solubility.**

Here h_{iE} is the specific enthalpy of the pure solute, while h_i is its partial enthalpy in solution. Equation (17.54) gives the effect of temperature on salt solubility.

Equations like (17.53) and (17.54) may also be written for the solvent. Hence, Eq. (17.50), given above, may describe the effect of solute on the boiling point of the solution. A similar equation for the effect on the freezing point is

$$\frac{dT}{dx_2} = \frac{RT^2}{h_{sf}} \frac{1}{1 - x_2} \tag{17.55}$$

where h_{sf} is the enthalpy change during melting.

When there is no change in concentration in the solution, $dx_i = 0$, and Eq. (17.48) simplifies to

$$\left(\frac{\partial T}{\partial p}\right)_x = \frac{(v_i - v_{iE})T}{h_i - h_{iE}} \tag{17.56}$$

Equation (17.56) is an extension of the Clapeyron equation. It shows the effect of pressure on the temperature of a phase transition in a solution. Indeed, for a pure substance, $x = 1$, and it simplifies to Eq. (13.32):

$$\left(\frac{\partial T}{\partial p}\right)^{sat} = \frac{T v_{fg}}{h_{fg}} \tag{17.57}$$

17.11 Osmosis

It was shown that given a semipermeable membrane a mixture can be in equilibrium with a pure solvent phase even though the pressures of the two phases are not equal. Indeed, it is possible for the pure component to transfer into the mixture even if the pressure of the latter is higher. This phenomenon is called osmosis. The transfer of solvent from the pure phase into the mixture stops when equilibrium is reached. At equilibrium there is a definite pressure difference between the phases. The pressure difference, required to maintain equilibrium, is called the osmotic pressure.

The osmotic pressure can be evaluated from Eq. (17.48) under the conditions of constant temperature, $dT = 0$, and constant pressure of the pure phase, $dp_{iE} = 0$:

$$dp = -\frac{RT}{v_1}\frac{dx_1}{x_1} = \frac{RT}{v_1}\frac{dx_2}{(1 - x_2)} \tag{17.58}$$

The osmotic pressure is obtained by integration of Eq. (17.58). Exact integration requires knowledge of how the partial volume, v_1, varies with solute concentration, x_2. For liquids v_1 may be assumed to be a constant, leading to

$$p - p_{iE} = \int_0^{x2} \frac{RT}{v_1}\frac{dx_2}{(1 - x_2)} \approx -\frac{RT}{v_1}\ln(1 - x_2) \approx \frac{RT}{v_1} x_2 \tag{17.59}$$

The difference $p - p_{iE}$ is the osmotic pressure, P:

$$P = p - p_{iE} \tag{17.60}$$

Osmosis may be used to separate the solvent from a mixture. As an example consider the desalination of sea water by a process called "reverse osmosis". In this process desalination is achieved by pressurizing the mixture above its osmotic pressure.

EXAMPLE 17.4

Estimate the osmotic pressure of ocean water at 20 °C assuming it is an ideal solution of 3.5 % by weight NaCl in water. The molecular weight of water is $M_1 = 18.02$ and that of NaCl is $M_2 = 58.5$. Thus for NaCl, consider two cases:
a. No dissociation of the salt molecule into ions.
b. The salt fully dissociates according to: $NaCl \Rightarrow Na^+ + Cl^-$

SOLUTION

a. Consider 1 kg of sea water. The number of moles of the solvent, denoted by index 1, and the solute, denoted by index 2, are

$$n_1 = \frac{m_1}{M_1} = \frac{0.965}{18.02} = 0.05355 \text{ kmol/kg} \qquad n_2 = \frac{m_2}{M_2} = \frac{0.035}{58.5} = 0.0005983 \text{ kmol/kg}$$

The mole fraction of the solute NaCl and the solvent water are

$$x_1 = \frac{n_1}{n_1 + n_2} = 0.98895 \qquad x_2 = \frac{n_2}{n_1 + n_2} = 0.01105$$

The expression for the change of osmotic pressure of an ideal solution is given as a special case of Eq. (17.48) in Table 17.1 as

$$\left(dP = \frac{RT}{v_f} \frac{dx_2}{1 - x_2} \right)_{T, P_{1E}}$$

Integration, assuming v_f= const., yields

$$P = -\frac{RT}{v_f} \ln(1 - x_2) \approx \frac{RT}{v_f} x_2 = \frac{(8.3143/18.02) \times 293.15}{0.001002} \times 0.01105 = 1491.4 \text{ kPa}$$

b. If the solute dissociates fully then the number of moles of the solute is doubled while the number of moles of the solvent is unchanged.
In this case:

$n_1 = 0.05355$ kmol/kg and $n_2 = 0.0011966$ kmol/kg
$x_1 = 0.97814$ kmol/kg and $x_2 = 0.021856$ kmol/kg

and the osmotic pressure is

$$P = -\frac{RT}{v_f} \ln(1 - x_2) \approx \frac{RT}{v_f} x_2 = \frac{(8.3143/18.02) \times 293.15}{0.001002} \times 0.021856 = 2950.3 \text{ kPa}$$

The calculations were performed above for two extreme conditions regardless of the actual composition of sea water. Sea water is not uniform in composition. It contains many solutes in addition to NaCl, and the solutes dissociate only partially. The actual osmotic pressure of sea water is approximately 2500 kPa.

17.12 Exergy analysis

Unless special care is taken, a mixing process is usually not reversible. Even though the energy during mixing may be conserved, there is, nevertheless, a loss of availability. The equations for maximum work, maximum useful work, exergy, availability, and irreversibility, that were developed in Chapter 10, are quite general and are, therefore, applicable also to multicomponent systems involving mixing.

The following example illustrates the application of exergy analysis to mixing processes.

EXAMPLE 17.5

A stream of liquid A is being mixed with a stream of liquid B inside a mixing chamber. Both streams enter the chamber at the pressure and temperature of the environment, $p_o = 100$ kPa and $T_o = 300$ K. Stream A enters at a rate of 0.5 kmol/s and stream B at 0.8 kmol/s. One mixed stream exits at the same pressure, p_o, and temperature, T_o, Assume that A and B form an ideal solution.

a. Determine the useful work of the process.
b. Determine the heat interaction of the process.
c. Find the maximum work associated with the process.
d. Find the irreversibility of the process.

SOLUTION

a. The mixing chamber is at steady state; therefore, the work and the useful work of the process are both zero:

$$\dot{W}_x = \dot{W}_x^u = 0$$

b. In the absence of work, the heat interaction of a control volume in steady state is equal to the change in enthalpy of the streams. For ideal solutions, however, the mixing enthalpy, as well as the mixing energy, are equal to zero. (See Eqs (17.16) and (17.22).) Thus there is no heat interaction in the process, i.e. $\dot{Q} = 0$.

c. From Eq. (10.52) for a control volume at steady state, we get

$$\left(\dot{W}_x^u\right)_{max} = \left(\dot{W}_x^u\right)_{rev} = \sum_i b_i \dot{n}_i = \sum_i \dot{n}_i [(h_i - h_i^0) - T_0(s_i - s_i^0) = -T_0 \sum_i \dot{n}_i (s_i - s_i^0)$$

$$\dot{W}_{max}^u = -\dot{n}RT_0 \sum_i x_i \ln x_i = 1.3 \times 8.3143 \times 300 \left(\frac{5}{13} \ln \frac{13}{5} + \frac{8}{13} \ln \frac{13}{8} \right) = 2630.5 \text{ kW}$$

d. From Eq. (10.54)

$$\dot{I} = (\dot{W}_x)_{rev} - \dot{W}_x = \left(\dot{W}_x^u\right)_{rev} - \dot{W}_x^u$$

Since no work was involved in the actual process, the irreversibility is equal to the maximum useful work, i.e.

$$\dot{I} = \left(\dot{W}_x^u\right)_{rev} = 2630.5 \text{ kW}$$

Table 17.1 **Applications of Eq. (17.47) for binary mixtures.**

Pure phase		Conditions	Equation	Remarks
Component	State			
Solvent	Solid	$p = p'$ $dT = 0$	$\left(\frac{\partial p}{\partial x_2}\right)_T = -\frac{RT}{v_{sf}}\frac{1}{1-x_2}$	Effect of solute addition on freezing pressure
		$p = p'$ $dp = 0$	$\left(\frac{\partial T}{\partial x_2}\right)_p = \frac{RT^2}{h_{sf}}\frac{1}{1-x_2}$	Effect of solute addition on freezing temperature
		$p = p'$ $dp = 0$	$\left(\frac{\partial p}{\partial T}\right)_x = \frac{h_{sf}}{Tv_{sf}}$	Clapeyron equation for freezing
Solute	Solid	$p = p'$ $dT = 0$	$\left(\frac{\partial x_2}{\partial p}\right)_T = -\frac{v_2^0 - v_{2E}}{RT}x_2$	Effect of pressure on solubility limit
		$p = p'$ $dp = 0$	$\left(\frac{\partial x_2}{\partial T}\right)_p = \frac{h_2^0 - h_{2E}}{RT^2}x_2$	Effect of temperature on solubility limit
Solvent	Vapor	$p = p'$ $dT = 0$	$\left(\frac{\partial p}{\partial x_2}\right)_T = -\frac{RT}{v_{fg}}\frac{1}{1-x_2}$	Effect of solute addition on boiling pressure
		$p = p'$ $dp = 0$	$\left(\frac{\partial T}{\partial x_2}\right)_p = \frac{RT^2}{h_{fg}}\frac{1}{1-x_2}$	Effect of solute addition on boiling temperature
		$p = p'$ $dp = 0$	$\left(\frac{\partial p}{\partial T}\right)_x = \frac{h_{fg}}{Tv_{fg}}$	Clapeyron equation for boiling
Solvent	Liquid	$p = p'$ $dp = 0$	$\left(\frac{\partial (p-p')}{\partial x_2}\right)_{T,p'} = \frac{RT}{v_i^0}\frac{1}{x_1}$	Effect of solute addition on osmotic pressure
		$dx = 0$ $dT = 0$	$v_1 dp = v_{1E} dp'$ or $\left(\frac{\partial p}{\partial p'}\right)_{T,x} = \frac{v_{1E}}{v_1}$	Effect of pressure of pure phase on the pressure of the solution

PROBLEMS

General assumptions and data for the following problems (unless stated otherwise) are as follows:

- The components dissolve with one another in any proportions.
- The solutions are ideal.
- Gases and vapors behave as ideal gases.

Data for several hydrocarbons in the range of temperatures 0–80 °C are given in the table below:

Substance	M	$\ln p^{sat}$ bar	v_f m³/kg	c_{p0}/R	T_c K	p_c bar
Propane (C_3H_8)	44.09	$9.83-2255/T$	0.00171	4.5	370.0	42.56
Butane (C_4H_{10})	58.12	$10.19-2770/T$	0.00166	6.0	425.2	38.00
Pentane (C_5H_{12})	72.15	$10.57-3271/T$	0.00159	7.5	470.3	33.44

17.1 a. Sketch a diagram of the saturation pressure of a propane–butane solution at 20 °C as a function of the propane mole fraction (liquid line).

b. Find the mole fraction of the propane in the gaseous phase as a function of its mole fraction in the liquid.

c. Add to the diagram the vapor line, i.e. the saturation pressure as a function of the mole fraction in the vapor.

d. How would the answers to a, b, and c change if the gases were not ideal gases?

17.2 A 100 liter tank contains 30 kg of cooking gas (a propane–butane solution) at 20 °C and 4.0 bars. Find:

a. The mole fraction of propane in the liquid and in the gaseous phases.
b. The specific volume of the liquid phase and of the gas phase.
c. The mass of the liquid phase and of the gas phase.

17.3 A 21 liter container holds 12 kg of cooking gas (a propane–butane solution) at 20 °C. The container is slowly emptied through an upper opening at a constant temperature of 20 °C. Find:

a. The pressure as a function of the mass of solution remaining in the container (neglect the mass of the vapor).
b. The composition of the liquid and the vapor as a function of the mass of solution remaining in the container.

Solve the problem for initial propane mole fractions of 0.8 and 0.3.

17.4 A gaseous mixture, at 125 kPa and 100 °C, contains 7.8 kmol of butane (C_4H_{10}) and pentane (C_5H_{12}), and 4.2 kmol of air (total 12 kmol). The mixture is cooled at a constant pressure to 7 °C when the first drop of liquid appears. Assume that the liquid contains no air, all the gases are ideal gases, and the liquid is an ideal solution.

a. Determine the mole fractions in the liquid and the gaseous phases.
b. Determine the initial and final volumes of the system.
c. Determine the heat interaction in the cooling process.

17.5 A vessel covered with a piston contains a binary solution of 3 gmol of Freon-12 and 7 gmol of Freon-21. The vessel is at 10 bars and −2 °C. The piston rises slowly while the temperature is kept constant and the pressure drops to 1 bar. Find:

a. The number of phases in the container at the initial and final states.
b. The mole fraction of each phase at the initial and final states.
c. The general number of moles of each phase at the initial and final states.
d. The volume of gas at the initial and final states.

Data: saturation pressure at −2 °C for Freon-12: $p^{sat} = 3.0$ bar
for Freon-21: $p^{sat} = 0.6$ bar

17.6 When 7.6 g of a compound that is used as a fuel additive is dissolved in 1 kg of benzene (C_6H_6) the boiling point at atmospheric pressure is raised from 80.10 °C to 80.24 °C. The enthalpy change in evaporation of pure benzene is 30740 kJ/kmol. Estimate the molecular weight of the solute.

17.7 A cylinder, covered with a frictionless heavy piston that maintains 500 kPa, contains 2 gmol of butane (C_4H_{10}) and 3.0 gmol of propane (C_3H_8) at 0 °C. The cylinder is heated slowly till the temperature reaches 20 °C.

a. Determine the initial and final states inside the cylinder (number of phases and their composition).
b. Find the work of the contents of the cylinder.
c. Find the heat interaction of the contents of the cylinder.

17.8 For each mole of a certain solute in 1.0 kg of water the boiling temperature rises by 0.515 °C. Assume an ideal solution.

a. Determine the chemical potential of water at the boiling point of a solution of 3.0 moles of solute in 1.0 kg of water.
b. Compare to the chemical potential of boiling pure water at the same temperature.

17.9 The osmotic pressure of a solution of a certain salt in water at 25 °C is 2.0 MPa. Determine the boiling temperature of the mixture at 100 kPa.

17.10 A certain non-volatile salt forms an ideal solution with water over a wide range of temperature and concentration. It was determined experimentally that the boiling point at atmospheric pressure (101.325 kPa) of a mixture with salt mole fraction x_2 was 100.34 °C.

a. Determine the osmotic pressure of the same solution at 25 °C.
b. Find the osmotic pressure of a solution with salt mole fraction $0.5x_2$.
c. Determine the relative humidity of air at 200 kPa, 25 °C, in equilibrium with a solution where the mole fraction of the salt is $5x_2$.
d. Determine the fugacity of the water in a solution at 200 kPa, 25 °C, where the mole fraction of the salt is $5x_2$.

17.11 Find the osmotic pressure of a mixture of H_2SO_4 in water at 25 °C when the molality is $m = 2$.

17.12 Find the osmotic pressure at 25 °C of sea water containing 3.5% by weight of NaCl of which 80% are dissociated into ions.

Given: $M_{Na} = 23$, $M_{Cl} = 35.5$, $v_f = 0.001002 \text{ m}^3/\text{kg}$

17.13 Sea water at 100 kPa, 20 °C, and a salt concentration of 3.5% by weight is pumped into a well-mixed chamber equipped with a membrane permeable to water only. The salt-free water leaves the system at atmospheric pressure while the concentrated brine is discharged through a throttling valve.

a. Draw the system schematically.
b. Find the pressure in the chamber and the pump work per unit product as functions of the ratio of the product water to the feed water (recovery factor).
c. At what recovery factor is the work input per unit desalted water minimal?

17.14 Sea water at 100 kPa, 20 °C, and a salt concentration of 3.5% by weight is pumped into a well-mixed chamber equipped with a membrane permeable to water only. The salt-free water leaves the system at atmospheric pressure while the concentrated brine passes through a turbine from which it exits at atmospheric pressure. Assume the adiabatic efficiencies of the pump and turbine to be 0.78 and 0.75, respectively.

a. Draw the system schematically.
b. Find the pressure in the chamber, the pump work, and the turbine work per unit product as functions of the ratio of the recovery factor.
c. At what recovery factor is the net work input per unit desalted water minimal?

17.15 The boiling point at 101.325 kPa of an aqueous solution of a certain salt was found to be 100.34 °C. Find the osmotic pressure of the same solution at 25 °C.

CHAPTER EIGHTEEN

Non-ideal solutions

Ordinarily, solutions are non-ideal, i.e. they do not behave like ideal solutions over all ranges of properties. In general, the fugacity of a solution depends on the temperature, pressure, and concentration of all the components, as shown in Chapter 15,

$$f_i = f_i(p, T, x_1, x_2, \ldots, x_i, \ldots, x_{c-1}) \tag{15.66}$$

The dependence on the concentrations of all the components makes the analysis of non-ideal solutions quite complicated. Furthermore, in many cases there is a limitation on the range of concentrations that a component in solution may attain. The component that may approach a mole fraction of unity, i.e. the major component, is called the solvent, and the components that are in smaller quantities are called the solutes. We denote the properties of the solvent by the index 1 (x_1, for example) and those of the solutes by the indices 2, 3, 4, etc.

Solutions for which the concentration of the solvent is close to unity and the concentrations of the solutes close to zero are called dilute solutions. This is a limiting case of real solutions. The chapter opens with Henry's and Raoult's laws that relate the fugacity of solute and solvent in a dilute solution, respectively.

In general, the properties of non-ideal solutions cannot be easily calculated from those of pure components. Data for non-ideal solutions are presented in the literature in the form of tables and diagrams. In this chapter we explain the structure of such diagrams by describing an equilibrium chart for a lithium bromide–water solution, and an enthalpy–concentration diagram for an ammonia–water solution. The latter diagram is then applied to the calculation of an ammonia–water absorption refrigeration system.

18.1 Henry's law

It was found experimentally that the fugacity of a solute in a solution is proportional to its mole fraction when the concentration of the solute is very low:

$$\lim_{x_i \to 0} f_i = x_i K_i$$

Henry's law is a modification of this observation stating that the fugacity of a solute at low concentration is proportional to its mole fraction:

$$f_i = x_i K_i \qquad i = 2,\ 3,\ \ldots,\ c \tag{18.1}$$

where $K_i = K_i(p,T)$ is a constant characteristic of the solute, called Henry's constant.

For ideal solutions this law is applicable to all ranges of concentrations. For real non-ideal solutions, Henry's law is applicable only at low solute concentrations. One can see here the analogy to the equation of state of an ideal gas that is applicable to real gases only at the limit of low pressures.

Henry's law may be used to define the standard state for a solute in solution. The standard state of a solute is usually selected by mathematically extrapolating Henry's law to the limit of pure solute. At that limit the mole fraction of the solute is $x_i = 1$ and the fugacity is

$$f_i^{std} = K_i \qquad i = 2,\ 3,\ \ldots,\ c \tag{18.2}$$

In most cases this standard state is a hypothetical rather than a real state, i.e. the pure component could not exist in the standard state. Still there is no problem in defining such a state for the purpose of comparison.

The activity of a component in solution was defined (Eq. 15.73) as the ratio of its fugacity to the fugacity of the pure component at the corresponding standard state. Hence, the activity of the solute that obeys Henry's law can be obtained from Eqs (18.1) and (18.2):

$$a_i = \frac{f_i}{f_i^{std}} = \frac{f_i}{K_i} = x_i \tag{18.3}$$

Equation (18.3) is valid as long as Henry's law is valid.

Originally, Henry's law was stated in terms of partial pressures of the solutes and not in terms of fugacities. For low pressures, however, when the fugacity is equal to the vapor pressure, the two forms are equivalent. Henry carried out his experiments at atmospheric pressure where the vapor pressures of the solutes were low enough to be equal to their respective fugacities. His results were correlated by

$$p_i = x_i K_i \qquad i = 2,\ 3,\ \ldots,\ c \tag{18.4}$$

18.2 Raoult's law

While Henry's law applies to solutes, Raoult's law applies to the solvent. Raoult's law is also based on experimental facts and states that the fugacity of the solvent is proportional to its mole fraction. The proportionality constant is the fugacity of the pure component:

$$f_1 = x_1 f_1^0 \tag{18.5}$$

The standard state for a solvent is usually selected as that of a pure solvent. Hence,

$$f_i^{std} = f_i^0 \tag{18.6}$$

The standard state for the solvent is always a real state, since the solvent can always be found at the limit of a pure phase. The activity of the solvent is, therefore,

$$a_i = \frac{f_i}{f_i^0} \tag{18.7}$$

and, as long as Raoult's law holds,

$$a_i = x_i \tag{18.8}$$

It should be noted that Raoult's law is not independent of Henry's law, as proven in the following example.

EXAMPLE 18.1

Prove Raoult's law from Henry's law. Hint: Use the Gibbs–Duhem equation.

SOLUTION

At a constant pressure and temperature the Gibbs–Duhem equation can be written as a sum over all the components, i.e. the solvent and all the solutes:

$$\left(\sum_{i=1}^{c} x_i dg_i\right)_{p,T} = RT\left(\sum_{i=1}^{c} x_i d\ln f_i\right)_{p,T} = 0$$

In the following analysis the subscripts p, T are omitted. It should be understood, however, that all derivatives are taken at a constant pressure and temperature. The summation over the solutes gives

$$\sum_{i=2}^{c} x_i dg_i = RT\sum_{i=2}^{c} x_i d\ln f_i = RT\sum_{i=2}^{c} dx_i = -RTdx_1$$

and the term for the solvent is

$$x_1 dg_1 = RTx_1 d\ln f_1$$

Thus

$$x_1 d\ln f_1 - dx_1 = 0$$

or

$$d\ln f_1 = \frac{dx_1}{x_1} = d\ln x_1$$

which is easily solved to give

$$f_1 = x_1 K_1$$

where K_1 is a constant of integration.

At $x_1 = 1$:

$$f_1 = f_1^0 \text{ and thus } K_1 = f_1^0$$

which proves Raoult's law.

18.3 Dilute solutions

A dilute solution is one which contains a major component for which the mole fraction is very close to unity. The major component is called the solvent, while all other components of a dilute solution are called solutes. It is customary to denote the properties of the solvent by the index 1, and those of the solutes by 2, 3, etc. Hence, in a dilute solution $x_1 \approx 1$ and $x_2 << 1$.

Dilute solutions obey both Henry's law and Raoult's law. Therefore, the behavior of a dilute solution is quite similar to that of an ideal solution, leading to a much simpler analysis. Hence, even though dilute solutions are relevant only as limiting cases of real solutions they are helpful in the analysis of the behavior of real solutions.

18.4 Binary non-ideal solutions

Equilibrium states of a binary solution are characterized by three independent properties. For ideal solutions, the properties can be easily calculated from data on the individual components and their mole (or mass) fractions. No additional tables or diagrams are needed. On the other hand, the properties of non-ideal solutions cannot be easily calculated from the properties of pure components. Data for non-ideal solutions appear in the literature in the form of tables and diagrams.

In this section we consider non-ideal solutions of liquid–gaseous binary systems. For such systems three regions may be distinguished, namely the gas phase, the gas–liquid two-phase region, and the liquid phase.

In most cases the gas phase may be considered as an ideal solution, thus requiring no special table or diagram. Two-phase solid, solid–liquid, or solid–vapor systems are of interest in the study of material sciences. These systems are not discussed here. Liquid–vapor two-phase systems are of interest to thermal cycles, such as dehumidification, refrigeration heat pumps, and power cycles.

Two-phase data appear in the literature in the form of tables and diagrams. Any two, independent, intensive properties may be used to define the intensive states of both phases of a binary solution. These could be the liquid temperature and concentration, or the liquid pressure and concentration, or the pressure and temperature of the gas. Once the two independent properties are fixed all other intensive properties of both phases are determined and may be listed in a table or a diagram. See, for example, the table for the H_2O–NH_3 system in the Appendix.

The saturation pressure of a two-phase binary mixture depends not only on the temperature (as in the case of a pure component) but also on the concentration. Such data can be presented in a diagram where the temperature of the solution is the abscissa, the concentration is the parameter, and the saturation pressure of the solution is the ordinate.

For a large class of solutions the solute is non-volatile, i.e. the vapor phase may contain only the pure solvent and none of the solute. The salt content of a salt–water solution is an example of a non-volatile solute. In the case of a non-volatile solute it is convenient to denote the ordinate as a linear function of the saturation temperature of the pure solvent.

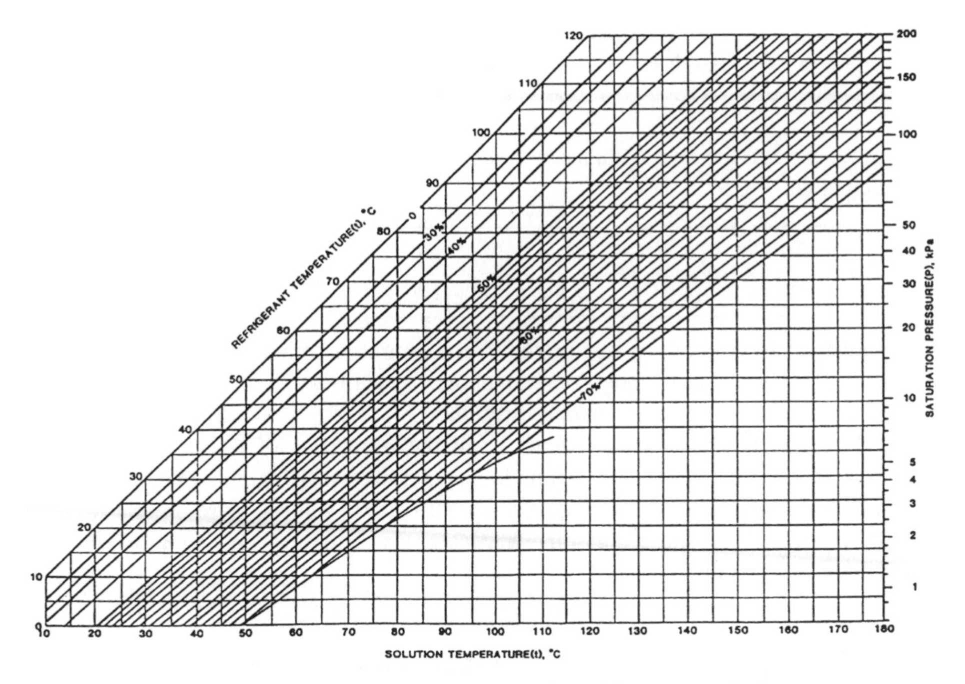

Figure 18.1 **Equilibrium chart for lithium bromide–water solution.**
(Source: 1993 ASHRAE Handbook, Fundamentals, American Society for Heating, Refrigerating and Air-conditioning Engineers, Inc.)

The corresponding pressure is also shown on a separate non-linear scale. A typical diagram of a non-volatile solute is given in Fig. 18.1 for an H_2O–LiBr solution.

EXAMPLE 18.2

Find the saturation pressure of 30% LiBr in a water solution at $T = 80$ °C.

SOLUTION

From Fig. 18.1 we read at 80 °C and 30%: $p^{sat} = 36.0$ kPa.

Note that the saturation pressure of pure water at 80 °C is 47.39 kPa.

EXAMPLE 18.3

What composition of H_2O–LiBr at 120 °C has the same vapor pressure as a solution of 30% LiBr at 80 °C? What is the equivalent temperature of pure water (that has the same vapor pressure)?

SOLUTION

For 120 °C and $p^{sat} = 36.0$ kPa we find in Fig. 18.1 that the concentration of LiBr is 56%. For pure water at p^{sat} = 36.0 kPa the temperature is 73 °C. This can be found either from the steam tables or from Fig. 18.1 at a concentration of 0% LiBr.

We now arrange the data obtained in Examples 18.2 and 18.3 for p^{sat} = 36 kPa in the following table:

% LiBr	0	30	56
Saturation temp. (°C)	73	80	120

As shown, at a constant pressure of 36 kPa the saturation temperature changes with the composition of the solution. This fact is exploited in various industrial applications such as absorption refrigeration and dehumidification.

The diagram in Fig. 18.1 does not list all the properties of the solution. Specific enthalpy and specific volume, for example, are not shown. Diagrams that include such information, and that also apply to mixtures with volatile solutes, were originally developed by Bosnjakovic. These are somewhat complex diagrams, and therefore they are described in some detail later on.

18.5 Enthalpy of mixing for non-ideal binary solutions

It was shown in Chapter 17 that the enthalpy of mixing is zero for an ideal solution. Thus the enthalpy of an ideal mixture, as given by Eq. (17.15), is a linear combination of the enthalpies of its pure components. For an ideal mixture Eq. (17.5) simplifies to

$$h = x_1 h_1^0 + x_2 h_2^0 = h_1^0 + x_2\left(h_2^0 - h_1^0\right) \tag{18.9}$$

For a non-ideal solution the enthalpy of mixing need not be zero. Lines a and b in Fig. 18.2 represent mixtures with positive and negative enthalpies of mixing, respectively. For

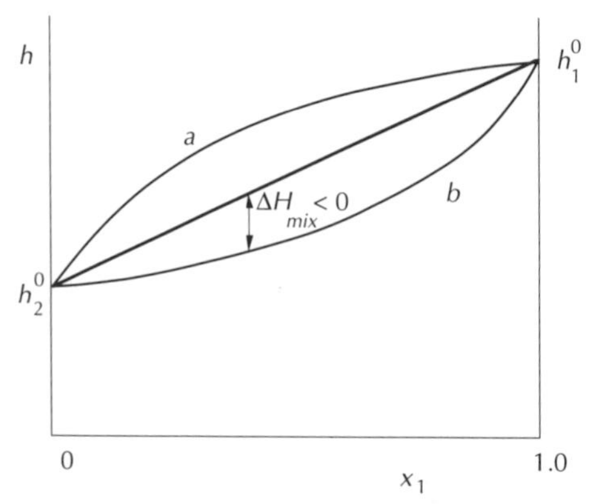

Figure 18.2 **Enthalpy–concentration diagram for a non-ideal solution.**

example, at $x = x_1$ the deviation in enthalpy between line b and the straight line is the enthalpy of mixing, which in this case is negative.

The enthalpy of mixing was defined in Eq. (17.12) as the difference between the enthalpy of the mixture and that of its pure components at the same pressure and temperature. Hence, when a binary mixture with a negative enthalpy of mixing is made up from its components, while the temperature is kept constant by means of a suitable reservoir, heat in the amount of the enthalpy of mixing must be removed. On the other hand, for mixtures of positive enthalpy of mixing, heat must be added if the temperature is to remain constant upon mixing.

18.6 Enthalpy diagrams

Binary mixtures in equilibrium have three independent properties. These may be selected as pressure, temperature, and concentration. In order to show data on a two-dimensional diagram it is customary to draw the diagram for a fixed pressure. The enthalpy at the fixed pressure is a function of temperature and concentration only:

$$h(p,T,x) \quad \Rightarrow \quad h(T,x)$$

In a typical diagram the enthalpy is the ordinate, the concentration is the abscissa, while the temperature appears in the diagram as a parameter.

Consider the enthalpy–concentration diagram shown schematically in Fig. 18.3. The diagram is drawn for one fixed pressure. Therefore, the enthalpy at that pressure depends on temperature and concentration only. In this diagram concentration is the independent variable, and temperature is the parameter. The concentration of the solute in the liquid is denoted by x and that in the vapor by y.

Three regions can be distinguished in the diagram: a compressed liquid region at the lower part, a superheated vapor region at the upper part, and a two-phase liquid–vapor region in between. The lines separating the regions are the saturation lines. The saturated liquid line is the locus of all liquid states that can be in equilibrium with corresponding states of vapor on the saturated vapor line.

An isotherm gives the dependence of enthalpy on concentration for a given p and T. For an ideal solution, where the enthalpy of mixing is zero, the isotherms are straight lines connecting the points of pure solvent and pure solute at a given p and T. Vapor mixtures may usually be considered ideal solutions, and therefore the isotherms in the superheated vapor region are straight lines. On the other hand, liquid solutions are typically non-ideal solutions. Hence, the isotherms in the compressed liquid region are generally curved, reflecting the non-zero enthalpy of mixing.

A typical isotherm in the compressed liquid region is depicted in Fig. 18.3 by T_1, while a typical isotherm in the vapor region is that of T_3. The isotherm T_2 is partly in the liquid region (at low concentrations) and partly in the vapor region (at high concentrations). The points common to the isotherm T_2 and the two saturation lines represent two states, liquid and vapor, in mutual equilibrium. These states have, of course, the same pressure and temperature, but different concentrations. The concentrations of the saturated liquid and

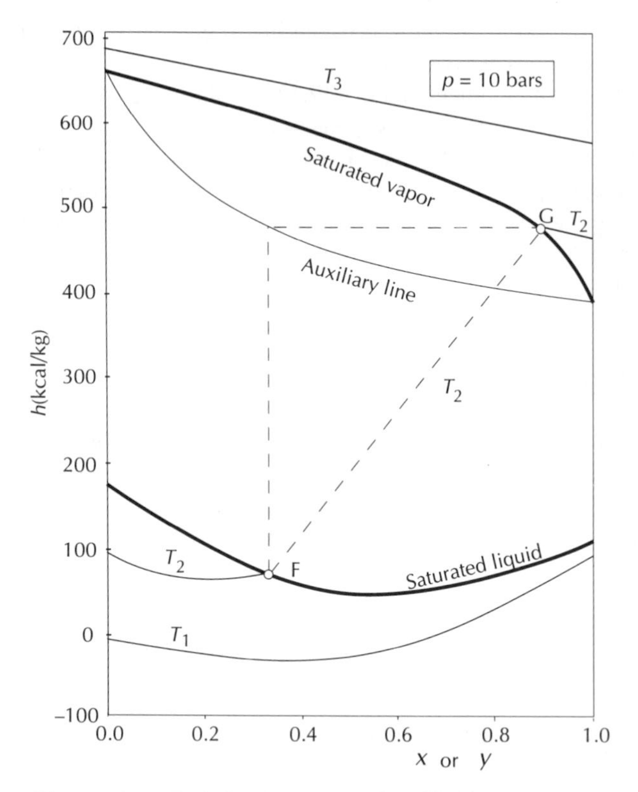

Figure 18.3 **Enthalpy–concentration diagram.**

that of the corresponding saturated vapor are functions of p and T. This follows directly from the Gibbs phase rule. Indeed, in the two-phase region any two independent properties, such as p and T, p and x, or h and T, are sufficient to determine a state.

When two phases coexist in equilibrium, the intensive state at any point within the system can be either a liquid or a vapor state. A point inside the two-phase region does not represent a real intensive state. Instead, such a point represents the average properties of a system consisting of two phases. Let the ratio of the mass of the vapor phase to the total mass of the two-phase system be denoted by ξ (similar to quality in a two-phase single-component system),

$$\xi = \frac{m^{v}}{m^{\ell} + m^{v}} \tag{18.10}$$

Then

$$\xi = \frac{h - h_f}{h_g - h_f} = \frac{x - x_f}{y_g - x_f} \tag{18.11}$$

Thus the isotherm T_2 may also be completed inside the two-phase region by connecting the appropriate saturation points along the liquid and vapor lines.

In many cases it is advantageous not to draw in the isotherm inside the two-phase region. In the absence of this isotherm in the two-phase region, an auxiliary line is added in order to facilitate the identification of the corresponding saturated liquid and saturated vapor states. A point on the auxiliary line has the concentration of the liquid and the enthalpy of the vapor. The location of a vapor point corresponding to a given liquid point is found by constructing a vertical line from a given point on the saturated liquid line up to the auxiliary line, and a horizontal line of constant enthalpy till it intersects the saturated vapor line.

The enthalpy diagram of Fig. 18.3 is limited to one pressure only. The diagram can be reproduced for other pressures as well. The enthalpy of a gaseous mixture, as well as that of a liquid mixture, are very weak functions of pressure. Therefore, the isotherms in the single-phase regions, both liquid and vapor, almost coincide in diagrams of different pressures. Thus a single h–x diagram with the temperature as a parameter is adequate for representing the enthalpies of single-phase mixtures at different pressures.

On the other hand, the saturation lines differ for different pressures. Bosnjakovic* proposed a diagram which is a superposition of the enthalpy charts of the various pressures. Figure 18.4 shows an SI version of his diagram for an NH_3–H_2O mixture. The line $x = 0$ represents the enthalpies of pure water in the liquid and vapor phases. These enthalpies can also be taken from the steam tables. At $x = 1$ the two points are the corresponding enthalpies of liquid and vapor ammonia.

The isotherms are shown in the liquid region. These are valid only below the saturated liquid line corresponding to the same pressure. All points between the saturated liquid line and the saturated vapor line at a given pressure describe average properties of the two phases. The isotherms are not shown in this two-phase region in order to avoid confusion. It is possible to reconstruct any given isotherm in the two-phase region by drawing a straight line between the two corresponding points of the saturated liquid and the saturated vapor.

EXAMPLE 18.4

Find the enthalpy of an ammonia–water mixture of 40% NH_3 at 10 bars and a. 40 °C, b. 60 °C, c. 80 °C, d. 100 °C, e. The maximum temperature for which a liquid phase exists.

SOLUTION

Let us first identify the saturation temperature for $p = 10$ bars and $x = 0.4$. From the diagram it is found to be 81 °C. Cases a, b, and c represent compressed liquid states and the enthalpies can be read off the diagram disregarding the pressure. Hence,

a. $h\ (x = 0.4,\ T = 40) = 16$ kcal/kg.
b. $h\ (x = 0.4,\ T = 60) = 31$ kcal/kg.
c. $h\ (x = 0.4,\ T = 80) = 64$ kcal/kg.
d. Point d lies above the saturation point. The isotherm of 100 °C is constructed in the two-phase region. The relevant state is the intersection of the isotherm with $x = 0.4$. The enthalpy at that point is $h\ (x = 0.4,\ T = 100) = 140$ kcal/kg.

* F. Bosnjakovic, *Technische Thermodynamik*, T. Steinkopff, Leipzig, 1935.

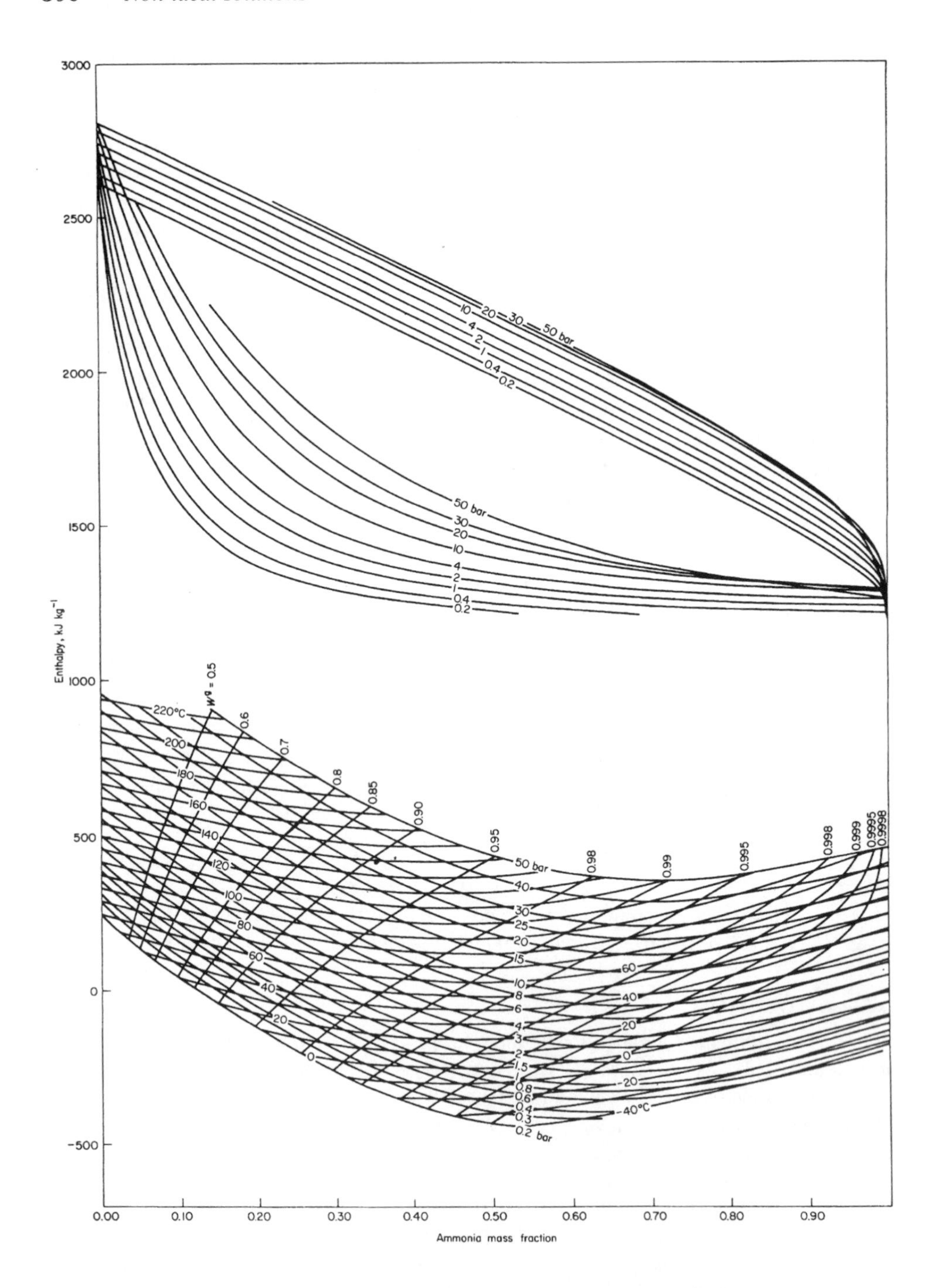

Figure 18.4 **Enthalpy–concentration diagram for ammonia–water solution.**
(Source: B. Ziegler and Ch. Trepp, 'Equations of state for ammonia–water mixtures', *Int. J. of Refrigeration*, 7, 1984, pp 101–6.

e. The maximum temperature is found by locating the liquid point corresponding to the vapor point e by reversing the construction procedure. It is found to be 157 °C. The enthalpy at point e is 580 kcal/kg.

18.7 Absorption refrigeration

Absorption machines perform similar duties to ordinary compressor-driven refrigerators and heat pumps, but require much less work input. Instead of work input they require a heat input at a temperature higher than that of the environment. Like ordinary compressor-driven refrigerators absorption machines include a condenser, a throttle valve, and an evaporator. No compressor, however, is used. It is replaced by a generator, absorber, valve, and pump that require very little work input. It is also possible to design absorption refrigerators that require no work input at all.

Figure 18.5 shows schematically a compressor-driven refrigerator and an equivalent absorption refrigerator. The compressor, shown by dashed line "A", that supplies the high pressure refrigerant to the condenser of an ordinary refrigerator, is replaced in the absorption refrigerator by a loop, shown by line "B" which contains a generator, throttling valve, absorber, and pump. These perform the same task of raising the pressure of the refrigerant from that of the evaporator to that of the condenser. Instead of compressing a vapor, as in a regular cycle, liquid is pumped in the absorption cycle. The work input, $-w_x$, in steady state compression is proportional to the specific volume of the substance, as can be seen from Eq. (9.17):

$$-w_x = \frac{1}{\varepsilon_c}\left(\int_1^2 v dp\right)_{rev} \tag{9.17}$$

Thus the larger the volume to be compressed, the higher the work input. Because the specific volume of the liquid is much lower than that of the vapor, the work of pumping a liquid in the absorption refrigerator is much less than that of compressing the vapor in an ordinary refrigerator.

The refrigerant vapor that emerges from the evaporator is absorbed into the lean liquid

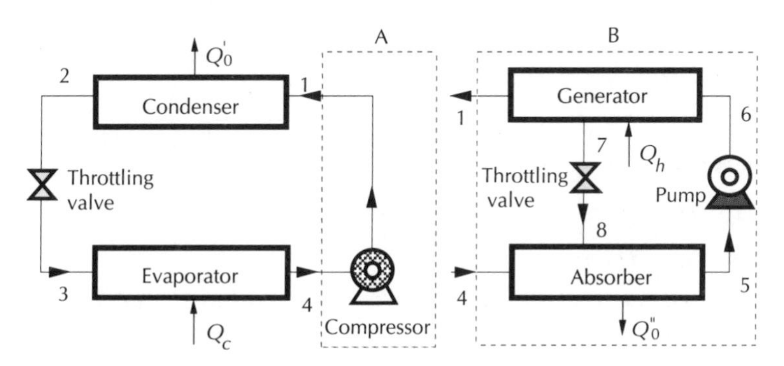

Figure 18.5 **Absorption refrigeration principle.**

solution in the absorber. This absorption process is exothermic and unless the absorber is cooled its temperature will rise until it is high enough to stop the absorption. In order to maintain the absorption process it is necessary to remove the heat from the absorber. The sink used for that purpose is the environment. Therefore the lowest temperature that can be maintained in the absorber is that of the environment to which the heat is transferred. The pressure in the evaporator is controlled by the temperature in the absorber. The lower the temperature in the absorber the lower the pressure of the vapor that will be absorbed. Of course, a lower vapor pressure at the evaporator means also a lower temperature to which the evaporator may be cooled.

An ordinary refrigerator "pumps" heat from a cold reservoir at temperature T_c to a warmer one at T_h. The performance of a refrigerator is measured by its coefficient of performance, *COP*, defined in Chapter 7 as the ratio of the desired output to the required input. Thus when we are interested in the cooling effect the coefficient of performance is $COP = |Q_c / W|$ and when we are interested in the heating effect the coefficient of performance is $COP = |Q_h / W|$.

An absorption system can be described as a cyclic device that has heat interactions with three reservoirs at temperatures T_c, T_0, and T_h, respectively. Such a cycle is shown schematically in Fig. 18.6. The cycle uses heat from the hot reservoir at T_h to "pump" heat from the cold reservoir at T_c to the warmer reservoir at T_0. The coefficient of performance is defined here as the ratio between the heat interaction of interest to the heat input at the high temperature. Thus the cooling and the heating *COP*s are, respectively,

$$COP_{cooling} = \left|\frac{Q_c}{Q_h}\right| \tag{18.12}$$

$$COP_{heating} = \left|\frac{Q_0}{Q_h}\right| \tag{18.13}$$

The highest coefficient of performance of a cycle interacting with three given reservoirs would be for an ideal absorption cycle for which all the processes are reversible. The *COP* of such a reversible cycle requires only the knowledge of the temperatures of the reservoirs but no other details of the system.

The first law for the cycle that involves only heat interactions requires that $\sum Q = 0$; thus for the system shown in Fig. 18.6

$$Q_h + Q_c - Q_0 = 0 \tag{18.14}$$

The second law for a reversible cycle states that the total change of entropy of all the reservoirs must be equal to zero:

$$-\frac{Q_h}{T_h} - \frac{Q_c}{T_c} + \frac{Q_0}{T_0} = 0 \tag{18.15}$$

Both cooling and heating *COP*s can be calculated from Eqs (18.14) and (18.15). By substituting Q_0 from Eq. (18.14) into Eq. (18.15) we get the cooling *COP* as

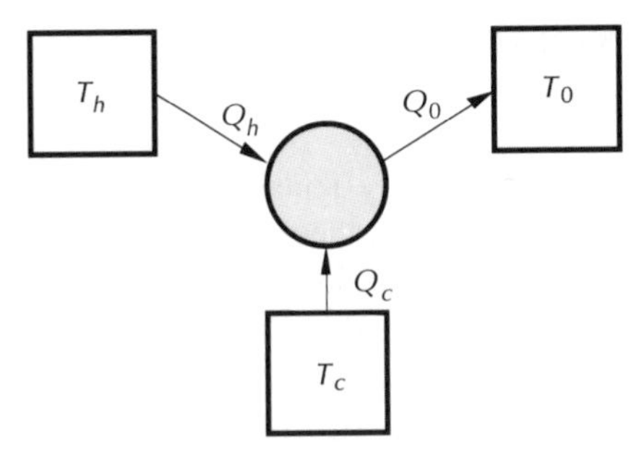

Figure 18.6 **An absorption refrigeration cycle.**

$$COP_{cooling} = \frac{Q_c}{Q_h} = \frac{T_c}{T_h}\frac{T_h - T_0}{T_0 - T_c} \tag{18.16}$$

And by substituting Q_c from Eq. (18.14) into Eq. (18.15) we get the heating *COP* as

$$COP_{heating} = \frac{Q_o}{Q_h} = \frac{T_0}{T_h}\frac{T_h - T_0}{T_0 - T_c} \tag{18.17}$$

The *COP*s calculated by Eqs (18.16) and (18.17) relate to reversible processes. They are, therefore, the most that any machine can provide for the three given temperatures. The *COP* of a real absorption machine depends on its detailed design and, in general, can be expected to be somewhat lower. We shall now outline a method for the evaluation of the performance of a real cycle.

Consider the absorption refrigeration cycle with a water–ammonia mixture shown in Fig. 18.5. The absorption cycle operates between three temperature levels: the heating temperature, T_h, the cold temperature, T_c, and the temperature of the environment at T_0.

Similarly to regular compressor-driven refrigeration cycles, absorption cycles also have two levels of pressures, the low evaporation pressure and the high condensation pressure. The condensation and evaporating pressures in an absorption cycle are not, however, unique functions of the temperature, as is the case for a pure refrigerant, but also depend on the respective concentrations of the refrigerant.

The condenser pressure must be high enough to condense, at the temperature of the environment, all the vapor that comes out of the generator. We usually select

$$p_c \geq p_{NH_3}^{sat}(T_0) \tag{18.18}$$

The evaporation pressure must be low enough to allow sufficient vapor to evaporate in the evaporator but not too low for it to be absorbed in the absorber at the temperature of the environment. Note that it is not required that *all* the refrigerant be evaporated in the evaporator.

The absorption system, shown in Fig. 18.5, has essentially two loops with different flowrates. One is the usual refrigerant loop (1–2–3–4) that is essentially the same as in the vapor compression cycle and includes the passage of the refrigerant through the condenser, the throttle valve, and the evaporator. The mass flow of this loop is

$$\dot{m}_{refrig} = \dot{m}_1 = \dot{m}_2 = \dot{m}_3 = \dot{m}_4 \tag{18.19}$$

The second loop is the solution loop that essentially replaces the compressor and includes the passage of the solution through the absorber, the solution pump, the generator, and the liquid throttle valve (5–6–7–8). The solution loop has two mass flows: the weak solution mass flow is

$$\dot{m}_{weak\ sol} = \dot{m}_7 = \dot{m}_8 \tag{18.20}$$

and the strong solution mass flow is

$$\dot{m}_{strong\ sol} = \dot{m}_5 = \dot{m}_6 \tag{18.21}$$

The ratio of the flowrate of the weak solution to the refrigerant flowrate is called the circulation ratio, and is denoted by c_r,

$$c_r = \frac{\dot{m}_{strong\ sol}}{\dot{m}_{refrig}} \tag{18.21}$$

Thus we can express each flow in terms of the refrigerant flow and the circulation ratio:

$$\dot{m}_{strong\ sol} = \dot{m}_5 = \dot{m}_5 = c_r\dot{m}_1 \tag{18.22}$$

$$\dot{m}_{weak\ sol} = \dot{m}_7 = \dot{m}_8 = (c_r - 1)\dot{m}_1 \tag{18.23}$$

The absorption system makes use of the fact that the vapor pressure of a refrigerant in a liquid solution is lower than that over a pure refrigerant at the same temperature. Indeed, the lower the concentration of the refrigerant in the solution the lower is the corresponding vapor pressure. Thus it is possible to absorb a cold refrigerant vapor that comes from the evaporator (point 4 in Fig. 18.5) into a warmer solution in the absorber provided it has a low concentration of the refrigerant.

Let us first look at the solution loop. The liquid solution, rich in refrigerant, leaves the absorber at the low pressure and at the temperature of the environment, T_0 (point 5). The concentration of the refrigerant can be assumed to be that of a saturated liquid solution.

The solution is pumped by a solution pump into the generator (point 6) at the higher pressure. We note that whereas the ideal cycle does not require any work input, in a practical cycle we may want to use some work to drive the solution pump. This work is usually quite small and indeed it is even possible to design absorption systems that require no work input at all. In the simpler version of the thermal analysis we shall neglect the pump work altogether.

Heat Q_h is supplied to the generator at the higher temperature (typical range 70–150 °C) causing some of the refrigerant to evaporate even though the pressure is higher. The vapor, which is rich in refrigerant, is directed to the condenser (point 1) and the remaining liquid, which is lean in refrigerant, is returned to the absorber via a throttling valve (point 7). The weak solution, which enters the absorber at point 8, is now ready to absorb the refrigerant that comes from the evaporator (point 4). The absorption process is exothermic and the heat of mixing Q_0' is removed from the solution and rejected to the environment at T_0.

The detailed calculation of the parameters of an absorption cycle and its performance is best explained by an example.

EXAMPLE 18.5

A cold storage room at −10 °C has a cooling load of 15 kW, while the environment is at 1.01 bars and 25 °C. The cooling effect is provided by an ammonia–water absorption refrigerator which receives heat from a reservoir at 125 °C. Assume that the heat exchangers require a minimum 5 °C temperature difference.

a. Describe schematically the absorption system. Show the reservoirs which interact with the system. Indicate the temperatures at all the points of the cycle.
b. Select the pressure levels.
c. Find the cycle points and draw an *h–x* diagram for the cycle.
d. Determine the circulation ratio.
e. Find the *COP* of the cycle and compare with the *COP* of a Carnot cycle that operates between the same reservoirs.
f. Could the *COP* of the real system be improved? Discuss briefly.

SOLUTION

a. The absorption system is shown schematically in Fig. 18.7.
b. The high pressure (points 1, 2, 6, 7) is determined so that point 2 represents a completely condensed liquid. Selection of p_2, so that pure ammonia is condensed, provides some safety. A somewhat lower pressure may be selected, but that can be determined by trial and error only. Hence, $p_2 = 12$ bars.

   Figure 18.8 shows the points of the process on a schematic ammonia–water *h–x* dia-

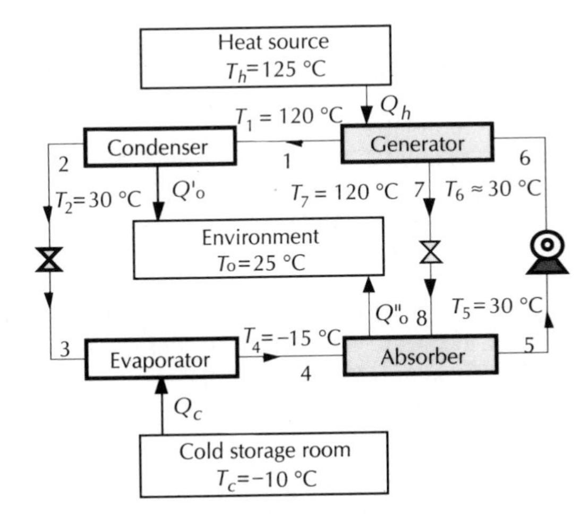

Figure 18.7 **Ammonia–water absorption refrigeration system.**

gram. The lower pressure points 3, 4, 8, and 5 must be selected low enough so that sufficient vapor is produced in the evaporator. If the evaporator were to receive pure ammonia, the pressure would be 2.5 bars. The selection of these pressures affects the performance of the cycle.

c. In order to keep track of the properties at the various points of the cycle we arrange the properties in a table. We underline those properties whose values are known without the need for an ammonia–water diagram.

	T °C	p bar	x_{ave}	h kJ/kg	*Phase*
1	120	12.0	0.86	1658.1	Saturated vapor
2	30	12.0	0.86	40.0	Liquid
3		1.4	0.86	40.0	Two phase
4	−15	1.4	0.86	639.0	Two phase
5	30	1.4	0.337	−103.0	Saturated liquid
6		12.0	0.337	−101.8	Liquid
7	120	12.0	0.253	343.7	Saturated liquid
8		1.4	0.253	343.7	Two phase

REMARKS

- Point 1 – A saturated vapor at 120 °C and 12 bars.
- Point 5 – A saturated liquid at 30 °C and 1.4 bars.
- Point 7 – A saturated liquid at 120 °C and 12 bars.
- The concentrations and the enthalpies of points 1, 5, and 7 are found directly from the ammonia–water diagram, Fig. 18.4, or from an ammonia–water table.
- Point 8 – For a throttling process $h_8 = h_7$. The temperature T_8 is not needed for the solution but could be found similarly to point 3.
- The average concentrations at points 2, 3, 4 are the same as in point 1.
- The average concentration at point 6 is equal to the concentration at 5.
- The average concentration at point 8 is equal to the concentration at 7.
- The enthalpy at point 2 is found from the diagram for a saturated liquid at −30 °C and $x_2 = 0.86$. The actual state is at a higher pressure than that of saturation but the enthalpy is almost independent of pressure.
- The enthalpy at point 3 is equal to that of point 2 (a throttling process). Point 3 is in a two-phase state. We do not need to know the temperature at point 3, T_3, for the solution of the problem. We can, however, determine T_3 by constructing by trial and error the isotherm that passes at 1.4 bars through the point of $x_3 = 0.86$, $h_3 = 40$ kJ/kg. We find that $T_3 = -22$ °C.
- Point 4 is also in a two-phase state. Here, however, we can easily construct the isotherm of −15 °C and find the enthalpy where the isotherm crosses the line of $x_4 = 0.86$.
- Point 6 has the same concentration as point 5 but at higher pressure. The enthalpy at point 6 can be estimated by Eq. (9.17) from the work of the pump:

$$h_6 - h_5 = \int v\,dp \approx v\Delta p = 0.0011 \times (1200 - 140) = 1.2 \text{ kJ/kg}$$

$$h_6 = -103 + 1.2 = -101.8 \text{ kJ/kg}$$

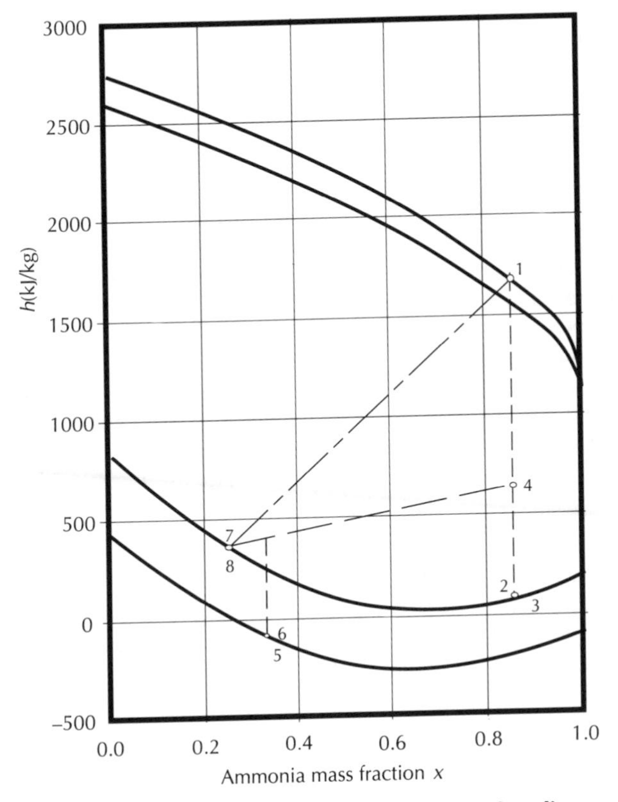

Figure 18.8 **Schematic of an ammonia–water *h*–*x* diagram.**

d. The circulation ratio is

$$c_r = \frac{x_4 - x_7}{x_5 - x_7} = \frac{0.860 - 0.253}{0.337 - 0.253} = 7.23$$

The flow of liquid through the pump is thus 7.23 times the flow of the vapor through the evaporator.

e. In order to find the *COP* of the cycle we need first to calculate the heat interactions. We shall calculate all quantities relative to a flow of 1 kg/s in the evaporator. Obviously, the appropriate flow in the pump is 7.23 kg/s. Hence,

$$\dot{m}_1 = \dot{m}_2 = \dot{m}_3 = \dot{m}_4 = 1.0 \text{ kg/s}$$

$$\dot{m}_5 = \dot{m}_6 = 7.23 \text{ kg/s}$$

$$\dot{m}_7 = \dot{m}_8 = 6.23 \text{ kg/s}$$

$$\frac{Q_h}{m_1} = h_1 + \frac{m_7}{m_1} h_7 - \frac{m_6}{m_1} h_6 = 1658.1 + 6.23 \times 343.7 - 7.23 \times (-1008) = 4535 \text{ kJ/kg}$$

$$\frac{Q_C}{m_1} = h_4 - h_3 = 639 - 40 = 599 \text{ kJ/kg}$$

$$COP = \frac{Q_C}{Q_h} = \frac{599}{4535} = 0.132$$

$$COP_{Carnot} = \frac{T_C}{T_h}\frac{T_H - T_a}{T_a - T_c} = \frac{263.115}{398.15}\frac{125-25}{25-(-10)} = 1.888$$

We see that the actual cycle performance falls short of the best thermodynamic performance. That means there is much room for improvements.

f. The *COP* could be greatly improved by a better design.
Just two examples for better design:

- The heat input into the generator could be reduced without decreasing the cooling load by making use of the hot solution emerging from the generator to preheat the cold solution (point 6). This requires of course an additional heat exchanger.
- The selection of the operating pressures could be optimized for maximum *COP*.

PROBLEMS

18.1 The vapor pressure of ammonia over an aqueous ammonia solution at 40 °C, having a mole fraction in the range $0 < x_A < 0.25$, is given in bars by the equation

$$p_A^V = 1.31x_A(1 + 6.58x_A)$$

Additional data are given in the table below:

	$v(m^3/kg)$	p^{sat} (bar)
Water	0.001005	0.0738
Ammonia	0.001717	14.5

Find:

a. The vapor pressure of the dissolved ammonia at standard conditions.
b. Expressions for the activity and the activity coefficient of the ammonia as a function of the mole fraction in the given range.
c. Expressions for the activity and the activity coefficient of water as a function of the mole fraction in the given range.
d. The activity and the activity coefficient of ammonia and of water at $x_A = 0.2$.
e. The approximate osmotic pressure of a 20% ammonia solution through a membrane semipermeable to water only.

18.2 Partial data for an ammonia–water solution at −18 °C are given below.

x_w %	y_w %	p kPa	v_f m^3/kg	v_g m^3/kg	h_f kJ/kg	h_g kJ/kg	M
0	0.00	213.7	0.00151	0.569	−82.5	1240.0	17
10	0.001	193.2					
100	100.00	0.133	0.00010	900.196	−33.8	1120.5	18

Assume that no solid phase is present, i.e. the water is a metastable liquid. Treat the solution of 10% water and 90% ammonia as a dilute solution. Find:

a. The Henry coefficient of the water in the solution.
b. The osmotic pressure of the solution.

c. The activity coefficient of the water in the solution.
d. The rise of the boiling point of ammonia by dissolving in it 10% of water.

18.3 An absorption cooling system used to cool a big hall works on a water–ammonia solution. The cooling load is 10 kW, and the vaporization temperature is 2 °C. The environment is at 30 °C and 1 bar. The maximum heating temperature is 115 °C.

a. Sketch the cycle including an ideal heat exchanger between the rich and lean solutions.
b. Define the states of the cycle on an $h - x$ diagram.
c. Compute the mass flowrate of solution through the pump in kg/h.
d. Find the power requirement of the pump, if its adiabatic effectiveness is 0.85.
e. Find the heat interaction of the condenser, the boiling vessel, and the absorber.
f. At what minimal heating temperature does the use of an absorbing cooler become ineffective?

18.4 A solution of 12.2 g of benzoic acid in 100 g of ethanol boils at 1.13 °C above the boiling temperature of pure ethanol at atmospheric pressure. A solution of 12.2 g of benzoic acid in 100 g of benzene boils at 1.36 °C above the boiling point of pure benzene at atmospheric pressure. Given below are saturation data at atmospheric pressure:

For ethanol: $T_{sat} = 78.4\ ^{\circ}\text{C}$ $\quad (\partial T / \partial \ln p)_{sat} = 24.5\ ^{\circ}\text{C}$

For benzene: $T_{sat} = 80.1\ ^{\circ}\text{C}$ $\quad (\partial T / \partial \ln p)_{sat} = 31.6\ ^{\circ}\text{C}$

a. Find the molecular weight of benzoic acid in each solution.
b. What is the molecular structure of benzoic acid (C_6H_5COOH) in each solution?

18.5 The boiling point of pure CS_2 is 45.8 °C. Find the boiling point elevation of CS_2 at 1 atm. The following information is available:

a. A solution of 3.2 g of naphthalene ($C_{10}H_8$) in 50 g of CS_2 boils at 1.17 °C above the boiling temperature of pure CS_2.
b. In measuring saturation pressures of pure CS_2 at atmospheric pressure it was found that dp/dT = 3.25 kPa/ °C.
c. The latent heat of vaporization of CS_2 at atmospheric pressure is 352 kJ/kg.

18.6 A solution of 3.795 g of sulfur in 100 g of CS_2 boils at 0.361 °C above the boiling point of pure CS_2.

a. Find the molecular weight of the sulfur in CS_2.
b. What can be concluded about the molecular structure of sulfur in that solvent?

18.7 An inventor proposes an improvement to the ammonia–water absorption cycle in which the vapor is enriched with ammonia before it passes to the condenser.

The new scheme, the main parts of which are shown in Fig. 18.9, includes a three-streams heat exchanger that transfers heat to the incoming rich liquid solution (2) from the liquid (9) and the vapor (4) that leave the generator. The cooled vapor (5) enters an adiabatic separation tank from which a richer vapor emerges and goes to the condenser. Saturated liquid leaves the separation tank and is pumped into the solution line from the absorber (1).

Known information is given in the table overleaf, where x is the mass fraction of ammonia.

You are charged with the task of checking the proposal. As part of the checking process you are asked to do the following:

a. Complete the table by filling in all the relevant missing properties.

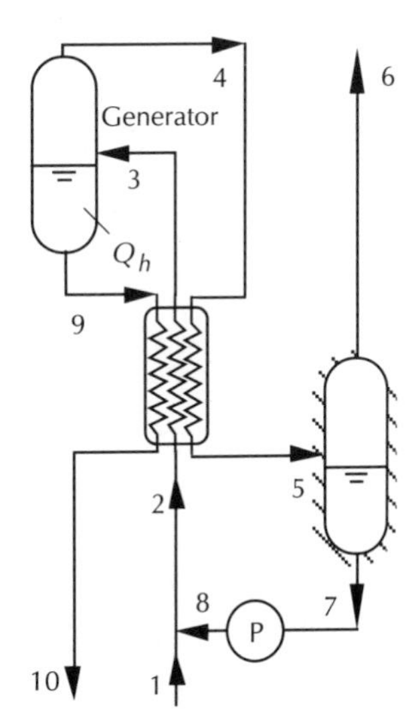

Figure 18.9

b. Determine the flowrate at each point in the loop.
c. Calculate the heat rate required to produce 1.0 kg/s of enriched vapor.

	p bar	T °C	x	h kJ/kg	m^v/m	m kg/s	Comments
1	20.3	30	0.400		–		Compressed liquid
2	20.3						
3	20.1	150					
4	20.0	150			1.00		Saturated vapor
5	20.0	80					
6	20.0	80			1.00	1.00	Saturated vapor
7	20.0	80			0.00		Saturated liquid
8	20.3						
9	20.0	150			0.00		Saturated liquid
10	20.0	80			–		Compressed liquid

18.8 The elements bismuth (Bi) and cadmium (Cd) form a liquid solution that can be considered ideal. The solid phases do not dissolve in each other. Estimate the melting temperature and the composition of a eutectic solution of Bi and Cd. Relevant data for the pure elements at atmospheric pressure are given in the table, where T_m is the melting temperature and h_{sf} is the enthalpy change in melting.

	M kJ/kmol	T_m K	h_{sf} kg/kmol
Bi	209.0	544.4	10488
Cd	112.4	594.0	6173

18.9 An industrial plant that has an effluent stream of sour water at 100 kPa, 30 °C, containing 3.0 ppm of H_2S, is required to reduce the concentration to 0.05 ppm without diluting it with fresh water. It was proposed to absorb the H_2S in air and treat it subsequently. The air in the environment is at 100 kPa, 30 °C, and 40% relative humidity. Henry's constant for H_2S in liquid water is K_H = 30 MPa. A mixing chamber was designed. Water and air are introduced into one side and emerge as an equilibrium stream from the other side.

a. Estimate the amount of air required to sweeten 1 m^3 of sour water.
b. Determine the conditions of the gas and liquid at the exit from the chamber.
c. Suggest a more efficient design for the mixing chamber that will decrease the need for fresh air to accomplish the same job.

CHAPTER NINETEEN

Chemical reactions

In the previous chapters we dealt with substances that did not react chemically, i.e. substances whose molecular structure did not change during a thermodynamic process. In many systems of engineering importance chemical reactions do take place. This chapter examines the effects of chemical reactions on thermodynamic systems.

19.1 Stoichiometry

A chemical reaction changes the molecular structure of the components of a system. However, the atoms which make up the molecules remain unchanged. This can be expressed by the *stoichiometric** equation which gives a possible change of molecular structure due to a chemical reaction but, at the same time, preserves the number of atoms of each type. An example of a stoichiometric equation is

$$CO + \frac{1}{2} O_2 \rightleftarrows CO_2 \tag{19.1}$$

Equation (19.1) by itself does not indicate the direction of the chemical reaction or its extent, nor does it imply whether a chemical reaction will occur or not. The equation only expresses an exchange rate. Specifically, it states that 1 mole of CO together with half a mole of O_2 are exchangeable for 1 mole of CO_2, and vice versa. What actually occurs in a chemical reaction is affected by other conditions that are discussed later.

In order to gain a better understanding of the difference between the stoichiometric equation and the actual chemical reaction consider the following analogy, taken from the world of banking. The currency exchange rates posted in most banks tell us how many yen may be exchanged for one dollar and vice versa. If, for example, the exchange rate is 150 yen/$ and Mr John Doe enters a bank with $10 in his pocket, it is not obvious that he comes out with 1500 yen. He may come out with his original $10, or exchange only part

* The term stoichiometry comes from two Greek words: *stoicheion* – element, and *metron* – measure. Stoichiometry deals with the balance of elements.

of it. The rate of exchange is analogous to the stoichiometric equation, while the actual transaction is analogous to the chemical reaction.

Consider a stoichiometric equation of the form

$$\nu_A A + \nu_B B \rightleftarrows \nu_K K + \nu_L L \tag{19.2}$$

where A, B, K, L stand for chemical compounds. The coefficients ν_A, ν_B, ν_K, and ν_L are called the *stoichiometric coefficients*; they indicate fixed proportions of the number of moles by which the compounds can be exchanged. It is customary to call the chemical compounds on the left hand side of the equation *reactants*, and those on the right hand side *products*. Such a distinction is quite arbitrary, since the stoichiometric equation may be written just as well in the reverse order, in which case the roles of reactants and products are also reversed.

A compact form of Eq. (19.2) is

$$\sum \nu_i N_i = 0 \tag{19.3}$$

where N_i is the i'th component in the stoichiometric equation, and ν_i is the respective stoichiometric coefficient, which is positive for a product and negative for a reactant.

Consider a vessel containing n_A moles of component A, n_B moles of component B, n_K moles of component K, and n_L moles of component L. When a chemical reaction takes place the proportions of the components change. We can describe an actual chemical reaction within the vessel by indicating the original composition of the reactants on the left side of a reaction equation and that of the products on the right side. Thus

$$n_A A + n_B B + n_K K + n_L L$$
$$\rightarrow (n_A + \Delta n_A)A + (n_B + \Delta n_B)B + (n_K + \Delta n_K)K + (n_L + \Delta n_L)L$$

or in compact form

$$\sum n_i N_i \rightarrow \sum (n_i + \Delta n_i) N_i \tag{19.4}$$

The changes from the initial number of moles of the various components to the final composition are not completely arbitrary. They must satisfy the stoichiometric equation, i.e. the change in the number of moles of each component is proportional to its stoichiometric coefficient,

$$\frac{\Delta n_A}{-\nu_A} = \frac{\Delta n_B}{-\nu_B} = \frac{\Delta n_K}{\nu_K} = \frac{\Delta n_L}{\nu_L} = \text{const.} \tag{19.5}$$

The constant is called the degree (or extent) of reaction and is denoted by ξ. Thus the change in the number of moles of each component depends on a single parameter, the degree of reaction:

$$\Delta n_A = -\nu_A \xi \qquad \Delta n_B = -\nu_B \xi$$
$$\Delta n_K = \nu_K \xi \qquad \Delta n_L = \nu_L \xi$$

or in compact form

$$\Delta n_i = \nu_i \xi \tag{19.6}$$

Equation (19.6) may also be written in terms of rates,

$$\dot{n}_i = \nu_i \dot{\xi} \tag{19.7}$$

where $\dot{\xi}$ is the reaction rate.

19.2 Fuel combustion

The term fuel refers usually to organic compounds containing mainly carbon and hydrogen and smaller amounts of oxygen, nitrogen, and sulfur. The fuel may also contain non-organic compounds which are referred to as ash.

Fuels appear in gaseous, liquid, and solid forms. Typical gaseous fuels are: hydrogen H_2, methane CH_4, propane C_3H_8, etc., or mixtures thereof. Most conventional liquid fuels are derived from crude oil and are either pure hydrocarbons like heptane C_7H_{16} and octane C_8H_{18}, or, more commonly, a mixture of hydrocarbons such as gasoline, kerosene, diesel oil, heavy oils, etc. Recently new classes of liquid fuels have become of interest; these include synthetic liquid fuels and alcohols. Solid fuels are various types of coals, lignites, peat, and wood.

Fuel combustion is an important branch of engineering that involves chemical reactions. The combustion of fuel is essentially a chemical reaction between a fuel and an oxidant that results in a substantial increase in temperature.

The oxidant is usually air or pure oxygen. For combustion calculations, air is usually considered to be a mixture of 21% oxygen and 79% nitrogen by volume. Argon and other trace components, present in the air, are lumped together with the nitrogen in the analysis. Thus air contains 3.762 moles of nitrogen for every mole of oxygen.

In this section we deal with the stoichiometry of fuel combustion. We consider questions of fuel composition, the amount of air (or other oxidant) consumed during combustion, and the amount and composition of the combustion gases that are produced. The composition of the fuel is easily determined if the fuel is a pure substance for which the chemical equation is known. In fuels which are mixtures the composition is given in terms of the weight percentage of the various elements that comprise the fuel. Such a description is called the *ultimate analysis*.

Complete combustion of a fuel is defined as a reaction that converts all the carbon in the fuel into CO_2 and all the hydrogen into H_2O. If some of the carbon is left either as carbon or as carbon monoxide, or if all the hydrogen is not completely converted, the reaction is considered to be incomplete. *Theoretical air* or *stoichiometric air* is defined as the minimum amount of air required for complete combustion of the fuel. Under conditions of complete combustion no oxygen remains in the combustion gases.

Several parameters are used to describe the relationships between the amounts of air and fuel in the combustion mixture. These are

The *air–fuel ratio* – AF
The *theoretical air–fuel ratio* – AF_{theor}
The *molar air–fuel ratio* – $\overline{AF}$
The *theoretical molar air–fuel ratio* – $\overline{AF}_{theor}$

These parameters are interrelated through the expression

$$\frac{AF}{\overline{AF}} = \frac{AF_{theor}}{\overline{AF}_{theor}} = \frac{M_{air}}{M_{fuel}} \tag{19.8}$$

The relative air–fuel ratio, λ, gives the ratio of the actual air to the theoretical air required for complete combustion:

$$\lambda = \frac{\text{actual air}}{\text{theoretical air}} = \frac{AF}{AF_{theor}} \tag{19.9}$$

In many combustion processes air is supplied in excess of the required theoretical air. We define the term *excess air* as

$$X = \frac{\text{actual air}}{\text{theoretical air}} - 1 = \frac{AF}{AF_{theor}} - 1 = \lambda - 1 \tag{19.10}$$

In automotive engineering practice it is not uncommon to find that the fuel–air mixture is rich, i.e. that the amount of fuel exceeds the one that would result in complete combustion. This excess fuel is required in order to assure consistent ignition and combustion of the mixture in the cylinders within the short time available for the process. The parameter used for the ratio of the actual fuel used to that of the stoichiometric ratio is called the equivalence ratio, ϕ. The equivalence ratio is the inverse of the relative air-fuel ratio, λ, and is given by

$$\phi = \frac{\text{actual fuel}}{\text{theoretical fuel}} = \frac{AF_{theor}}{AF} \tag{19.11}$$

EXAMPLE 19.1

The analysis of the flue gases from the combustion of a hydrocarbon fuel in air is given on a dry basis in the following table.

Gas	CO_2	CO	O_2	N_2
% volume	8.0	0.9	8.8	82.3

a. Determine the composition of the fuel.
b. Find the excess air used in the combustion process.
c. Find the mass air–fuel ratio

SOLUTION

a. We calculate all the quantities required to produce 100 kmol of dry flue gases.

Let the composition of the hydrocarbon fuel be equivalent to C_xH_y.

The amount of oxygen that is actually supplied for the combustion of the fuel is denoted by z. Since the combustion is in air, we also include in the equation 79/21=3.762 kmol of nitrogen that accompany each kmol of oxygen in the air.

The equation of the chemical reaction that results in 100 kmol of dry flue gases is therefore

$$x\,C + y\,H + z(O_2 + 3.762N_2) \rightarrow 8CO_2 + 0.9CO + 8.8O_2 + 82.3N_2 + w\,H_2O$$

where x, y, z, and w are unknown. The unknown quantities can be evaluated using the condition that each element is conserved in the reaction. Thus,

Balance on N_2 yields	$z = 82.3/3.762$	$z = 21.88$
Balance on C yields	$x = 8 + 0.9$	$x = 8.90$
Balance on O_2 yields	$z = 8 + 0.9/2 + 8.8 + w/2$	$w = 9.25$
Balance on H yields	$y = 2w$	$y = 18.50$

The hydrogen/carbon (H/C) ratio in the fuel is H/C = 18.50/8.9 = 2.079.

The fuel is not a pure chemical compound, but rather a mixture of several compounds.

b. The theoretical oxygen is calculated from the known fuel composition, by noting that for each C 1 kmol of O_2 is needed, while for each H a quarter of a kmol of O_2 is required for complete combustion. Hence, per 100 kmol of flue gases

Theoretical oxygen = C + H/4 = 8.9 + 18.5/4 = 13.525 kmol

The excess air is found from Eq. (19.10):

$$X = \frac{z}{\text{theoretical oxygen}} - 1 = \frac{21.88}{13.525} - 1 = 0.618 \qquad (61.8\%)$$

c. The air–fuel mass ratio, *AF*, is found from the equation of the chemical reaction:

$$AF = \frac{m_{air}}{m_{fuel}} = \frac{z(32 + 3.762 \times 28)}{12x + y} = \frac{21.88 \times (32 + 3.762 \times 28)}{12 \times 8.90 + 18.50} = 23.98$$

19.3 The first law for chemical reactions

The first law of thermodynamics is also valid in the presence of chemical reactions. Thus for a simple compressible system in which a chemical reaction takes place we have

$$\Delta U = Q - W$$

and

$$\frac{dU}{dt} = \dot{Q} - \dot{W}$$

For a control volume the first law may be written in terms of molar fluxes as

$$(\Delta U)_{cv} = Q - W_x + \sum \bar{h}_i^0 n_i = Q - W_x + \sum_{inlet} \bar{h}_i^0 n_i - \sum_{exit} \bar{h}_i^0 n_i \tag{19.12}$$

and

$$\left(\frac{dU}{dt}\right)_{cv} = \dot{Q} - \dot{W}_x + \sum \bar{h}_i^0 \dot{n}_i = \dot{Q} - \dot{W}_x + \sum_{inlet} \bar{h}_i^0 \dot{n}_i - \sum_{exit} \bar{h}_i^0 \dot{n}_i \tag{19.13}$$

It should be noted that because a chemical reaction changes the composition of the system the calculation of its properties has to be carefully defined. In the absence of chemical reactions the quantity of each component does not change. Properties such as enthalpy are tabulated in a table for each component. There is, of course, an arbitrary constant in the value of enthalpy. This constant, however, cancels out when changes in

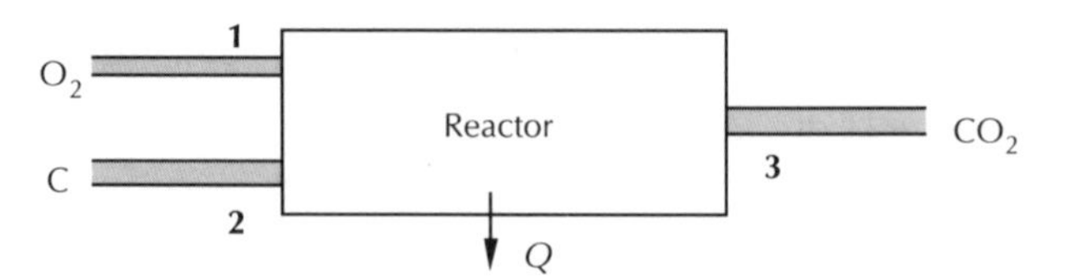

Figure 19.1 **Formation of carbon dioxide from its elements.**

enthalpy are calculated. The constants in the ordinary tables are selected in an arbitrary way. There is no need to worry about any specific relations between these constants, since there is no conversion from one table to another, as there is no conversion from one substance to another. This is not the case in the presence of chemical reactions. Here a common base state has to be defined, so that the data agree with each other.

The base state for determining the derived properties of any substance is the state where the *elements* of the substance are in their most stable form at 25 °C and 0.1 MPa. At this *reference state* the enthalpy of the elements is taken as zero.

Now consider a reactor, as shown in Fig. 19.1, that is fed carbon and oxygen at stoichiometric ratios, each at 25 °C and 0.1 MPa. A chemical reaction takes place in the reactor that converts the reactants into carbon dioxide

$$C + O_2 \rightarrow CO_2 \tag{19.14}$$

An appropriate quantity of heat is transferred so that the product, carbon dioxide, leaves the reactor at 25 °C, 0.1 MPa. The first law of thermodynamics, Eq. (19.12), written in terms of specific molar quantities for the reactor operating at steady state during a period of time required to produce 1 kmol of CO_2 is

$$0 = Q - \sum n_i \bar{h}_i \tag{19.15}$$

In our case for the reactants $n_1 = n_2 = -1$ and for the product $n_3 = 1$. Hence,

$$Q = \sum n_i \bar{h}_i = \bar{h}_{CO_2} - \bar{h}_{O_2} - \bar{h}_C \tag{19.16}$$

The heat interaction during the formation of 1 kmol of carbon dioxide from its elements at the reference state of 25 °C and 0.1 MPa is called the *enthalpy of formation* of carbon dioxide and is denoted by h_f. Thus,

$$\bar{h}^f_{CO_2} = \bar{h}_{CO_2} - \bar{h}_{O_2} - \bar{h}_C \tag{19.17}$$

It was found experimentally that $\bar{h}^f_{CO_2} = -393520$ kJ/kmol, which means that in the production of 1 kmol of CO_2 from its elements at the reference state 393520 kJ must be removed.

The enthalpy of formation of an element is also determined by measuring the heat interaction associated with the production of 1 kmol of the element at 25 °C and 0.1 MPa from the same element at its most stable form. Thus the enthalpy of formation of O_2 is zero since this is the most stable state of oxygen. The enthalpy of formation of O_3, however, is not zero. It can be determined experimentally by measuring the heat interaction of the reaction

$$\tfrac{3}{2}O_2 \rightarrow O_3$$

which yields $\bar{h}^f_{O_3} = 141820$ kJ/kmol.

Similarly, the enthalpy of formation of atomic oxygen is determined by measuring the heat interaction of the reaction

$$\tfrac{1}{2}O_2 \rightarrow O \qquad \bar{h}^f_O = 247640 \text{ kJ/kmol}$$

Each pure substance, of fixed chemical composition, is thus assigned the property *enthalpy of formation* at the reference state of 25 °C and 0.1 MPa. The enthalpy of formation of elements in their most stable state is always zero, while for other compounds it may take any value. A list of enthalpies of formation of various substances is given in Table 19.1.

During a chemical reaction other extensive properties may change. For example, the volume of the product may be different from the combined volume of the reactants. The difference between the volume of the compound product and the total volume of the reactant elements is called the *volume of formation.* In a similar way it is possible to define *entropy of formation, energy of formation, free energy of formation*, etc.

Consider now a more general chemical reaction, given by the stoichiometric equation

$$\nu_A A + \nu_B B \rightleftarrows \nu_K K + \nu_L L$$

where the substances are not necessarily elements and the reactant and product states are arbitrary, and not necessarily the reference state.

Let n_A, n_B, n_K, and n_L kmol of substances A, B, K, and L, respectively, enter the reaction chamber at respective pressures and temperatures p_A, T_A, p_B, T_B, p_K, T_K, and p_L, T_L. A chemical reaction takes place and the composition at the exit changes. We denote the properties at the exit by primes; thus the quantities of the products are denoted by n'_A, n'_B, n'_K and n'_K, respectively. Of course, there is a relationship between the products and the reactants according to Eq. (19.8). Thus

$$n'_i = n_i + \nu_i \xi$$

The enthalpy change, ΔH, in the reaction chamber may be broken into three terms, as follows:

$$\begin{aligned} H'(p',T',c') - H(p,T,c) = &\left[H'(p',T',c') - H'(p_0,T_0,c') \right] \\ &- \left[H(p,T,c) - H(p_0,T_0,c) \right] \\ &+ \left[H(p_0,T_0,c') - H(p_0,T_0,c) \right] \end{aligned} \tag{19.18}$$

The first term in square brackets describes the enthalpy change of the mixture of the final composition from the reference state (p_0, T_0) to the final state at (p', T'). No change of composition is involved in this term. Thus

Table 19.1 **Enthalpies and free energies of formation of several compounds at standard state of 1 bar, 25 °C.**

Compound (phase)	Formula	M	h^f MJ/kmol	g^f MJ/kmol
Acetylene (g)	C_2H_2	26.04	226.75	209.20
Ammonia (g)	NH_3	17.04	−46.19	−16.64
Benzene (g)	C_6H_6	78.11	82.93	129.66
Carbon–graphite (s)	C	12.01	0	0
Carbon–diamond (s)	C	12.01	1.88	2.89
Carbon dioxide (g)	CO_2	44.01	−393.52	−394.36
Carbon monoxide (g)	CO	28.01	−110.53	−137.15
Ethane (g)	C_2H_6	30.07	−84.68	−32.89
Ethanol (g)	C_6H_5OH	46.07	−235.31	−168.57
Ethene (g)	C_2H_4	28.05	52.28	68.12
Hydrogen (g)	H_2	2.016	0	0
Hydrogen peroxide (l)	H_2O_2	34.02	−187.61	−117.99
Hydrogen sulfide (l)	H_2S	34.00	−20.15	−33.02
Methane (g)	CH_4	16.04	−74.85	−50.69
Methanol (g)	CH_3OH	32.05	−200.67	−162.00
Nitrogen (g)	N_2	28.01	0	0
Nitrogen atomic (g)	N	14.01	472.65	455.50
n-Butane (g)	C_4H_{10}	58.12	−124.73	−15.71
n-Heptane (g)	C_7H_{16}	100.20	−187.82	−8.11
n-Hexane (g)	C_6H_{14}	86.17	−167.20	−0.29
n-Octane (l)	C_8H_{18}	114.22	209.45	16.53
n-Pentane (l)	C_5H_{12}	72.15	−146.44	−8.20
Oxygen (g)	O_2	32.00	0	0
Oxygen atomic(g)	O	16.00	249.20	231.76
Ozone (g)	O_3	48.00	34.00	39.06
Propane (g)	C_3H_8	44.09	−103.85	−23.49
Propene (g)	C_3H_6	42.08	20.41	62.72
Sulfur rhombic (s)	S	32.00	0	0
Sulfur monoclinic (s)	S	32.00	0.30	0.10
Sulfur dioxide (g)	SO_2	64.07	−296.90	−300.37
Sulfur trioxide (g)	SO_3	80.06	−395.18	−370.37
Water (l)	H_2O	18.02	−285.84	−237.19
Water (g)	H_2O	18.02	−241.83	−228.60

$$H'(p',T',c')-H'(p_0,T_0,c')=\sum_{product} n_i'\left[h(p',T')-h(p_0,T_0)\right]_i \tag{19.19}$$

The specific enthalpy for each substance can be read off the table of properties for that substance, or calculated from an appropriate equation, if available.

The second term in square brackets is also of fixed composition corresponding to the reactants. Thus

$$H(p,T,c)-H(p_0,T_0,c)=\sum_{reactants} n_i\left[h(p,T)-h_i(p_0,T_0)\right]_i \tag{19.20}$$

The last term represents the change of enthalpy from reactants to products each at the reference state (p_0, T_0). It is thus equal to the change of the enthalpy of formation from the reactants to the products:

$$H'(p_0,T_0,c')-H(p_0,T_0,c)=\sum_{products} n_i'h_i^f-\sum_{reactants} n_ih_i^f$$

$$=\sum(n_i'-n_i)h_i^f=(\sum \nu_ih_i^f)\xi \tag{19.21}$$

Combining all three terms yields the total enthalpy change in a chemical reaction,

$$H'(p',T',c')-H(p,T,c)=\sum_{product} n_i'\left[h(p',T')-h(p_0,T_0)\right]_i$$

$$-\sum_{reactants} n_i\left[h(p,T)-h(p_0,T_0)\right]_i+\left(\sum \nu_ih_i^f\right)\xi \tag{19.22}$$

Equation (19.22) may be combined with Eq. (19.12) to yield the expression of the first law of thermodynamics for a control volume in the presence of a chemical reaction. Note that Eq. (19.22) gives the enthalpy change from reactants to products which is equivalent to the enthalpy change from inlet to exit in the control volume.

$$(\Delta U)_{cv}=Q-W_x-\sum_{products} n_i'\left[h(p',T')-h(p_0,T_0)\right]_i$$

$$+\sum_{reactants} n_i\left[h(p,T)-h(p_0,T_0)\right]_i-\left(\sum \nu_ih_i^f\right)\xi \tag{19.23}$$

Similarly, in terms of rates Eq. (19.13) becomes

$$\left(\frac{dU}{dt}\right)_{cv}=\dot{Q}-\dot{W}_x-\sum_{products} \dot{n}_i'\left[h(p',T')-h(p_0,T_0)\right]_i$$

$$+\sum_{reactants} \dot{n}_i\left[h(p,T)-h(p_0,T_0)\right]_i-\left(\sum \nu_ih_i^f\right)\dot{\xi} \tag{19.24}$$

For the special case of steady state and $W_x = 0$, Eqs (19.23) and (19.24) yield the heat interaction and the rate of heat transfer, respectively,

$$Q=\sum_{products} n_i'\left[h(p',T')-h(p_0,T_0)\right]_i-\sum_{reactants} n_i\left[h(p,T)-h(p_0,T_0)\right]_i+\left(\sum \nu_ih_i^f\right)\xi \tag{19.25}$$

and

$$\dot{Q} = \sum_{products} \dot{n}'_i \left[h(p',T') - h(p_0,T_0)\right]_i$$

$$- \sum_{reactants} \dot{n}_i \left[h(p,T) - h(p_0,T_0)\right]_i + \left(\sum \nu_i h_i^f\right)\xi \tag{19.26}$$

For an ideal gas $\Delta H = c_p \Delta T$. Thus Eqs (19.25) and (19.26) can be simplified for this case as follows:

$$Q = \sum_{products} n'_i c_{p_i} (T' - T_o)_i - \sum_{reactants} n_i c_{p_i} (T - T_0)_i + \left(\sum \nu_i h_i^f\right)\xi \tag{19.27}$$

$$\dot{Q} = \sum_{products} \dot{n}'_i c_{p_i} (T' - T_0)_i - \sum_{reactants} \dot{n}_i c_{p_i} (T - T_0)_i + \left(\sum \nu_i h_i^f\right)\xi \tag{19.28}$$

EXAMPLE 19.2

A reaction chamber receives a stream of 24 kg/min of oxygen at 2 bars, 25 °C, and a stream of 28 kg/min of carbon monoxide, CO, at 1.5 bars, 100 °C. The two streams react chemically according to the following stoichiometric equation:

$$CO + \frac{1}{2}O_2 \rightleftarrows CO_2$$

The degree of the reaction is 0.5 and the product gases emerge at 1 bar and 1800 °C.

a. Find the composition of the product gases.

b. Find the heat interaction of the reaction chamber.

Data:

Formula	M	k	c_p/R	h^f(25 °C)	g^f(25 °C)
O_2	32	1.40	3.50	0	0
CO	28	1.40	3.50	−110529	−137150
CO_2	44	1.28	4.57	−393522	−394374

SOLUTION

Consider the reaction chamber as the control volume, shown in Fig. 19.2. Two streams enter the control volume and one stream leaves it. The control volume operates at steady state. Denote stream 1 as oxygen, stream 2 as carbon monoxide, and stream 3 as the reaction products:

$$\dot{m}_1 = 24\,\text{kg/min} \qquad \dot{n}_1 = \frac{\dot{m}_1}{M_1} = \frac{24}{32} = 0.75\,\text{kmol/min}$$

$$\dot{m}_2 = 28\,\text{kg/min} \qquad \dot{n}_2 = \frac{\dot{m}_2}{M_2} = \frac{28}{28} = 1.00\,\text{kmol/min}$$

a. The equation describing the chemical reaction is

$$CO + 0.75\,O_2 \rightarrow n_{CO}CO + n_{O_2}O_2 + n_{CO_2}CO_2$$

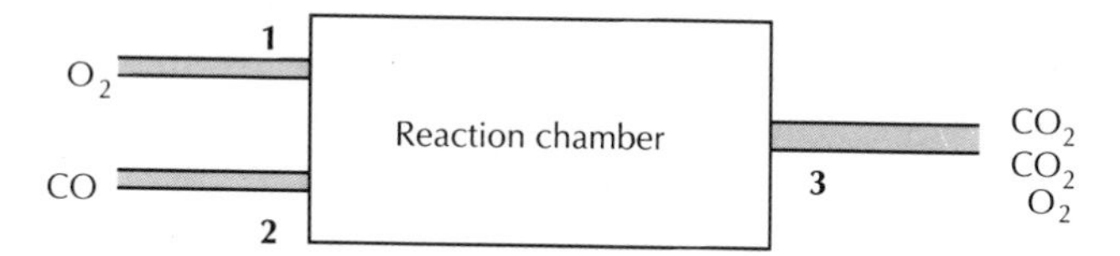

Figure 19.2 **Control volume for reaction chamber.**

where the fluxes of the components in the product stream can be calculated from Eq. (19.7):

$$\dot{n}_{O_2} = \dot{n}_1 - \tfrac{1}{2}\dot{\xi} = 0.75 - \frac{1}{2} \times \frac{1}{2} = 0.5\,\text{kmol/min}$$

$$\dot{n}_{CO} = \dot{n}_2 - \dot{\xi} = 1 - \frac{1}{2} = 0.5\,\text{kmol/min}$$

$$\dot{n}_{CO_2} = 0 + \dot{\xi} = 0 + \frac{1}{2} = 0.5\,\text{kmol/min}$$

$$\dot{n} = \sum \dot{n}_i = 1.5\,\text{kmol/min}$$

The composition of the gases at the exit of the reaction chamber is given by

$$y_i = \frac{\dot{n}_i}{\dot{n}}$$

$$y_{CO_2} = y_{CO} = y_{O_2} = \frac{1}{3}$$

b. The flow through the reaction chamber is at steady state. Assuming ideal gas behavior, the heat interaction is found from Eq. (19.28):

$$\dot{Q} = (\dot{n}co\; c_{p_{CO_2}} + \dot{n}_{CO} c_{p_{CO}} + \dot{n}_{O_2} c_{p_{O_2}})(T_3 - T_0)$$
$$-\left[\dot{n}_1 c_{p_{O2}}(T_1 - T_0) + \dot{n}_2 c_{p_{CO}}(T_2 - T_0)\right] + \dot{\xi}\left(h^f_{CO_2} - h^f_{CO} - \tfrac{1}{2} h^f_{O_2}\right)$$

Hence,

$$\dot{Q} = (0.5 \times 4.57 + 0.5 \times 3.5 + 0.5 \times 3.5) \times 8.3143(1800 - 25)$$
$$-\left[0.75 \times 3.5 \times 8.3143(25 - 25) + 1 \times 3.5 \times 8.3143(100 - 25)\right]$$
$$+0.5\left[(-393522) - (-110529) - 0\right] = -58300\ \text{kJ/min} = -972\ \text{kW}$$

Note that even though the temperature of the products is substantially higher than that of the reactants the heat interaction is still negative, i.e. heat is being removed.

19.4 Adiabatic flame temperature

We have seen that once the initial and final states and the degree of reaction are known, it is possible to calculate the heat interaction from the first law.

If the heat interaction is known the final temperature can be calculated. A case where the final temperature is of special interest is that of an adiabatic reaction, i.e. a reaction in which the heat interaction is zero. The final temperature of the product is called the *adiabatic flame temperature*. The adiabatic flame temperature is a useful concept in fuel combustion. It indicates the highest temperature that can be reached in the combustion process. Under actual conditions, heat is removed from the combustion gases and therefore the temperature is lower than the adiabatic flame temperature.

The adiabatic flame temperature is calculated from Eq. (19.25) by setting $Q = 0$,

$$\sum_{products} n_i'\left[h(p',T') - h(p_0,T_0)\right] - \sum_{reactants} n_i\left[h(p,T) - h(p_0,T_0)\right]_i + \left(\sum \nu_i h_i^f\right)\xi = 0 \quad (19.29)$$

The only unknown in Eq. (19.29) is the final temperature T'. The solution for T' may involve a numerical trial and error procedure. If, however, the gases are ideal, then their enthalpies are linear functions of temperature, and the solution for T' follows easily from Eq. (19.27):

$$T = T_0 + \frac{\sum_{reactants} n_i c_{p_i}(T_i - T_0) - \left(\sum \nu_i h_i^f\right)\xi}{\sum_{products} n_i' c_{p_i}} \quad (19.30)$$

EXAMPLE 19.3

Find the adiabatic flame temperature in a complete combustion of propane (C3H8) at 2.5 bars, 25 °C, with 200% excess air at 1.0 bar, 220 °C. Assume all the gases to be ideal.

Formula	M	k	h^f (25 °C)
O_2	32	1.40	0
N_2	28	1.40	0
CO_2	44	1.29	−393522
$H_2O(g)$	18	1.29	−241830
C_3H_8	44	1.25	−103850

SOLUTION

The stoichiometric equation is

$$C_3H_8 + 5O_2 \rightleftarrows 3CO_2 + 4H_2O$$

The actual reaction is

$$C_3H_8 + 3\times 5(O_2 + 3.762N_2) \rightarrow 3CO_2 + 4H_2O + 10O_2 + 56.43N_2$$

Equation (19.30) is used to calculate the adiabatic flame temperature. Hence,

$$T' = 25 + \frac{c_{PC_3H_8}(25-25) + 15\times 4.762c_{p_{air}}(220-25) - \left(3h^f_{CO_2} + 4h^f_{H_2O(g)} - h^f_{C_3H_8}\right)}{3c_{PCO_2} + 4c_{PH_2O} + 10c_{PO_2} + 56.43c_{PN_2}}$$

or

$$T' = 25 + \frac{15 \times 4.762 \times \dfrac{1.4 \times 8.3143}{0.4} \times 195 - [3 \times (-393520) + 4 \times (-241830) - (-103850)]}{\left((3+4) \times \dfrac{1.29}{0.29} + (10 + 56.43) \times \dfrac{1.4}{0.4}\right) \times 8.3143}$$

and finally

$$T' = 25 + 1117 = 1142\ ^\circ C$$

EXAMPLE 19.4

Repeat Example 19.3 without the assumption that water is an ideal gas.

SOLUTION

The stoichiometric equation and the chemical reaction are exactly the same as in Example 19.3. The only difference is in the calculation of the enthalpy of water. Here the enthalpy of water must be found from the steam tables. Two enthalpies are needed, the enthalpy of water at the reference state of $p_0 = 100$ kPa, $T_0 = 25$ °C, and at the final state. The enthalpy of formation of liquid water at 100 kPa and 25 °C is

$$h^f_{H_2O} = -285840 \text{ kJ/kmol}$$

The partial pressure of water at the final state is related to the total pressure through its mole fraction

$$p'_{H_2O} = p' \frac{n_{H_2O}}{n} = 100 \frac{4}{73.43} = 5.447 \text{ kPa}$$

The final temperature is not known a priori, and the enthalpy change of water cannot be expressed in terms of the final temperature. Thus Eq. (19.30) cannot be used, and a trial and error procedure must be employed.

We guess a final temperature, and calculate from Eq. (19.25) the resulting heat interaction. In that equation we can calculate the enthalpy changes of all other gases from the ideal gas equation $\Delta h = c_p \Delta T$. A successful guess will result in a zero heat interaction.

$$\begin{aligned} Q &= \left[\left(3c_{p_{CO_2}} + 10\,c_{p_{N_2}} + 56.43\,c_{p_{N_2}}\right)(T - T_0) + 4\left(h(p',T') - h(p_0 T_0)\right)_{H_2O}\right] \\ &\quad - \left[15 \times 4.762 c_{p_{air}} (220 - 25)\right] + \left[3(-393520) + 4(-285840) - (-103850)\right] \\ &= 2044.1(T' - 25) + 4 \times 18.02\left(h(p', T') - 104.89\right) - 2625360 \end{aligned}$$

or

$$Q = 2044.1T' + 72.08h\left(p', T'\right) - 2684022$$

We arrange the guesses in a table:

Guess no.	p'	T'	$h(p',T')$	Q
1	5.447	1100	4891.2	–82989
2	5.447	1200	5147.8	139914
3	5.447	1137.2	4896.0	0

The obtained temperature of 1137.2 °C is fairly close to the one calculated in Example 19.3 where water was assumed to be an ideal gas.

19.5 Enthalpy of formation at any temperature

The enthalpy of formation is usually listed in the literature for one reference state, namely $p_0 = 1$ atm, $T_0 = 25$ °C. It is possible to calculate the enthalpy of formation at any other state (p, T) using Eq. (19.21). Let the products in Eq. (19.21) be the component at p and T and the reactants the elements at the same p and T. The left hand side of Eq. (19.21) will then be equal to the enthalpy of formation of the component at p and T, and the last term on the right hand side will be the enthalpy of formation at p_0 and T_0. Thus

$$h^f(p,T) = \sum \nu_i \left[h_i(p,T) - h_i(p_0,T_0)\right] + h^f(p_0,T_0) \tag{19.31}$$

The summation is over the enthalpy changes from (p_0,T_0) to (p, T) of the component and its elements. For the special case where all the substances are ideal gases Eq. (19.31) is simplified to

$$h^f(p,T) = \sum \nu_i c_{p_i}(T - T_0) + h^f(p_0,T_0) \tag{19.32}$$

19.6 Free energy of formation at any temperature

The free energy of formation is also listed in the literature at one reference state. For many applications it is necessary to know the free energy of formation, i.e. the change of the free energy from elements to compounds at different states. We now develop the relationship for the free energy of formation at any temperature.

Applying Eq. (15.81) to the free energy of formation we find that

$$\left[\frac{d(\mu^f/T)}{dT}\right]_p = -\frac{h^f}{T^2} \tag{19.33}$$

Multiplication of both sides of Eq. (19.33) by dT and integration yields

$$\frac{\mu^f(T)}{T} - \frac{\mu^f(T_0)}{T_0} = -\int_0^T \frac{h^f}{T^2} dT \tag{19.34}$$

The integral on the right hand side of Eq. (19.34) can be evaluated by substituting h^f from Eq. (19.31). In the general case a numerical solution is required. For the special case where all the gases are ideal it is possible to obtain a closed solution by substituting h^f from Eq. (19.32). The solution is then

$$\frac{\mu^f(T)}{T} - \frac{\mu^f(T_0)}{T_0} = \left(h^f(p_0,T_0) - \sum_i \nu_i c_{p_i} T_0\right)\left(\frac{1}{T} - \frac{1}{T_0}\right) - \left(\sum_i \nu_i c_{p_i}\right) \ln\frac{T}{T_0} \tag{19.35}$$

EXAMPLE 19.5

Find the enthalpy of formation of water at 1000 °C, assuming that all the gases are ideal. Use the following data:

	Formula	M	k	h^f (25 °C)	c_p/ R
1	H_2	2	1.40	0	3.50
2	O_2	32	1.40	0	3.50
3	H_2O	18	1.29	−241820	4.45

SOLUTION

We use Eq. (19.32) to find the enthalpy of formation of water at 1000°C. We first find

$$\sum v_i c_{pi} = \left(4.45 - \frac{3}{2} \times 3.5\right) R = -0.8017R$$

Hence,

$$h^f\left(1000\ °\mathrm{C}\right) = h^f\left(25\ °\mathrm{C}\right) + \sum v_i c_{pi}\left(T - T_0\right)$$
$$= -241820 - 0.8017 \times 8.3143(1000 - 25) = -248320\ \mathrm{kJ/kmol}$$

Note that the enthalpy of formation of water does not vary much with temperature.

19.7 Chemical equilibrium

Consider a system consisting of n_A moles of substance A, n_B moles of B, n_K moles of K, and n_L moles of L. The system is held at constant pressure and temperature.

A chemical reaction of the following type is possible:

$$v_A A + v_B B \rightleftarrows v_K K + v_L L \tag{19.2}$$

The chemical reaction, if present, would change the number of moles of each component according to

$$n_A A + n_B B + n_K K + n_L L$$
$$\rightarrow (n_A + \Delta n_A)A + (n_B + \Delta n_B)B + (n_K + \Delta n_K)K + (n_L + \Delta n_L)L \tag{19.4}$$

The changes in the number of moles in the reaction are not completely independent. They are related according to the corresponding stoichiometric coefficient $dn_i = v_i d\xi$ where $d\xi$ is the degree of reaction.

Changes in the Gibbs free energy of the system depend in general on changes in pressure, temperature, and composition, according to

$$dG = -SdT + Vdp + \sum \mu_i dn_i \tag{15.48}$$

The process under consideration is carried out at constant pressure and temperature; therefore, the changes in Gibbs free energy, Eq. (15.48), depend only on the changes in composition. As the chemical reaction proceeds, the composition changes and so does the

Gibbs free energy

$$(dG)_{p,T} = \sum \mu_i dn_i = \left(\sum \nu_i \mu_i\right) d\xi \tag{19.36}$$

The process at constant p and T may continue, however, only as long as the Gibbs free energy is decreasing

$$(dG)_{p,T} \le 0 \tag{19.37}$$

An equilibrium composition is reached when the Gibbs free energy attains its minimum value. The requirement for a minimum value of the Gibbs free energy imposes, therefore, a condition on the equilibrium composition.

For equilibrium to exist $(dG)_{p,T}$ is minimum, i.e.

$$(dG)_{p,T} = 0 \tag{19.38}$$

Substitution of Eq. (19.36) into Eq. (19.38) yields for equilibrium,

$$\sum \nu_i \mu_i = 0 \tag{19.39}$$

Equation (19.39) states the condition for chemical equilibrium. It gives a relation between the chemical potentials of the components, μ_i, that must hold in equilibrium. Since, in general, the chemical potentials are functions of pressure, temperature, and composition of the system,

$$\mu_i = \mu_i(p, T, x_1, \ldots, x_{c-1}) \tag{19.40}$$

Equation (19.39) gives an implicit condition on the composition of the system in equilibrium at any given pressure and temperature. The form of this equation, however, is not very convenient for everyday use, and hence we restate the same condition in a different, more useful, form by expressing the same condition in terms of the fugacities. By definition, the changes in the chemical potential of a component are related to changes in the fugacity by

$$(d\mu_i)_T = RTd\ln f_i \tag{19.41}$$

Upon integration of Eq. (19.41) at constant temperature we find that

$$\mu_i = RT \ln f_i + \mu_i^*(T) \tag{19.42}$$

where $\mu_i^*(T)$ is the integration constant that may be a function of the temperature. It is obvious from Eq. (19.42) that $\mu_i^*(T)$ can be interpreted as the chemical potential of the component i at a specific state where $f_i = 1$. Substitution of Eq. (19.42) for each of the components of Eq. (19.39) yields

$$\sum_i \nu_i \mu_i^*(T) + \sum_i \nu_i RT \ln f_i = 0 \tag{19.43}$$

or

$$\sum_i \nu_i \ln f_i = -\frac{\sum \nu_i \mu_i^*(T)}{RT} \tag{19.44}$$

For a given stoichiometric equation the right hand side of Eq. (19.44) is a function of temperature only. It is therefore a constant for any given temperature and does not depend on the specific composition of the system. There are many possible compositions that may be in equilibrium at a given temperature depending on the original composition of the system.

Consider, for example, a system composed of O_2, CO, and CO_2 in equilibrium at a given temperature T. Different initial proportions between the carbon and the oxygen will result in different equilibrium compositions. All these compositions, however, must conform to Eq. (19.44) with the same constant on the right hand side. The right hand side is called, therefore, the equilibrium constant for the reaction and is denoted by ln $K(T)$. It is, of course, a function of temperature. It imposes a condition on the relative values of the fugacities of all the components. Thus:

$$\sum_i \nu_i \ln f_i = \ln K(T) \tag{19.45}$$

$$K(T) = \prod_i f_i^{\nu_i} \tag{19.46}$$

The equilibrium constant $K(T)$ is not dimensionless. Indeed, its dimensions depend on the respective stoichiometric equation. The units of the equilibrium constant can be determined from Eq. (19.46), noting that the fugacity has the same units as the pressure. Thus the units of $K(T)$ are the same as those of $p^{\Sigma \nu_i}$.

For the special case of a mixture of ideal gases, where $f_i = p_i = y_i p$, Eq. (19.45) simplifies to

$$\sum \nu_i \ln p_i = \ln \prod_i p_i^{\nu_i} = \ln K(T)$$

or

$$K(T) = \prod_i p_i^{\nu_i} \tag{19.47}$$

Thus, for the reaction given in Eq. (19.2), the equilibrium constant is given as

$$K(T) = \frac{p_K^{\nu_k} \, p_L^{\nu_l}}{p_A^{\nu_a} \, p_B^{\nu_b}} \tag{19.48}$$

Another form of the equilibrium equation is obtained by expressing p_i in terms of the mole fractions, i.e. $p_i = y_i p$,

$$K(T) = \frac{y_K^{\nu_k} \, y_L^{\nu_l}}{y_A^{\nu_a} \, y_B^{\nu_b}} p^{(\nu_k + \nu_l - \nu_a - \nu_b)} = \prod y_i^{\nu_i} \, p^{\Sigma \nu_i} \tag{19.49}$$

The equilibrium constant $K(T)$ may be evaluated experimentally for any stoichiometric equation by measuring the composition of the components at one equilibrium state. For an ideal gas mixture Eq. (19.49) can be used to calculate $K(T)$ directly. If the components are not ideal gases then the fugacities must be calculated and used in Eq. (19.46). This method is quite cumbersome since it requires an experimental test for each stoichiometric equation at each temperature.

Another method for evaluating the equilibrium constant is by applying Eq. (19.42) to the standard state; thus

$$\mu_i^{std} = RT\ln f_i^{std} + \mu_i^*(T) \tag{19.50}$$

If the standard state is selected as a pure ideal gas at unit pressure then its fugacity is unity, $f_i^{std} = 1$ atm. For this case the chemical potential of the standard state, given by Eq. (19.50), becomes

$$\mu_i^{std}(T, p=1) = \mu_i^*(T) \tag{19.51}$$

Combining Eqs (19.45) and (19.44) with Eq. (19.51) yields

$$\ln K(T) = -\frac{\sum \nu_i \mu_i^{std}(T, p=1)}{RT} \tag{19.52}$$

Values of chemical potentials are tabulated in the literature for many substances at unit pressure, usually at 25 °C. These are the free energies of formation of those substances. Thus, at $T_0 = 25$ °C

$$K(T_0) = e^{-\frac{\sum \nu_i \mu_i^f}{RT_0}} = e^{-\frac{\sum \nu_i g_i^f}{RT_0}} \tag{19.53}$$

The equilibrium constant at any other temperature may be related to that at $T_0 = 25$ °C by means of Eq. (19.34),

$$\ln\frac{K(T)}{K(T_0)} = -\sum\frac{\nu_i}{R}\left(\frac{\mu_i^f(T)}{T} - \frac{\mu_i^f(T_0)}{T_0}\right) = \int_{T_0}^{T}\frac{\sum \nu_i h_i^f(T)}{RT^2}dT \tag{19.54}$$

where the summation is over the components of the stoichiometric equation.

For the special case of ideal gases Eq. (19.35) may be used to yield a more explicit relationship:

$$\ln\frac{K(T)}{K(T_0)} = \left(1 - \frac{T_0}{T}\right)\sum_i \nu_i\left[\frac{h_i^f(T_0)}{RT_0} - \frac{c_{pi}}{R}\right] + \frac{\sum \nu_i c_{pi}}{R}\ln\frac{T}{T_0} \tag{19.55}$$

Equation (19.55) is used to calculate the equilibrium constant at any temperature.

EXAMPLE 19.6

Find the equilibrium constant for the reaction

$$\frac{1}{2}N_2 + \frac{3}{2}H_2 \rightleftarrows NH_3$$

a. At 25 °C.
b. At 450 °C.

Data:

Substance	M	c_p/R	h^f(25 °C) kJ/kmol	g^f(25 °C) kJ/kmol
N_2	28	3.5	0	0
H_2	2	3.5	0	0
NH_3	17	5.0	−46190	−16590

SOLUTION

a. The equilibrium constant at T_0 = 25 °C is calculated from Eq. (19.53):

$$K(T_0) = e^{-\frac{g_A^f}{RT_0}} = e^{-\frac{-16590}{8.3143 \times 298.15}} = e^{6.69} = 806.3 \text{ bar}^{-1}$$

The units are bar $^{-1}$ since $\Sigma v_i = -1$ for the stoichiometric equation and the free energy of formation is defined at 1 bar, 25 °C.

b. The equilibrium constant at 450 °C is calculated with the aid of Eq. (19.55) with

$$\sum \frac{v_i C_{pi}}{R} = 5 - 2 \times 3.5 = -2$$

$$\ln \frac{K(723.15)}{K(298.15)} = \left(1 - \frac{298.15}{723.15}\right) \sum_i v_i \left[\frac{h_i^f(T_0)}{RT_0} - \frac{c_{pi}}{R} \right] + \frac{\sum v_i c_{pi}}{R} \ln \frac{723.15}{298.15}$$

$$= \left(1 - \frac{298.15}{723.15}\right)\left(\frac{-46190}{8.3143 \times 298.15} + 2\right) - 2 \ln \frac{723.15}{298.15} = -11.553$$

Hence,

$$K(723.15) = K(298.15) \times e^{-11.553} = e^{6.69} \times e^{-11.553} = e^{-4.86} = 0.00773 \text{ bar}^{-1}$$

EXAMPLE 19.7

Find the composition that would emerge from the reaction chamber of Example 19.2 if the gases were in equilibrium at 1 bar, 1500 °C.

SOLUTION

The final composition in this case depends on the degree of reaction ξ that takes place in the reactor. The equation that describes the process taking place in the reactor is

$$CO + 0.75 O_2 \rightarrow (1 - \xi) CO + (0.75 - 0.5\xi) O_2 + \xi CO_2$$

where the only unknown is ξ.

On the other hand we know that the exit stream is in equilibrium. We assume that the emerging gas is a mixture of ideal gases in equilibrium and use Eq. (19.49) to calculate the equilibrium constant that corresponds to the stoichiometric equation,

$$CO + \tfrac{1}{2} O_2 \rightleftarrows CO_2$$

Hence,

$$K(T) = \frac{y_{CO_2}}{y_{CO}\, y_{O_2}^{0.5}} p^{-0.5}$$

Now the respective mole fractions are given as

$$y_i = \frac{\dot{n}_i}{\sum \dot{n}_i}$$

where

$$\sum \dot{n}_i = \dot{n}_{CO_2} + \dot{n}_{CO} + \dot{n}_{O_2} = 1.75 - 0.5\xi$$

Hence,

$$y_{CO_2} = \frac{\dot{n}_{CO_2}}{\sum \dot{n}_i} = \frac{\xi}{1.75 - 0.5\xi}$$

$$y_{CO} = \frac{\dot{n}_{CO}}{\dot{n}} = \frac{1 - \xi}{1.75 - 0.5\xi}$$

$$y_{O_2} = \frac{\dot{n}_{O_2}}{\dot{n}} = \frac{0.75 - 0.5\xi}{1.75 - 0.5\xi}$$

Thus the condition of equilibrium is expressed as

$$K(T) = \frac{\left(\dfrac{\xi}{1.75 - 0.5x}\right)}{\left(\dfrac{1 - \xi}{1.75 - 0.5\xi}\right)\left(\dfrac{0.75 - 0.5\xi}{1.75 - 0.5\xi}\right)^{0.5}} = \frac{\xi(1.75 - 0.5\xi)^{0.5}}{(1 - \xi)(0.75 - 0.5\xi)^{0.5}}$$

which may be simplified to

$$K(T) = \frac{\xi}{(1 - \xi)}\left(\frac{7 - 2\xi}{3 - 2\xi}\right)^{0.5}$$

To find ξ we have to determine $K(T)$. This is done by first finding ln $K(T_0)$ using Eq. (19.52) and data from Table 19.1:

$$\ln K(T_0) = -\frac{\sum \nu_i \mu_i^f}{RT_0} = \frac{\mu_{CO_2}^f - \mu_{CO}^f - \frac{1}{2}\mu_{O_2}^f}{RT_0}$$

$$= -\frac{(-394374) - (-137150) - 0}{8.3143 \times 298.15} = 103.765$$

$K(T)$ is found from Eq. (19.55), where

$$\frac{\sum \nu_i c_{pi}}{R} = \frac{c_{pCO_2} - c_{pCO} - \frac{1}{2}c_{pO_2}}{R} = 4.57 - 3.5 - \frac{1}{2} \times 3.5 = -0.6800$$

For T = 1500 °C = 1773.15 K:

$$\ln\frac{K(T)}{K(T_0)} = \left(1-\frac{T_0}{T}\right)\sum_i v_i\left[\frac{h_i^f(T_0)}{RT_0}-\frac{c_{pi}}{R}\right]+\frac{\sum v_i c_{pi}}{R}\ln\frac{T}{T_0}$$

$$= \left(1-\frac{298.15}{1773.15}\right)\left[\frac{-393522-(-110529)}{8.3143\times 298.15}+0.6800\right]-0.6800\ln\frac{1773.15}{298.15}$$

$$= -95.611$$

$$\ln K(T) = \ln K(T_0) - 95.611 = 103.765 - 95.611 = 8.154$$

Thus

$$K(T) = 3477$$

We now find the degree of reaction ξ by solving the third order equation

$$\frac{\xi}{(1-\xi)}\left(\frac{7-2\xi}{3-2\xi}\right)^{0.5} = 3477$$

This equation can be solved by trial and error to yield

$\xi = 0.99936$

For T = 2500 °C = 2773.15 K:

$$\ln\frac{K(T)}{K(T_0)} = \left(1-\frac{T_0}{T}\right)\sum_i v_i\left(\frac{h_i^f(T_0)}{RT_0}-\frac{c_{pi}}{R}\right)+\frac{\sum v_i c_{pi}}{R}\ln\frac{T}{T_0}$$

$$= \left(1-\frac{298.15}{2773.15}\right)\left(\frac{-393522-(-110529)}{8.3143\times 298.15}+0.6800\right)-0.6800\ln\frac{2773.15}{298.15}$$

$$= -102.796$$

$$\ln K(T) = \ln K(T_0) - 102.796 = 103.765 - 102.796 = 0.969$$

and

$K(T) = 2.635$

leading to

$\xi = 0.5952$

The results for the two temperatures are summarized in the following table:

Temp. °C	$K(T)$	ξ	$y_{CO_2} = \frac{\xi}{1.75-0.5\xi}$	$y_{CO} = \frac{1-\xi}{1.75-0.5\xi}$	$y_{O_2} = \frac{0.75-0.5\xi}{1.75-0.5\xi}$
1500	3477	0.99936	0.79927	0.000052	0.20021
2500	2.635	0.5952	0.40980	0.278710	0.31148

We note that at 1500 °C the combustion is practically complete, with only negligible quantities of CO present in the product gas. At 2500 °C the combustion is far from being complete, and a large quantity of CO remains unreacted.

19.8 Exergy considerations

In Chapter 10 we have shown that exergy analysis is an important tool for measuring the effectiveness of thermodynamic processes. Exergy analysis applies also to processes with chemical reactions. Both steady and unsteady state processes can be analyzed. The presence of chemical reactions does not change the basic equations that were developed in Chapter 10, and the only difference is in the way the properties of the reactants and products are evaluated. We have already seen that whenever enthalpy is used in calculations of heat and work interactions in reacting systems the enthalpy of formation must be accounted for. Other extensive properties, such as entropy, energy, free energy, etc., must also be similarly evaluated. We demonstrate exergy analysis in reacting systems by several examples.

EXAMPLE 19.8

What is the maximum work that can be obtained from 1 kg of carbon and a sufficient amount of oxygen for complete combustion, relative to an environment at p_0 = 101 kPa, T_0 = 25 °C? Assume that the components do not mix with the environment.

SOLUTION

The stoichiometric equation of the reaction is

$$C + O_2 \rightleftarrows CO_2$$

For CO_2 at 25 °C: $h^f = -393520$ kJ/kmol and $g^f = -394360$ kJ/kmol.

The maximum work is obtained when the reaction is carried out reversibly and the final products are in equilibrium with the environment, i.e. at the pressure and temperature of the environment. The maximum work is then equal to the decrease in the exergy, or the decrease in the free energy from reactants to products, namely

$$W_{max} = W_{rev} = B_{reactants} - B_{products} = 0 - \left(h - T_0 s\right)_{CO_2} = -g^f_{CO_2}$$

$$W_{max} = 394360 \text{ kJ/kmol of carbon} = 394360/12 = 32863 \text{ kJ/kg of carbon}$$

Note that

$$g^f = h^f - T_0 s^f = b^f$$

defines the exergy of formation which is equal to the Gibbs free energy of formation.

The calculations in Example 19.8 assume that each component is always maintained at the pressure of the atmosphere, say by a semi permeable membrane. If mixtures are produced then the maximum work must be calculated with respect to the partial pressure of each component, reactants, and products.

A practical combustion process, such as the one taking place in a steam boiler, is not reversible and part of the exergy of the fuel is always lost during combustion.

EXAMPLE 19.9

Coal with atmospheric air at p_0 = 101 kPa and T_0 = 25 °C enter an adiabatic combustion chamber. Assuming

excess air of 20%,

coal is made up of pure carbon,

complete combustion (the products contain no CO),

all gases are ideal (for diatomic gases $k = 1.34$, for polyatomic gases $k = 1.27$), and combustion gases do not mix with the environment, find:

a. The final temperature of the product gases.
b. The exergy of the reactants per kilogram of coal.
c. The exergy of the products per kilogram of coal.
d. The change of exergy in the combustion process per kilogram of coal.
e. The loss relative to the available work.

SOLUTION

The stoichiometric equation of the reaction is

$$C + O_2 \rightleftarrows CO_2$$

For CO_2 at 25 °C: $h^f = -393520$ kJ/kmol and $g^f = -394360$ kJ/kmol.

The chemical reaction that takes place in the boiler is

$$C + 1.2(O_2 + 3.762N_2) \Rightarrow CO_2 + 0.2O_2 + 4.5144N_2$$

The enthalpy, entropy, and exergy of each component are calculated from the following equations:

$$(h - h_0)_i = c_{p_i}(T - T_0)_i + h_i^f = \frac{k_i R}{k_i - 1}(T - T_0)_i + h_i^f \qquad c_{p_i} = \frac{k_i R}{k_i - 1}$$

$$(s - s_0)_i = c_{p_i} \ln\frac{T_i}{T_0} - R\ln\frac{p_i}{p_0} + s_i^f = \frac{k_i R}{k_i - 1}\ln\frac{T_i}{T_0} - R\ln\frac{p_i}{p_0} + s_i^f$$

$$s_i^f = \frac{h^f - g^f}{T_0}$$

and

$$(b - b_0)_i = (h - h_0)_i - T_0(s - s_0)_i$$

where the subscript 0 indicates the reference state. Thus

$$c_{pCO_2} = \frac{1.27 \times 8.3143}{1.27 - 1} = 39.1080 \ \frac{\text{kJ}}{\text{kmol K}}$$

$$c_{pO_2} = c_{pN_2} = \frac{1.34 \times 8.3143}{1.34 - 1} = 32.7681 \ \frac{\text{kJ}}{\text{kmol K}}$$

a. The outlet temperature, which is the adiabatic flame temperature, is calculated on the basis of the first law by using Eq. (19.30):

$$T' = T + \frac{\sum n_i c_{p_i}(T_i - T_0) - \left(\sum \nu_i h_i^f\right)\xi}{\sum n'_i c_{p_i}}$$

$$= 25 + \frac{-(-393520)}{\left(1\times\frac{1.27}{1.27-1} + (0.2+4.5144)\times\frac{1.34}{1.34-1}\right)\bar{R}} = 2057.75\ ^\circ\mathrm{C}$$

Thus the adiabatic flame temperature is $T' = 2057.75$ °C = 2330.90 K.

b. We select the conditions of the environment as the reference state. The reactants enter the combustion chamber at the conditions of the environment. Each reactant is a stable element under these conditions, and the "properties of formation" are zero by definition. As the exergy of the reactants, relative to the reference state, is zero, then

$$B_{in} = \sum_{in} n_i b_i = 0$$

c. At the outlet

$$(h-h_0)_{CO_2} = \frac{1.27\times 8.3143}{1.27-1}(2330.90-298.15) + (-393520) = -314023\ \frac{\mathrm{kJ}}{\mathrm{kmol}}$$

$$(s-s_0)_{CO_2} = \frac{1.27\times 8.3143}{1.27-1}\ln\frac{2330.90}{298.15} + \frac{-393520+394360}{298.15} = 83.240\ \frac{\mathrm{kJ}}{\mathrm{kmol\ K}}$$

If the gases are always at the same pressure and are not allowed to mix with the environment the pressure term in the calculation of entropy may be ignored. If, however, in the equilibrium state the gases are allowed to mix with the environment, the pressure term must be considered in a similar way that was presented in Example 17.5. For the sake of simplicity, we ignore here the pressure terms.

$$(b-b_0)_{CO_2} = (h-h_0)_{CO_2} - T_0(s-s_0)_{CO_2}$$

$$= -314023 - 298.15\times 83.240 = -338841\ \frac{\mathrm{kJ}}{\mathrm{kmol}}$$

Similarly,

$$(h-h_0)_{O_2} = (h-h_0)_{N_2} = \frac{1.34\times 8.3143}{1.34-1}(2330.90-298.15) = 66609\ \frac{\mathrm{kJ}}{\mathrm{kmol}}$$

$$(s-s_0)_{O_2} = (s-s_0)_{N_2} = \frac{1.34\times 8.3143}{1.34-1}\ln\frac{2330.90}{298.15} = 67.385\ \frac{\mathrm{kJ}}{\mathrm{kmol\ K}}$$

and

$$(b-b_0)_{O_2} = (b-b_0)_{N_2} = 66609 - 298.15\times 67.385 = 46519\ \frac{\mathrm{kJ}}{\mathrm{kmol}}$$

d. The exergy of the products per kilomole of coal is

$$B_{out} = \sum n_i (b-b_0)_i = -338841 + (0.2+4.5144)\times 46519 = -119534\ \mathrm{kJ}$$

and per kilogram of coal

$$B_{out} = \frac{-119534}{12} = -9961 \text{ kJ}$$

For convenience we arrange the relevant properties in two tables, one for the inlet and one for the outlet conditions.

Inlet	p MPa	T °C	$h-h_0$ kJ/kmol	$s-s_0$ kJ/kmol	$b-b_0$ kJ/kmol	n kmol	$B-B_0$ kJ
C	0.101	25.0	0	0.000	0.0	1.0000	0.0
O_2, N_2	0.101	25.0	0	0.000	0.0	5.7144	0.0
Total							0.0

Outlet	p MPa	T °C	$h-h_0$ kJ/kmol	$s-s_0$ kJ/kmol	$b-b_0$ kJ/kmol	n kmol	$B-B_0$ kJ
CO_2	0.101	2057.25	−314023	83.2396	−338841	1.0000	−338841
O_2, N_2	0.101	2057.25	66609	67.3848	46519	4.7144	219307
Total							−119534

e. The combustion process of coal in atmospheric air is not reversible, as can be seen from the fact that there is a loss of exergy in the process not compensated by an equivalent amount of work. The maximum work of reversible combustion of carbon with oxygen was calculated in Example 19.8 as

$$W_{max} = W_{rev} = -g^f = -b^f = 394360 \text{ kJ/kmol of carbon} = 32,863 \text{ kJ/kg carbon}$$

Here over 30% (9961/32863 = 0.303) of the exergy is lost just by the decision to burn the coal in atmospheric air. Note, however, that from the point of view of the first law the combustion process, as described, may be considered perfect since it has no losses whatsoever.

The selection of the reference state is quite arbitrary and can be done to be most convenient to the problem at hand. Selecting a different reference state does not alter the final conclusions but only shifts by a constant the values assigned to the properties energy, enthalpy, entropy, free energy, exergy, etc.

We may note that the reference state selected in example 19.9 is not the state of equilibrium for the fuel–air mixture. Indeed, the equilibrium state (the dead state) is one in which all the carbon is in the form of CO_2 which has a different composition than that of the environment. The advantage of selecting the equilibrium state to be the reference state is that absolute exergies will always be non-negative and equal in value to the maximum work that can be obtained from that state in a steady state process.

Let us repeat the calculations for the equilibrium state as the reference. In this case the calculation of the exergy of the products is simply the difference of $h - T_0 s$ between the state of the products and the reference state. In calculating the exergy of the reactants we must also account for the exergy of the reaction.

Thus, at the outlet

$$(h-h_0)_{CO_2} = \frac{1.27 \times 8.3143}{1.27-1}(2330.90-298.15) = 79497 \frac{\text{kJ}}{\text{kmol}}$$

$$(s-s_0)_{CO_2} = \frac{1.27 \times 8.3143}{1.27-1} \ln \frac{2330.90}{298.15} = 80.422 \frac{\text{kJ}}{\text{kmol K}}$$

$$(b-b_0)_{CO_2} = 79497 - 298.15 \times 80.422 = 55519 \frac{\text{kJ}}{\text{kmol}}$$

and

$$(h-h_0)_{O_2} = (h-h_0)_{N_2} = \frac{1.34 \times 8.3143}{1.34-1}(2330.90-298.15) = 66609 \frac{\text{kJ}}{\text{kmol}}$$

$$(s-s_0)_{O_2} = (s-s_0)_{N_2} = \frac{1.34 \times 8.3143}{1.34-1} \ln \frac{2330.90}{298.15} = 67.385 \frac{\text{kJ}}{\text{kmol K}}$$

$$(b-b_0)_{O_2} = (b-b_0)_{N_2} = 66609 - 298.15 \times 67.385 = 46519 \frac{\text{kJ}}{\text{kmol}}$$

Again we arrange the properties in two tables:

Inlet	p MPa	T °C	$h\text{-}h_0$ kJ/kmol	$s\text{-}s_0$ kJ/kmol	$b\text{-}b_0$ kJ/kmol	n kmol	$B\text{-}B_0$ kJ
C	0.101	25.0	393520	−2.8174	394360	1.0000	394360
O_2, N_2	0.101	25.0	0	0.000	0	5.7144	0
Total							394360

Outlet	p MPa	T °C	$h\text{-}h_0$ kJ/kmol	$s\text{-}s_0$ kJ/kmol	$b\text{-}b_0$ kJ/kmol	n kmol	$B\text{-}B_0$ kJ
CO_2	0.101	2057.25	79497	80.4222	55519	1.0000	55519
O_2, N_2	0.101	2057.25	66609	67.3848	46519	4.7144	219307
Total							274826

Comparison of these two tables with the former ones shows that there is no difference in the properties of the nitrogen and oxygen but there is a difference in the values assigned to carbon and carbon dioxide. The final result, however, of the net exergy change in the process is not affected by the selection of the reference. Thus the exergy of the products per kilomole of coal is

$$B_{out} = \sum_{out} n_i (b-b_0)_i = 55519 + (0.2 + 4.5144) \times 46519 = 274826 \text{ kJ}$$

and per kilogram of coal

$$B_{out} = \frac{274826}{12} = 22902 \text{ kJ}$$

At the inlet, the products are at the pressure and temperature of the reference state, but at a different composition. The exergy of the carbon relative to the reference state where it is in the form of CO_2 is the negative of the Gibbs free energy of the reaction.

Thus,

$$B_{in} = (B_C)_{in} = -g^f_{CO_2} = 394360 \ \frac{\text{kJ}}{\text{kmol}}$$

and the net change of exergy in the process becomes

$$\Delta B = 274826 - 394360 = -119534 \ \frac{\text{kJ}}{\text{kmol}}$$

$$\Delta B = \frac{-119534}{12} = -9961 \ \frac{\text{kJ}}{\text{kg}}$$

EXAMPLE 19.10

A coal-fired utility steam boiler raises steam at 15 MPa, 550 °C from feed water at 20 MPa, 200 °C. The coal and the combustion air, with excess air of 20%, are supplied to the burner at p_1 = 105 kPa and T_1 = 25 °C and burn completely before leaving the boiler at p_2 = 101 kPa and T_2 = 400 °C.

Assume:

The environment is at: p_0 = 101 kPa and T_0 = 25 °C.
Coal is pure carbon.
Air is composed of nitrogen and oxygen with a ratio of 3.76:1.
Complete combustion (the products contain no CO).
All gases are ideal; for diatomic gases k = 1.34, for polyatomic gases k = 1.27.
The insulation of the boiler is perfect (no heat loss from the walls).

Find:

a. The change in the exergy of the steam from inlet to outlet of the boiler.
b. The amount of coal and combustion air supplied per kilogram of steam produced.
c. The work and heat interactions of the air/flue gases.
d. The change in the exergy of the air/flue gases from inlet to outlet of the boiler.
e. What percent of the decrease in exergy of the gases was gained by the steam?

SOLUTION

The relevant properties of steam are arranged in a table including values of exergy calculated by $b = h - T_0 s$ and $b = b - b_0$.

Outlet	p MPa	T °C	x	h kJ/kg	s kJ/kg K	b kJ/kg	$b–b_0$ kJ/kg
s_0	0.101	25.0	–	419.04	1.3069	29.39	0.00
s_1	20.00	200.0	–	860.5	2.3031	173.83	144.44
s_2	15.00	550.0		3448.6	6.5199	1504.69	1475.30

a. The change of exergy of the steam can be easily calculated from the values in the table:

$$\Delta B_{steam} = 1475.30 - 144.44 = 1330.86 \text{ kJ/kg}$$

b. The amount of coal needed is calculated by equating the heat required per kilogram of steam to the heat provided by the appropriate amount of coal.

Heat supplied in the boiler per kilogram steam is

$$Q = h_2 - h_1 = 3448.6 - 860.5 = 2588.1 \text{ kJ/kg}$$

The stoichiometric equation of the reaction is

$$C + O_2 \rightleftarrows CO_2$$

For CO_2 at 25 °C: $h^f = -393520$ kJ/kmol and $g^f = -394360$ kJ/kmol.

The air/fuel mixture reacts chemically in the boiler and produces flue gases according to the following equation:

$$C + 1.2(O_2 + 3.762N_2) \Rightarrow CO_2 + 0.2O_2 + 4.5144N_2$$

The amount of heat supplied by 1 mole of coal (12 kg of coal) is then calculated by

$$Q_{coal} = \sum_{products} n_i c_{pi}(T_2 - T_0) - \sum_{reactants} n_i c_{pi}(T_1 - T_0) + \sum n_i h_i^f$$

where

$$c_{PCO_2} = \frac{1.27 \times 8.3143}{1.27 - 1} = 39.1080 \ \frac{\text{kJ}}{\text{kmol K}}$$

$$c_{PO_2} = c_{PN_2} = \frac{1.34 \times 8.3143}{1.34 - 1} = 32.7681 \ \frac{\text{kJ}}{\text{kmol K}}$$

Here

$$\sum n_i h_i^f = -393520 \text{ kJ/kmol}$$

$$\sum_{reactants} n_i c_{pi}(T_1 - T_0) = 0$$

$$\sum_{products} n_i c_{pi}(T_2 - T_0) = [39.108 + (0.2 + 4.5144) \times 32.768](400 - 25) = 72596 \ \frac{\text{kJ}}{\text{kmol}}$$

Thus,

$$Q_{coal} = \frac{72596 - 393520}{12} = -26744 \text{ kJ/kg}$$

And the amount of coal required to produce 1 kilogram of steam in the boiler is

$$m_{coal} = \frac{2588.1}{26744} = 0.09677 \ \frac{\text{kg coal}}{\text{kg steam}} \qquad n_{coal} = \frac{0.09677}{12} = 0.008065 \ \frac{\text{kmol çoal}}{\text{kg steam}}$$

The mass ratios of air to coal and flue gases to coal are for this case, respectively,

$$\frac{m_{air}}{m_{coal}} = \frac{\sum n_i M_i}{12} = \frac{1.2 \times (32 + 3.76 \times 28)}{12} = 13.728 \frac{\text{kg}}{\text{kg}}$$

$$\frac{m_{gas}}{m_{coal}} = \frac{\sum n_i M_i}{12} = \frac{44 + 0.2 \times 32 + 4.512 \times 28}{12} = 14.728 \frac{\text{kg}}{\text{kg}}$$

The masses of the air and of the flue gases, per kilogram of steam, are, respectively,

$$m_{air} = 13.728 \times 0.09677 = 1.328 \text{ kg/kg}$$

$$m_{gas} = 14.728 \times 0.09677 = 1.425 \text{ kg/kg}$$

c. The air/fuel and the flue gases passing through the boiler have no work interaction.
   The heat interaction of the steam in the boiler is equal to that of the air/fuel/flue gas mixture, but opposite in sign.
   The heat per kilogram of steam was calculated in b to be 2588.1 kJ/kg.

d. In order to calculate the properties of the gaseous components we select the reference state to be at the pressure and temperature of the environment but containing only CO2 and no unreacted carbon. Thus, carbon at reference pressure and temperature is credited with the exergy $b - b_0 = -g^f = 394360$ kJ/kmol relative to the dead state.
   Molecular weights of the gaseous mixtures are calculated by

$$M = \sum y_i M_i$$

Heat capacities of the gaseous mixtures are calculated by

$$C_p = \sum n_i c_{pi}$$

We list the properties at the inlet and at the outlet, respectively, relative to the dead state per kilomole of carbon in the reaction.

Inlet	p MPa	T °C	$h-h_0$ kJ/kmol	$s-s_0$ kJ/kmol	$b-b_0$ kJ/kmol	n kmol	$B-B_0$ kJ
C	0.101	25.0	393520	−2.8174	−394360	1.0000	−394360
O_2, N_2	0.105	25.0	0	0.0000	0	5.7144	0.0
Total							−394360

Outlet	p MPa	T °C	$h-h_0$ kJ/kmol	$s-s_0$ kJ/kmol	$b-b_0$ kJ/kmol	n kmol	$B-B_0$ kJ
CO_2	0.101	400.0	14666	31.8484	5169.9	1.0000	5169.9
O_2, N_2	0.105	400.0	12288	26.6854	4331.8	4.7144	20421.8
Total							25591.7

The net exergy change per kilomole of coal is

$$\Delta B_{fuel/air} = 25592 - 394360 = -368768 \text{ kJ/kmol }^o\text{C}$$

and per kilogram of steam

$$\Delta B_{fuel/air} = -368768 \times 0.008065 = -2974.26 \text{ kJ/kg of steam}$$

Thus the net change of exergy per kilogram of steam is

$$\Delta B_{net} = \Delta B_{steam} + \Delta B_{fuel/air} = 1330.86 - 2974.26 = -1643.40 \text{ kJ/kg of steam}$$

e. The percent exergy in the original fuel that was gained by the steam is

$$\% \text{ gain by steam} = 1330.86/2974.26 = 0.4475$$

This number represents the real efficiency of the process in the boiler.

Note that from the point of view of the first law, the boiler efficiency is defined as the "heat" into the steam over the "heat" in the fuel. The latter is the heat of combustion of the fuel.

The boiler efficiency, thus defined, is

$$\eta_{boiler} = \frac{Q_{steam}}{n_{coal}\left(-h^{f}_{CO_2}\right)} = \frac{2588.1}{0.008065 \times 393520} = 0.8155$$

The first-law analysis is not concerned with what is the maximum potential utilization of the fuel, in this case the coal. It is only concerned with what is the maximum utilization that can be obtained from the fuel when burned in a boiler. If, for example, an ideal fuel cell is used to combine coal with oxygen in a reversible way, the result could far exceed that of the "best" combustion process in a boiler.

PROBLEMS

19.1 An Orsat analysis of the flue gases from the combustion of a hydrocarbon fuel is shown in the table.

a. Find the fuel composition.
b. Find the excess air.

Gas	% volume
CO_2	7.8
CO	1.1
O_2	8.2
N_2	82.9

19.2 An industrial boiler is fired by 500 kg/h of heavy oil. The combustion air is supplied at 20% excess and 1.2 bars, 120 °C, while the flue gases leave at 1.0 bar and 280 °C. The chemical analysis of the fuel is given in the table.

a. Find the rate of air supply to the boiler.
b. Find the flowrate, mass and volumetric, of the flue gases.
c. Find the dew point of the flue gases.

Element	% mass
C	80
H	15
S	2
O	1
Ash	2

19.3 Octane (C_8H_{18}) is burned at constant pressure with theoretical air at 1 bar, 30 °C. The combustion products are cooled to 30 °C. Find the amount of water condensed from the flue gas if:

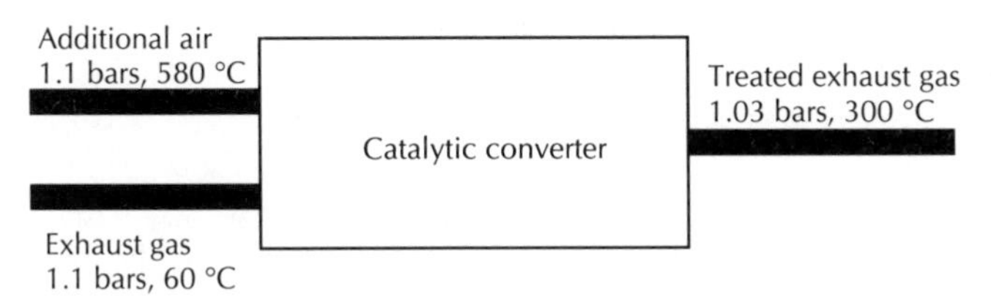

Figure 19.3 **Catalytic converter.**

a. The combustion air is dry.
b. The air has a 90% relative humidity.

19.4 An analysis of the exhaust gas from an internal combustion engine, using liquid hydrocarbon fuel, is given in the table. In order to prevent air pollution by carbon monoxide the exhaust gas together with additional air are passed through a catalytic converter (Fig. 19.3) where the carbon monoxide is oxidized. It is known from experience that in order to eliminate carbon monoxide emission the gas leaving the converter should contain at least 6% oxygen.

Gas	% volume
CO_2	11.3
CO	2.8
O_2	2.3
N_2	83.6

Assume the gases are ideal with $c_p = 3.5R$ for diatomic and $c_p = 4.6R$ for triatomic gases.

a. Find the composition of the fuel.
b. Find the mass ratio of the additional air to the exhaust gas.
c. Find the heat interaction in the catalytic converter.

19.5 Propane (C_3H_8) is burned in oxygen-enriched air. The analysis on a dry basis of the combustion gases is shown in the table:

a. Determine the composition of the oxygen-enriched air.
b. Determine the excess air.

Gas	% volume
CO_2	8.2
CO	1.4
O_2	7.0
N_2	83.4

19.6 Propane (C_3H_8) at 0.1 MPa, 25 °C, is mixed with air at 0.1 MPa, 150°C, and subsequently is completely burned adiabatically. The final temperature is 900 °C.

a. Determine the excess air.
b. Find the change of volume in the process.

19.7 A rigid vessel contains 0.01 kmol of O_2 and 0.01 kmol of CO at 0.1 MPa, 25 °C. The mixture is ignited and complete combustion takes place. Then the vessel is cooled to 1100 °C.

a. Find the final pressure in the vessel.
b. Find the heat interaction.

19.8 a. Is the reaction $H_2 = 2H$ endothermic or exothermic at 3000 K?
b. Is the reaction $2NH_3 = N_2 + 3H_2$ endothermic or exothermic at 1500 K?

19.9 Water vapor at 0.1 MPa, 400 K, is heated in a steady state to 3000 K at a rate of 20.0 kg/s. The final state may contain only H_2O, H_2, and O_2.

a. Determine the specific volume at the final state.
b. Find the heat interaction.

19.10 Determine the adiabatic flame temperature when sulfur at 25 °C is converted to SO_2 by burning it in 50% excess air at 300 °C. Treat nitrogen, oxygen, and SO_2 as ideal gases. The specific heat of diatomic gases is $c_p = 3.5R$ and that of SO_2 is given by

$$\left(\frac{c_p}{R}\right)_{SO_2} = 3.85 + 2.63\left(\frac{T}{1000}\right) - 0.424\left(\frac{T}{1000}\right)^2$$

where T is in K.

19.11 Natural gas, consisting of 80% by volume of CH_4 and 20% C_2H_6, is burned in 40% excess air. The air enters the combustion chamber at 1 bar, 120 °C while the fuel is supplied at 1.02 bars, 25 °C. The combustion products leave at 0.98 bars, 430 °C. Determine the heat interaction of the process.

19.12 A reactor is fed by two streams: one stream is steam at 430 °C, 1.6 bars, at a rate of 2 kmol/min; the other, at 25 °C and 1 bar, is a mixture of CO_2, CO, and N_2 at rates of 2, 4, and 2 kmol/min, respectively. An equilibrium stream leaves the reaction chamber at 1 bar and 827 °C. Assuming that the only possible reaction is

$$CO + H_2O \rightleftarrows CO_2 + H_2$$

a. Determine the flowrate of hydrogen at the exit.
b. Determine the heat interaction in the reactor.

19.13 During a test of a small air-cooled gasoline engine the power obtained at 5000 rpm was 10 kW. The fuel, octane, was supplied at 25 °C at a rate of 5.5 kg/h, while the oxidant was dry air at ambient 25 °C. The exhaust gas left the engine at 400 °C and had an Orsat analysis as given in the table.

a. Determine the excess air.
b. Determine the volume of the cylinders.
c. Determine the heat interaction of the engine.
d. Determine the efficiency of the engine. Define the efficiency for this case.

Gas	% volume
CO_2	11.23
CO	2.80
O_2	1.84
N_2	84.13

19.14 An insulated vessel is divided into three parts of 50 L each. One part contains oxygen (M = 32, k = 1.4) at 25 °C, 100 kPa, another hydrogen (M = 2, k = 1.4) at 25 °C, 100 kPa, and the third part is empty, Fig. 19.4. The partitions are removed, the gases mix and fill the vessel.

a. Find the final temperature and pressure assuming no chemical reactions.
b. Find the changes in enthalpy and in entropy.
c. Find the final temperature and pressure assuming a chemical reaction according to stoichiometric equation $2H_2 + O_2 = 2H_2O$ till all the hydrogen is exhausted.
d. Find the final temperature and pressure assuming a chemical reaction according to stoichiometric equation $2H_2 + O_2 = 2H_2O$ till complete equilibrium.

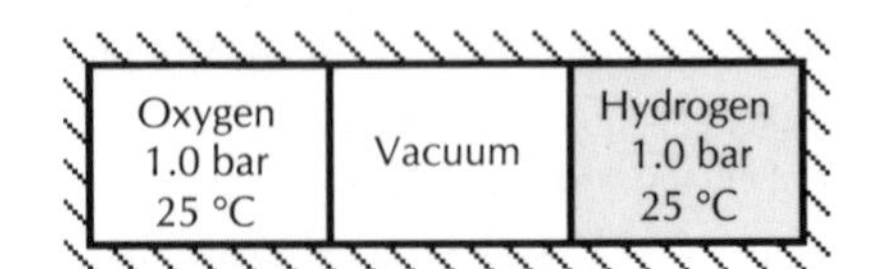

Figure 19.4

19.15 In a static test of an adiabatic rocket engine a

stoichiometric mixture of H_2 and O_2 at 25 °C was supplied to the engine at an appropriate pressure. At the exit section of the engine there was pure water vapor at 3.0 MPa, 1600 °C.

Assume that all the gases are ideal (for O_2: $M = 32$, $k = 1.4$; H_2: $M = 4$, $k = 1.4$; H_2O: $M = 18$, $k = 1.25$).

a. Determine the velocity of the gases at the exit of the engine.
b. How much would the velocity increase if the gases were to expand till their temperature reaches 100 °C.
c. What would be the pressure in that case?

19.16 One kmol of (solid) carbon together with 50% excess oxygen at 0.2 MPa, 25 °C, are placed in a closed adiabatic container. The carbon is ignited and burns completely. Assuming that the equilibrium constant for the reaction

$$CO + \frac{1}{2}O_2 \rightleftarrows CO_2$$

is $K = \infty$ and that the reaction is possible, find the final pressure and temperature inside the container.

19.17 A cylinder covered by a weighted piston contains 11 g of CO_2 at 0.3 MPa, 25 °C. The cylinder is brought into contact with a heat reservoir at 2500 K and allowed to reach equilibrium, Fig. 19.5. Given that the only reaction possible is

$$CO + \frac{1}{2}O_2 \rightleftarrows CO_2$$

find the heat and work interactions of the gases in the cylinder.

Figure 19.5

19.18 For an aqueous ammonia solution at 40 °C Henry's constant is $K = 1.2$ bars, while the equilibrium constant for the reaction

$$\frac{1}{2}N_2 + \frac{3}{2}H_2 \rightleftarrows NH_3(g)$$

is $K_p = 800$ bars. A 1% aqueous ammonia solution is held at 40 °C and high pressure. The pressure is slowly lowered until a gas phase begins to form. Estimate the partial pressures of the hydrogen and the oxygen in the gas phase.

19.19 Acetylene and oxygen at 25 °C are fed to an acetylene burner with oxygen at 40% excess. The only possible reactions are

$$C_2H_2 + 2.5O_2 \rightleftarrows 2CO_2 + H_2O$$

$$CO + \frac{1}{2}O_2 \rightleftarrows CO_2$$

a. Determine the adiabatic flame temperature assuming complete combustion.
b. Determine the adiabatic flame temperature assuming the existence of chemical equilibrium.

19.20 A hydrogen–oxygen fuel cell operates under steady state conditions according to the following reactions:

at the anode $\quad H_2 \rightarrow 2H^+ + 2e^-$

at the cathode $\quad \frac{1}{2}O_2 + 2H^+ + 2e^- \rightarrow H_2O$

the overall effect is $\quad H_2 + \frac{1}{2}O_2 \rightarrow H_2O$

The following data were obtained during a test at 200 °C and 50 bars:

Current density (A/cm²)	0.680	0.500	0.250	0.100	0.010
Voltage (V)	0.585	0.667	0.805	0.905	1.020

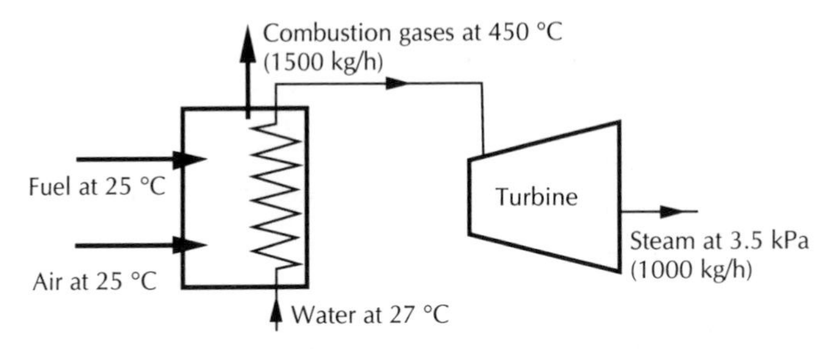

Figure 19.6

Given an environment at 1 bar and 27 °C, determine per square centimeter of electrode area for the above test conditions:

a. The cell power output.
b. The rate of fuel consumption.
c. The rate of heat interaction of the cell.
d. The irreversibility of the cell.

19.21 The fuel of the boiler shown in Fig. 19.6 is methane which is burned with a stoichiometric amount of air. The heat of reaction at 25 °C is equal to 2500 kJ/kg of reactants or products. The specific heat of the products may be assumed constant at 1.2 kJ/kg K. The total reactant mass flowrate into the boiler is 1500 kg/h. The reactants enter the boiler at 25 °C and the combustion products come out of the boiler at 450 °C. The boiler produces steam at a rate of 1000 kg/h from liquid water which enters the boiler at 27 °C. The steam is supplied to an adiabatic turbine which exhausts at a pressure of 3.5 kPa. Find:

a. The power produced by the turbine in kW.
b. The minimum pressure at states 1 and 2 (assuming negligible pressure drop in the boiler) which is compatible with the second law.

19.22 A cylinder is maintained under a constant pressure of 70 kPa by means of a weighted piston. The cylinder contains 3 m^3 of a mixture of N_2, H_2, and NH_3 with respective mole fractions 0.1, 0.3, and 0.6 at equilibrium at 75 °C. The mixture is then heated slowly till the temperature reaches 175 °C. Consider all the species as ideal gases with $k = 1.4$ for N_2 and H_2 and $k = 1.28$ for NH_3, and find:

a. An expression for the heat of reaction ΔH° at any temperature T.
b. The ratio K_2/K_1 of the equilibrium constants at temperatures 75 °C and 350 °C.
c. The final partial pressures.
d. The final volume.

19.23 A test rocket is supplied with a stoichiometric mixture of gaseous hydrogen and oxygen at 60 °C. The high velocity exhaust gas leaves the engine at 1000 °C. The heat loss from the rocket is negligible.

a. What is the heat of combustion per kilogram of products?
b. Assuming that the water vapor has a constant specific heat of 32 kJ/kmol K, what is the exhaust velocity?
c. If the exhaust gas was further expanded until its temperature was 0 °C, by what percentage would the exhaust velocity increase?
d. Which non-stoichiometric mixture, $3H_2 + O_2$ or $2H_2 + 2O_2$, would give a higher exhaust velocity if the gases are expanded to 0 °C?

19.24 The primary reaction during discharge of a lead storage cell is

$$Pb(s) + PbO_2(s) + 2H_2SO_4(aq) \rightarrow 2PbSO_4(s) + 2H_2O$$

where (s) denotes a solid state and (aq) denotes a large aqueous solution of sulfuric acid. The enthalpies of formation at 25 °C (in kJ/kmol) are given in the table.

Substance	h^f (kJ/kmol)
PbO_2(s)	−272100
$PbSO_4$(s)	−914600
H_2SO_4(l)	−811000
H_2O(l)	−286300

The enthalpy of solution of H_2SO_4 in a large aqueous solution of sulfuric acid is - 75300 kJ/kmol of H_2SO_4.

a. Find the heat interaction with the environment when 1 mole of Pb is consumed in the cell at 1 atm and 25 °C if the change occurs while the cell is on the shelf and not connected electrically to any external device.
b. An array of 16 such cells at 25 °C and a voltage of 28 V drives an electric motor, which produces 0.5 hp at 90% efficiency. Each mole of lead consumed delivers 193000 coulombs (2 farads) of electricity. Estimate the heat interaction between the cells and the environment, in kJ per hp-h of work performed by the motor.

19.25 Consider n_A, n_B, n_K, and n_L kilomoles of chemical species in chemical equilibrium at temperature T and pressure p. Let the stoichiometric equation be

$$aA + bB \rightleftarrows kK + lL$$

We may define the specific heat at constant pressure c_{pm} of the mixture as the heat required to increase the temperature of the mixture by 1 °C while the mixture passes through equilibrium states at constant pressure. The mixture is assumed to be a Gibbs–Dalton mixture of perfect gases.

a. Express c_{pm} as a function of the number of kilomoles of the components, their specific heats c_{pi}, the enthalpy of reaction ΔH°, and the change of the degree of reaction ξ with temperature, namely the ratio $d\xi/dT$.
b. Show that the ratio $d\xi/dT$ may be expressed in the form

$$\frac{d\xi}{dT} = \frac{d \ln K/dT}{\sum \frac{\nu_i^2}{n_i} - \frac{1}{n}\left(\sum \nu_i\right)^2}$$

where K is the equilibrium constant of the mixture and ν_i denotes successively k, l, $-a$, $-b$.

c. Show that by means of the equation of chemical equilibrium

$$\frac{d \ln K}{dT} = \frac{\Delta H^\circ}{RT^2}$$

where R is the universal gas constant, and then express c_{pm} in terms of the specific heats c_{pi}, the temperature T, the gas constant R, the number of moles n_i, the coefficients ν_i, and the enthalpy of reaction ΔH°.

19.26 Hydrogen and oxygen at 25 °C enter, in stoichiometric proportions, an adiabatic combustion chamber followed by an adiabatic turbine, as shown in Fig 19.7. The exhaust gases leave the turbine as H_2O at 120 kPa and 900 °C, and pass through a heat exchanger, emerging at 100 kPa and 160 °C. The heat exchanger produces saturated steam at 700 kPa from liquid water at 25 °C.

a. Find the amount of steam produced in the heat exchanger per kilogram of H_2O passing the turbine.
b. Find the work delivered by the turbine per kilogram of H_2O.

19.27 Two kmols of gas A_2 and 1kmol of gas B_2 at 1.0 bar and 300 K in steady flow enter a combus-

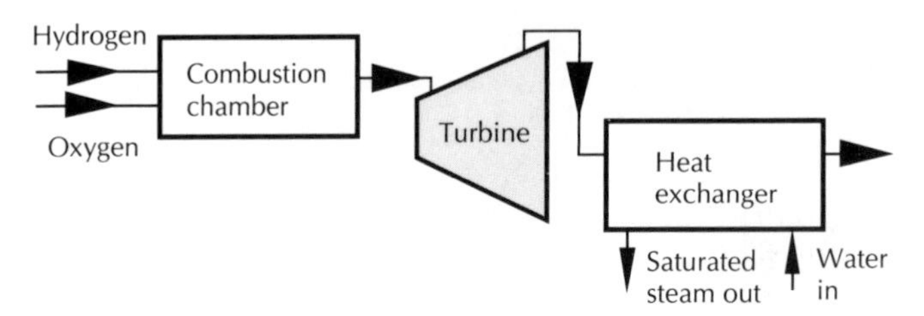

Figure 19.7

tion chamber where the pressure is maintained at 1.0 bar.

Assume:
the only reaction possible is $A_2 + \frac{1}{2}B_2 = A_2B$,
ideal gases ($k = 1.4$ for diatomic gases and 1.3 for triatomic gases),
the enthalpy of formation at 300 K is $\Delta H^\circ = 40000$ kJ/A_2B, and the equilibrium constant of the reaction $A_2 + \frac{1}{2}B_2 = A_2B$ is

$$K_p(T) = 22.24 - \frac{60000}{T}$$

where T is in kelvin and p is in bars.

Analysis of the combustion chamber exhaust gases indicates that the reaction has proceeded to equilibrium according to the following equation:

$$A_2 + \frac{1}{2}B_2 \rightarrow \frac{1}{2}A_2B + \frac{1}{2}A_2 + \frac{1}{4}B_2$$

a. Find the temperature of the exhaust gases.
b. Find the heat transferred to the walls of the combustor per kilomole of A_2B formed.

19.28 A hydrocarbon fuel and air at 25 °C are fed at a rate of 1500 kg/h to a steam generator, as shown in Fig. 19.8. The combustion gases enter the stack at 450 °C. Water at 25 °C and 100 kPa is supplied by a pump at a rate of 1000 kg/h to the steam generator where it is converted to steam that drives a turbine. Steam leaves the turbine at 60 °C and 10 kPa.

The enthalpy of combustion of the fuel at the inlet temperature of 25 °C is −2650 kJ/kg of fuel/air mixture, and the combustion products may be considered as an ideal gas with $c_p = 1.25$ kJ/kg K. Find for a steady state operation:

a. The power produced by the turbine.
b. The minimum pressure at the turbine inlet consistent with the second law.

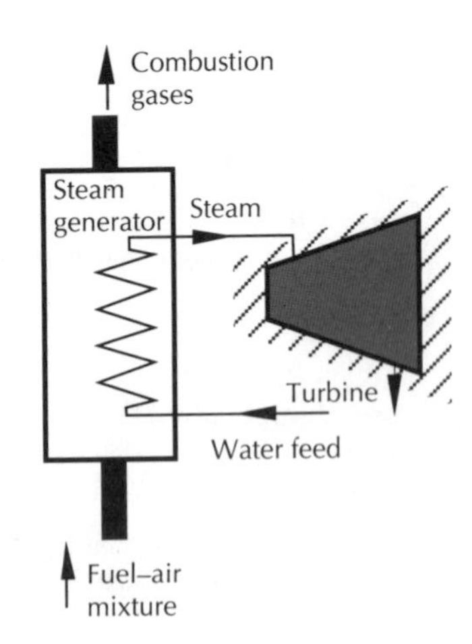

Figure 19.8

19.29 A cylinder in equilibrium with a constant-temperature bath at 700 K contains a mixture of NO, O_2, and NO_2 in equilibrium. The partial pressures of NO, O_2, and NO_2 are 200, 100, and 200 kPa, respectively, when the piston is locked in position 1. The lock is released and the gas expands until a new equilibrium is attained when the weight of the piston is balanced by the total final pressure which is 100 kPa.

Assume: NO, O_2, and NO_2 are ideal gases with $k = 1.4$, 1.4, and 1.3, respectively. Find the amount of heat transferred to the bath during this process.

The enthalpies of formation at 700 K, 100 kPa, are

$$h_{NO_2}^{f,1000} = 38600 \text{ kJ/kmol} \qquad h_{NO}^{f,1000} = 90400 \text{ kJ/kmol} \qquad h_{O_2}^{f,1000} = 0$$

19.30 A mixture of $n_I = 2.63$ kmol of I_2 and $n_H = 1.82$ kmol of H_2 is introduced into a chamber and held at a constant temperature till equilibrium is reached. It is found that finally the number of kilomoles of I_2 was reduced to $n'_I = 0.88$ kmol. The possible reaction is $H_2 + I_2 = 2\ HI$.

What would be the equilibrium number of kilomoles of I_2 in *another* chamber, held at the same temperature as the first, if originally it was filled with 8 kmol of HI?

19.31 A boiler is supplied with methane (CH_4) and the necessary oxygen (O_2) for complete combustion. The inlet temperatures of the CH_4 and O_2 are 15 °C and 60 °C, respectively. The products of the reaction leave the boiler at a temperature of 180 °C and a pressure of 140 kPa. Assume:

i. Steady flow.
ii. The equilibrium constant for the reaction

$$CH_4 + 2O_2 \rightleftarrows CO_2 + 2H_2O$$

is $K_p(T) = 422 + 2200/T$, where T is in K.

iii. Specific heats for CH_4, O_2, and CO_2 are 10, 7, and 10 kcal/(kmol K), respectively.
iv. For the reaction at (ii) $\Delta H^0 = 380000$ kJ at $T_0 = 25$ °C and $p_0 = 100$ kPa.

a. Find the partial pressures of the products.
b. Determine the heat transferred per kilomole of CH_4 and its direction.

19.32 When diatomic oxygen is heated to high temperatures it dissociates partially into monatomic oxygen. In a certain test, a system containing 0.32 kg of oxygen was brought to equilibrium at 0.1 kPa and 2500 K. Equal numbers of moles of diatomic and monatomic oxygen were found in the system.

Assume that diatomic and monatomic oxygen are ideal gases with specific heats at constant pressure of $3R$ and $4R$, respectively. The enthalpy of formation of monatomic oxygen at 100 kPa, 300 K, is 248 MJ/kmol.

a. Find the equilibrium mole ratio at 10 kPa and 2500 K.
b. Find the entropy of formation of monatomic oxygen at 100 kPa, 300 K.
c. Find the heat and work interactions when the system is cooled at 1.0 bar from 2500 K to 300 K.

19.33 A cylinder, covered by a piston that maintains a constant pressure of 100 kPa, contains a system of 0.30 kmol of SO and 0.15 kmol of O_2 separated by a thin membrane. Initially the temperature was 40 °C. The membrane is ruptured and the contents mix and react till they reach equilibrium at 500 °C.

Assume the only possible chemical reaction is $2SO + O_2 = 2SO_2$. SO, O_2, and SO_2 are ideal gases with $c_p/R = 3.7$, 3.5, and 4.3, respectively. Determine the heat interaction of the system.

19.34 A mixture of NO_2 and NO_4 reaches equilibrium relatively quickly over a wide range of temperatures. It was proposed to use such a mixture as a heat transfer substance having a high effective specific heat, $(\partial H/\partial T)_p$.

Evaluate the effective specific heat of the mixture at 100 kPa, 27 °C and 100 °C. Repeat the calculations for a pressure of 1.0 MPa.

Assume the gases are ideal, where $k = 1.25$ for NO_2 and $k = 1.20$ for NO_4.

19.35 A mixture of an equal number of moles of nitrogen and oxygen at 0.1 MPa, 27 °C, is heated at a constant pressure to 2000 K. Assume that a chemical reaction is possible according to the stoichiometric equation $N_2 + O_2 = 2NO$.

a. Find the equilibrium constant at 2000 K.
b. Find the percentage of the original nitrogen that was oxidized.
c. Find the percentage of the original nitrogen that is oxidized if air is heated to 2000 K.

19.36 It is possible to calculate the rate of dissociation of CO_2 by measuring the pressure, temperature and volume of 1 mole of CO_2.

a. Find the relation between the volume at given p and T and the dissociation constant.
b. Find the relation between the equilibrium constant and the dissociation constant.

19.37 The maximum and minimum volumes of an engine cylinder are 1.0 L and 0.1 L, respectively. A stoichiometric mixture of octane (C_8H_{18}) at 0.1 MPa, 27 °C, is compressed adiabatically. The mixture is ignited at the end of the compression stroke resulting in combustion at constant volume. Then the gases expand to the maximum volume. Assume that the cylinder and piston are adiabatic, the gases (except for the liquid fuel whose volume is negligible) are ideal ($k = 1.4$ for diatomic gases and $k = 1.28$ for multiatomic gases), and also assume complete combustion in the cylinder.

a. Find the pressure and temperature at the end of the compression stroke.
b. Find the pressure and temperature at the end of combustion.
c. Find the pressure and temperature at the end of expansion.

19.38 Molecular oxygen (O_2) is heated at a constant pressure till there are an equal number of moles of molecular and atomic oxygen (O). Then the pressure is doubled at a constant temperature. Find the final composition of the mixture. Assume the gases are ideal.

19.39 Molecular oxygen (O_2) is heated at a constant volume till there are an equal number of moles of molecular and atomic oxygen (O). Then the system is compressed to half of its volume at a constant temperature. Find the final composition of the mixture. Assume the gases are ideal.

19.40 Two streams enter a heated reaction chamber, as shown in Fig. 19.9. One stream is 0.8 kmol/s of a mixture of 25% CO_2, 50% CO, and 25% N_2. The second stream is 0.2 kmol/s of steam at 0.16 MPa, 700 K. A single stream exits in equilibrium at 0.1MPa, 1100 K.

Only the reaction $CO + H_2O = CO_2 + H_2$ is possible for which the equilibrium constant is $K_p(1100\ K) = 1$. Assume all gases are ideal. Select $k = 1.4$ for diatomic gases and $k = 1.3$ for triatomic gases.

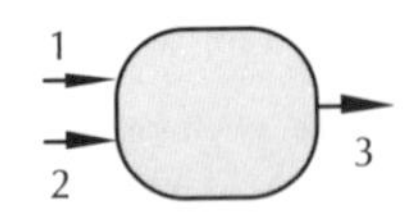

Figure 19.9

a. Find the amount of hydrogen at the exit.
b. Find the heat interaction of the chamber.

19.41 A gas turbine used to power a jet plane is required to supply 100000 N of thrust during take-off. The airfield is at 7 km above sea level, at a temperature of –30 °C, pressure of 60 kPa, and composition by volume of 80% N_2 and 20% O_2.

The following data are available:
The pressure ratio in the compressor of the gas turbine is 6.
The maximum allowed temperature is 1000 °C.
The compression and expansion are adiabatic at an isentropic efficiency of 0.96.
The fuel is C_8H_8 at 25 °C.

a. Find the excess air needed for combustion.
b. Find the composition of the flue gases.
c. Determine the rate of fuel consumption.
d. What is the state of the gas entering the nozzle?

19.42 A rigid container is divided into two parts by partitions. One part contains 56 g of N_2 and the other 12 g of H_2, each gas being at 0.2 MPa, 40 °C. The partition is broken and the contents undergo a chemical reaction according to the stoichiometric equation $0.5N_2 + 1.5H_2 = NH_3$. Finally a state of equilibrium is reached at 450 °C.

a. Find the equilibrium constant at the end.
b. Find the final pressure in the container.
c. Find the work and heat interactions of the system.
d. Determine the irreversibility relative to an environment at 0.1 MPa, 40 °C.

APPENDIX

Thermodynamic properties

Tables

Figures

Table A.1.1 **Saturated steam – by temperature.**
(Adapted from J.H. Keenan, F.G. Keyes, P.G. Hill and J.G. Moore, *Steam Tables (S.I. Units)*, Wiley, New York, 1978)

T °C	p	v_f m³/kg	v_g m³/kg	u_f kJ/kg	u_{fg} kJ/kg	u_g kJ/kg	h_f kJ/kg	h_{fg} kJ/kg	h_g kJ/kg	s_f kJ/kg K	s_{fg} kJ/kg K	s_g kJ/kg K
0.01	0.6113 kPa	0.001000	206.14	0.00	2375.3	2375.3	0.00	2501.3	2501.3	0.0000	9.1562	9.1562
5	0.8721	0.001000	147.12	20.97	2361.3	2382.3	20.97	2489.6	2510.6	0.0761	8.9496	9.0257
10	1.2276	0.001000	106.38	42.00	2347.2	2389.2	42.00	2477.8	2519.8	0.1510	8.7498	8.9008
15	1.7051	0.001001	77.93	62.99	2333.1	2396.1	62.99	2466.0	2529.0	0.2245	8.5569	8.7814
20	2.339	0.001002	57.79	83.95	2319.0	2402.9	83.95	2454.1	2538.1	0.2966	8.3706	8.6672
25	3.169	0.001003	43.36	104.88	2304.9	2409.8	104.88	2442.3	2547.2	0.3674	8.1906	8.5580
30	4.246	0.001004	32.89	125.78	2290.8	2416.6	125.78	2430.5	2556.3	0.4369	8.0164	8.4533
35	5.628	0.001006	25.22	146.67	2276.7	2423.4	146.68	2418.7	2565.3	0.5053	7.8478	8.3531
40	7.384	0.001008	19.52	167.56	2262.5	2430.1	167.57	2406.7	2574.2	0.5725	7.6845	8.2570
45	9.593	0.001010	15.26	188.44	2248.4	2436.8	188.45	2394.7	2583.2	0.6387	7.5261	8.1648
50	12.349	0.001012	12.03	209.32	2234.2	2443.5	209.33	2382.7	2592.1	0.7038	7.3725	8.0763
55	15.758	0.001015	9.5680	230.21	2219.9	2450.1	230.23	2370.6	2600.9	0.7679	7.2234	7.9913
60	19.94	0.001017	7.6710	251.11	2205.5	2456.6	251.13	2358.4	2609.6	0.8312	7.0784	7.9096
65	25.03	0.001020	6.1970	272.02	2191.1	2463.1	272.05	2346.2	2618.2	0.8935	6.9375	7.8310
70	31.19	0.001023	5.0420	292.95	2176.7	2469.6	292.98	2333.9	2626.9	0.9549	6.8004	7.7553
75	38.58	0.001026	4.1310	313.90	2162.0	2475.9	313.94	2321.3	2635.3	1.0155	6.6669	7.6824
80	47.39	0.001029	3.4070	334.86	2147.3	2482.2	334.91	2308.7	2643.7	1.0753	6.5369	7.6122
85	57.83	0.001033	2.8280	355.84	2132.6	2488.4	355.90	2296.0	2651.9	1.1343	6.4102	7.5445
90	70.14	0.001036	2.3610	376.85	2117.7	2494.5	376.92	2283.2	2660.1	1.1925	6.2866	7.4791
95	84.55	0.001040	1.9820	397.88	2102.7	2500.6	397.97	2270.2	2668.2	1.2500	6.1659	7.4159
100	101.325	0.001044	1.6729	418.94	2087.6	2506.5	419.05	2257.0	2676.0	1.3069	6.0480	7.3549
105	0.12082 MPa	0.001048	1.4194	440.02	2072.4	2512.4	440.15	2243.7	2683.9	1.3630	5.9328	7.2958
110	0.14327	0.001052	1.2102	461.14	2057.0	2518.1	461.29	2230.2	2691.5	1.4185	5.8202	7.2387
115	0.16906	0.001056	1.0396	482.30	2041.4	2523.7	482.48	2217.0	2699.5	1.4734	5.7099	7.1833
120	0.19853	0.001060	0.8919	503.50	2025.8	2529.3	503.71	2202.7	2706.4	1.5276	5.6020	7.1296
125	0.2321	0.001065	0.7706	524.74	2009.9	2534.6	524.99	2188.5	2713.5	1.5813	5.4962	7.0775

Table A.1.1 (continued)

T	p	v_f	v_g	u_f	u_{fg}	u_g	h_f	h_{fg}	h_g	s_f	s_{fg}	s_g
°C		m^3/kg	m^3/kg	kJ/kg	kJ/kg	kJ/kg	kJ/kg	kJ/kg	kJ/kg	kJ/kg K	kJ/kg K	kJ/kg K
130	0.2701	0.001070	0.6685	546.02	1993.9	2539.9	546.31	2174.2	2720.5	1.6344	5.3925	7.0269
135	0.3130	0.001075	0.5822	567.35	1977.7	2545.0	567.69	2159.5	2727.2	1.6870	5.2907	6.9777
140	0.3613	0.001080	0.5089	588.74	1961.3	2550.0	589.13	2144.7	2733.9	1.7391	5.1908	6.9299
145	0.4154	0.001085	0.4463	610.18	1944.7	2554.9	610.63	2129.7	2740.3	1.7907	5.0926	6.8833
150	0.4758	0.001091	0.3928	631.68	1927.8	2559.5	632.20	2114.2	2746.4	1.8418	4.9961	6.8379
155	0.5431	0.001096	0.3468	653.24	1910.9	2564.1	653.84	2098.6	2752.4	1.8925	4.9010	6.7935
160	0.6178	0.001102	0.3071	674.87	1893.5	2568.4	675.55	2082.6	2758.1	1.9427	4.8075	6.7502
165	0.7005	0.001108	0.2727	696.56	1875.9	2572.5	697.34	2066.2	2763.5	1.9925	4.7153	6.7078
170	0.7917	0.001114	0.2428	718.33	1858.2	2576.5	719.21	2049.5	2768.7	2.0419	4.6244	6.6663
175	0.8920	0.001121	0.2168	740.17	1840.0	2580.2	741.17	2032.4	2773.6	2.0909	4.5347	6.6256
180	1.0021	0.001127	0.19405	762.09	1821.6	2583.7	763.22	2014.9	2778.2	2.1396	4.4461	6.5857
185	1.1227	0.001134	0.17409	784.10	1802.9	2587.0	785.37	1997.1	2782.5	2.1879	4.3586	6.5465
190	1.2544	0.001141	0.15654	806.19	1783.8	2590.0	807.62	1978.7	2786.4	2.2359	4.2720	6.5079
195	1.3978	0.001149	0.14105	828.37	1764.4	2592.8	829.98	1960.0	2790.0	2.2835	4.1863	6.4698
200	1.5538	0.001157	0.12736	850.65	1744.7	2595.3	852.45	1940.7	2793.2	2.3309	4.1014	6.4323
205	1.7230	0.001164	0.11521	873.04	1724.5	2597.5	875.05	1921.0	2796.0	2.3780	4.0172	6.3952
210	1.9062	0.001173	0.10441	895.53	1704.0	2599.5	897.77	1900.8	2798.5	2.4248	3.9337	6.3585
215	2.1040	0.001181	0.09479	918.14	1683.0	2601.1	920.62	1879.9	2800.5	2.4714	3.8507	6.3221
220	2.318	0.001190	0.08619	940.87	1661.5	2602.4	943.63	1858.6	2802.2	2.5178	3.7683	6.2861
225	2.548	0.001199	0.07849	963.73	1639.6	2603.3	966.79	1836.5	2803.3	2.5639	3.6864	6.2503
230	2.795	0.001209	0.07158	986.74	1617.2	2603.9	990.12	1813.8	2804.0	2.6099	3.6047	6.2146
235	3.060	0.001219	0.06537	1009.89	1594.2	2604.1	1013.62	1790.5	2804.1	2.6558	3.5233	6.1791
240	3.344	0.001229	0.05976	1033.21	1570.8	2604.0	1037.32	1766.5	2803.8	2.7015	3.4422	6.1437
245	3.648	0.001240	0.05471	1056.71	1546.7	2603.4	1061.23	1741.7	2803.0	2.7472	3.3611	6.1083
250	3.973	0.001251	0.05013	1080.39	1522.0	2602.4	1085.36	1716.2	2801.6	2.7927	3.2803	6.0730
255	4.319	0.001263	0.04598	1104.28	1496.6	2600.9	1109.73	1689.8	2799.5	2.8383	3.1992	6.0375
260	4.688	0.001276	0.04221	1128.39	1470.6	2599.0	1134.37	1662.5	2796.9	2.8838	3.1181	6.0019
265	5.081	0.001289	0.03877	1152.74	1443.9	2596.6	1159.29	1634.3	2793.6	2.9294	3.0368	5.9662
270	5.499	0.001302	0.03564	1177.36	1416.3	2593.7	1184.52	1605.2	2789.7	2.9751	2.9550	5.9301
275	5.942	0.001317	0.03279	1202.25	1388.0	2590.2	1210.08	1575.0	2785.0	3.0208	2.8730	5.8938

Table A.1.1 (continued)

T °C	p	v_f m³/kg	v_g m³/kg	u_f kJ/kg	u_{fg} kJ/kg	u_g kJ/kg	h_f kJ/kg	h_{fg} kJ/kg	h_g kJ/kg	s_f kJ/kg K	s_{fg} kJ/kg K	s_g kJ/kg K
280	6.412	0.001332	0.03017	1227.46	1358.6	2586.1	1236.00	1543.5	2779.6	3.0668	2.7903	5.8571
285	6.909	0.001348	0.02777	1253.00	1328.4	2581.4	1262.31	1510.9	2773.3	3.1130	2.7069	5.8199
290	7.436	0.001366	0.02557	1278.92	1297.1	2576.0	1289.08	1477.1	2766.1	3.1594	2.6227	5.7821
295	7.993	0.001384	0.02354	1305.20	1264.7	2569.9	1316.26	1441.8	2758.1	3.2062	2.5375	5.7437
300	8.581	0.001404	0.02167	1332.00	1231.0	2563.0	1344.05	1404.9	2749.0	3.2534	2.4511	5.7045
305	9.202	0.001425	0.019948	1359.30	1195.9	2555.2	1372.41	1366.3	2738.8	3.3010	2.3633	5.6643
310	9.856	0.001447	0.018350	1387.10	1159.3	2546.4	1401.36	1325.9	2727.3	3.3493	2.2737	5.6230
315	10.547	0.001472	0.016867	1415.50	1121.1	2536.6	1431.03	1283.5	2714.5	3.3982	2.1822	5.5804
320	11.274	0.001499	0.015488	1444.60	1080.9	2525.5	1461.50	1238.6	2700.1	3.4480	2.0882	5.5362
330	12.845	0.001561	0.012996	1505.30	993.6	2498.9	1525.35	1140.5	2665.8	3.5507	1.8910	5.4417
340	14.586	0.001638	0.010797	1570.30	894.3	2464.6	1594.19	1027.9	2622.1	3.6594	1.6763	5.3357
350	16.513	0.001740	0.008813	1641.90	776.5	2418.4	1670.63	893.3	2563.9	3.7777	1.4335	5.2112
360	18.651	0.001893	0.006945	1725.20	626.3	2351.5	1760.51	720.5	2481.0	3.9147	1.1379	5.0526
370	21.030	0.002213	0.004925	1844.00	384.5	2228.5	1890.54	441.5	2332.1	4.1106	0.6865	4.7971
374.14	22.090	0.003155	0.003155	2029.60	0.0	2029.6	2099.29	0.0	2099.3	4.4298	0.0000	4.4298

Table A.1.2 **Saturated steam – by pressure.**
(Adapted from J.H. Keenan, F.G. Keyes, P.G. Hill and J.G. Moore, *Steam Tables (S.I. Units)*, Wiley, New York, 1978)

p	T	v_f	v_g	u_f	u_{fg}	u_g	h_f	h_{fg}	h_g	s_f	s_{fg}	s_g
kPa	°C	m³/kg			kJ/kg			kJ/kg			kJ/kg K	
0.6113	0.01	0.001000	206.14	0.00	2375.3	2375.3	0.00	2501.3	2501.3	0.0000	9.1562	9.1562
1.0	6.98	0.001000	129.21	29.30	2355.7	2385.0	29.30	2484.9	2514.2	0.1059	8.8697	8.9756
1.5	13.03	0.001001	87.98	54.71	2338.6	2393.3	54.71	2470.6	2525.3	0.1957	8.6322	8.8279
2.0	17.50	0.001001	67.00	73.48	2325.8	2399.3	73.48	2459.8	2533.3	0.2607	8.4630	8.7237
2.5	21.08	0.001002	54.25	88.48	2315.9	2404.4	88.48	2451.5	2540.0	0.3120	8.3312	8.6432
3.0	24.08	0.001003	45.67	101.04	2307.5	2408.5	101.04	2444.5	2545.5	0.3545	8.2231	8.5776
4.0	28.96	0.001004	34.80	121.45	2293.8	2415.2	121.45	2432.9	2554.4	0.4226	8.0520	8.4746
5.0	32.88	0.001005	28.19	137.81	2282.7	2420.5	137.82	2423.6	2561.5	0.4764	7.9187	8.3951
7.5	40.29	0.001008	19.24	168.78	2261.7	2430.5	168.79	2406.0	2574.8	0.5764	7.6751	8.2515
10	45.81	0.001010	14.67	191.82	2246.1	2437.9	191.83	2392.8	2584.6	0.6493	7.5009	8.1502
15	53.97	0.001014	10.02	225.92	2222.8	2448.7	225.94	2373.1	2599.0	0.7549	7.2536	8.0085
20	60.06	0.001017	7.6490	251.38	2205.3	2456.7	251.40	2358.3	2609.7	0.8320	7.0765	7.9085
25	64.97	0.001020	6.2040	271.90	2191.2	2463.1	271.93	2346.3	2618.2	0.8931	6.9383	7.8314
30	69.10	0.001022	5.2290	289.20	2179.2	2468.4	289.23	2336.0	2625.3	0.9439	6.8247	7.7686
40	75.87	0.001027	3.9930	317.53	2159.5	2477.0	317.57	2319.1	2636.7	1.0259	6.6441	7.6700
50	81.33	0.001030	3.2400	340.44	2143.5	2483.9	340.49	2305.4	2645.9	1.0910	6.5029	7.5939
75	91.78	0.001037	2.2170	384.31	2112.4	2496.7	384.39	2278.6	2663.0	1.2130	6.2434	7.4564
100	99.63	0.001043	1.6940	417.36	2088.7	2506.1	417.46	2258.0	2675.5	1.3026	6.0568	7.3594
125	105.99	0.001048	1.3749	444.19	2069.3	2513.5	444.32	2241.0	2685.4	1.3740	5.9104	7.2844
150	111.37	0.001053	1.1593	466.94	2052.8	2519.7	467.10	2226.5	2693.6	1.4336	5.7897	7.2233
175	116.06	0.001057	1.0036	486.80	2038.1	2524.9	486.98	2213.5	2700.5	1.4839	5.6878	7.1717
200	120.23	0.001061	0.8857	504.49	2025.0	2529.5	504.70	2201.9	2706.6	1.5301	5.5970	7.1271
225	124.00	0.001064	0.7933	520.47	2013.1	2533.6	520.71	2191.4	2712.1	1.5706	5.5172	7.0878
250	127.44	0.001067	0.7187	535.10	2002.1	2537.2	535.37	2181.5	2716.9	1.6072	5.4455	7.0527
275	130.60	0.001070	0.6573	548.59	1991.9	2540.5	548.88	2172.4	2721.3	1.6408	5.3801	7.0209
300	133.55	0.001073	0.6058	561.15	1982.5	2543.6	561.47	2163.9	2725.3	1.6718	5.3201	6.9919

Table A.1.2 (continued)

p	T	v_f	v_g	u_f	u_{fg}	u_g	h_f	h_{fg}	h_g	s_f	s_{fg}	s_g
kPa	°C	m^3/kg		kJ/kg			kJ/kg			kJ/kg K		
325	136.30	0.001076	0.5620	572.90	1973.5	2546.4	573.25	2155.8	2729.1	1.7006	5.2646	6.9652
350	138.88	0.001079	0.5243	583.95	1965.0	2548.9	584.33	2148.1	2732.4	1.7275	5.2130	6.9405
375	141.32	0.001081	0.4914	594.40	1956.9	2551.3	594.81	2140.8	2735.6	1.7528	5.1647	6.9175
400	143.63	0.001084	0.4625	604.31	1949.3	2553.6	604.74	2133.9	2738.6	1.7766	5.1193	6.8959
450	147.93	0.001088	0.4140	622.77	1934.8	2557.6	623.26	2120.6	2743.9	1.8207	5.0358	6.8565
500	151.86	0.001093	0.3749	639.68	1921.5	2561.2	640.23	2108.4	2748.7	1.8607	4.9606	6.8213
550	155.48	0.001097	0.3427	655.32	1909.2	2564.5	655.92	2097.1	2753.0	1.8973	4.8920	6.7893
600	158.85	0.001101	0.3157	669.90	1897.5	2567.4	670.56	2086.3	2756.8	1.9312	4.8288	6.7600
650	162.01	0.001104	0.2927	683.56	1886.5	2570.1	684.28	2076.1	2760.4	1.9627	4.7704	6.7331
700	164.97	0.001108	0.2729	696.44	1876.1	2572.5	697.22	2066.3	2763.5	1.9922	4.7158	6.7080
750	167.78	0.001112	0.2556	708.64	1866.1	2574.7	709.47	2056.9	2766.4	2.0200	4.6647	6.6847
800	170.43	0.001115	0.2404	720.22	1856.6	2576.8	721.11	2048.0	2769.1	2.0462	4.6166	6.6628
850	172.96	0.001118	0.2270	731.27	1847.4	2578.7	732.22	2039.4	2771.7	2.0710	4.5711	6.6421
900	175.38	0.001121	0.2150	741.83	1838.7	2580.5	742.84	2031.2	2774.0	2.0946	4.5280	6.6226
950	177.69	0.001124	0.2042	751.95	1830.2	2582.1	753.02	2023.1	2776.1	2.1172	4.4869	6.6041
1000	179.91	0.001127	0.194440	761.09	1822.5	2583.6	762.22	2015.8	2778.0	2.1387	4.4478	6.5865
1100	184.09	0.001133	0.177530	780.09	1806.3	2586.4	781.34	2000.3	2781.7	2.1792	4.3744	6.5536
1200	187.99	0.001139	0.163330	797.29	1791.5	2588.8	798.66	1986.1	2784.8	2.2166	4.3067	6.5233
1300	191.07	0.001144	0.151250	813.44	1777.6	2591.0	814.93	1972.7	2787.6	2.2515	4.2438	6.4953
1400	195.07	0.001149	0.140840	828.70	1764.1	2592.8	830.31	1959.7	2790.0	2.2842	4.1851	6.4693
1500	198.32	0.001154	0.131770	743.16	1851.3	2594.5	744.89	2047.3	2792.2	2.3150	4.1298	6.4448
1750	205.76	0.001166	0.113490	876.46	1721.3	2597.8	878.50	1917.9	2796.4	2.3851	4.0045	6.3896
2000	212.42	0.001177	0.099630	906.44	1693.9	2600.3	908.79	1890.8	2799.6	2.4474	3.8935	6.3409
2250	218.45	0.001187	0.088750	933.83	1668.2	2602.0	936.50	1865.2	2801.7	2.5035	3.7937	6.2972
2500	223.99	0.001197	0.079980	959.11	1644.0	2603.1	962.10	1840.9	2803.1	2.5547	3.7028	6.2575
3000	233.90	0.001217	0.066680	1004.78	1599.3	2604.1	1008.43	1795.7	2804.1	2.6457	3.5412	6.1869
3500	242.60	0.001235	0.057070	1045.43	1558.3	2603.7	1049.75	1753.7	2803.4	2.7253	3.4000	6.1253
4000	250.40	0.001252	0.049780	1082.31	1520.0	2602.3	1087.32	1714.1	2801.4	2.7964	3.2737	6.0701
5000	263.99	0.001286	0.039440	1147.81	1449.3	2597.1	1154.24	1640.1	2794.3	2.9202	3.0532	5.9734

Table A.1.2 (continued)

p	T	v_f	v_g	u_f	u_{fg}	u_g	h_f	h_{fg}	h_g	s_f	s_{fg}	s_g
kPa	°C	m^3/kg		kJ/kg			kJ/kg			kJ/kg K		
6000	275.64	0.001319	0.032440	1205.44	1384.3	2589.7	1213.35	1571.0	2784.3	3.0267	2.8625	5.8892
7000	285.88	0.001351	0.027370	1257.55	1323.0	2580.5	1267.01	1505.1	2772.1	3.1211	2.6922	5.8133
8000	295.06	0.001384	0.023520	1305.57	1264.2	2569.8	1316.64	1441.3	2758.0	3.2068	2.5364	5.7432
9000	303.40	0.001418	0.020480	1350.51	1207.3	2557.8	1363.27	1378.8	2742.1	3.2858	2.3914	5.6772
10000	311.06	0.001452	0.018026	1393.04	1151.4	2544.4	1407.56	1317.1	2724.7	3.3596	2.2545	5.6141
11000	318.15	0.001489	0.015987	1433.70	1096.1	2529.8	1450.08	1255.6	2705.7	3.4295	2.1232	5.5527
12000	324.75	0.001527	0.014263	1473.00	1040.7	2513.7	1491.32	1193.5	2684.9	3.4962	1.9962	5.4924
13000	330.93	0.001567	0.012780	1511.10	985.0	2496.1	1531.47	1130.8	2662.2	3.5606	1.8717	5.4323
14000	336.75	0.001611	0.011485	1548.60	928.2	2476.8	1571.15	1066.4	2637.6	3.6232	1.7485	5.3717
15000	342.24	0.001658	0.010337	1585.60	869.9	2455.5	1610.47	1000.1	2610.6	3.6848	1.6250	5.3098
16000	347.44	0.001711	0.009306	1622.70	809.0	2431.7	1650.08	930.5	2580.6	3.7461	1.4994	5.2455
17000	352.37	0.001770	0.008364	1660.20	744.8	2405.0	1690.29	856.9	2547.2	3.8079	1.3698	5.1777
18000	357.06	0.001840	0.007489	1698.90	675.4	2374.3	1732.02	777.1	2509.1	3.8715	1.2329	5.1044
19000	361.54	0.001924	0.006657	1739.90	598.2	2338.1	1776.46	688.1	2464.6	3.9388	1.0840	5.0228
20000	365.81	0.002036	0.005834	1785.60	507.4	2293.0	1826.32	583.4	2409.7	4.0139	0.9130	4.9269
21000	369.89	0.002207	0.004952	1842.10	388.5	2230.6	1888.45	446.1	2334.6	4.1075	0.6938	4.8013
22000	373.80	0.002742	0.003568	1961.90	125.2	2087.1	2022.22	143.4	2165.6	4.3110	0.2217	4.5327
22090	374.14	0.003155	0.003155	2029.60	0.0	2029.6	2099.29	0.0	2099.3	4.4298	0.0000	4.4298

Table A.1.3 **Superheated steam.**
(Adapted from J.H. Keenan, F.G. Keyes, P.G. Hill and J.G. Moore, *Steam Tables (S.I. Units)*, Wiley, New York, 1978)

$p = 0.01$ MPa				
T	v	u	h	s
45.81	14.6740	2437.9	2584.6	8.1502
100	17.1960	2515.5	2687.5	8.4479
150	19.5120	2587.9	2783.0	8.6882
200	21.8250	2661.3	2879.6	8.9038
250	24.1360	2736.0	2977.4	9.1002
300	26.4450	2812.1	3076.6	9.2813
400	31.0630	2968.9	3279.5	9.6077
500	35.6790	3132.3	3489.1	9.8978
600	40.2950	3302.5	3705.5	10.1608
700	44.9110	3479.6	3928.7	10.4028
800	49.5260	3663.8	4159.1	10.6281
900	54.1410	3855.0	4396.4	10.8396
1000	58.7570	4053.0	4640.6	11.0393
1100	63.3720	4257.5	4891.2	11.2287
1200	67.9870	4467.9	5147.8	11.4091
1300	72.6020	4683.7	5409.7	11.5811

$p = 0.05$ MPa				
T	v	u	h	s
81.33	3.2400	2483.9	2645.9	7.5939
100	3.4180	2511.6	2682.5	7.6947
150	3.8890	2585.6	2780.1	7.9401
200	4.3560	2659.9	2877.7	8.1580
250	4.8200	2735.0	2976.0	8.3556
300	5.2840	2811.3	3075.5	8.5373
400	6.2090	2968.5	3279.0	8.8642
500	7.1340	3132.0	3488.7	9.1546
600	8.0570	3302.2	3705.1	9.4178
700	8.9810	3479.4	3928.5	9.6599
800	9.9040	3663.6	4158.8	9.8852
900	10.8280	3854.9	4396.3	10.0967
1000	11.7510	4052.9	4640.5	10.2964
1100	12.6740	4257.4	4891.1	10.4859
1200	13.5970	4467.8	5147.7	10.6662
1300	14.5210	4683.6	5409.7	10.8382

$p = 0.10$ MPa				
T	v	u	h	s
99.63	1.6940	2506.1	2675.5	7.3594
100	1.6958	2506.7	2676.3	7.3614
150	1.9364	2582.8	2776.4	7.6134
200	2.1720	2658.1	2875.3	7.8343
250	2.4060	2733.7	2974.3	8.0333
300	2.6390	2810.4	3074.3	8.2158
400	3.1030	2967.9	3278.2	8.5435
500	3.5650	3131.6	3488.1	8.8342
600	4.0280	3301.9	3704.7	9.0976
700	4.4900	3479.2	3928.2	9.3398
800	4.9520	3663.5	4158.7	9.5652
900	5.4140	3854.8	4396.2	9.7767
1000	5.8750	4052.8	4640.3	9.9764
1100	6.3370	4257.3	4891.0	10.1659
1200	6.7990	4467.7	5147.6	10.3463
1300	7.2600	4683.5	5409.5	10.5183

$p = 0.20$ MPa				
T	v	u	h	s
151.86	0.8857	2529.5	2706.6	7.1272
150	0.9596	2576.9	2768.8	7.2795
200	1.0803	2654.4	2870.5	7.5066
250	1.1988	2731.2	2971.0	7.7086
300	1.3162	2808.6	3071.8	7.8926
400	1.5493	2966.7	3276.6	8.2218
500	1.7814	3130.8	3487.1	8.5133
600	2.0130	3301.4	3704.0	8.7770
700	2.2440	3478.8	3927.6	9.0194
800	2.4750	3663.1	4158.1	9.2449
900	2.7060	3854.5	4395.7	9.4566
1000	2.9370	4052.5	4639.9	9.6563
1100	3.1680	4257.0	4890.6	9.8458
1200	3.3990	4467.3	5147.1	10.0262
1300	3.6300	4683.2	5409.2	10.1982

$p = 0.30$ MPa				
T	v	u	h	s
133.55	0.6058	2543.6	2725.3	6.9919
150	0.6339	2570.8	2761.0	7.0778
200	0.7163	2650.7	2865.6	7.3115
250	0.7964	2728.7	2967.6	7.5166
300	0.8753	2806.7	3069.3	7.7022
400	1.0315	2965.6	3275.1	8.0330
500	1.1867	3130.0	3486.0	8.3251
600	1.3414	3300.8	3703.2	8.5892
700	1.4957	3478.4	3927.1	8.8319
800	1.6499	3662.9	4157.9	9.0576
900	1.8041	3854.2	4395.4	9.2692
1000	1.9581	4052.3	4639.7	9.4690
1100	2.1121	4256.8	4890.4	9.6585
1200	2.2661	4467.2	5147.0	9.8389
1300	2.4201	4683.0	5409.0	10.0110

$p = 0.40$ MPa				
T	v	u	h	s
143.63	0.4625	2553.6	2738.6	6.8959
150	0.4708	2564.5	2752.8	6.9299
200	0.5342	2646.8	2860.5	7.1706
250	0.5951	2726.1	2964.1	7.3789
300	0.6548	2804.8	3066.7	7.5662
400	0.7726	2964.4	3273.4	7.8995
500	0.8893	3129.2	3484.9	8.1913
600	1.0055	3300.2	3702.4	8.4558
700	1.1215	3477.9	3926.5	8.6987
800	1.2372	3662.4	4157.3	8.9244
900	1.3529	3853.9	4395.1	9.1362
1000	1.4685	4052.0	4639.4	9.3360
1100	1.5840	4256.5	4890.1	9.5256
1200	1.6996	4467.0	5146.8	9.7060
1300	1.8151	4682.8	5408.8	9.8780

Table A.1.3 (continued)

p = 0.50 MPa				
T	v	u	h	s
151.86	0.37490	2561.2	2748.7	6.8213
200	0.42490	2642.9	2855.4	7.0592
250	0.47440	2723.5	2960.7	7.2709
300	0.52260	2802.9	3064.2	7.4599
350	0.57010	2882.6	3167.7	7.6329
400	0.61730	2963.2	3271.9	7.7938
500	0.71090	3128.4	3483.9	8.0873
600	0.80410	3299.6	3701.7	8.3522
700	0.89690	3477.5	3926.0	8.5952
800	0.98960	3662.1	4156.9	8.8211
900	1.08220	3853.6	4394.7	9.0329
1000	1.17470	4051.8	4639.2	9.2328
1100	1.26720	4256.3	4889.9	9.4224
1200	1.35960	4466.8	5146.6	9.6029
1300	1.45210	4682.5	5408.6	6.7749

p = 0.60 MPa				
T	v	u	h	s
158.85	0.31570	2567.4	2756.8	6.7600
200	0.35200	2638.9	2850.1	6.9665
250	0.39380	2720.9	2957.2	7.1816
300	0.43400	2801.0	3061.4	7.3724
350	0.47420	2881.2	3165.7	7.5464
400	0.51370	2962.1	3270.3	7.7079
500	0.59200	3127.6	3482.8	8.0021
600	0.66970	3299.1	3700.9	8.2674
700	0.74720	3477.0	3925.3	8.5107
800	0.82450	3661.8	4156.5	8.7367
900	0.90750	3853.4	4397.9	8.9486
1000	0.97880	4051.5	4638.8	9.1485
1100	1.05590	4256.1	4889.6	9.3381
1200	1.13300	4466.5	5146.3	9.5185
1300	1.21010	4682.3	5408.4	9.6906

p = 0.80 MPa				
T	v	u	h	s
170.43	0.24040	2576.8	2769.1	6.6628
200	0.26080	2630.6	2839.2	6.8158
250	0.29310	2715.5	2950.0	7.0384
300	0.32410	2797.2	3056.5	7.2328
350	0.35440	2878.2	3161.7	7.4089
400	0.38430	2959.7	3267.1	7.5716
500	0.44330	3126.0	3480.6	7.8673
600	0.50180	3297.9	3699.3	8.1333
700	0.56010	3476.2	3924.3	8.3770
800	0.61810	3661.1	4155.6	8.6033
900	0.67610	3852.8	4393.7	8.8153
1000	0.73400	4051.0	4638.2	9.0153
1100	0.79190	4255.6	4889.1	9.2050
1200	0.84970	4466.1	5145.9	9.3855
1300	0.90760	4681.8	5407.9	9.5575

p = 1.00 MPa				
T	v	u	h	s
179.91	0.19444	2583.6	2789.6	6.5865
200	0.20600	2621.9	2827.9	6.6940
250	0.23270	2709.9	2942.6	6.9247
300	0.25790	2793.2	3051.1	7.1229
350	0.28250	2875.2	3157.7	7.3011
400	0.30660	2957.3	3263.9	7.4651
500	0.35410	3124.4	3478.5	7.7622
600	0.40110	3296.8	3697.9	8.0290
700	0.44780	3475.3	3923.1	8.2731
800	0.49430	3660.4	4154.7	8.4996
900	0.54070	3852.2	4392.9	8.7118
1000	0.58710	4050.5	4637.6	8.9119
1100	0.63350	4255.1	4888.6	9.1017
1200	0.67980	4465.6	5145.4	9.2822
1300	0.72610	4681.3	5407.4	9.4543

p = 1.20 MPa				
T	v	u	h	s
187.99	0.16333	2588.8	2792.0	6.5233
200	0.16930	2612.8	2816.0	6.5898
250	0.19234	2704.2	2935.0	6.8294
300	0.21380	2789.2	3045.8	7.0317
350	0.23450	2872.2	3153.6	7.2121
400	0.25480	2954.9	3260.7	7.3774
500	0.29460	3122.8	3476.3	7.6759
600	0.33390	3295.6	3696.3	7.9435
700	0.37290	3474.4	3921.9	8.1881
800	0.41180	3659.7	4153.9	8.4148
900	0.45050	3851.6	4392.2	8.6272
1000	0.48920	4050.0	4637.0	8.8274
1100	0.52780	4254.6	4888.0	9.0172
1200	0.56650	4465.1	5144.9	9.1977
1300	0.60510	4680.9	5407.0	9.3698

p =1.40 MPa				
T	v	u	h	s
195.07	0.14084	2592.8	2793.0	6.4693
200	0.14302	2603.1	2803.3	6.4975
250	0.16350	2698.3	2927.2	6.7467
300	0.18228	2785.2	3040.4	6.9534
350	0.20030	2869.2	3149.6	7.1360
400	0.21780	2952.5	3257.4	7.3026
500	0.25210	3121.1	3474.1	7.6027
600	0.28600	3294.4	3694.8	7.8710
700	0.31950	3473.6	3920.9	8.1160
800	0.35280	3659.0	4152.9	8.3431
900	0.38610	3851.1	4391.6	8.5556
1000	0.41920	4049.5	4636.4	8.7559
1100	0.45240	4254.1	4887.5	8.9457
1200	0.48550	4464.7	5144.4	9.1262
1300	0.51860	4680.4	5406.4	9.2984

Table A.1.3 (continued)

	p = 1.60 MPa			
T	v	u	h	s
201.40	0.12380	2596.0	2794.1	6.4218
250	0.14184	2692.3	2919.2	6.6732
300	0.15862	2781.1	3034.9	6.8844
350	0.17456	2866.1	3145.4	7.0694
400	0.19005	2950.1	3254.2	7.2374
500	0.22030	3119.5	3472.0	7.5390
600	0.25000	3293.3	3693.3	7.8080
700	0.27940	3472.7	3919.7	8.0535
800	0.30860	3658.3	4152.1	8.2808
900	0.33770	3850.5	4390.8	8.4935
1000	0.36680	4049.0	4635.9	8.6938
1100	0.39580	4253.7	4887.0	8.8837
1200	0.42480	4464.2	5143.9	9.0643
1300	0.45380	4679.9	5406.0	9.2364

	p =1.80MPa			
T	v	u	h	s
207.15	0.11042	2598.4	2797.2	6.3794
250	0.12497	2686.0	2910.9	6.6066
300	0.14021	2776.9	3029.3	6.8226
350	0.15457	2863.0	3141.2	7.0100
400	0.16847	2947.7	3250.9	7.1794
500	0.19550	3117.9	3469.8	7.4825
600	0.22200	3292.1	3691.7	7.7523
700	0.24820	3471.8	3918.6	7.9983
800	0.27420	3657.6	4151.2	8.2258
900	0.30010	3849.9	4390.1	8.4386
1000	0.32600	4048.5	4635.3	8.6391
1100	0.35180	4253.2	4886.4	8.8290
1200	0.77600	4463.7	5860.5	9.0096
1300	0.40340	4679.5	5405.6	9.1818

	p = 2.00 MPa			
T	v	u	h	s
212.42	0.09963	2600.3	2799.6	6.3409
250	0.11144	2679.6	2902.5	6.5453
300	0.12547	2772.6	3023.5	6.7664
350	0.13857	2859.8	3136.9	6.9563
400	0.15120	2945.2	3247.6	7.1271
500	0.17568	3116.2	3467.6	7.4317
600	0.19960	3290.9	3690.1	7.7024
700	0.22320	3470.9	3917.3	7.9487
800	0.24600	3657.0	4149.0	8.1765
900	0.27000	3849.3	4389.3	8.3895
1000	0.29330	4048.0	4634.6	8.5901
1100	0.31660	4252.7	4885.9	8.7800
1200	0.33980	4463.3	5142.9	8.9607
1300	0.36310	4679.0	5405.2	9.1329

	p = 2.50 MPa			
T	v	u	h	s
223.99	0.07998	2603.1	2803.1	6.2675
250	0.08700	2662.6	2880.1	6.4085
300	0.09890	2761.6	3008.9	6.6438
350	0.10976	2851.9	3126.3	6.8403
400	0.12010	2939.1	3239.4	7.0148
450	0.13014	3025.5	3350.9	7.1746
500	0.13998	3112.1	3462.1	7.3234
600	0.15930	3288.0	3686.3	7.5960
700	0.17832	3468.7	3914.5	7.8435
800	0.19716	3655.3	4148.2	8.0720
900	0.21590	3847.9	4387.7	8.2853
1000	0.23460	4046.7	4633.2	8.4861
1100	0.25320	4251.5	4884.5	8.6762
1200	0.27180	4462.1	5141.6	8.8569
1300	0.29050	4677.8	5404.1	9.0291

	p = 3.00 MPa			
T	v	u	h	s
233.90	0.06668	2604.1	2804.1	6.1869
250	0.07058	2644.0	2855.7	6.2872
300	0.08114	2750.1	2993.5	6.5390
350	0.09053	2843.7	3115.3	6.7428
400	0.09936	2932.8	3230.9	6.9212
450	0.10787	3020.4	3344.0	7.0834
500	0.11619	3108.0	3456.6	7.2338
600	0.13243	3285.0	3682.3	7.5085
700	0.14838	3466.5	3911.6	7.7571
800	0.16414	3653.5	4145.9	7.9862
900	0.17980	3846.5	4385.9	8.1999
1000	0.19541	4045.4	4631.6	8.4009
1100	0.21098	4250.3	4883.2	8.5912
1200	0.22652	4460.9	5140.5	8.7720
1300	0.24206	4676.5	5402.7	8.9442

	p = 3.50 MPa			
T	v	u	h	s
242.60	0.05707	2603.7	2803.4	6.1253
250	0.05872	2623.7	2829.2	6.1749
300	0.06842	2738.0	2977.5	6.4461
350	0.07678	2835.3	3104.0	6.6579
400	0.08453	2926.4	3222.3	6.8405
450	0.09196	3015.3	3337.2	7.0052
500	0.09918	3103.0	3450.1	7.1572
600	0.11324	3282.1	3678.4	7.4339
700	0.12699	3464.3	3908.8	7.6837
800	0.14056	3651.8	4143.8	7.9134
900	0.15402	3845.0	4384.1	8.1276
1000	0.16743	4044.1	4630.1	8.3288
1100	0.18080	4249.2	4882.0	8.5192
1200	0.19415	4459.8	5139.3	8.7000
1300	0.20749	4675.5	5401.7	8.8723

Table A.1.3 (continued)

T	$p = 4.00$ MPa v	u	h	s
250.40	0.04978	2602.3	2801.4	6.0701
300	0.05884	2725.3	2960.7	6.3615
350	0.06645	2826.7	3092.5	6.5821
400	0.07341	2919.9	3213.5	6.7690
450	0.08002	3010.2	3330.3	6.9363
500	0.08643	3099.5	3445.2	7.0901
600	0.09885	3279.1	3674.5	7.3688
700	0.11095	3462.1	3905.9	7.6198
800	0.12287	3650.0	4141.5	7.8502
900	0.13469	3843.6	4382.4	8.0647
1000	0.14645	4042.9	4628.7	8.2662
1100	0.15817	4248.0	4880.7	8.4567
1200	0.16987	4458.6	5138.1	8.6376
1300	0.18156	4674.3	5400.5	8.8100

T	$p = 4.50$ MPa v	u	h	s
257.49	0.04406	2600.1	2798.4	6.0198
300	0.05135	2712.0	2943.1	6.2828
350	0.05840	2817.8	3080.6	6.5131
400	0.06475	2913.3	3204.7	6.7047
450	0.07074	3005.0	3323.3	6.8746
500	0.07651	3095.3	3439.6	7.0301
600	0.08765	3276.0	3670.4	7.3110
700	0.09847	3459.9	3903.0	7.5631
800	0.10911	3648.4	4139.4	7.7942
900	0.11965	3842.2	4380.6	8.0091
1000	0.13013	4041.6	4627.2	8.2108
1100	0.14056	4246.8	4879.3	8.4015
1200	0.15098	4457.5	5136.9	8.5825
1300	0.16139	4673.1	5399.4	8.7549

T	$p = 5.00$ MPa v	u	h	s
263.99	0.03944	2597.1	2794.3	5.9734
300	0.04532	2698.0	2924.6	6.2084
350	0.05194	2808.7	3068.4	6.4493
400	0.05781	2906.6	3195.7	6.6459
450	0.06330	2999.7	3316.2	6.8186
500	0.06857	3091.0	3433.9	6.9759
600	0.07869	3273.0	3666.5	7.2589
700	0.08849	3457.6	3900.1	7.5122
800	0.09811	3646.6	4137.2	7.7440
900	0.10762	3840.7	4378.8	7.9593
1000	0.11707	4040.4	4625.8	8.1612
1100	0.12648	4245.6	4878.0	8.3520
1200	0.13587	4456.3	5135.7	8.5331
1300	0.14526	4672.0	5398.3	8.7055

T	$p = 6.00$ MPa v	u	h	s
275.64	0.03244	2589.7	2784.3	5.8892
300	0.03616	2667.2	2884.2	6.0674
350	0.04223	2789.6	3043.0	6.3335
400	0.04739	2892.9	3177.2	6.5408
450	0.05214	2988.9	3301.7	6.7193
500	0.05665	3082.2	3422.1	6.8803
600	0.06525	3266.9	3658.4	7.1677
700	0.07352	3453.1	3894.2	7.4234
800	0.08160	3643.1	4132.7	7.6566
900	0.08958	3837.8	4375.3	7.8727
1000	0.09749	4037.8	4622.7	8.0751
1100	0.10536	4243.3	4875.5	8.2661
1200	0.11321	4454.0	5133.3	8.4474
1300	0.12106	4669.6	5396.0	8.6199

T	$p = 7.00$ MPa v	u	h	s
265.88	0.02737	2580.5	2772.1	5.8133
300	0.02947	2632.2	2838.5	5.9305
350	0.03524	2769.4	3016.1	6.2283
400	0.03993	2878.6	3158.1	6.4478
450	0.04416	2978.0	3287.1	6.6327
500	0.04814	3073.4	3410.4	6.7975
600	0.05565	3260.7	3650.3	7.0894
700	0.06283	3448.5	3888.3	7.3476
800	0.06981	3639.5	4128.2	7.5822
900	0.07669	3835.0	4371.8	7.7991
1000	0.08350	4035.3	4619.8	8.0020
1100	0.09027	4240.9	4872.8	8.1933
1200	0.09703	4451.7	5130.9	8.3747
1300	0.10377	4667.3	5393.7	8.5473

T	$p = 8.00$ MPa v	u	h	s
295.06	0.02352	2569.8	2758.0	5.7432
300	0.02426	2590.9	2785.0	5.7906
350	0.02995	2747.7	2987.3	6.1301
400	0.03432	2863.8	3138.4	6.3634
450	0.03817	2966.7	3272.1	6.5551
500	0.04176	3064.3	3398.4	6.7240
600	0.04845	3254.4	3642.0	7.0206
700	0.05481	3443.9	3882.4	7.2812
800	0.06097	3636.0	4123.8	7.5173
900	0.06702	3832.1	4368.3	7.7351
1000	0.07301	4032.8	4616.9	7.9384
1100	0.07896	4238.6	4870.3	8.1300
1200	0.08489	4449.5	5128.6	8.3115
1300	0.09080	4665.0	5391.4	8.4842

Table A.1.3 (continued)

$p = 9.00$ MPa					$p = 10.00$ MPa					$p = 12.50$ MPa				
T	v	u	h	s	T	v	u	h	s	T	v	u	h	s
303.40	0.02048	2557.8	2742.1	5.6772	**311.06**	0.01803	2544.4	2724.7	5.6141	**327.89**	0.01350	2505.1	2673.8	5.4624
350	0.02580	2724.4	2956.6	6.0361	**350**	0.02242	2699.2	2923.4	5.9443	**350**	0.01613	2624.6	2826.2	5.7118
400	0.02993	2848.4	3117.8	6.2854	**400**	0.02641	2832.4	3096.5	6.2120	**400**	0.02000	2789.3	3039.3	6.0417
450	0.03350	2955.1	3256.6	6.4844	**450**	0.02975	2943.4	3240.9	6.4190	**450**	0.02299	2912.5	3199.9	6.2719
500	0.03677	3055.2	3386.1	6.6576	**500**	0.03279	3045.8	3373.7	6.5966	**500**	0.02560	3021.7	3341.7	6.4618
600	0.04285	3248.1	3633.8	6.9589	**600**	0.03837	3241.7	3625.4	6.9029	**600**	0.03029	3225.4	3604.0	6.7810
700	0.04857	3439.4	3876.5	7.2221	**700**	0.04358	3434.7	3870.5	7.1687	**700**	0.03460	3422.9	3855.4	7.0536
800	0.05409	3632.5	4119.3	7.4596	**800**	0.04859	3628.9	4114.8	7.4077	**800**	0.03869	3620.0	4103.6	7.2965
900	0.05950	3829.3	4364.8	7.6783	**900**	0.05349	3826.3	4361.2	7.6272	**900**	0.04267	3819.1	4352.5	7.5182
1000	0.06485	4030.4	4614.1	7.8821	**1000**	0.05832	4027.8	4611.0	7.8315	**1000**	0.04658	4021.6	4603.9	7.7237
1100	0.07016	4236.3	4867.7	8.0740	**1100**	0.06312	4234.0	4865.2	8.0237	**1100**	0.05045	4228.2	4858.8	7.9165
1200	0.07544	4447.2	5126.2	8.2556	**1200**	0.06789	4444.9	5123.8	8.2055	**1200**	0.05430	4439.3	5118.1	8.0987
1300	0.08072	4662.7	5389.2	8.4284	**1300**	0.07265	4660.5	5387.0	8.3783	**1300**	0.05813	4654.8	5381.4	8.2717

$p = 15.00$ MPa					$p = 17.50$ MPa					$p = 20.00$ MPa				
T	v	u	h	s	T	v	u	h	s	T	v	u	h	s
342.24	0.01034	2455.5	2610.6	5.3098	**354.75**	0.00792	2390.2	2528.8	5.1419	**365.81**	0.00583	2293.0	2409.7	4.9269
400	0.01565	2740.7	2975.4	5.8811	**400**	0.01245	2685.0	2902.8	5.7213	**400**	0.00994	2619.3	2818.1	5.5540
450	0.01845	2879.5	3156.2	6.1404	**450**	0.01517	2844.2	3109.7	6.0184	**450**	0.01270	2806.2	3060.1	5.9017
500	0.02080	2996.6	3308.6	6.3443	**500**	0.01736	2970.3	3274.1	6.2383	**500**	0.01477	2942.9	3238.3	6.1401
600	0.02491	3208.6	3582.3	6.6776	**600**	0.02106	3191.5	3560.1	6.5866	**600**	0.01818	3174.0	3537.6	6.5048
700	0.02861	3410.9	3840.1	6.9572	**700**	0.02434	3398.7	3824.7	6.8736	**700**	0.02113	3386.4	3809.0	6.7993
800	0.03210	3610.9	4092.4	7.2040	**800**	0.02738	3601.8	4081.0	7.1244	**800**	0.02385	3592.7	4069.7	7.0544
900	0.03546	3811.9	4343.8	7.4279	**900**	0.03031	3804.7	4335.1	7.3507	**900**	0.02645	3797.5	4326.5	7.2830
1000	0.03875	4015.4	4596.7	7.6348	**1000**	0.03316	4009.3	4589.6	7.5589	**1000**	0.02897	4003.1	4582.5	7.4925
1100	0.04200	4222.6	4852.6	7.8283	**1100**	0.03597	4216.9	4846.4	7.7531	**1100**	0.03145	4211.3	4840.3	7.6874
1200	0.04523	4433.8	5112.3	8.0108	**1200**	0.03876	4428.3	5106.6	7.9360	**1200**	0.03391	4422.8	5101.0	7.8707
1300	0.04845	4649.1	5375.9	8.1840	**1300**	0.04154	4643.5	5370.5	8.1093	**1300**	0.03636	4638.0	5365.2	8.0442

Table A.1.3 (continued)

T	$p = 25.00$ MPa v	u	h	s	$p = 30.00$ MPa v	u	h	s	$p = 35.00$ MPa v	u	h	s
375	0.00197	1798.7	1848.0	4.0320	0.00179	1737.8	1791.5	3.9305	0.00170	1702.9	1762.4	3.8722
400	0.00600	2430.1	2580.2	5.1418	0.00279	2067.4	2151.1	4.4728	0.00210	1914.1	1987.6	4.2126
450	0.00916	2720.7	2949.8	5.6744	0.00674	2619.3	2821.4	5.4424	0.00496	2498.7	2672.3	5.1962
500	0.01112	2884.3	3162.4	5.9592	0.00868	2820.7	3081.0	5.7905	0.00693	2751.9	2994.3	5.6282
600	0.01414	3137.9	3491.3	6.3602	0.01145	3100.5	3443.9	6.2331	0.00953	3062.0	3395.4	6.1179
700	0.01665	3361.3	3777.5	6.6707	0.01366	3335.8	3745.6	6.5606	0.01153	3309.8	3713.5	6.4631
800	0.01891	3574.3	4047.1	6.9345	0.01562	3555.5	4024.2	6.8332	0.01328	3536.7	4001.4	6.7450
900	0.02105	3783.0	4309.1	7.1680	0.01745	3768.5	4291.9	7.0718	0.01488	3754.0	4274.9	6.9886
1000	0.02310	3990.9	4568.4	7.3802	0.01920	3978.8	4554.7	7.2867	0.01641	3966.7	4541.1	7.2064
1100	0.02512	4200.2	4828.2	7.5765	0.02090	4189.2	4816.3	7.4845	0.01790	4178.3	4804.6	7.4057
1200	0.02711	4412.0	5089.8	7.7605	0.02259	4401.3	5079.0	7.6692	0.01936	4390.7	5068.3	7.5910
1300	0.02910	4626.9	5354.4	7.9342	0.02427	4616.0	5344.0	7.8432	0.02082	4605.1	5333.6	7.7653

T	$p = 40.00$ MPa v	u	h	s	$p = 50.00$ MPa v	u	h	s	$p = 60.00$ MPa v	u	h	s
375	0.00164	1677.1	1742.7	3.8290	0.00156	1638.6	1716.6	3.7639	0.00150	1609.4	1699.6	3.7141
400	0.00191	1854.6	1930.9	4.1135	0.00173	1788.1	1874.6	4.0031	0.00163	1745.4	1843.4	3.9318
450	0.00369	2365.1	2512.8	4.9459	0.00249	2159.6	2283.9	4.5884	0.00209	2053.9	2179.0	4.4121
500	0.00562	2678.4	2903.3	5.4700	0.00389	2525.5	2720.1	5.1726	0.00296	2390.6	2568.0	4.9321
600	0.00809	3022.6	3346.4	6.0114	0.00611	2942.0	3247.6	5.8178	0.00483	2861.1	3151.1	5.6452
700	0.00994	3283.6	3681.2	6.3750	0.00773	3230.5	3616.9	6.2189	0.00627	3177.2	3553.5	6.0824
800	0.01152	3517.8	3978.7	6.6662	0.00908	3479.8	3933.6	6.5290	0.00746	3441.5	3889.0	6.4109
900	0.01296	3739.4	4257.9	6.9150	0.01028	3710.3	4224.5	6.7882	0.00851	3681.0	4191.5	6.6805
1000	0.01432	3954.6	4527.6	7.1356	0.01141	3930.5	4501.1	7.0146	0.00948	3906.4	4475.2	6.9127
1100	0.01564	4167.4	4793.1	7.3364	0.01250	4145.7	4770.5	7.2184	0.01041	4124.1	4748.6	7.1195
1200	0.01694	4380.1	5057.7	7.5224	0.01356	4359.1	5037.2	7.4058	0.01132	4338.2	5017.2	7.3083
1300	0.01823	4594.3	5323.5	7.6969	0.01462	4572.8	5303.6	7.5808	0.01222	4551.4	5284.3	7.4837

Table A.1.4 **Compressed liquid water.**
(Adapted from J.H. Keenan, F.G. Keyes, P.G. Hill and J.G. Moore, *Steam Tables (S.I. Units)*, Wiley, New York, 1978)

p = 5.00 MPa					p = 10.00 MPa					p = 15.00 MPa				
T	v	u	h	s	T	v	u	h	s	T	v	u	h	s
0	0.0009977	0.04	5.03	0.0001	**0**	0.0009952	0.09	10.04	0.0002	**0**	0.0009928	0.15	15.04	0.0004
20	0.0009995	83.65	88.65	0.2956	**20**	0.0009972	83.36	93.33	0.2945	**20**	0.0009950	83.06	97.99	0.2934
40	0.0010056	166.95	171.98	0.5705	**40**	0.0010034	166.35	176.38	0.5686	**40**	0.0010013	165.76	180.78	0.5666
60	0.0010149	250.23	255.30	0.8285	**60**	0.0010127	249.36	259.49	0.8258	**60**	0.0010105	248.51	263.67	0.8232
80	0.0010268	333.72	338.85	1.0720	**80**	0.0010245	332.59	342.84	1.0688	**80**	0.0010222	331.48	346.81	1.0656
100	0.0010576	417.52	422.81	1.3030	**100**	0.0010385	416.12	426.51	1.2992	**100**	0.0010361	414.74	430.28	1.2955
120	0.0010576	501.80	507.09	1.5233	**120**	0.0010549	500.08	510.63	1.5189	**120**	0.0010522	498.40	514.18	1.5145
140	0.0010768	586.76	592.14	1.7343	**140**	0.0010737	584.68	595.42	1.7292	**140**	0.0010707	582.66	598.72	1.7242
160	0.0010988	672.62	678.11	1.9375	**160**	0.0010953	670.13	681.08	1.9317	**160**	0.0010918	667.71	684.09	1.9260
180	0.0011240	759.63	765.25	2.1341	**180**	0.0011199	756.65	767.85	2.1275	**180**	0.0011159	753.76	770.50	2.1210
200	0.0011530	848.10	853.87	2.3255	**200**	0.0011480	844.50	855.98	2.3178	**200**	0.0011433	841.00	858.15	2.3104
220	0.0011866	938.40	944.33	2.5128	**220**	0.0011805	934.10	945.91	2.5039	**220**	0.0011748	929.90	947.52	2.4953
240	0.0012264	1031.40	1037.53	2.6979	**240**	0.0012187	1026.00	1038.19	2.6872	**240**	0.0012114	1020.80	1038.97	2.6771
260	0.0012749	1127.90	1134.27	2.8883	**260**	0.0012645	1121.10	1133.75	2.8699	**260**	0.0012550	1114.60	1133.43	2.8576
					280	0.0013216	1220.90	1234.12	3.0548	**280**	0.0013084	1212.50	1232.13	3.0393
					300	0.0039720	1328.40	1368.12	3.2469	**300**	0.0013770	1316.60	1337.26	3.2260
										320	0.0014724	1431.10	1453.19	3.4247
										340	0.0016311	1567.50	1591.97	3.6546
263.99	0.0012859	1147.80	1154.23	2.9202	**311.06**	0.0014524	1393.00	1407.52	3.3596	**342.24**	0.0016581	1585.10	1609.97	3.6848

Table A.1.4 (continued)

p = 20.00 MPa					p = 30.00 MPa					p = 50.00 MPa				
T	v	u	h	s	T	v	u	h	s	T	v	u	h	s
0	0.0009904	0.19	20.00	0.0004	**0**	0.0009856	0.25	29.82	0.0001	**0**	0.0009766	0.20	49.03	−0.0014
20	0.0009904	82.77	102.58	0.2923	**20**	0.0009886	82.17	111.83	0.2899	**20**	0.0009804	81.00	130.02	0.2848
40	0.0009992	165.17	185.15	0.5646	**40**	0.0009951	164.04	193.89	0.5607	**40**	0.0009872	161.86	211.22	0.5527
60	0.0010084	247.68	267.85	0.8206	**60**	0.0010042	246.06	276.19	0.8154	**60**	0.0009962	242.98	292.79	0.8052
80	0.0010199	330.40	350.80	1.0624	**80**	0.0010156	328.30	358.77	1.0561	**80**	0.0010073	324.34	374.71	1.0440
100	0.0010337	413.39	434.06	1.2917	**100**	0.0010290	410.78	441.65	1.2844	**100**	0.0010201	405.88	456.89	1.2703
120	0.0010496	496.76	517.75	1.5102	**120**	0.0010445	493.59	524.93	1.5018	**120**	0.0010348	487.65	539.39	1.4857
140	0.0010678	580.69	602.05	1.7193	**140**	0.0010621	576.88	608.74	1.7098	**140**	0.0010515	569.77	622.35	1.6915
160	0.0010885	665.35	687.12	1.9204	**160**	0.0010821	660.82	693.28	1.9096	**160**	0.0010703	652.41	705.93	1.8891
180	0.0011120	750.95	773.19	2.1147	**180**	0.0011047	745.59	778.73	2.1024	**180**	0.0010912	735.69	790.25	2.0794
200	0.0011388	837.70	860.48	2.3031	**200**	0.0011302	831.40	865.31	2.2893	**200**	0.0011146	819.70	875.43	2.2634
220	0.0011693	925.90	949.29	2.4870	**220**	0.0011590	918.30	953.07	2.4711	**220**	0.0011408	904.70	961.74	2.4419
240	0.0012046	1016.00	1040.09	0.6674	**240**	0.0011920	1006.90	1042.66	2.6490	**240**	0.0011702	990.70	1049.21	2.6158
260	0.0012462	1108.60	1133.52	0.8459	**260**	0.0012303	1097.40	1134.31	2.8243	**260**	0.0012034	1078.10	1138.27	2.7860
280	0.0012965	1204.70	1230.63	3.0248	**280**	0.0012755	1190.70	1228.97	2.9986	**280**	0.0012415	1167.20	1229.28	2.9537
300	0.0013596	1306.10	1333.29	3.2071	**300**	0.0013304	1287.90	1327.81	3.1741	**300**	0.0012860	1258.70	1323.00	3.1200
320	0.0014437	1415.70	1444.57	3.3979	**320**	0.0013997	1390.70	1432.69	3.3539	**320**	0.0013388	1353.30	1420.24	3.2868
340	0.0015684	1539.70	1571.07	3.6075	**340**	0.0014920	1501.70	1546.46	3.5426	**340**	0.0014032	1452.00	1522.16	3.4557
360	0.0018226	1702.80	1739.25	3.8772	**360**	0.0016265	1626.60	1675.40	3.7494	**360**	0.0014838	1556.00	1630.19	3.6291
365.81	0.0020360	1147.80	1158.00	2.9202										

Table A.1.5 **Ice–vapor saturation (sublimation).**
(Adapted from J.H. Keenan, F.G. Keyes, P.G. Hill and J.G. Moore, *Steam Tables (S.I. Units)*, Wiley, New York, 1978)

T °C	p kPa	v_s m³/kg	v_g m³/kg	u_s kJ/kg	u_{sg} kJ/kg	u_g kJ/kg	h_s kJ/kg	h_{sg} kJ/kg	h_g kJ/kg	s_s kJ/kg K	s_{sg} kJ/kg K	s_g kJ/kg K
0.01	0.6113	0.0010908	206.1	−333.40	2708.7	2375.3	−333.40	2834.7	2501.3	−1.221	10.377	9.156
0	0.6108	0.0010908	206.3	−333.43	2708.7	2375.3	−333.43	2834.7	2501.3	−1.221	10.378	9.157
−2	0.5176	0.0010904	241.7	−337.62	2710.2	2372.6	−337.62	2835.3	2497.7	−1.237	10.456	9.219
−4	0.4375	0.0010901	283.8	−341.78	2711.6	2369.8	−341.78	2835.7	2494.0	−1.253	10.536	9.283
−6	0.3689	0.0010898	334.2	−345.91	2712.9	2367.0	−345.91	2836.2	2490.3	−1.268	10.616	9.348
−8	0.3102	0.0010894	394.4	−350.02	2714.2	2364.2	−350.02	2836.6	2486.5	−1.284	10.698	9.414
−10	0.2602	0.0010891	466.7	−354.09	2715.5	2361.4	−354.09	2836.9	2482.8	−1.299	10.780	9.481
−12	0.2176	0.0010888	553.7	−358.14	2716.8	2358.7	−358.14	2837.3	2479.2	−1.315	10.845	9.530
−14	0.1815	0.0010884	658.8	−362.15	2718.1	2355.9	−362.15	2837.6	2475.5	−1.331	10.950	9.619
−16	0.1510	0.0010881	786.0	−366.14	2719.2	2353.1	−366.14	2837.9	2471.8	−1.346	11.036	9.690
−18	0.1252	0.0010878	940.5	−370.10	2720.4	2350.3	−370.10	2838.2	2468.1	−1.362	11.124	9.762
−20	0.1035	0.0010874	1128.6	−374.03	2721.5	2347.5	−374.03	2838.3	2464.3	−1.377	11.212	9.835
−22	0.0853	0.0010871	1358.4	−377.90	2722.6	2344.7	−377.90	2838.5	2460.6	−1.393	11.302	9.909
−24	0.0701	0.0010868	1640.1	−381.80	2723.8	2342.0	−381.80	2838.8	2457.0	−1.408	11.393	9.985
−26	0.0574	0.0010864	1986.4	−385.64	2724.8	2339.2	−385.64	2838.9	2453.2	−1.424	11.486	10.062
−28	0.0469	0.0010861	2413.7	−389.45	2725.9	2336.4	−389.45	2839.1	2449.6	−1.439	11.580	10.141
−30	0.0381	0.0010858	2943.0	−393.23	2726.8	2333.6	−393.23	2839.0	2445.7	−1.455	11.676	10.221
−32	0.0309	0.0010854	3600.0	−396.98	2727.8	2330.8	−396.98	2839.0	2442.0	−1.471	11.774	10.303
−34	0.0250	0.0010851	4419.0	−400.71	2728.7	2328.0	−400.71	2839.2	2438.5	−1.486	11.872	10.386
−36	0.0201	0.0010848	5444.0	−404.40	2729.6	2325.2	−404.40	2839.0	2434.6	−1.501	11.971	10.470
−38	0.0161	0.0010844	6731.0	−408.06	2730.5	2322.4	−408.06	2838.8	2430.8	−1.517	12.073	10.556
−40	0.0129	0.0010841	8354.0	−411.70	2731.3	2319.6	−411.70	2839.1	2427.4	−1.532	12.176	10.644

Table A.2.1 **Saturated ammonia – by temperature.**
(Adapted from National Bureau of Standards Circular No. 142, *Tables of Thermodynamic Properties of Ammonia*)

T °C	p kPa	v_f m³/kg	v_{fg} m³/kg	v_g m³/kg	u_f kJ/kg	u_{fg} kJ/kg	u_g kJ/kg	h_f kJ/kg	h_{fg} kJ/kg	h_g kJ/kg	s_f kJ/kg K	s_{fg} kJ/kg K	s_g kJ/kg K
–50	40.88	0.001424	2.6240	2.6254	–44.4	1309.4	1265.1	–44.3	1416.7	1372.4	–0.1942	6.3503	6.1561
–48	45.96	0.001429	2.3519	2.3533	–35.6	1303.2	1267.6	–35.5	1411.3	1375.8	–0.1547	6.2696	6.1149
–46	51.55	0.001434	2.1126	2.1140	–26.7	1296.9	1270.2	–26.6	1405.8	1379.2	–0.1156	6.1902	6.0746
–44	57.69	0.001439	1.9018	1.9032	–17.9	1290.6	1272.7	–17.8	1400.3	1382.5	–0.0768	6.1120	6.0352
–42	64.42	0.001444	1.7156	1.7170	–9.0	1284.2	1275.2	–8.9	1394.7	1385.8	–0.0382	6.0349	5.9967
–40	71.77	0.001449	1.5507	1.5521	–0.1	1277.7	1277.6	0.0	1389.0	1389.0	0.0000	5.9589	5.9589
–38	79.80	0.001454	1.4043	1.4058	8.8	1271.2	1280.0	8.9	1383.3	1392.2	0.0380	5.8840	5.9220
–36	88.54	0.001460	1.2742	1.2757	17.7	1264.8	1282.5	17.8	1377.6	1395.4	0.0757	5.8101	5.8858
–34	98.05	0.001465	1.1582	1.1597	26.7	1258.1	1284.8	26.8	1371.7	1398.5	0.1132	5.7372	5.8504
–32	108.37	0.001470	1.0547	1.0562	35.5	1251.6	1287.1	35.7	1365.9	1401.6	0.1504	5.6652	5.8156
–30	119.55	0.001476	0.9620	0.9635	44.5	1244.9	1289.4	44.7	1359.9	1404.6	0.1873	5.5942	5.7815
–28	131.64	0.001481	0.8790	0.8805	53.4	1238.3	1291.7	53.6	1354.0	1407.6	0.2240	5.5241	5.7481
–26	144.70	0.001487	0.8044	0.8059	62.4	1231.5	1293.9	62.6	1347.9	1410.5	0.2605	5.4548	5.7153
–24	158.78	0.001492	0.7373	0.7388	71.4	1224.7	1296.1	71.6	1341.8	1413.4	0.2967	5.3864	5.6831
–22	173.93	0.001498	0.6768	0.6783	80.4	1217.8	1298.2	80.7	1335.5	1416.2	0.3327	5.3188	5.6515
–20	190.22	0.001504	0.6222	0.6237	89.4	1210.9	1300.4	89.7	1329.3	1419.0	0.3684	5.2521	5.6205
–18	207.71	0.001510	0.5728	0.5743	98.5	1203.9	1302.4	98.8	1322.9	1421.7	0.4040	5.1860	5.5900
–16	226.45	0.001515	0.5281	0.5296	107.5	1197.0	1304.5	107.8	1316.6	1424.4	0.4393	5.1207	5.5600
–14	246.51	0.001521	0.4874	0.4889	116.5	1190.0	1306.5	116.9	1310.1	1427.0	0.4744	5.0561	5.5305
–12	267.95	0.001528	0.4505	0.4520	125.6	1182.8	1308.4	126.0	1303.5	1429.5	0.5093	4.9922	5.5015
–10	290.85	0.001534	0.4170	0.4185	134.8	1175.5	1310.3	135.2	1296.8	1432.0	0.5440	4.9309	5.4749
–8	315.25	0.001540	0.3863	0.3878	143.8	1168.3	1312.1	144.3	1290.1	1434.4	0.5785	4.8664	5.4449
–6	341.25	0.001546	0.3584	0.3599	153.0	1161.0	1314.0	153.5	1283.3	1436.8	0.6128	4.8045	5.4173
–4	368.90	0.001553	0.3327	0.3343	162.1	1153.7	1315.8	162.7	1276.4	1439.1	0.6469	4.7432	5.3901
–2	398.27	0.001559	0.3093	0.3109	171.3	1146.2	1317.5	171.9	1269.4	1441.3	0.6808	4.6825	5.3633
0	429.44	0.001566	0.2879	0.2895	180.4	1138.8	1319.2	181.1	1262.4	1443.5	0.7145	4.6224	5.3369

Table A.2.1 (continued)

T °C	p kPa	v_f m³/kg	v_{fg} m³/kg	v_g m³/kg	u_f kJ/kg	u_{fg} kJ/kg	u_g kJ/kg	h_f kJ/kg	h_{fg} kJ/kg	h_g kJ/kg	s_f kJ/kg K	s_{fg} kJ/kg K	s_g kJ/kg K
2	462.49	0.001573	0.2682	0.2698	189.7	1131.1	1320.8	190.4	1255.2	1445.6	0.7481	4.5627	5.3108
4	497.49	0.001580	0.2501	0.2517	198.8	1123.6	1322.4	199.6	1248.0	1447.6	0.7815	4.5037	5.2852
6	534.51	0.001587	0.2335	0.2351	208.1	1115.9	1323.9	208.9	1240.7	1449.6	0.8148	4.4451	5.2599
8	573.64	0.001594	0.2182	0.2198	217.4	1108.0	1325.4	218.3	1233.2	1451.5	0.8479	4.3871	5.2350
10	614.95	0.001601	0.2040	0.2056	226.6	1100.3	1326.9	227.6	1225.7	1453.3	0.8808	4.3296	5.2104
12	658.52	0.001608	0.1910	0.1926	235.9	1092.3	1328.3	237.0	1218.1	1455.1	0.9136	4.2725	5.1861
14	704.44	0.001616	0.1789	0.1805	245.3	1084.4	1329.6	246.4	1210.4	1456.8	0.9463	4.2158	5.1621
16	752.79	0.001623	0.1677	0.1693	254.7	1076.4	1331.1	255.9	1202.6	1458.5	0.9788	4.1597	5.1385
18	803.66	0.001631	0.1574	0.1590	264.1	1068.1	1332.2	265.4	1194.6	1460.0	1.0112	4.1039	5.1151
20	857.12	0.001639	0.1478	0.1494	273.5	1060.0	1333.4	274.9	1186.6	1461.5	1.0434	4.0486	5.0920
22	913.27	0.001647	0.1389	0.1405	282.9	1051.7	1334.6	284.4	1178.5	1462.9	1.0755	3.9937	5.0692
24	972.19	0.001655	0.1305	0.1322	292.4	1043.4	1335.8	294.0	1170.3	1464.3	1.1075	3.9392	5.0467
26	1033.97	0.001663	0.1228	0.1245	301.9	1035.0	1336.9	303.6	1162.0	1465.6	1.1394	3.8850	5.0244
28	1098.71	0.001671	0.1156	0.1173	311.4	1026.6	1337.9	313.2	1153.6	1466.8	1.1711	3.8312	5.0023
30	1166.49	0.001680	0.1089	0.1106	320.9	1017.9	1338.9	322.9	1145.0	1467.9	1.2028	3.7777	4.9805
32	1237.41	0.001689	0.1027	0.1044	330.5	1009.3	1339.8	332.6	1136.4	1469.0	1.2343	3.7246	4.9589
34	1311.55	0.001698	0.0969	0.0986	340.1	1000.5	1340.6	342.3	1127.6	1469.9	1.2656	3.6718	4.9374
36	1389.03	0.001707	0.0914	0.0931	349.7	991.8	1341.5	352.1	1118.7	1470.8	1.2969	3.6192	4.9161
38	1469.92	0.001716	0.0863	0.0880	359.4	982.8	1342.1	361.9	1109.6	1471.5	1.3281	3.5669	4.8950
40	1554.33	0.001726	0.0816	0.0833	369.0	973.7	1342.7	371.7	1100.5	1472.2	1.3591	3.5149	4.8740
42	1642.35	0.001735	0.0771	0.0788	378.8	964.6	1343.4	381.6	1091.2	1472.8	1.3901	3.4629	4.8530
44	1734.09	0.001745	0.0729	0.0746	388.5	955.4	1343.8	391.5	1081.7	1473.2	1.4209	3.4113	4.8322
46	1829.65	0.001756	0.0689	0.0707	398.3	945.9	1344.1	401.5	1072.0	1473.5	1.4518	3.3595	4.8113
48	1929.13	0.001766	0.0651	0.0669	408.1	936.5	1344.6	411.5	1062.2	1473.7	1.4826	3.3079	4.7905
50	2032.62	0.001777	0.0617	0.0635	418.1	926.5	1344.6	421.7	1052.0	1473.7	1.5135	3.2561	4.7696

Table A.2.2 **Superheated ammonia.**
(Adapted from National Bureau of Standards Circular No. 142, *Tables of Thermodynamic Properties of Ammonia*)

$p = 50$ kPa				
T °C	v m³/kg	u kJ/kg	h kJ/kg	s kJ/kg K
−20	2.4474	1313.4	1435.8	6.3256
−10	2.5481	1329.6	1457.0	6.4077
0	2.6482	1345.7	1478.1	6.4865
10	2.7479	1361.8	1499.2	6.5625
20	2.8473	1378.0	1520.4	6.6360
30	2.9464	1394.4	1541.7	6.7073
40	3.0453	1410.7	1563.0	6.7766
50	3.1441	1427.3	1584.5	6.8441
60	3.2427	1444.0	1606.1	6.9099
70	3.3413	1460.7	1627.8	6.9743
80	3.4397	1477.7	1649.7	7.0372
100				

$p = 75$ kPa				
T °C	v m³/kg	u kJ/kg	h kJ/kg	s kJ/kg K
−20	1.6233	1311.3	1433.0	6.3119
−10	1.6915	1327.8	1454.7	6.2028
0	1.7591	1344.2	1476.1	6.2828
10	1.8263	1360.5	1497.5	6.3597
20	1.8932	1376.9	1518.9	6.4339
30	1.9597	1393.3	1540.3	6.5058
40	2.0261	1409.8	1561.8	6.5756
50	2.0923	1426.5	1583.4	6.6434
60	2.1584	1443.2	1605.1	6.7096
70	2.2244	1460.1	1626.9	6.7742
80	2.2903	1477.1	1648.9	6.8373
100				

$p = 100$ kPa				
T °C	v m³/kg	u kJ/kg	h kJ/kg	s kJ/kg K
−20	1.2110	1309.0	1430.1	5.9695
−10	1.2631	1325.9	1452.2	6.0552
0	1.3145	1342.7	1474.1	6.1366
10	1.3654	1359.2	1495.7	6.2144
20	1.4160	1375.7	1517.3	6.2894
30	1.4664	1392.3	1538.9	6.3618
40	1.5165	1408.9	1560.5	6.4321
50	1.5664	1425.6	1582.2	6.5003
60	1.6163	1442.5	1604.1	6.5668
70	1.6659	1459.4	1626.0	6.6316
80	1.7155	1476.5	1648.0	6.6950
100	1.8145	1511.2	1692.6	6.8177

$p = 125$ kPa				
T °C	v m³/kg	u kJ/kg	h kJ/kg	s kJ/kg K
−20	0.9635	1306.8	1427.2	5.8512
−10	1.0059	1324.1	1449.8	5.9389
0	1.0476	1341.1	1472.0	6.0217
10	1.0889	1357.8	1493.9	6.1006
20	1.1297	1374.5	1515.7	6.1763
30	1.1703	1391.2	1537.5	6.2494
40	1.2107	1408.0	1559.3	6.3201
50	1.2509	1424.7	1581.1	6.3887
60	1.2909	1441.6	1603.0	6.4555
70	1.3309	1458.6	1625.0	6.5206
80	1.3707	1475.9	1647.2	6.5842
100	1.4501	1510.5	1691.8	6.7072

$p = 150$ kPa				
T °C	v m³/kg	u kJ/kg	h kJ/kg	s kJ/kg K
−20	0.7984	1304.3	1424.1	5.7526
−10	0.8344	1322.1	1447.3	5.8424
0	0.8697	1339.3	1469.8	5.9206
10	0.9045	1356.4	1492.1	6.0066
20	0.9388	1373.3	1514.1	6.0831
30	0.9729	1390.2	1536.1	6.1568
40	1.0068	1407.0	1558.0	6.2280
50	1.0405	1423.9	1580.0	6.2970
60	1.0740	1440.9	1602.0	6.3641
70	1.1074	1458.0	1624.1	6.4295
80	1.1408	1475.2	1646.3	6.4933
100	1.2072	1510.0	1691.1	6.6167

$p = 200$ kPa				
T °C	v m³/kg	u kJ/kg	h kJ/kg	s kJ/kg K
−20				
−10	0.6199	1318.0	1442.0	5.6863
0	0.6471	1336.1	1465.5	5.7737
10	0.6738	1353.6	1488.4	5.8559
20	0.7001	1370.9	1510.9	5.9342
30	0.7261	1388.0	1533.2	6.0091
40	0.7519	1405.1	1555.5	6.0813
50	0.7774	1422.2	1577.7	6.1512
60	0.8029	1439.3	1599.9	6.2189
70	0.8282	1456.6	1622.2	6.2849
80	0.8533	1473.9	1644.6	6.3491
100	0.9035	1508.9	1689.6	6.4732

Table A.2.2 (continued)

p = 250 kPa				
T °C	v m³/kg	u kJ/kg	h kJ/kg	s kJ/kg K
−10	0.4910	1313.9	1436.6	5.5609
0	0.5135	1332.6	1461.0	5.6517
10	0.5354	1350.7	1484.5	5.7365
20	0.5568	1368.4	1507.6	5.8165
30	0.5780	1385.8	1530.3	5.8928
40	0.5989	1403.2	1552.9	5.9661
50	0.6096	1423.0	1575.4	6.0368
60	0.6401	1437.8	1597.8	6.1052
70	0.6605	1455.2	1620.3	6.1717
80	0.6809	1472.6	1642.8	6.2365
100	0.7212	1507.9	1688.2	6.3613

p = 300 kPa				
T °C	v m³/kg	u kJ/kg	h kJ/kg	s kJ/kg K
−10				
0	0.4243	1329.0	1456.3	5.5493
10	0.4430	1347.7	1480.6	5.6366
20	0.4613	1365.8	1504.2	5.7186
30	0.4792	1383.6	1527.4	5.7963
40	0.4968	1401.3	1550.3	5.8707
50	0.5143	1418.7	1573.0	5.9423
60	0.5316	1436.2	1595.7	6.0114
70	0.5488	1453.8	1618.4	6.0785
80	0.5658	1471.4	1641.1	6.1437
100	0.5997	1500.8	1680.7	6.2693

p = 350 kPa				
T °C	v m³/kg	u kJ/kg	h kJ/kg	s kJ/kg K
−10				
0	0.3605	1325.3	1451.5	5.4600
10	0.3770	1344.6	1476.5	5.5502
20	0.3929	1363.2	1500.7	5.6342
30	0.4084	1381.5	1524.4	5.7135
40	0.4239	1399.2	1547.6	5.7890
50	0.4391	1417.0	1570.7	5.8615
60	0.4541	1434.7	1593.6	5.9314
70	0.4689	1452.4	1616.5	5.9990
80	0.4837	1470.0	1639.3	6.0647
100	0.5129	1505.7	1685.2	6.1910

p = 400 kPa				
T °C	v m³/kg	u kJ/kg	h kJ/kg	s kJ/kg K
0	0.3125	1321.5	1446.5	5.3803
10	0.3274	1341.4	1472.4	5.4735
20	0.3417	1360.5	1497.2	5.5597
30	0.3556	1379.1	1521.3	5.6405
40	0.3692	1397.2	1544.9	5.7173
50	0.3826	1415.3	1568.3	5.7907
60	0.3959	1433.1	1591.5	5.8613
70	0.4090	1450.9	1614.5	5.9296
80	0.4220	1468.8	1637.6	5.9957
100	0.4478	1504.6	1683.7	6.1228
120				
140				

p = 450 kPa				
T °C	v m³/kg	u kJ/kg	h kJ/kg	s kJ/kg K
0	0.2752	1317.5	1441.3	5.3078
10	0.2887	1338.2	1468.1	5.4042
20	0.3017	1357.8	1493.6	5.4926
30	0.3143	1376.8	1518.2	5.5752
40	0.3266	1395.2	1542.2	5.6532
50	0.3387	1413.5	1565.9	5.7275
60	0.3506	1431.5	1589.3	5.7989
70	0.3624	1449.5	1612.6	5.8678
80	0.3740	1467.5	1635.8	5.9345
100	0.3971	1503.5	1682.2	6.0623
120				
140				

p = 500 kPa				
T °C	v m³/kg	u kJ/kg	h kJ/kg	s kJ/kg K
0				
10				
20	0.2698	1355.0	1489.9	5.4314
30	0.2813	1374.4	1515.0	5.5157
40	0.2926	1393.2	1539.5	5.5950
50	0.3036	1411.6	1563.4	5.6704
60	0.3144	1429.9	1587.1	5.7425
70	0.3251	1448.1	1610.6	5.8120
80	0.3357	1466.2	1634.0	5.8793
100	0.3565	1502.5	1680.7	6.0079
120	0.3771	1539.0	1727.5	6.1301
140	0.3975	1576.0	1774.7	6.2472

Table A.2.2 (continued)

p = 600 kPa				
T °C	v m³/kg	u kJ/kg	h kJ/kg	s kJ/kg K
20	0.2217	1349.4	1482.4	5.3222
30	0.2317	1369.6	1508.6	5.4102
40	0.2414	1389.0	1533.8	5.4923
50	0.2508	1408.0	1558.5	5.5697
60	0.2600	1426.7	1582.7	5.6436
70	0.2691	1445.1	1606.6	5.7144
80	0.2781	1463.5	1630.4	5.7826
100	0.2957	1500.3	1677.7	5.9129
120	0.3130	1537.1	1724.9	6.0363
140	0.3302	1574.3	1772.4	6.1541
160				

p = 700 kPa				
T °C	v m³/kg	u kJ/kg	h kJ/kg	s kJ/kg K
20	0.1874	1343.3	1474.5	5.2259
30	0.1963	1364.5	1501.9	5.3179
40	0.2048	1384.7	1528.1	5.4029
50	0.2131	1404.2	1553.4	5.4826
60	0.2212	1423.4	1578.2	5.5582
70	0.2291	1442.2	1602.6	5.6303
80	0.2369	1461.0	1626.8	5.6997
100	0.2522	1498.1	1674.6	5.8316
120	0.2672	1535.4	1722.4	5.9562
140	0.2821	1572.7	1770.2	6.0749
160				

p = 800 kPa				
T °C	v m³/kg	u kJ/kg	h kJ/kg	s kJ/kg K
20	0.1615	1337.1	1466.3	5.1387
30	0.1696	1359.3	1495.0	5.2351
40	0.1773	1380.4	1522.2	5.3232
50	0.1848	1400.5	1548.3	5.4053
60	0.1920	1420.1	1573.7	5.4827
70	0.1991	1439.3	1598.6	5.5562
80	0.2060	1458.3	1623.1	5.6268
100	0.2196	1495.9	1671.6	5.7603
120	0.2329	1533.6	1719.9	5.8861
140	0.2459	1571.3	1768.0	6.0057
160	0.2589	1609.3	1816.4	6.1202

p = 900kPa				
T °C	v m³/kg	u kJ/kg	h kJ/kg	s kJ/kg K
30	0.1488	1354.1	1488.0	5.1593
40	0.1559	1375.9	1516.2	5.2508
50	0.1627	1396.6	1543.0	5.3354
60	0.1693	1416.7	1569.1	5.4147
70	0.1757	1436.3	1594.4	5.4897
80	0.1820	1455.6	1619.4	5.5614
100	0.1942	1493.7	1668.5	5.6968
120	0.2061	1531.6	1717.1	5.8237
140	0.2178	1569.7	1765.7	5.9442
160	0.2294	1607.9	1814.4	6.0594
180				

p = 1000 kPa				
T °C	v m³/kg	u kJ/kg	h kJ/kg	s kJ/kg K
30	0.1321	1348.5	1480.6	5.0889
40	0.1388	1371.2	1510.0	5.1840
50	0.1450	1392.7	1537.7	5.2713
60	0.1511	1413.3	1564.4	5.3525
70	0.1570	1433.3	1590.3	5.4292
80	0.1627	1452.9	1615.6	5.5021
100	0.1739	1491.5	1665.4	5.6392
120	0.1847	1532.8	1717.5	5.7674
140	0.1954	1568.0	1763.4	5.8888
160	0.2058	1606.6	1812.4	6.0047
180	0.2162	1645.5	1861.7	6.1159

p = 1200 kPa				
T °C	v m³/kg	u kJ/kg	h kJ/kg	s kJ/kg K
30				
40	0.1129	1361.6	1497.1	5.0629
50	0.1185	1384.4	1526.6	5.1560
60	0.1238	1406.1	1554.7	5.2416
70	0.1289	1427.0	1581.7	5.3215
80	0.1338	1447.4	1608.0	5.3970
100	0.1434	1487.1	1659.2	5.5379
120	0.1526	1526.1	1709.2	5.6687
140	0.1616	1565.0	1758.9	5.7919
160	0.1705	1603.9	1808.5	5.9091
180	0.1792	1643.2	1858.2	6.0214

Table A.2.2 (continued)

	p = 1400 kPa			
T °C	v m³/kg	u kJ/kg	h kJ/kg	s kJ/kg K
40	0.0944	1351.2	1483.4	4.9534
50	0.0995	1375.8	1515.1	5.0530
60	0.1042	1398.8	1544.7	5.1434
70	0.1088	1420.7	1573.0	5.2270
80	0.1132	1441.7	1600.2	5.3053
100	0.1216	1482.6	1652.8	5.4501
120	0.1297	1522.3	1703.9	5.5836
140	0.1376	1561.7	1754.3	5.7087
160	0.1452	1601.2	1804.5	5.8273
180	0.1528	1640.6	1854.5	5.9406

	p = 1600 kPa			
T °C	v m³/kg	u kJ/kg	h kJ/kg	s kJ/kg K
40				
50	0.0851	1366.7	1502.9	4.9584
60	0.8950	102.4	1534.4	5.0543
70	0.0937	1414.1	1564.0	5.1419
80	0.0977	1436.0	1592.3	5.2232
100	0.1053	1477.9	1646.4	5.3722
120	0.1125	1518.5	1698.5	5.5084
140	0.1195	1558.5	1749.7	5.6355
160	0.1263	1598.4	1800.5	5.7555
180	0.1330	1638.4	1851.2	5.8699

	p = 1800kPa			
T °C	v m³/kg	u kJ/kg	h kJ/kg	s kJ/kg K
40				
50	0.0739	1357.0	1490.0	4.8693
60	0.0781	1382.9	1523.5	4.9715
70	0.0820	1407.0	1554.6	5.0635
80	0.0856	1430.0	1584.1	5.1482
100	0.0926	1473.1	1639.8	5.3018
120	0.0992	1514.5	1693.1	5.4409
140	0.1055	1555.2	1745.1	5.5699
160	0.1116	1595.6	1796.5	5.6914
180	0.1177	1635.8	1847.7	5.8069

	p = 2000 kPa			
T °C	v m³/kg	u kJ/kg	h kJ/kg	s kJ/kg K
50	0.0648	1346.5	1476.1	4.7834
60	0.0688	1374.4	1512.0	4.8930
70	0.0725	1399.9	1544.9	4.9902
80	0.0760	1423.6	1575.6	5.0786
100	0.0824	1468.4	1633.2	5.2371
120	0.0885	1510.6	1687.6	5.3793
140	0.0943	1551.8	1740.4	5.5104
160	0.0999	1592.6	1792.4	5.6333
180	0.1054	1633.3	1844.1	5.7499

Table A.3.1 **Saturated refrigerant 12 (Freon-12) – by temperature.**
(Source: G.J. Van Wylen and R.E. Sonntag, *Fundamentals of Classical Thermodynamics*, 3rd edn, Wiley, New York, 1986, as based on data from E.I. du Pont de Nemours & Company, Inc.)

T °C	p MPa	v_f m³/kg	v_{fg} m³/kg	v_g m³/kg	u_f kJ/kg	u_{fg} kJ/kg	u_g kJ/kg	h_f kJ/kg	h_{fg} kJ/kg	h_g kJ/kg	s_f kJ/kg K	s_{fg} kJ/kg K	s_g kJ/kg K
–90	0.0028	0.000608	4.414937	4.415545	–43.245	177.256	134.011	–43.243	189.618	146.375	–0.2084	1.0352	0.8268
–85	0.0042	0.000612	3.036704	3.037316	–38.971	174.854	135.883	–38.968	187.608	148.640	–0.1854	0.9970	0.8116
–80	0.0062	0.000617	2.137728	2.138345	–34.692	172.358	137.666	–34.688	185.612	150.924	–0.1630	0.9609	0.7979
–75	0.0088	0.000622	1.537029	1.537651	–30.406	170.099	139.693	–30.401	183.625	153.224	–0.1411	0.9266	0.7855
–70	0.0123	0.000627	1.126653	1.127280	–26.111	167.781	141.670	–26.103	181.639	155.536	–0.1197	0.8941	0.7744
–65	0.0168	0.000632	0.840534	0.841166	–21.804	165.529	143.725	–21.793	179.650	157.857	–0.0987	0.8630	0.7643
–60	0.0226	0.000637	0.637273	0.637910	–17.483	163.250	145.767	–17.469	177.653	160.184	–0.0782	0.8334	0.7552
–55	0.0300	0.000642	0.490358	0.491000	–13.148	160.930	147.782	–13.129	175.641	162.512	–0.0581	0.8051	0.7470
–50	0.0391	0.000648	0.382457	0.383105	–8.797	158.658	149.861	–8.772	173.612	164.840	–0.0384	0.7780	0.7396
–45	0.0504	0.000654	0.302028	0.302682	–4.429	156.337	151.908	–4.396	171.559	167.163	–0.0190	0.7519	0.7329
–40	0.0642	0.000659	0.241251	0.241910	–0.042	153.990	153.948	0.000	169.479	169.479	0.0000	0.7269	0.7269
–35	0.0807	0.000666	0.194732	0.195398	4.362	151.653	156.015	4.416	167.368	171.784	0.0187	0.7027	0.7214
–30	0.1004	0.000672	0.158703	0.159375	8.787	149.288	158.075	8.854	165.222	174.076	0.0371	0.6794	0.7165
–25	0.1237	0.000679	0.130487	0.131166	13.231	146.896	160.127	13.315	163.037	176.352	0.0552	0.6569	0.7121
–20	0.1509	0.000685	0.108162	0.108847	17.697	144.488	162.185	17.800	160.810	178.610	0.0730	0.6352	0.7082
–15	0.1826	0.000693	0.090325	0.091018	22.185	142.041	164.226	22.312	158.534	180.846	0.0906	0.6140	0.7046
–10	0.2191	0.000700	0.075946	0.076646	26.698	139.567	166.265	26.851	156.207	183.058	0.1079	0.5935	0.7014
–5	0.2610	0.000708	0.064255	0.064963	31.235	137.053	168.288	31.420	153.823	185.243	0.1250	0.5736	0.6986
0	0.3086	0.000716	0.054673	0.055389	35.801	134.503	170.304	36.022	151.375	187.397	0.1418	0.5542	0.6960
5	0.3626	0.000724	0.046761	0.047485	40.396	131.904	172.300	40.659	148.859	189.518	0.1585	0.5352	0.6937
10	0.4233	0.000733	0.040181	0.040914	45.027	129.256	174.283	45.337	146.265	191.602	0.1750	0.5166	0.6916
15	0.4914	0.000743	0.034670	0.035413	49.693	126.549	176.242	50.058	143.586	193.644	0.1914	0.4983	0.6897
20	0.5673	0.000752	0.030028	0.030780	54.401	123.779	178.180	54.828	140.813	195.641	0.2076	0.4803	0.6879
25	0.6516	0.000763	0.026091	0.026854	59.156	120.932	180.088	59.653	137.933	197.586	0.2237	0.4626	0.6863
30	0.7449	0.000774	0.022734	0.023508	63.962	118.002	181.964	64.539	134.936	199.475	0.2397	0.4451	0.6848

Table A.3.1 (continued)

T °C	p MPa	v_f m³/kg	v_{fg} m³/kg	v_g m³/kg	u_f kJ/kg	u_{fg} kJ/kg	u_g kJ/kg	h_f kJ/kg	h_{fg} kJ/kg	h_g kJ/kg	s_f kJ/kg K	s_{fg} kJ/kg K	s_g kJ/kg K
35	0.8477	0.000786	0.025624	0.026410	68.828	110.083	178.911	69.494	131.805	201.299	0.2557	0.4277	0.6834
40	0.9607	0.000798	0.017373	0.018171	73.760	111.834	185.594	74.527	128.524	203.051	0.2716	0.4104	0.6820
45	1.0843	0.000811	0.015221	0.016032	78.768	108.571	187.339	79.647	125.075	204.722	0.2875	0.3931	0.6806
50	1.2193	0.000826	0.013344	0.014170	83.861	105.160	189.021	84.868	121.430	206.298	0.3034	0.3758	0.6792
55	1.3663	0.000841	0.011701	0.012542	89.052	101.578	190.630	90.201	117.565	207.766	0.3194	0.3583	0.6777
60	1.5259	0.000858	0.010253	0.011111	94.356	97.799	192.155	95.665	113.444	209.109	0.3355	0.3405	0.6760
65	1.6988	0.000877	0.008970	0.009847	99.789	93.786	193.575	101.279	109.024	210.303	0.3518	0.3224	0.6742
70	1.8858	0.000897	0.007828	0.008725	105.375	89.492	194.867	107.067	104.254	211.321	0.3683	0.3038	0.6721
75	2.0874	0.000920	0.006803	0.007723	111.138	84.867	196.005	113.058	99.068	212.126	0.3851	0.2846	0.6697
80	2.3046	0.000946	0.005875	0.006821	117.111	79.834	196.945	119.291	93.374	212.665	0.4023	0.2644	0.6667
85	2.5380	0.000976	0.005029	0.006005	123.341	74.283	197.624	125.818	87.047	212.865	0.4201	0.2430	0.6631
90	2.7885	0.001012	0.004246	0.005258	129.886	68.066	197.952	132.708	79.906	212.614	0.4385	0.2200	0.6585
95	3.0569	0.001056	0.003507	0.004563	136.840	60.937	197.777	140.068	71.658	211.726	0.4579	0.1947	0.6526
100	3.3440	0.001113	0.002790	0.003903	144.354	52.437	196.791	148.076	61.767	209.843	0.4788	0.1656	0.6444
105	3.6509	0.001197	0.002045	0.003242	152.715	41.548	194.263	157.085	49.014	206.099	0.5023	0.1296	0.6319
110	3.9784	0.001364	0.001098	0.002462	162.632	24.057	186.689	168.059	28.425	196.484	0.5322	0.0742	0.6064
112	4.1155	0.001792	0.000005	0.001797	167.545	0.130	167.675	174.920	0.151	175.071	0.5651	0.0004	0.5655

Table A.3.2 **Superheated refrigerant 12 (Freon-12).**
(Source: G.J. Van Wylen and R.E. Sonntag, *Fundamentals of Classical Thermodynamics*, 3rd edn, Wiley, New York, 1986, as based on data from E.I. du Pont de Nemours & Company, Inc.)

$p = 0.050$ MPa					$p = 0.100$ MPa					$p = 0.150$ MPa				
T °C	v m³/kg	u kJ/kg	h kJ/kg	s kJ/kg K	T °C	v m³/kg	u kJ/kg	h kJ/kg	s kJ/kg K	T °C	v m³/kg	u kJ/kg	h kJ/kg	s kJ/kg K
−20	0.341857	163.949	181.042	0.7912	**−20**	0.167701	163.091	179.861	0.7401	**−20**				
−10	0.356227	168.946	186.757	0.8133	**−10**	0.175222	168.185	185.707	0.7628	**−10**	0.114716	167.412	184.619	0.7318
0	0.370508	174.042	192.567	0.8350	**0**	0.182647	173.363	191.628	0.7849	**0**	0.119866	172.680	190.660	0.7543
10	0.384716	179.235	198.471	0.8562	**10**	0.189994	178.629	197.628	0.8064	**10**	0.124932	178.022	196.762	0.7763
20	0.398863	184.526	204.469	0.8770	**20**	0.197277	183.979	203.707	0.8275	**20**	0.129930	183.438	202.927	0.7977
30	0.412959	189.909	210.557	0.8974	**30**	0.204506	189.415	209.866	0.8482	**30**	0.134873	188.929	209.160	0.8186
40	0.427012	195.382	216.733	0.9175	**40**	0.211691	194.935	216.104	0.8684	**40**	0.139768	194.498	215.463	0.8390
50	0.441030	200.946	222.997	0.9372	**50**	0.218839	200.537	222.421	0.8883	**50**	0.144625	200.141	221.835	0.8591
60	0.455017	206.593	229.344	0.9565	**60**	0.225955	206.220	228.815	0.9078	**60**	0.149450	205.860	228.277	0.8787
70	0.468978	212.325	235.774	0.9755	**70**	0.233044	211.981	235.285	0.9269	**70**	0.154247	211.652	234.789	0.8980
80	0.482917	218.136	242.282	0.9942	**80**	0.240111	217.818	241.829	0.9457	**80**	0.159020	217.518	241.371	0.9169
90	0.496838	224.026	248.868	1.0126	**90**	0.247159	223.730	248.446	0.9642	**90**	0.163774	223.454	248.020	0.9354

$p = 0.200$ MPa					$p = 0.250$ MPa					$p = 0.300$ MPa				
T °C	v m³/kg	u kJ/kg	h kJ/kg	s kJ/kg K	T °C	v m³/kg	u kJ/kg	h kJ/kg	s kJ/kg K	T °C	v m³/kg	u kJ/kg	h kJ/kg	s kJ/kg K
0	0.088608	171.947	189.669	0.7320	**0**	0.069752	171.206	188.644	0.7139	**0**	0.057150	170.438	187.583	0.6984
10	0.092550	177.368	195.878	0.7543	**10**	0.073024	176.713	194.969	0.7366	**10**	0.059984	176.039	194.034	0.7216
20	0.096418	182.851	202.135	0.7760	**20**	0.076218	182.268	201.322	0.7587	**20**	0.062734	181.670	200.490	0.7440
30	0.100228	188.400	208.446	0.7972	**30**	0.079350	187.878	207.715	0.7801	**30**	0.065418	187.344	206.969	0.7658
40	0.103989	194.016	214.814	0.8178	**40**	0.082431	193.545	214.153	0.8010	**40**	0.068049	193.065	213.480	0.7869
50	0.107710	199.701	221.243	0.8381	**50**	0.085470	199.275	220.642	0.8214	**50**	0.070635	198.840	220.030	0.8075
60	0.113970	204.941	227.735	0.8578	**60**	0.088474	205.067	227.185	0.8413	**60**	0.073185	204.672	226.627	0.8276
70	0.115055	211.280	234.291	0.8772	**70**	0.091449	210.923	233.785	0.8608	**70**	0.075705	210.562	233.273	0.8473
80	0.118690	217.172	240.910	0.8962	**80**	0.094398	216.844	240.443	0.8800	**80**	0.078200	216.511	239.971	0.8665
90	0.122304	223.132	247.593	0.9149	**90**	0.097327	222.828	247.160	0.8987	**90**	0.080673	222.521	246.723	0.8853
100	0.125901	229.159	254.339	0.9332	**100**	0.100238	228.877	253.936	0.9171	**100**	0.083127	228.592	253.530	0.9038
110	0.129483	235.250	261.147	0.9512	**110**	0.103134	234.987	260.770	0.9352	**110**	0.085566	234.721	260.391	0.9220

Table A.3.2 (continued)

$p = 0.400$ MPa					$p = 0.500$ MPa					$p = 0.600$ MPa				
T °C	v m³/kg	u kJ/kg	h kJ/kg	s kJ/kg K	T °C	v m³/kg	u kJ/kg	h kJ/kg	s kJ/kg K	T °C	v m³/kg	u kJ/kg	h kJ/kg	s kJ/kg K
20	0.045836	180.428	198.762	0.7199	**20**	0.035646	179.112	196.935	0.6999	**20**				
30	0.047971	186.240	205.428	0.7423	**30**	0.037464	185.082	203.814	0.7230	**30**	0.030422	183.863	202.116	0.7065
40	0.050046	192.077	212.095	0.7639	**40**	0.039214	191.049	210.656	0.7452	**40**	0.031966	189.974	209.154	0.7291
50	0.052072	197.950	218.779	0.7849	**50**	0.040911	197.029	217.484	0.7667	**50**	0.033450	196.071	216.141	0.7511
60	0.054059	203.864	225.488	0.8054	**60**	0.042565	203.033	224.315	0.7875	**60**	0.034887	202.172	223.104	0.7723
70	0.056014	209.824	232.230	0.8253	**70**	0.044184	209.069	231.161	0.8077	**70**	0.036285	208.291	230.062	0.7929
80	0.057941	215.836	239.012	0.8448	**80**	0.045774	215.144	238.031	0.8275	**80**	0.037653	214.435	237.027	0.8129
90	0.059846	221.899	245.837	0.8638	**90**	0.047340	221.262	244.932	0.8467	**90**	0.038995	220.612	244.009	0.8324
100	0.061731	228.015	252.707	0.8825	**100**	0.048886	227.426	251.869	0.8656	**100**	0.040316	226.826	251.016	0.8514
110	0.063600	234.184	259.624	0.9008	**110**	0.050415	233.638	258.845	0.8840	**110**	0.041619	233.082	258.053	0.8700
120	0.065455	240.408	266.590	0.9187	**120**	0.051929	239.898	265.862	0.9021	**120**	0.042907	239.380	265.124	0.8882
130	0.067298	246.686	273.605	0.9364	**130**	0.053430	246.208	272.923	0.9198	**130**	0.044181	245.722	272.231	0.9061

$p = 0.700$ MPa					$p = 0.800$ MPa					$p = 0.900$ MPa				
T °C	v m³/kg	u kJ/kg	h kJ/kg	s kJ/kg K	T °C	v m³/kg	u kJ/kg	h kJ/kg	s kJ/kg K	T °C	v m³/kg	u kJ/kg	h kJ/kg	s kJ/kg K
40	0.026761	188.847	207.580	0.7148	**40**	0.022830	187.660	205.924	0.7016	**40**	0.019744	186.400	204.170	0.6982
50	0.028100	195.075	214.745	0.7373	**50**	0.024068	194.036	213.290	0.7248	**50**	0.020912	192.944	211.765	0.7131
60	0.029387	201.283	221.854	0.7590	**60**	0.025247	200.360	220.558	0.7469	**60**	0.022012	199.401	219.212	0.7358
70	0.030632	207.489	228.931	0.7799	**70**	0.026380	206.662	227.766	0.7682	**70**	0.023062	205.808	226.564	0.7575
80	0.031843	213.707	235.997	0.8002	**80**	0.027477	212.959	234.941	0.7888	**80**	0.024072	212.191	233.856	0.7785
90	0.033027	219.947	243.066	0.8199	**90**	0.028545	219.265	242.101	0.8088	**90**	0.025051	218.567	241.113	0.7987
100	0.034189	226.214	250.146	0.8392	**100**	0.029588	225.590	249.260	0.8283	**100**	0.026005	224.951	248.355	0.8184
110	0.035332	232.515	257.247	0.8579	**110**	0.030612	231.938	256.428	0.8472	**110**	0.026937	231.350	255.593	0.8376
120	0.036458	238.853	264.374	0.8763	**120**	0.031619	238.318	263.613	0.8657	**120**	0.027851	237.773	262.839	0.8562
130	0.037572	245.331	271.631	0.8943	**130**	0.032612	244.730	270.820	0.8838	**130**	0.028751	244.224	270.100	0.8745
140	0.038673	251.649	278.720	0.9119	**140**	0.033592	251.181	278.055	0.9016	**140**	0.029639	250.706	277.381	0.8923
150	0.039764	258.111	285.946	0.9292	**150**	0.034563	257.670	285.320	0.9189	**150**	0.030515	257.224	284.687	0.9098

Table A.3.2 (continued)

p = 1.000 MPa				
T °C	v m³/kg	u kJ/kg	h kJ/kg	s kJ/kg K
50	0.018366	191.796	210.162	0.7021
60	0.019410	198.400	217.810	0.7254
70	0.020397	204.922	225.319	0.7476
80	0.021341	211.398	232.739	0.7689
90	0.022251	217.850	240.101	0.7895
100	0.023133	224.297	247.430	0.8094
110	0.023993	230.750	254.743	0.8287
120	0.024835	237.218	262.053	0.8475
130	0.025661	243.708	269.369	0.8659
140	0.026474	350.225	376.699	0.8839
150	0.027275	256.772	284.047	0.9015
160	0.028068	263.351	291.419	0.9187

p = 1.200 MPa				
T °C	v m³/kg	u kJ/kg	h kJ/kg	s kJ/kg K
50	0.014483	189.281	206.661	0.6812
60	0.015463	196.249	214.805	0.7060
70	0.016368	203.045	222.687	0.7293
80	0.017221	209.733	230.398	0.7514
90	0.018032	216.357	237.995	0.7727
100	0.018812	222.944	245.518	0.7931
110	0.019567	229.513	252.993	0.8129
120	0.020301	236.080	260.441	0.8320
130	0.021018	242.653	267.875	0.8507
140	0.021721	249.242	275.307	0.8689
150	0.022412	255.851	282.745	0.8867
160	0.023093	262.483	290.195	0.9041

p = 1.400 MPa				
T °C	v m³/kg	u kJ/kg	h kJ/kg	s kJ/kg K
50				
60	0.012579	193.846	211.457	0.6876
70	0.013448	200.995	219.822	0.7123
80	0.014147	208.085	227.891	0.7355
90	0.014997	214.770	235.766	0.7575
100	0.015710	221.518	243.512	0.7785
110	0.016393	228.220	251.170	0.7988
120	0.017053	234.896	258.770	0.8183
130	0.017695	241.561	266.334	0.8373
140	0.018321	248.228	273.877	0.8558
150	0.018934	254.903	281.411	0.8738
160	0.019535	261.597	288.946	0.8914

p =1.600MPa				
T °C	v m³/kg	u kJ/kg	h kJ/kg	s kJ/kg K
70	0.011208	198.717	216.650	0.6959
80	0.011984	206.003	225.177	0.7204
90	0.012698	213.073	233.390	0.7433
100	0.013366	220.011	241.397	0.7651
110	0.014000	226.864	249.264	0.7859
120	0.014608	233.662	257.035	0.8059
130	0.015195	240.430	264.742	0.8253
140	0.015765	247.182	272.406	0.8440
150	0.016320	253.932	280.044	0.8623
160	0.016864	260.687	287.669	0.8801
170	0.017398	267.453	295.290	0.8975
180	0.017923	274.237	302.914	0.9145

p = 1.800 MPa				
T °C	v m³/kg	u kJ/kg	h kJ/kg	s kJ/kg K
70	0.009406	196.118	213.049	0.6794
80	0.010187	203.861	222.198	0.7057
90	0.010884	211.244	230.835	0.7298
100	0.011526	218.408	239.155	0.7524
110	0.012126	225.437	247.264	0.7739
120	0.012697	232.373	255.228	0.7944
130	0.013244	239.255	263.094	0.8141
140	0.013772	246.101	270.891	0.8332
150	0.014284	252.931	278.642	0.8518
160	0.014784	259.753	286.364	0.8698
170	0.015272	266.579	294.069	0.8874
180	0.015752	273.413	301.767	0.9046

p = 2.000 MPa				
T °C	v m³/kg	u kJ/kg	h kJ/kg	s kJ/kg K
70				
80	0.008704	201.451	218.859	0.6909
90	0.009406	209.244	228.056	0.7166
100	0.010035	216.690	236.760	0.7402
110	0.010615	223.924	245.154	0.7624
120	0.011159	231.023	253.341	0.7835
130	0.011676	238.032	261.384	0.8037
140	0.012172	244.983	269.327	0.8232
150	0.012651	251.899	277.201	0.8420
160	0.013116	258.795	285.027	0.8603
170	0.013570	265.682	292.822	0.8781
180	0.014013	272.572	300.598	0.8955

Table A.3.2 (continued)

$p = 2.500$ MPa				
T °C	v m^3/kg	u kJ/kg	h kJ/kg	s kJ/kg K
90	0.006595	203.075	219.562	0.6823
100	0.007264	211.692	229.852	0.7103
110	0.007837	219.679	239.271	0.7352
120	0.008351	227.315	248.192	0.7582
130	0.008827	234.727	256.794	0.7798
140	0.009273	241.998	265.180	0.8003
150	0.009697	249.172	273.414	0.8200
160	0.010104	256.280	281.540	0.8390
170	0.010497	263.347	289.589	0.8574
180	0.010879	270.386	297.583	0.8752
190	0.011250	277.415	305.540	0.8926
200	0.011614	284.437	313.472	0.9095

$p = 3.000$ MPa				
T °C	v m^3/kg	u kJ/kg	h kJ/kg	s kJ/kg K
90				
100	0.005231	204.836	220.529	0.6770
110	0.005886	214.410	232.068	0.7075
120	0.006419	222.951	242.208	0.7336
130	0.006887	230.971	251.632	0.7573
140	0.007313	238.681	260.620	0.7793
150	0.007709	246.192	269.319	0.8001
160	0.008083	253.568	277.817	0.8200
170	0.008439	260.854	286.171	0.8391
180	0.008782	268.076	294.422	0.8575
190	0.009114	275.255	302.597	0.8753
200	0.009436	282.410	310.718	0.8927

$p = 3.500$ MPa				
T °C	v m^3/kg	u kJ/kg	h kJ/kg	s kJ/kg K
90				
100				
110	0.004324	206.987	222.121	0.6750
120	0.004959	217.519	234.875	0.7078
130	0.005456	226.565	245.661	0.7349
140	0.005884	234.930	255.524	0.7591
150	0.006270	242.901	264.846	0.7814
160	0.006626	250.626	273.817	0.8023
170	0.006961	258.182	282.545	0.8222
180	0.007279	265.624	291.100	0.8413
190	0.007584	272.984	299.528	0.8597
200	0.007878	280.291	307.864	0.8775

$p = 4.000$ MPa				
T °C	v m^3/kg	u kJ/kg	h kJ/kg	s kJ/kg K
120	0.003736	209.919	224.863	0.6771
130	0.004325	221.143	238.443	0.7111
140	0.004781	230.579	249.703	0.7386
150	0.005172	239.216	259.904	0.7630
160	0.005522	247.404	269.492	0.7854
170	0.005845	255.304	278.684	0.8063
180	0.006147	263.014	287.602	0.8262
190	0.006434	270.590	296.326	0.8453
200	0.006708	278.074	304.906	0.8636
210	0.006972	285.492	313.380	0.8813
220	0.007228	292.862	321.774	0.8985
230	0.007477	300.200	330.108	0.9152

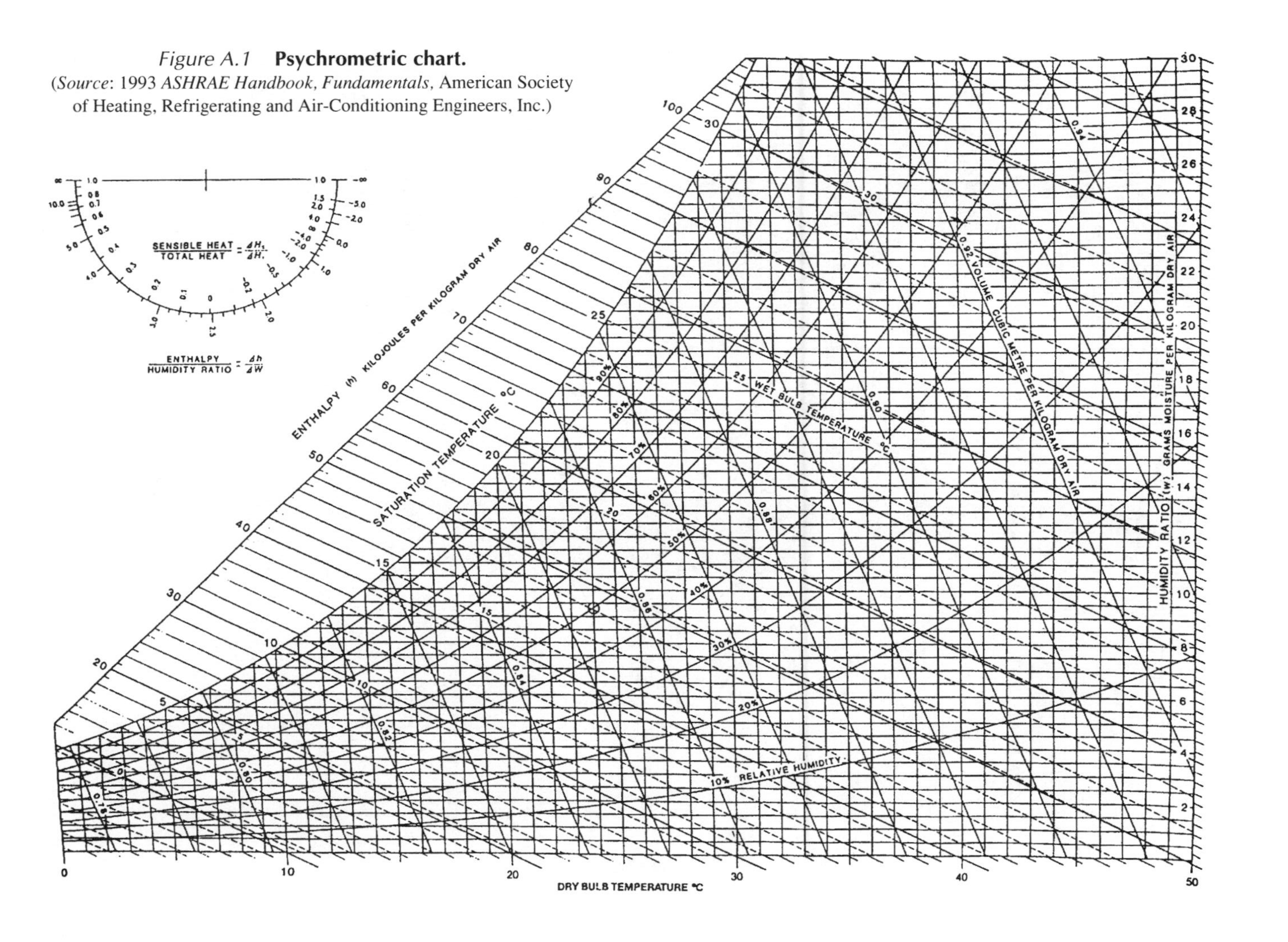

Figure A.1 **Psychrometric chart.**
(*Source*: 1993 *ASHRAE Handbook, Fundamentals*, American Society of Heating, Refrigerating and Air-Conditioning Engineers, Inc.)

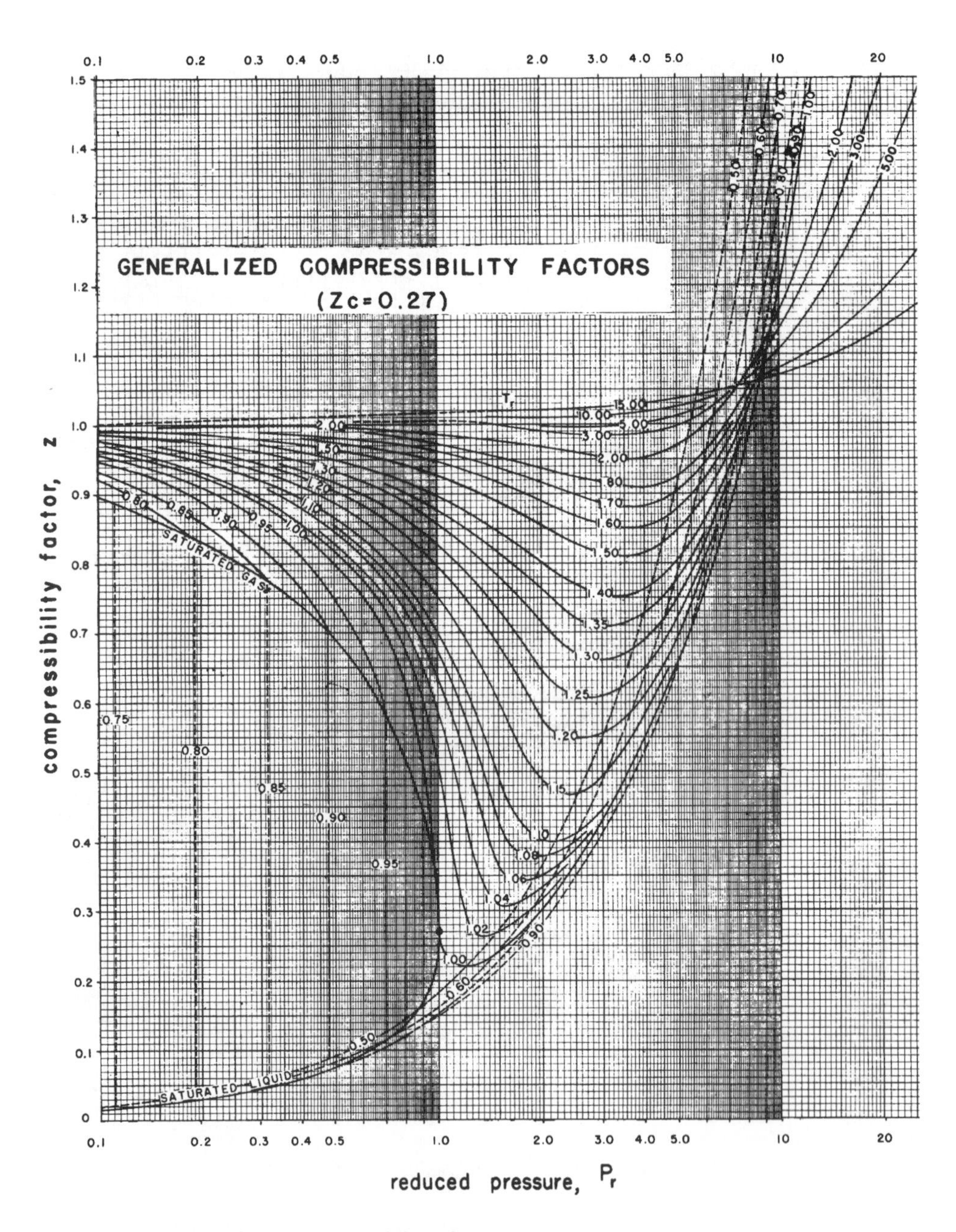

Figure A.2 **Generalized compressibility chart.**
(*Source*: G.J. Van Wylen and R.E. Sonntag, *Fundamentals of Classical Thermodynamics*, 3rd edn, Wiley, New York, 1986)

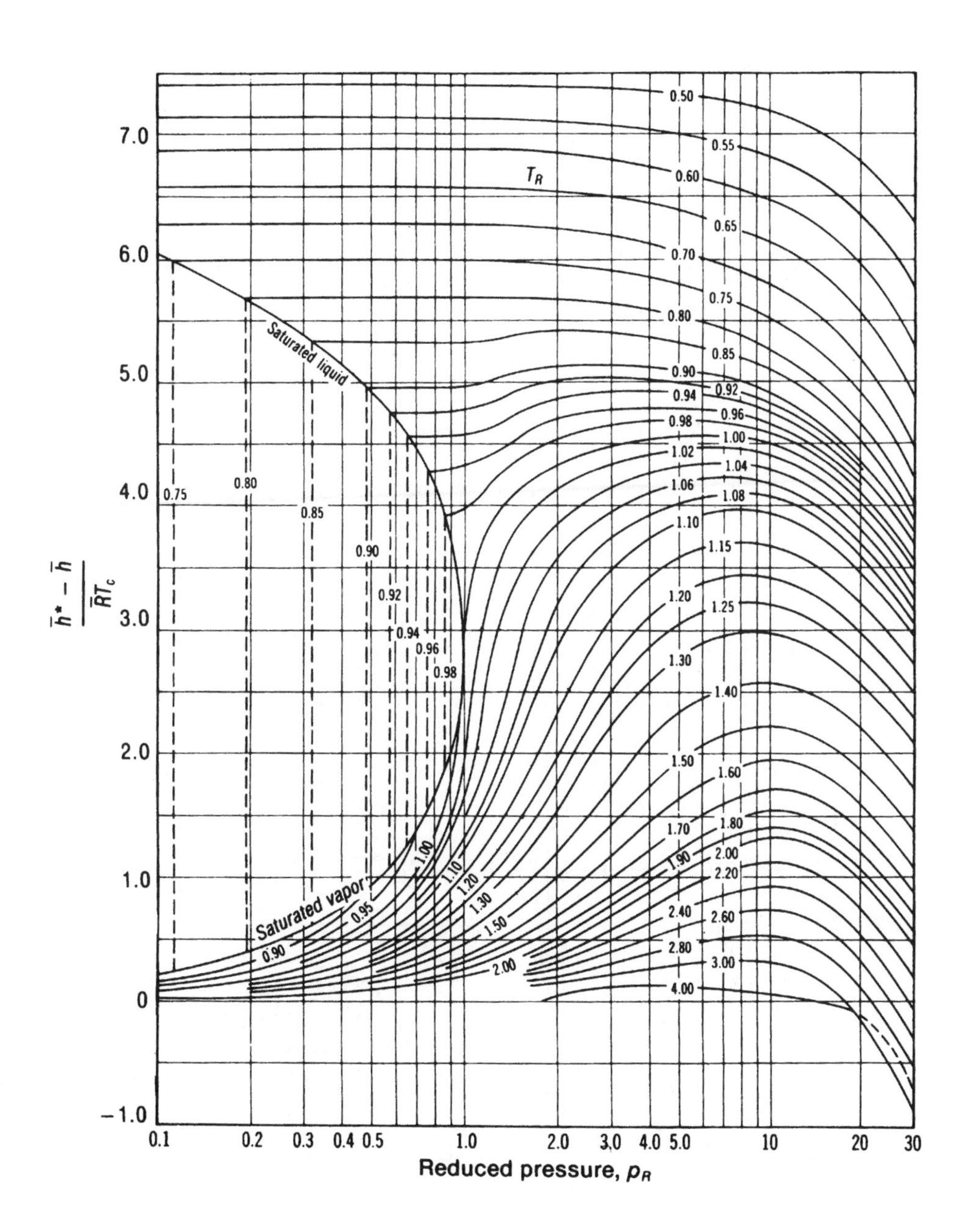

Figure A.3 **Generalized enthalpy chart.**
(*Source:* G.J. Van Wylen and R.E. Sonntag, *Fundamentals of Classical Thermodynamics*, 3rd edn, Wiley, New York, 1986)

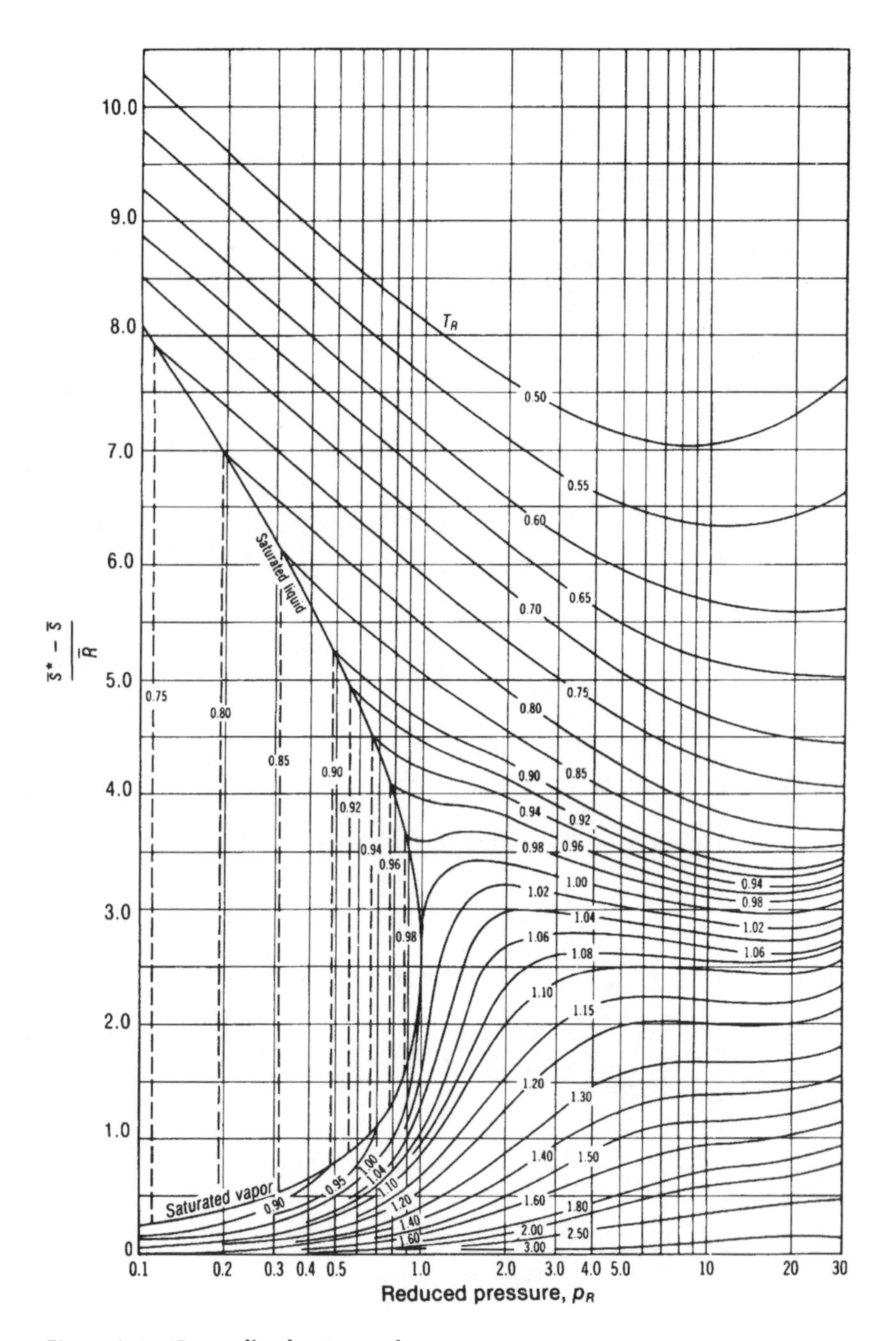

Figure A.4 **Generalized entropy chart.**
(*Source*: G.J. Van Wylen and R.E. Sonntag, *Fundamentals of Classical Thermodynamics*, 3rd edn, Wiley, New York, 1986)

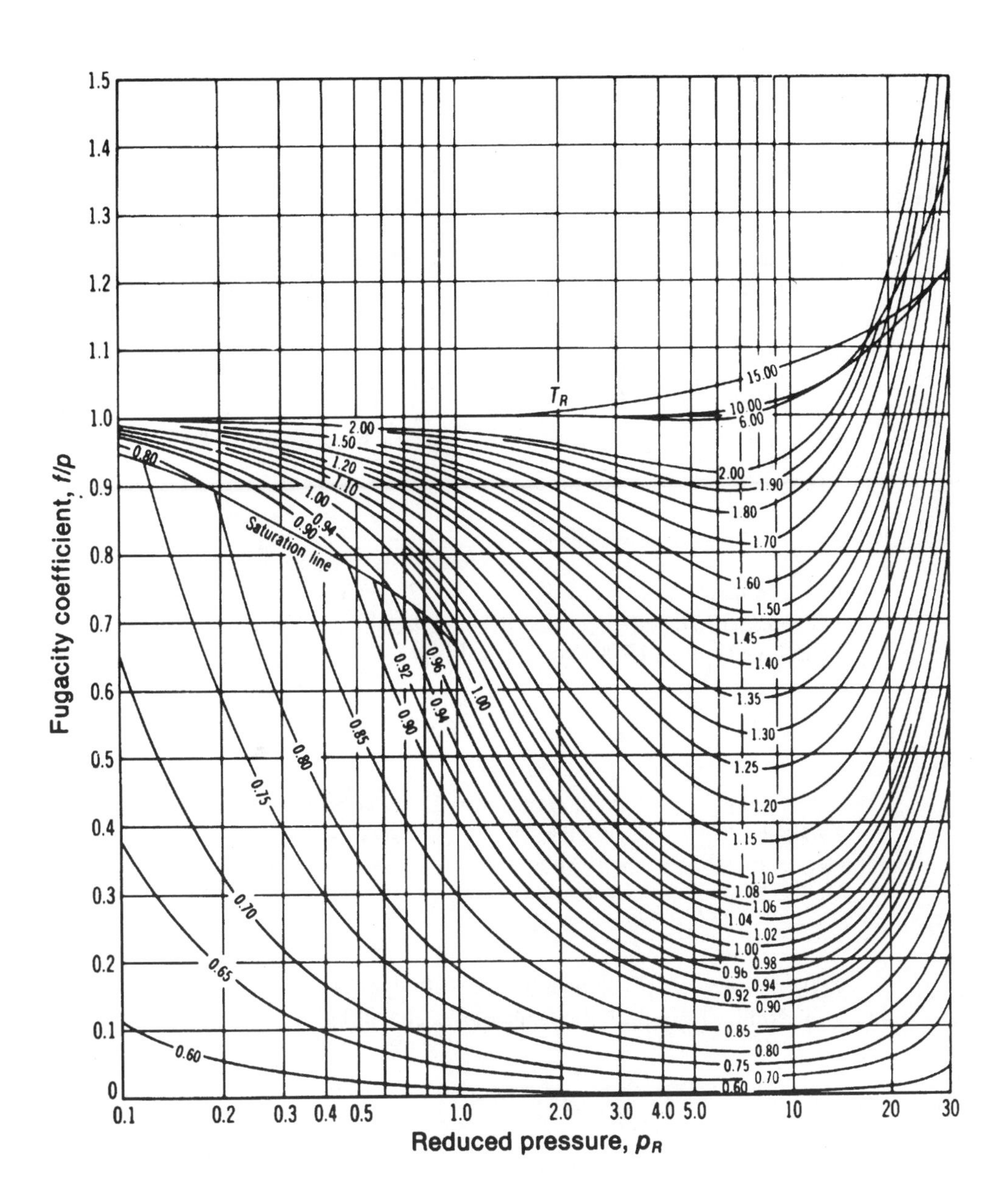

Figure A.5 **Generalized fugacity coefficient chart.**
(*Source:* G.J. Van Wylen and R.E. Sonntag, *Fundamentals of Classical Thermodynamics*, 3rd edn, Wiley, New York, 1986)

Unit conversion factors

Each of the conversion factors given below is dimensionless and equals unity. An expression may be multiplied or divided by any of these factors without changing its physical magnitude. Underlined numbers are exact by definition.

Length

$\underline{2.540}$ cm/in	$\underline{12}$ in/ft	3.281 ft/m	$\underline{30.48}$ cm/ft
1.609 km/mi	$\underline{5280}$ ft/mi	$\underline{10^{10}}$ Å/m	91.44 cm/yd

Area

6.452 cm^2/in^2	929.0 cm^2/ft^2	10.764 ft^2/m^2	144 in^2/ft^2

Volume

16.387 in^3/cm^3	28.317 L/ft^3	1728 in^3/ft^3	35.315 ft^3/m^3
3.7845 L/gal(US)	7.48 gal(US)/ft^3	$\underline{4}$ qt/gal	0.946 L/qt(US)
4.545 L/gal(Imp.)	1.2009 gal(US)/gal(Imp.)		

Mass

453.59 g/lbm	$\underline{2000}$ lbm/ton(short)	$\underline{2240}$ lbm/ton(long)	
2.2046 lbm/kg	32.174 lbm/slug	14.594 kg/slug	28.349 g/oz

Force

$\underline{9.80665}$ N/kgf	7.233 poundal/N	$\underline{10^5}$ dyne/N
4.448 N/lbf	32.174 poundal/lbf	2.205 lbf/kgf

Density

$$\underline{1000}\,\frac{kg/m^3}{g/cm^3} \qquad 62.428\,\frac{lbm/ft^3}{g/cm^3} \qquad 32.174\,\frac{lbm/ft^3}{slug/ft^3}$$

$$1.9403\,\frac{slug/ft^3}{g/cm^3} \qquad 16.018\,\frac{kg/m^3}{lbm/ft^3} \qquad 8.345\,\frac{lbm/gal}{g/cm^3}$$

Viscosity

$\underline{100}\,\dfrac{\text{cp}}{\text{g/(cm s)}}$ $\underline{1000}\,\dfrac{\text{cp}}{\text{kg/(m s)}}$ $0.6723\,\dfrac{\text{lbm/(ft s)}}{\text{kg/(m s)}}$

$2.42\,\dfrac{\text{lbm/(ft h)}}{\text{cp}}$ $0.06723\,\dfrac{\text{lbm/(ft s)}}{\text{g/(cm s)}}$

Thermal conductivity

$1.730278\,\dfrac{\text{W/m °C}}{\text{Btu/h ft °F}}$ $241.9\,\dfrac{\text{Btu/hft °F}}{\text{cal/scm °C}}$

Pressure

$\underline{1.01325}$ bar/atm $1.0332\,\dfrac{\text{kgf/cm}^2}{\text{atm}}$ 14.696 psi/atm 6.8949 kPa/psi

$\underline{10^5}\,\dfrac{\text{N/m}^2}{\text{bar}}$ $\underline{144}\,\dfrac{\text{lbf/ft}^2}{\text{psi}}$ $\underline{0.1}\,\dfrac{\text{dyne/cm}^2}{\text{Pa}}$ $2116.2\,\dfrac{\text{lbf/ft}^2}{\text{atm}}$

$\underline{100}$ kPa/bar 760 mm Hg/atm 2.036 in Hg/psi 27.71 in H_2O/psi

Energy and power

$\underline{1.8}\,\dfrac{\text{Btu/lbm}}{\text{kcal/kg}}$ $\underline{550.0}\,\dfrac{\text{ft lbf/s}}{\text{hp}}$ $737.56\,\dfrac{\text{ft lbf/s}}{\text{kW}}$

4.18676 kJ/kcal 3412.8 Btu/kWh 1.35582 J/(ft bf)

2.6552×10^6 ft lbf/kWh 3600.0 kJ/kWh 0.25199 kcal/Btu

1.3410 hp/kW 778.16 ft lbf/Btu $\underline{860.0}$ kcal/kWh

0.252 kcal/Btu 2544.46 Btu/(hp h) 101.92 kgf m/kJ

1.05505 kJ/Btu 1.98×10^6 ft lbf/(hp h) 0.746 kW/hp

Specific heat, specific entropy

$$1\frac{\text{kcal/(kg K)}}{\text{Btu/(lbm °R)}} \qquad 4.1868\frac{\text{kJ/(kg K)}}{\text{kcal/(kg K)}} \qquad 0.23885\frac{\text{Btu/(lbm °R)}}{\text{kJ/(kg K)}}$$

Universal gas constant

$$\overline{R} = 8.3143\ \frac{\text{kJ}}{\text{kmol K}} = 1.986\ \frac{\text{kcal}}{\text{kmol K}} = 1.986\ \frac{\text{Btu}}{\text{lbmol R}} = 0.082057\frac{\text{m}^3\ \text{atm}}{\text{kmol K}}$$

$$= 847.8\ \frac{\text{kgf m}}{\text{kmol K}} = 1545.3\ \frac{\text{ft lbf}}{\text{lbmol °R}} = 10.73\frac{\text{psia ft}^3}{\text{lbmol °R}} = 0.7302\frac{\text{ft}^3\ \text{atm}}{\text{lbmol °R}}$$

Bibliography

There are two major methods of presenting thermodynamics. The classical method, which does not require a model of the substance, looks at the system as a macroscopic continuum. The statistical method, on the other hand, deduces the properties of the system by making models of its microstructure.

Classical thermodynamics

Classical thermodynamics may be developed from several different points of view. Some may be very mathematical, while others put a higher emphasis on the physics. The following books present different expositions of classical thermodynamics. Generally, these books are on a higher level than the present textbook.

Buchsdahl, H.A. (1966) *The Concepts of Classical Thermodynamics*, Cambridge University Press, Cambridge.

Callen, H.B. (1960) *Thermodynamics*, John Wiley, New York.

Giles, R. (1964) *Mathematical Foundations of Thermodynamics*, Pergamon Press, Oxford.

Hatsopoulos, G.N. and J.H. Keenan (1965) *Principles of General Thermodynamics,* John Wiley, New York.

Lewis, G.N. and M. Randall (1961) *Thermodynamics*, 2nd edn (revised by K.S. Pitzer and L. Brewer), McGraw-Hill, New York.

Tribus, M. (1961) *Thermostatics and Thermodynamics*, D. Van Nostrand, Princeton, NJ.

Statistical thermodynamics

Callen, H.B. (1963) *Thermodynamics and Statistical Physics*, Harcourt Brace & World, New York.

Chang, L.T. and J.H. Lienhard (1979) *Statistical Thermodynamics*, Hemisphere, Washington, DC.

Davidson, N. (1962) *Statistical Mechanics*, McGraw-Hill, New York.

Hill, T.L. (1960) *Statistical Thermodynamics*, Addison-Wesley, Reading, MA.

Lawden, D.F. (1987) *Principles of Thermodynamics and Statistical Mechanics*, John Wiley, New York.

Lee, J.F., F.W. Sears and D.L. Turcotte (1973) *Statistical Thermodynamics*, Addison-Wesley, Reading, MA.

Socrates, G. (1971) *Thermodynamics and Statistical Mechanics*, Butterworths, London.

Sommerfeld, A. (1956) *Thermodynamics and Statistical Mechanics*, Academic Press, New York.

Sonntag, R.E. and G.V. Van Wylen (1966) *Fundamentals of Statistical Thermodynamics*, John Wiley, New York.

Tien, C.L. (1971) *Statistical Thermodynamics*, Holt, Rinehart & Winston, New York.

Theory development

Some historical landmarks in the development of the theory of thermodynamics are listed below.

Caratheodory, C. (1909) 'Grundlagen die Thermodynamik', *Math. Ann.*, **67**, 355.

Clausius, R. (1850) 'Über die bewegende Krafte der Wärme und Gesetze, welche sich daraus für die Wärmelehre selbt albeiten lassen', *Pogg. Ann.*, Series III, Book 79.

Gibbs, J.W. (1948) *Collected Works*, Yale University Press, New Haven, CT.

Kelvin, Lord (Sir William Thomson) (1911) *Mathematical and Physical Papers*, Cambridge University Press, Cambridge.

Kline, S.J. and F.O. Koenig (1957) 'The state principle', *J. Appl. Mech.*, **24**, 29.

Maxwell, J.C. (1891) *The Theory of Heat*, Longmans Green, London.

Mendoza, E. (ed.) (1960) *Reflections on the Motive Power of Fire by S. Carnot; and Other Papers on the Second Law by Clapeyron and Clausius*, Dover, New York.

General textbooks

Many textbooks have been published in the field of thermodynamics, some of which are listed below. These are different from each other by the method of presentation of the subject matter and the degree of rigor.

Cengel, Y.A. and M.A. Boles (1989) *Thermodynamics, an Engineering Approach*, McGraw-Hill, New York.

Eastop, T.D. and A. McConkey (1986) *Applied Thermodynamics for Engineering Technologists*, 4th edn, Longman, London.

Hall, N.A. and W.E. Ibele (1960) *Engineering Thermodynamics*, Prentice Hall, Englewood Cliffs, NJ.

Holman, J.P. (1988) *Thermodynamics*, 4th edn, McGraw-Hill, New York.

Hsieh, J.S. (1975) *Principles of Thermodynamics*, McGraw-Hill, New York.

Huang, F.F. (1976) *Engineering Thermodynamics – Fundamentals and Applications*, Macmillan.

Jones, J.B. and G.A. Hawkins (1985) *Engineering Thermodynamics*, 2nd edn, John Wiley, New York.

Kirkwood, J.G. and I. Oppenheim (1961) *Chemical Thermodynamics*, McGraw-Hill, New York.

Moran, J.M. and H.N. Shapiro (1993) *Fundamentals of Engineering Thermodynamics*, 2nd edn, John Wiley, New York.

Obert, E.F. (1960) *Concepts of Thermodynamics*, McGraw-Hill, New York.

Obert, E.F. and R.A. Gaggioli (1963) *Thermodynamics*, McGraw-Hill , New York.

Reynolds, W.C. (1968) *Thermodynamics*, 2nd edn, McGraw-Hill, New York.

Rogers, G.F.C. and Y.R. Mayhew (1980). *Thermodynamics, Work and Heat Transfer*, Longman.

Sears, F.W. (1953) *Thermodynamics*, 2nd edn, Addison-Wesley, Reading, MA.

Van Wylen, G.J. and R.E. Sonntag (1985) *Fundamentals of Classical Thermodynamics*, 3rd edn, John Wiley, New York.

Wark, K. (1983) *Thermodynamics*, 4th edn, McGraw-Hill, New York.

Thermodynamic properties

Thermodynamic properties play an important role in the science of thermodynamics. Various sources of these properties may be found in the following publications.

Barber, C.R. (1969) 'The International Practice Temperature Scale of 1968', *Metrologia*, **5**, (2), 35.

Beattie, J.A. and O.C. Bridgeman (1928) 'A new equation of state for fluids', *Proc. Am. Acad. Arts Sci.*, **63,** 229.

Benedict, M., G. Webb and R. Rubin (1940) 'An empirical equation for the thermodynamic properties of light hydrocarbons and their mixtures', *J. Chem. Physics*, **8**, 334.

Gouq-Jen Su (1946) 'Modified law of corresponding states for real gases', *Ind. Engr. Chem.*, **38**, p. 803.

Hickson, D.C. and F.R. Taylor (1980) *Enthalpy–Entropy Diagram for Steam*, Blackwell, Oxford.

Rogers, G.F.C. and Y.R. Mayhew (1980) *Thermodynamic and Transport Properties of Fluids, SI Units*, Blackwell, Oxford.

Simson, H.F. (1949) 'The international temperature scale of 1948', *J. Res. Natl. Bur. Std.* (paper, 1962), **42,** 211.

'The metric system of measurement: Interpretation and Modification of the International System of Units for the United States' (1976) *Federal Register*, **41**, (239), 54018–19.

Property tables

Hilsenrath, J. *et al.* (1955). 'Tables of thermal properties of gases', *Natl. Bur. Std, Circ. 564*, US Government Printing Office, Washington, DC.

Irvine, T.F. and J.P. Hartnett (1976) *Steam and Air Tables in SI Units*, Hemisphere, Washington, DC.

JANAF Thermochemical Tables (1965) *Document PB 168-370,* Clearinghouse for Federal Scientific and Technical Information, August.

Keenan, J.H. and J. Kaye (1948) *Gas Tables,* John Wiley, New York.

Keenan, J.H. and F.G. Keyes (1965) *Thermodynamic Properties of Steam*, John Wiley, New York.

Mechtly, E.A. (1973) 'The International System of Units, physical constants, and conversion factors, revised', NASA SP-7012.

National Engineering Laboratory (1964) *Steam Tables*, HMSO, Edinburgh.

Nelson, L.C. and E.F. Obert (1954) 'Generalized *pvT* properties of gases', *Trans. ASME*, 1057.

Reynolds, W.C. (1979) *Thermodynamic Properties in SI: Graphs, Tables and Computational Equations for 40 Substances*, Dept. of Mechanical Eng., Stanford University, CA.

Selected Values of Chemical Thermodynamic Properties (1955) NBS Technical Notes, 270–1, 270–2.

Applications – compressors, pumps, nozzles, etc.

Chapman, A.J. and W.F. Walker (1971) *Introductory Gas Dynamics*, Holt, Rinehart & Winston, New York.

Dixon, S.L. (1978) *Fluid Mechanics and Thermodynamics of Turbomachinery*, Pergamon, Oxford.

Gibbs, C.W. (ed.) (1971) *Compressed Air and Gas Data*, Ingersol Rand, Woodcliff Lake, NJ.

Liepmann, H.W. and A. Roshko (1957) *Elements of Gas Dynamics*, John Wiley, New York.

Shapiro, A.H. (1987) *The Dynamics and Thermodynamics of Compressible Fluid Flow*, vols 1 and 2, Krieger, Malabar, FL.

Turton, R.K. (1984) *Principles of Turbomachinery*, E. & F.N. Spon, London.

Applications – power systems

Benson, R.S. (ed. by Harlock, J.H. and D.E. Winterbone) (1982). *The Thermodynamics and Gas Dynamics of Internal-combustion Engines*, 2 vols, Clarendon Press, Oxford.

Benson, R.S. and N.D. Whitehouse (1979) *Engines*, Vols 1 – 2, Pergamon Press, Oxford.

Boyce, M.P. (1982) *Gas Turbine Engineering Handbook*, Gulf, Houston, TX.

Central Electricity Generating Board (1982) *Modern Power Station Practice*, Vols 2, 3 and 4, Pergamon Press, Oxford.

Cohen, H., Rogers, G.F.C. and H.I.H. Saravanamutto (1979) *Gas Turbine Theory*, Halstead Press, New York.

Cole, D.E. (1972) The Wankel Engine, *Scientific American*, **227**, 1423

Dales, D.N. (1982) *Diesel Fundamentals*, Reston, Reston, PA,

Gaffert, G.A. (1952) *Steam Power Stations*, 4th edn, McGraw-Hill, New York.

Greene, A.B. and G.G. Lucas (1969) *The Testing of Internal Combustion Engines*, English Universities Press, London.

Haddad, S. and N. Watson (1984) *Principles and Performance in Diesel Engineering*, Ellis Horwood, London.

Hartman, R.T.C. (1981) *Gas Turbine Engineering*, Macmillan.

Heywood, J.B. (1989) *Internal Combustion Engine Fundamentals*, McGraw-Hill, New York.

Hill, P.G. and C.R. Peterson (1965) *Mechanics and Thermodynamics of Propulsion*, Addison-Wesley, Reading, MA.

Pyke, D.R. (1953). *The Internal Combustion Engine*, Oxford University Press, Oxford.

Ricardo, H.R. (1960) *The High Speed Internal Combustion Engine*, Blackie, London.

Taylor, C.F. (1977) *The Internal Combustion Engine in Theory and Practice*; Vol. 1, *Thermodynamics, Fluid Flow, Performance*; Vol. 2, *Combustion, Fuels, Materials, Design*, MIT Press, Cambridge, MA.

Walker, G. (1978) *Stirling Engines*, Oxford University Press, Oxford.

Watson, N. and M.W. Janota (1984) *Turbocharging the IC Engine*, Macmillan, New York.

Williams, T.T. (ed.) (1978) *A History of Technology*, Vol. VII, 20, *The Internal Combustion Engine*, Clarendon Press, Oxford.

Applications – refrigeration

ASHRAE Handbook on Heating, Ventilating and Air-conditioning Systems and Applications (1991) American Society of Heating, Refrigerating and Air-conditioning Engineers, Atlanta, GA.

ASHRAE Handbook Fundamentals (1989) American Society of Heating, Refrigerating and Air-conditioning Engineers, Atlanta, GA.

Barron, Randall (1966) *Cryogenic Systems*, McGraw-Hill, New York.

Croome, D.J. and B.M. Roberts (1981) *Air Conditioning and Ventilation of Buildings*, Pergamon Press, Oxford.

Dossat, R.J. (1981) *Principles of Refrigeration*, John Wiley, New York.

Elonka, S.M. and Q.W. Minich (1983) *Standard Refrigeration and Air Conditioning*, Tata McGraw-Hill, New Delhi.

Gosney, W.B. (1982) *Principles of Refrigeration*, Cambridge University Press, Cambridge.

Holland, F.A., F.A. Watson and S. Derotta (1982) *Thermodynamic Design Data for Heat Pump Systems*, Pergamon Press, Oxford.

Ita, E.G. (1984) *Refrigeration Principles and Systems*, John Wiley, New York.

Ludwig von Cube, H., and F. Steimle (1981) *Heat Pump Technology*, Butterworths, London.

Meacock, H.M. (1979) *Refrigeration Processes*, Pergamon Press, Oxford.

Stoecker, W.F. (1958) *Refrigeration and Air Conditioning*, McGraw-Hill, New York.

Applications – combustion

Fryling, G.R. (1966) *Combustion Engineering*, Combustion Engineering, New York.

Glassman, I. (1977) *Combustion,* Academic Press, New York.

Merrick, D. (1984) *Coal Combustion and Conversion Technology*, Macmillan, London.

Spalding, D.B. (1979) *Combustion Mass Transfer*, Pergamon Press, Oxford.

Strehlow, R.A. (1984) *Combustion Fundamentals*, McGraw-Hill, New York.

Index